Comparative Primate Biology
Volume 3

Reproduction and Development

Comparative Primate Biology

J. Erwin, Series Editor

Volume 1 **Systematics, Evolution, and Anatomy**
Edited by Daris R. Swindler and J. Erwin

Volume 2 Published in 2 Parts
Part A: **Behavior, Conservation, and Ecology**
Part B: **Behavior, Cognition, and Motivation**
Edited by G. Mitchell and J. Erwin

Volume 3 **Reproduction and Development**
Edited by W. Richard Dukelow and J. Erwin

Volume 4 **Neurosciences**
Edited by Horst D. Steklis and J. Erwin

Comparative Primate Biology
Volume 3

Reproduction
and Development

Editors

W. Richard Dukelow

Endocrine Research Center
Michigan State University
East Lansing, Michigan

J. Erwin

National Geographic Society
Washington, D.C.

Alan R. Liss, Inc., New York

Library of Congress Cataloging in Publication Data

Comparative primate biology.

Includes indexes.
Contents: v. 1. Systematics, evolution, and anatomy /
editors, Daris R. Swindler, J. Erwin — v. 2. pt. A.
Behavior, conservation and ecology / editors, G. Mitchell,
J. Erwin. pt. B. Behavior, cognition and motivation /
editors, G. Mitchell, J. Erwin — v. 3. Reproduction
and development / editors, W. Richard Dukelow, J. Erwin —
[etc.]
1. Primates—Collected works.   I. Swindler, Daris Ray.
II. Erwin, J. (Joseph)
QL737.P9C577   1986   599.8   85-5243
ISBN 0-8451-4000-0 (v. 1)
ISBN 0-8451-4003-5 (v. 3)

Contents

Contributors

Terry G. Baker, School of Medical Sciences, University of Bradford, Bradford BD7 1DP, United Kingdom **[195]**

Michael S. Blank, Yerkes Regional Primate Research Center, Emory University, Atlanta, GA 30322 **[17]**

Kenneth R. Brizzee, Department of Neurobiology, Delta Regional Primate Research Center, Tulane University, Covington, LA 70433 **[363]**

W. Richard Dukelow, Endocrine Research Center, Michigan State University, East Lansing, MI 48824 **[xi,263,277]**

William P. Dunlap, Department of Psychology, Tulane University, New Orleans, LA 70118 **[363]**

Allen C. Enders, Department of Human Anatomy, University of California School of Medicine, Davis, CA 95616 **[291]**

J. Erwin, National Geographic Society, Washington, D.C. 20035 **[ix]**

Bi-qin Fan, Endocrine Research Center, Michigan State University, East Lansing, MI 48824 **[263]**

Robert W. Goy, University of Wisconsin Regional Primate Research Center, Madison, WI 53706 **[63]**

Charles E. Graham, Primate Research Institute, New Mexico State University, Holloman AFB, NM 88330 **[93]**

Richard M. Harrison, Department of Urology/Reproductive Physiology, Delta Regional Primate Research Center, Tulane University, Covington, LA 70433 **[101]**

Andrew G. Hendrickx, California Primate Research Center, University of California, Davis, CA 95616 **[333]**

Barry F. King, Department of Human Anatomy, University of California School of Medicine, Davis, CA 95616 **[311]**

Marilyn J. Koering, Department of Anatomy, George Washington University Medical Center, Washington, D.C. 20037 **[215]**

Ronald W. Lewis, Department of Urology/Reproductive Physiology, Delta Regional Primate Research Center, Tulane University, Covington, LA 70433 **[101]**

Gary R. Marshall, Max Planck Clinical Research Unit for Reproductive Medicine, University Women's Hospital, D-4400 Münster, Federal Republic of Germany **[149]**

Eberhard Nieschlag, Max Planck Clinical Research Unit for Reproductive Medicine, University Women's Hospital, D-4400 Münster, Federal Republic of Germany **[149]**

Reid L. Norman, Department of Anatomy, Texas Tech University Health Sciences Center, Lubbock, TX 79430 **[1]**

Srinivasa Prahalada, California Primate Research Center, University of California, Davis, CA 95616 **[333]**

Jerry A. Robinson, University of Wisconsin Regional Primate Research Center, Madison, WI 53706 **[63]**

A.G. Sacco, Department of Obstetrics and Gynecology, Wayne State University, Detroit, MI 48202 **[263]**

The number in brackets is the opening page number of the contributor's article.

Sandra Schlafke, Department of Human Anatomy, University of California School of Medicine, Davis, CA 95616 **[291]**

Elizabeth S. Watts, Department of Anthropology, Tulane University, New Orleans, LA 70118 **[415]**

E. Jean Wickings, Department of Experimental Endocrinology, University Women's Hospital, D-4400 Münster, Federal Republic of Germany; present address: Institute of Obstetrics and Gynaecology, Hammersmith Hospital, London W12 0HS, United Kingdom **[149]**

David E. Wildt, National Zoological Park, Smithsonian Institution, Washington, D.C. 20008 **[171]**

Yutaka Yorozu, Endocrine Research Center, Michigan State University, East Lansing, MI 48824; present address: Department of Obstetrics and Gynecology, Asahikawa Red Cross Hospital, Asahikawa, Japan **[277]**

Foreword

This is Volume 3 of **Comparative Primate Biology**. It is designed to provide current comprehensive reviews of topics in endocrinology, development, and reproduction. The information is valuable for basic research on these topics and for application to a variety of purposes. Like much information in primatology, there are direct and practical values for understanding mechanisms and processes in humans and other animals. The comparative perspective provides a basis for generalization that has practical significance as well as theoretical value.

It is not uncommon for nonhuman primates to be studied as very general models, on the order of comparison of "the rodent, the fish, the bird, and the primate." There is increasing recognition that such general animals do not exist, and that the relativity of information from any species must be established by comparison with other species. Basic knowledge of behavior and ecology (Volume 2, Parts A and B), anatomy, systematics, and evolution (Volume 1), and neurological factors (Volume 4), are all essential for those working in the areas covered in this volume to optimize the value of their research.

The primary editor of this volume, Dr. W. Richard Dukelow, is eminently qualified to put together a book of this kind. He has worked with several different species and recognizes the value of coordinated comparative research. He recognizes that his work has potential application for biotechnological uses as well as for the preservation of biological diversity. He is aware of the need for basic understanding of processes that operate in humans as in nonhuman primates, in sickness and in health. Fortunately, more and more of those who wish to preserve primates are coming to appreciate the value of basic knowledge about reproduction and development.

My association with Dr. Dukelow extends back to 1976, when he agreed to serve on the steering committee that was set up to form the American Society of Primatologists. He was primarily responsible for getting that society developed into a fiscally viable entity. He served for several years as the treasurer of the society. He has also served as president elect, and will be sworn in as president of the society shortly after this volume comes off press. The first time I met Dr. Dukelow was at the congress of the International Primatological Society in Cambridge, England. Since that time we have had many occasions to discuss the development of the interdisciplinary field of primatology. I recall one conversation in Nairobi, Kenya, regarding possible conservation strategies for the muriqui of Brazil. It became clear to me on that occasion that Richard Dukelow had remarkable breadth, intellectually and emotionally. Most important of all, he has the ability to get things done, and he demonstrated that once again in completing this volume.

As with all the volumes of **Comparative Primate Biology**, this volume is intended as a point of departure—as a stimulus for further work. When we see (as is often apparent in the reviews in this volume) that we have good information on only a few species for many topics, I hope we will all be inspired to redouble our efforts to fill the huge gaps in knowledge that must be filled if we are to fully understand primates and the role of humans in natural systems. Let us hope that this work will progress unimpeded in time to prevent the extinction of additional primate species that are currently threatened by human activities. As in all the volumes of **Comparative Primate Biology**, the goal of this work is a deeper and broader understanding of primates and to point to the promise of primatology as an area of interface between the social, behavioral, biological, and health sciences.

J. Erwin
Series Editor
Washington, D.C.

Preface

The fate of many nonhuman primate species lies in the hands of man! The increasing use of primates in research over the last several decades and the gradual encroachment of man (primarily through the lumbering industry) on the natural habitat of many nonhuman species have resulted in the decimation of native populations and even near extinction of some species. Early capture of nonhuman primates for the pet and circus trade as well as extensive use of some species for vaccine production have also taken their toll. Traditionally, the nonhuman primate species utilized by man have been wild-caught and it has only been in the last decade that extensive efforts have been undertaken for captive breeding and rearing.

In the late 1950s the production of polimyelitis vaccine from *Macaca mulatta* caused the government of India to place an embargo upon the exportation of this species. That action reflected concern of that government of the high incidence of transit losses and the decimation of native populations. It had a secondary effect which was, although not intended, a salvation for a number of nonhuman primate species. Prior to that time there was a strong belief, rightly or wrongly, that most biomedical research programs must involve the rhesus monkey because of the background of available data. When that source of supply was cut off, scientists turned their attention to other, more readily available, nonhuman primates (particularly macaque species) and realized that alternative species would be necessary. Before this could be done it was necessary to initiate basic biological studies of a number of different species to provide the background information. Coupled with this was the realization that the captive breeding of a number of primate species was necessary not only for production of animals for research usage, but also for the maintenance of species in captivity in zoos or for the final salvation of very endangered species in their native countries. The results of this increased education on the basic reproductive biology of nonhuman primates have been more intelligent usage of the animals for research, improved breeding in captivity, and sounder conservation programs for the management of animals in their native environment. The basic concept in modern zoos has changed from one of merely display to self-perpetuating units and the interchange of animals between zoos for breeding purposes has greatly increased. Many nearly extinct species now find their final refuge in such environments. Primate research facilities are orienting their research programs towards reproductive physiology in an effort to solve some of these most pressing problems.

In view of this increased emphasis in the area of reproductive physiology and endocrinology, it is entirely fitting that the present volume be assembled featuring a current update on the major fields relating to captive breeding and reproduction. The extent of knowledge in some of these fields (i.e., menstrual cycle endocrinology, in vitro fertilization, etc.) is substantial, reflecting the use of nonhuman primates as research models for human-related problems. On the other hand, some aspects of the reproductive cycle (i.e., aging, advanced biotechnology) are in their infancy and require more advanced study.

This volume should provide the reader with basic background information relating to the endocrinology of reproduction in nonhuman primates as it exists at the time of publication. This not only will provide a history of previous studies but also the basis for research in the future.

W. Richard Dukelow
East Lansing

Central Nervous System Regulation of Anterior Pituitary Function

Reid L. Norman

Oregon Regional Primate Research Center, Beaverton, Oregon 97006, and Department of Anatomy, Texas Tech University Health Sciences Center, Lubbock, Texas 79430

INTRODUCTION

In this essay I will attempt to review the existing data on how the central nervous system (CNS) controls the activity of the pars distalis (anterior pituitary) gland in primates. Most of these neuroendocrine studies have been conducted within the past few years and within only a few primate species. For several reasons, the rhesus macaque *(Macaca mulatta)* and man are the most studied species. There exists a stereotaxic atlas for the brain of the rhesus macaque, and, until just recently, this species has been available and moderately priced. The rhesus macaque has been a favorite in reproductive neuroendocrine studies because of its size, availability, and the fact that it has a menstrual cycle comparable to that in women. A great deal of descriptive work has been conducted in human primates concerning neuroendocrine relationships. However, experimental approaches are more difficult to conduct except when inborn errors or disease states require surgical modifications that create unique opportunities for neuroendocrine studies. It is important to note that primate neuroendocrine research owes a great deal of inspiration to similar, previous studies in nonprimates. Although it is not within the scope of this review to cite contributions in nonprimate species, I will have to occasionally because the pertinent data do not exist in primates.

The primary influence of the CNS on pituitary function is stimulatory. When physically or physiologically removed from the control of the CNS, specifically the hypothalamus, secretion of adrenocorticotropin (ACTH), follicle-stimulating hormone (FSH), growth hormone (GH), luteinizing hormone (LH), and thyroid-stimulating hormone (TSH), are depressed, only the secretion of prolactin (PRL) is enhanced. Several recent reviews may be consulted for a more complete discussion of the anatomy, immunocytochemistry, receptor analysis, and peptide physiology of the hypophysiotropic hypothalamus [Hayward, 1977; Reichlin et al, 1978].

In general, the CNS exerts both stimulatory and inhibitory influence on each pituitary hormone. Although all of the hypothalamic factors that affect adenohypophysial function have not been identified, they include traditional neurotransmitters such as dopamine as well as small peptides. Through these neurohumoral agents, the CNS is able to control the secretion of some of the most powerful metabolic stimulators within the body.

This neuroendocrine link, anatomically represented by the hypophysial-portal system, is one way the CNS adjusts and synchronizes the internal environment with the external environment. Primates as well as other organisms have internally generated biological rhythms [Moore-Ede et al, 1982]. Individuals are most successful if they can synchronize these internal rhythms (ie, cortisol production) with the environment. In addition, individuals must also react to temporary (suckling) or discrete (stressful) external stimuli with appropriate physiological responses (hormone release). The pituitary serves as the primary avenue through

Comparative Primate Biology, Volume 3: Reproduction and Development, pages 1–16
© 1986 Alan R. Liss, Inc.

which the CNS acts to bring about internal metabolic changes that are of prime importance to both the individual and the species.

This review is not comprehensive but should be used as an avenue into the pertinent literature.

CONTROL OF ADRENOCORTICOTROPIN SECRETION

It is appropriate that we first consider the CNS regulation of the pituitary-adrenal axis since it was this physiological interaction that was responsible for providing the impetus for the intense search for the hypothalamic factors or hormones that influence the pituitary.

Seven years after Harris [1948] proposed a neuroendocrine link in the release of stress-related hormones, Saffran and Schally [1955] and Guillemin and Rosenberg [1955] independently presented convincing evidence that something in hypothalamic extracts would stimulate the release of ACTH. This substance was named corticotropin-releasing factor (CRF) by Saffran and Schally [1955], and this designation has served as the generic precursor for other brain peptides that influence pituitary function. After over 25 years of dedicated research, a material that qualified as CRF has been identified and synthesized [Vale et al, 1981; Spiess et al, 1981]. In comparison to the other hypothalamic releasing factors thus far identified, CRF is unique in that it is larger (41 amino acid residues) than the hormone it releases (ACTH, 39 amino acid residues). The tissue concentration of CRF has been studied in several species, including man, and has been found by Yasuda and Greer [1978] to be highest in hypophysial stalk.

With the identification of a specific CRF and the attendant enthusiasm to describe the wide-ranging effects of this material as the stress-related hormone, it is important that we do not forget that previous candidates for CRF, such as vasopressin, may also serve to regulate ACTH secretion [Yasuda et al, 1982]. The observation by Zimmerman et al [1973] that high levels of vasopressin are present in hypophysial portal blood of rhesus monkeys lends credibility to the suggestion that this hormone may be a physiological regulator of ACTH. In addition to vasopressin, there may exist other nonneural factors that influence the release of ACTH under extreme conditions [Brodish, 1979].

Because of methodological problems in the measurement of circulating levels of ACTH, most of the information concerning the control of this pituitary hormone has been gained by analyzing serum or urine levels of adrenal corticosteroids.

In adult rhesus macaques and human beings, serum corticosteroids show rhythms that have a periodicity of about 24 hours [Migeon et al, 1956; Perkoff et al, 1959; Krieger et al, 1971; Weitzman et al, 1971; Michael et al, 1974; Leshner et al, 1978; Spies et al, 1979; Quabbe et al, 1982]. In both species serum cortisol is highest in the morning and reaches a nadir in late afternoon, and reflects changes in ACTH secretion [Krieger et al, 1971; Gallagher et al, 1973]. Although the corticosteroid rhythm has not been described in children until the midprepubertal period [Franks, 1967], it appears to be present in rhesus monkeys from the day of birth [Hess and Plant, 1981]. This rhythm is the reverse of that seen in nocturnal animals such as the rat [Critchlow et al, 1963] and is probably entrained to the activity cycle of the animal rather than the light-dark cycle. As is the case for several other pituitary hormones, the smooth 24-hour rhythm in serum cortisol is a simplified view of how this hormone, and presumably ACTH, is secreted. By analyzing blood samples collected at frequent intervals, the episodic or pulsatile nature of cortisol secretion was revealed in man [Weitzman et al, 1971], in baboons [McIntosh et al, 1981], and in rhesus monkeys [Jacoby et al, 1974]. In man these episodes or secretory bursts occur at 40- to 280-minute intervals during the daytime. The interval between the last secretory episode during waking hours and the first nocturnal episode may be as long as 8 hours [Weitzman et al, 1971]. In monkeys, early studies indicated the episodes have a predominant periodicity of 85–90 minutes, and are synchronized between individuals that are separately maintained in identical environments [Holaday et al, 1977]. However, more recent studies in animals not socially deprived have revealed a 30- to 60-minute periodicity in episodic cortisol secretion [Quabbe et al, 1982].

Attempts to temporally relate nocturnal cortisol secretion with sleep stages have generally shown that in neither the rhesus monkey [Jacoby et al, 1974; Quabbe et al, 1982] nor man [Takahashi et al, 1968; Weitzman et al, 1974] is there a correlation between these events. However, although there is no correlation between sleep and nocturnal episodes, the circadian cortisol pattern is entrained to the sleep-wake cycle [Krieger, 1974].

It is apparent that both the regulation of the circadian pattern of ACTH and cortisol secretion as well as the activation of the pituitary-adrenal axis in response to stress [Fortier, 1966] depend on communication between the CNS and pituitary. It is generally understood and accepted that the CNS is responsible for generating these rhythms [Moore, 1978]. Predictably, when the pituitary is removed from hypothalamic influence in monkeys by cutting the hypophysial stalk and placement of a barrier to prevent revascularization of the pituitary, the circadian variation in serum cortisol is lost [Spies et al, 1979]. In these stalk-sectioned (SS) monkeys, cortisol levels remain stable at a level below the daily nadir. Several studies in adult monkeys have shown that when the medial basal hypothalamus is surgically isolated from the rest of the brain, the diurnal cortisol rhythm is abolished [McHugh, 1970; Krey et al, 1975; Ferin et al, 1977; Spies et al, 1979], but serum concentrations are not diminished as in SS animals [Spies et al, 1979]. Neither rostral hypothalamic lesions (which destroyed the suprachiasmatic nuclei) nor removal of caudal hypothalamic connections disrupted the diurnal secretion of cortisol. However, when the posterior hypothalamic connections were cut in animals with rostral hypothalamic lesions, the cortisol rhythms persisted but were free-running [Spies et al, 1979]. Thus it appears that although some extrahypothalamic input is required to generate the diurnal cortisol rhythm in monkeys, considerably more input is required to entrain this rhythm to the light-dark cycle.

In contrast to observations in adult monkeys, diurnal fluctuations in cortisol persist after complete hypothalamic disconnection in young monkeys [Krey et al, 1981; Norman and Spies, 1981]. The reason for this discrepancy between adult and young animals is not apparent at this time.

In man, diseases of the hypothalamus or limbic system result in altered circadian patterns of ACTH and cortisol in about 50% of patients with diseases in these areas [Krieger, 1973]. However, massive lesions in the temporal lobe of young monkeys do not grossly disturb cortisol rhythms [Norman and Spies, 1981].

Our understanding of the specific neurotransmitters involved in regulation of CRF-ACTH secretion is, at best, primitive. Weiner and Ganong [1978] recently reviewed this area and stated that our knowledge of it is conflicting and inconclusive.

In most species studied, including monkeys and man, the data are consistent with norepinephrine having an inhibitory effect on CRF release. In monkeys, resting ACTH levels were suppressed by amphetamine, a catecholamine-releasing drug [Marantz et al, 1976], but L-dopa had no effect on plasma corticoid concentrations [Chambers and Brown, 1976].

Serotonin may also be inhibitory to the secretion of ACTH. Infusion of tryptophan, the precursor to serotonin, decreased plasma cortisol concentrations and blunted the cortisol response to hypoglycemia [Woolf and Lee, 1977]. Serotonin may influence ACTH secretion through the circadian control mechanisms within the CNS, but this remains to be established [Weiner and Ganong, 1978].

CONTROL OF GROWTH HORMONE SECRETION

The secretion of GH from the pituitary is regulated by both stimulatory and inhibitory hypothalamic factors. Whereas the structure of GH release-inhibiting factor (GIF) or somatostatin first reported by Krulich and co-workers [1972] is known [Brazeau et al, 1973], the nature of GH-releasing factor (GHRF) has not been established. However, a 44-amino acid peptide with growth hormone-releasing activity has been isolated from a pancreatic tumor that caused acromegaly [Guillemin et al, 1982]. Initial studies with this GHRF-like peptide indicate that GH is under simultaneous physiological regulation by GHRF and somatostatin [Wehrenberg et al, 1982]. The neurotransmitters that affect secretion of GH and appear to regulate GHRF and GIF release are dopamine, norepinephrine, and serotonin [Martin et al, 1977a]. Two recent reviews on the neuroendocrine [Martin et al, 1978] and rhythmic [Parker et al, 1979] control of GH secretion are recommended.

The major influence of the hypothalamus on pituitary GH secretion in the primate is stimulatory. In both rhesus monkeys [Shintani et al, 1972; Vaughn et al, 1980] and man [Powell et al, 1966], transection of the pituitary stalk results in a decrease in both basal and hypoglycemia-induced GH secretion.

As for most other pituitary hormones, GH is secreted in an episodic manner, presumably as a consequence of CNS activation. Some of these secretory episodes appear to be a result of endogenous activation, and others are provoked by environmental stimuli. In the baboon [Parker et al, 1972] and man [Quabbe et al, 1966; Honda et al, 1969; Parker et al, 1969], but not in the rhesus macaque [Jacoby et al, 1974; Quabbe et al, 1981], there is an association between major GH secretory episodes and the onset of sleep. This association between GH release and sleep appears within the first year of life in relation to the organization of sleep-wake cycles [Finkelstein et al, 1971; Shaywitz et al, 1971] and the appearance of slow-wave sleep [Vigneri and D'Agata, 1971]. Although there appears to be a correlation between slow-wave sleep and growth hormone release since they both cluster in early sleep [Parker et al, 1973], there does not seem to be a cause-and-effect relationship between the two phenomena [Parker et al, 1979]. However, because of the strong correlation between GH release and sleep, there is a circadian periodicity or rhythm in GH secretion. The impact of the sleep-wake cycle on the GH rhythm has been demonstrated in individuals on a 30-hour sleep-wake cycle. In these subjects, GH rhythms showed a periodicity equivalent to the sleep-wake cycle rather than a circadian periodicity [Parker et al, 1979].

There is also an ultradian rhythm in GH release. This rhythm has a period of about 4 hours in baboons [Steiner et al, 1978], 3–6 hours in monkeys [Quabbe et al, 1981], and about 6 hours in man [Parker et al, 1979]. In all three species, episodes of GH release were synchronized among individuals, except in the rhesus macaques during daytime [Quabbe et al, 1981]. This synchrony may have been the result of standard feeding time within each study and limited freedom of movement, since both of these environmental variables affect GH release [Roth et al, 1963; Glick et al, 1965]. An excellent discussion of the ultradian rhythm in GH release in man and its dependency on and synchronization to feeding can be found in the article by Parker and colleagues [1979].

As might be expected, the magnitude and frequency of spontaneous GH surges in man are age-dependent, with the highest frequency observed in adolescence [Finkelstein et al, 1972]. Another factor that affects the frequency of GH release is availability of food. Daytime GH release was es-sentially silenced in individuals fed every 2 hours [Parker et al, 1979], whereas the frequency of GH release increases with fasting [Glick and Goldsmith, 1968].

The control of GH release is influenced by metabolic factors; but how, and to what extent, variations in glucose, amino acids, and free fatty acids influence hypothalamic regulation of GH is still poorly understood. Hypoglycemia induced by insulin injection has become a widely used provocative test for GH release [Roth et al, 1963]. Presumably, there are cells within the hypothalamus that are sensitive to circulating blood glucose and that can cause GH release in response to low levels of blood glucose. Intravenous administration of 2-deoxy-D-glucose (2DG), a metabolic inhibitor of glycolysis [Tower, 1958], also causes GH release [Roth et al, 1963]. When 2DG is infused directly into a restricted area of the lateral hypothalamus, just lateral to the ventromedial nucleus, GH is released in a pattern identical to that induced by intravenous insulin or 2DG [Himsworth et al, 1972]. These cells within the lateral hypothalamus are thought to be responsible for initiation of the GH response to insulin- and vasopressin-induced hypoglycemia since surgical isolation of the medial basal hypothalamus in monkeys effectively blocked this response [Krey et al, 1975].

Hypothalamic peptides other than GHRF and somatostatin that have been implicated in the control of GH release are vasopressin [Meyer and Knobil, 1966; Zimmerman et al, 1973], α-melanocyte stimulating hormone (α-MSH) [Strauch et al, 1973], glucagon [Eddy et al, 1974], and possibly others [Martin et al, 1978].

The aminergic control of GH secretion has been extensively reviewed by Weiner and Ganong [1978] and by Martin et al [1978]. In primates, norepinephrine, dopamine, and serotonin will all release GH [Martin, 1976]. Administration of L-dopa, the precursor of dopamine and norepinephrine, or clomidene, both selective noradrenergic receptor agonists, will elevate plasma GH levels in man [Lal et al, 1975; Lancranian and Marbach, 1977], monkeys [Jacoby et al, 1974; Chambers and Brown, 1975], and baboons [McWilliam and Meldrum, 1983]. Although the GH-releasing effect of L-dopa is probably mediated through its conversion to norepinephrine [Martin, 1976], it is possible that dopamine as well may be involved in the control of GH secretion since a specific dopamine agonist, apomorphine, will also release GH in man [Lal et al, 1973; Smythe et al, 1976]. However, the intrahypothalamic administration of norepinephrine but not dopamine in baboons resulted in GH release and this effect was blocked by phentolamine [Toivola and Gale, 1972; Toivola et al, 1972]. This would suggest that the GH-releasing action of dopamine may be at the pituitary or median eminence. Most of the stimuli that cause GH release in man (insulin hypoglycemia, exercise, vasopressin, L-dopa, and stress) probably act through central α-adrenergic receptors since their ability to release GH can be blocked by phentolamine, an α-receptor blocking agent [Martin, 1976]. Conversely, when β-adrenergic receptor agonists are given to monkeys, GH release is inhibited [Schaub et al, 1980], whereas β-adrenergic receptor antagonists augment the hypoglycemia-, exercise-, and L-dopa-induced release of GH in man [Blackard and Heidingsfelder, 1968; Hansen, 1971; Camanni et al, 1974; MacLaren et al, 1975]. Since blockade of the dopaminergic and α- and β-adrenergic receptors with chlorpromazine did not affect the physiologic sleep-related GH release, it is likely that some other mechanism controls this aspect of GH secretion [Martin, 1973].

The involvement of serotonin in the regulation of GH secretion is unclear. Administration of 5-hydroxytryptophan will cause some GH release in monkeys [Jacoby et al, 1974; Chambers and Brown, 1976] and man [Imura et al, 1973; Nakai and Imura, 1974]. In addition, GH release in response to physiologic (sleep, hypoglycemia) stimuli is reduced by cyproheptadine, a serotonin-blocking drug [Bivens et al, 1973; Chihara et al, 1976].

CONTROL OF THYROTROPIN SECRETION

The first hypothalamic releasing factor to be purified [Burgus et al, 1970; Nair et al, 1970] and synthesized [Burgus et al, 1969; Folkers et al, 1969; Baush et al, 1970] was named thyrotropin-releasing hormone (TRH). This tripeptide, pyroglutamyl-histidyl-proline-amide, not only acts on the thyrotropes to release TSH, but will also stimulate mammotrophs to release PRL in vitro [Tashjian et al, 1971] and in vivo [Jacobs et al, 1971]. Since 70–80% of this peptide in the nervous system is found in extrahypothalamic brain, it is likely to have additional employment unrelated to its hypophysiotropic effects. Other neurotransmitters that appear to regulate TSH secretion are dopa-

mine, norepinephrine, and somatostatin. Several recent reviews on the control of TSH secretion are recommended [Martin et al, 1977; Scanlon et al, 1980; Morley, 1981].

Pituitary TSH secretion depends on stimulation from the CNS. When hypothalamic influence on pituitary function is removed by stalk section in rhesus monkeys, serum thyroxine (T_4) levels fall [Norman et al, 1982]. Tertiary or hypothalamic hypothyroidism is thought to result from a deficit in hypothalamic TRH [Kaplan et al, 1972; Morley, 1981]. Complete surgical disconnection of the medial basal hypothalamus of female rhesus monkeys caused a 50% decrease in T_4 levels in six of ten animals. In the remaining four animals T_4 was unchanged as it was after anterior disconnection [Butler et al, 1975]. The thyrotropic area has been localized in the anterior hypothalamus [Greer, 1952], probably involving the paraventricular nuclei and surrounding area [Aizawa and Greer, 1981].

Analysis of circulating TSH levels in man indicates that both ultradian [Alford et al, 1973; Parker et al, 1976] and circadian [Vanhaelst et al, 1972; Weeke, 1973; Azukizawa et al, 1976] rhythms are present. Very few data exist on patterns of TSH secretion in primates other than man owing to the lack of appropriate assays. The circadian pattern of TSH secretion in man is different from the ACTH pattern in that peak levels are observed between 2100 and 2300 hours with the nadir at 1100 hours [Patel et al, 1974; Weeke, 1973]. The nighttime increase in serum TSH begins before the onset of sleep [Weeke, 1973; Chan et al, 1978] and is larger and broader during sleep deprivation [Parker et al, 1976], suggesting that secretion is inhibited by sleep. Although adrenal steroids, thyroid hormones (T_3 and T_4), and dopamine influence TSH secretion, none of these account for the circadian TSH rhythm [Scanlon et al, 1980].

Both physical and psychological stress and changes in environmental temperature are stimuli that affect TSH secretion. Physical stresses including starvation [Vinik et al, 1975; Croxson et al, 1977], shock [Oppenheimer et al, 1958], and surgery [Goldenberg et al, 1957; Kehlet et al, 1979] inhibit thyroid function in man. Presumably these responses are a result of decreased TSH secretion. Psychological stressors such as conditioned avoidance situations [Harrison et al, 1968; Mason et al, 1968] and exposure to simulated battle conditions [Levi, 1972] result in increased thyroid activity.

However, it is not clear that the classic neuroendocrine pathway is activated by these situations. Because of the rich autonomic innervation of the thyroid and the sensitivity of the thyroid to monoaminergic stimulation, stressful stimuli might increase thyroid activity directly [Melander et al, 1973; Melander, 1977].

The increased TSH secretion in response to decreased environmental temperature is more dramatic in neonates [Fisher and Odell, 1964; Wilbur and Baum, 1970] than in adults [Hershman and Pittman, 1970; Golstein-Golaire et al, 1970; Tuomisto et al, 1976]. Based on our current understanding of temperature regulation by the hypothalamus, activation of the pituitary by TRH would result from increased norepinephrine secretion [Cox and Lomax, 1977] induced by temperature-sensitive neurons in the anterior hypothalamus [Nakayama et al, 1963].

The monoamine that has been most thoroughly studied in regard to its effect on TSH secretion is dopamine. Scanlon et al [1980] have written an in-depth review of literature pertaining to this subject. The consensus is that in man dopamine has an inhibitory effect on TSH secretion. Dopamine and L-dopa depress TSH levels in normal and hypothyroid individuals and block the TSH response to TRH [Hidaka, 1971; Spaulding et al, 1972; Refetoff et al, 1974; Besses et al, 1975; Delitala, 1977; Lamberg et al, 1977; Leebaw et al, 1978; Massara et al, 1978; Kapstein et al, 1980]. It is most likely that this inhibitory effect of dopamine on TSH secretion is at the level of the pituitary since dopamine does not cross the blood brain barrier [Weil-Malherbe et al, 1961; Oldendorf, 1971] and the median eminence probably does not have dopamine receptors [Brown et al, 1976].

As discussed above, it is very likely that the cold-induced release of TSH is mediated by norepinephrine [Cox and Lomax, 1977]. The α-adrenergic stimulation of TSH is believed to be mediated through TRH [Morley, 1981].

The role of serotonin in control of TSH secretion is unclear. Administration of L-tryptophan decreased TRH-induced TSH release in vervet monkeys [Morley et al, 1980], but had no effect on basal TSH secretion in man [Woolf and Lee, 1977]. In general serotonin does not appear to be intimately involved in regulation of TSH secretion.

Other than TRH, the hypothalamic peptide that exerts considerable effect on TSH secretion is somatostatin. This peptide, in addition to inhibiting GH secretion, appears to be inhibitory to TSH secretion as well. Infusion of this peptide will block the nocturnal TSH elevation in normal subjects [Weeke et al, 1975, 1980; Azukizawa et al, 1976], elevate TSH levels in hypothyroid individuals [Lucke et al, 1975] and the TSH response to TRH [Hall et al, 1973; Siler et al, 1974; Weeke et al, 1974; Carr et al, 1975]. This effect may be directly on the pituitary since TSH secretion is inhibited by somatostatin in vitro [Belanger et al, 1974; Vale et al, 1974].

CONTROL OF PROLACTIN SECRETION

Intense interest in the control of prolactin secretion in primates has developed in the past decade. After it became possible to measure prolactin activity separate from growth hormone activity [Frantz and Kleinberg, 1970], it gradually emerged that abnormal prolactin secretion was symptomatic of what appears to be hypothalamic infertility. The inhibition of prolactin secretion by pituitary cells in vitro is also used to broadly define the dopaminergic activity of various pharmacologic agents.

Prolactin is unique in that it is the only pituitary hormone that remains under tonic hypothalamic inhibition. This was first observed in the rat by Everett [1954] and has since been confirmed in monkeys [Diefenbach et al, 1976; Vaughn et al, 1980; Norman et al, 1980] and man [Woolf et al, 1974]. When the pituitary is removed from hypothalamic influence, either by transection of the hypophysial portal system or by transplantation of the pituitary to a remote site, prolactin secretion increases manyfold. The descripton of a tuberoinfundibular dopaminergic set of neurons, independent of brainstem dopamine systems [Fuxe and Hökfelt, 1966], and the demonstration that dopamine would suppress prolactin secretion in vitro [MacLeod et al, 1970] helped establish dopamine as a physiologic prolactin-inhibiting hormone (PIH).

In addition to the generally accepted role for dopamine as the most potent PIH, there is good evidence for a prolactin-releasing hormone (PRH) as well. Weiner and Bethea [1981] have recently reviewed evidence indicating that both TRH and vasoactive intestinal peptide (VIP) could serve as physiologic prolactin-releasing factors (PRFs). Other catecholamines and peptides such as the endogenous opiates can influence prolactin secretion [Weiner and Bethea, 1981] but probably do so through their influence on dopamine or PRH.

Peripheral estrogen levels can also affect prolactin secretion in both macaques [Quadri et al, 1979] and humans [Vekeman et al, 1977]. However, physiologic fluctuations in estrogen levels do not appear to cause major changes in prolactin secretion [Ehara et al, 1973; Tyson and Friesen, 1973; Quadri and Spies, 1976].

In rhesus monkeys, the pattern of prolactin secretion has both episodic and diurnal components. The frequent secretory episodes of prolactin secretion are superimposed on the diurnal rhythm and may actually have an ultradian rhythm of their own [Quabbe et al, 1982]. Serum prolactin levels are higher at night than during the day in both rhesus monkeys [Quadri and Spies, 1976; Spies et al, 1979; Norman and Spies, 1981; Quabbe et al, 1982] and humans [Sassin et al, 1972; Parker et al, 1973; Copinschi et al, 1978]; however, the exact pattern of secretion is somewhat different between the two species. This diurnal rhythm in adult monkeys is dependent on influence from outside the medial basal hypothalamus since surgical isolation of this area abolishes the rhythm [Spies et al, 1979]. This nocturnal prolactin increase is associated with the onset of sleep in monkeys [Quabbe et al, 1982], and the tendency is for prolactin to be elevated during slow-wave sleep. Prolactin release in man can be triggered by feeding [Sassin et al, 1972; Quigley et al, 1981] and by daytime sleep [Sassin et al, 1973; Parker et al, 1973].

The stimulus for the episodic pattern of prolactin secretion observed in both man [Sassin et al, 1972] and monkeys [Norman et al, 1981; Quabbe et al, 1982] is not known. However, in some instances in both rhesus monkeys [Belchetz et al, 1978; Norman et al, 1981] and man [Yen, 1978], the episodic release of prolactin is synchronized with the release of luteinizing hormone (LH). Since there are many instances when LH and prolactin release are not synchronized, the pulse generator responsible for LH release is probably not a primary stimulator for prolactin.

The most potent physiologic stimulus for prolactin release is nursing in postpartum women [Frantz et al, 1972] and postpartum monkeys [Frawley et al, 1983]. The prolactin released by suckling not only provides for the production of milk but also is an important regulator of fertility [Short, 1983]. Indeed, hyperprolactinemia from causes other than nursing is associated with reduced fertility [Besser, 1983].

CONTROL OF GONADOTROPIN SECRETION

The secretion of the gonadotropic hormones, luteinizing hormone (LH) and follicle-stimulating hormone (FSH), appears to be controlled by a common central mechanism. These two hormones are secreted by the same cell, and although there are occasions when they are released separately, it is not clear how the separate release is effected. Because of the similarity in the secretion profiles of LH and FSH, I will discuss them as a single entity.

The primary central message for the synthesis and release of the gonadotropins from the anterior pituitary is a peptide hormone, luteinizing hormone-releasing hormone (LHRH), or more commonly called gonadotropin-releasing hormone (GnRH) because it releases FSH as well as LH. GnRH was isolated and synthesized in 1971 [Matsuo et al, 1971] and has since become a powerful tool in the armamentarium of both basic and clinical scientists. Together with GnRH, the ovarian steroids, estradiol and progesterone, are the other most important regulators of gonadotropin secretion. Recent reports by Ferin et al [1983] show that changes in endogenous opioids are correlated with hormonal events during the menstrual cycle of monkeys. From studies in humans, it appears that these peptides inhibit the pulsatile secretion of LH [Delitala et al, 1981; Ropert et al, 1981] by inhibiting the release of GnRH from the hypothalamus [Rasmussen et al, 1981]. Several recent reviews should be consulted for more complete discussions on the regulation of gonadotropin secretion in primates [Rebar and Yen, 1979; Knobil, 1980; Norman et al, 1983].

Serum gonadotropin levels exhibit ultradian, infradian, and, at least at puberty, circadian profiles. Ultradian rhythms have been described in rhesus monkeys [Dierschke et al, 1970; Plant, 1980; Steiner et al, 1980; Marut et al, 1981; Norman et al, 1984] and man [Yen et al, 1972a; Boyar et al, 1972; Santen and Bardin, 1973; Filicori and Crowley, 1983]. These secretory episodes are almost certainly driven by the episodic release of GnRH from the hypothalamus [Carmel et al, 1976; Levine et al, 1983; Clarke and Cummins, 1983]. The frequency of these secretory gonadotropin episodes changes throughout the day in male monkeys [Plant, 1980; Steiner et al, 1980], during puberty [Boyar et al, 1972, 1976], and in females, throughout the menstrual cycle [Yen et al, 1972a; Filicori and Crowley, 1983; Norman et al, 1984]. The frequency and amplitude of the LH pulses increase in most male primates in the evening, and this results in a diurnal rhythm of gonadotropin secretion [see Judd, 1979, for a more complete discussion]. In female primates, the frequency of LH secretory episodes probably increases somewhat through the follicular phase of the menstrual cycle, but shows a dramatic decrease in the luteal phase. A diurnal rhythm in gonadotropin secretion in female primates has not been documented. The monthly menstrual cycle is the most apparent infradian rhythm in gonadotropin secretion in female primates. The ultradian or episodic mode of gonadotropin release is superimposed on the monthly rhythm, including the midcycle, preovulatory surge of gonadotropin [Naftolin et al, 1973; Marut et al, 1981; Filicori and Crowley, 1983; Norman et al, 1984]. In fact, the dramatic elevation of LH and FSH that occurs at the time of the preovulatory surge is probably a result of the increased frequency and quantity of GnRH released [Neill et al, 1977; Levine et al, 1984] coupled with a greater pituitary sensitivity to that GnRH [Yen et al, 1972b; Jaffe and Keye, 1974; Krey et al, 1973; Adams et al, 1981]. This monthly cycle of gonadotropin release is governed by a "pelvic clock" [Corner, 1943] in which the steroid production by the ovary informs the hypothalamo-hypophysial axis what "time" it is. The follicles begin to grow in response to the gonadotropin secretion early in menstrual cycle. The tempo of pulsatile gonadotropin secretion gradually increases and the follicle matures, producing more and more estrogen (estradiol). When the follicle is mature, estradiol has reached a threshold level that will trigger the ovulatory surge of gonadotropin from the pituitary [Knobil, 1980]. The pulse generator for GnRH release begins to slow after ovulation in response to elevated progesterone levels. The corpus luteum regresses after 14 days and the process begins again. That this process can operate, at least for a time, under unvarying GnRH stimulation [Knobil, 1980] indicates the flexibility of the pituitary-gonadal axis that ultimately ensures reproductive success. However, the central nervous system of primates does respond to steroid modulation from within and, most environmental influences as well [Van Horn, 1980]. That the hypothalamus, surgically isolated from surrounding brain tissue, can support cyclic ovarian function [Krey et al, 1975, 1981; Ferin et al, 1977; Norman and Spies, 1981] does not obviate the importance of the regulatory capacity of other CNS areas [Norman et al, 1976; Spies et al, 1980]. Chronic emotional or psychological problems that result in anovulatory cycles (hypothalamic amenorrhea) most likely do so through the inhibitory action of higher nervous

centers on GnRH-driven LH pulses [Yen et al, 1978].

Considerable effort has been devoted to elucidating the role of various monoamines in the regulation of gonadotropin secretion. Both norepinephrine and dopamine participate in this regulation [see Weiner and Ganong, 1978], probably through their action on the release of GnRH.

ACKNOWLEDGMENTS

I thank Carol McLain, Lois Hasebe, and Mary Anne Foley for excellent assistance in the preparation of this manuscript. Support during the preparation of this manuscript was provided by the Oregon Regional Primate Research Center (RR-00163) and the Department of Anatomy, Texas Tech University Health Sciences Center. Publication No. 1293 of the Oregon Regional Primate Research Center.

REFERENCES

Adams, T.E.; Norman, R.L.; Spies, H.G. Gonadotropin-releasing hormone receptor binding characteristics and pituitary responsiveness in estradiol-primed monkey. SCIENCE 213:1388–1390, 1981.

Aizawa, T.; Greer, M.A. Delineation of the hypothalamic area controlling thyrotropin secretion in the rat. ENDOCRINOLOGY 109:1731–1738, 1981.

Alford, F.P.; Baker, H.W.G.; Burger, H.G.; De Krestser, D.M.; Hudson, B.; Johns, M.W.; Masterson, J.P.; Patel, Y.C.; Rennie, G.C. Temporal patterns of integrated plasma hormone levels during sleep and wakefulness. I. Thyroid stimulating hormone, growth hormone and cortisol. JOURNAL OF CLINICAL ENDOCRINOLOGY AND METABOLISM 37:841–847, 1973.

Azukizawa, M.; Pekary, A.E.; Hershman, J.M.; Parker, D.C. Plasma thyrotropin, thyroxine and triiodothyronine relationships in man. JOURNAL OF CLINICAL ENDOCRINOLOGY AND METABOLISM 43:533–542, 1976.

Baush, C.M.; Krumdieck, C.L.; Hershman, J.M.; Pittman, J.A. Jr. Synthesis and biological activity of thyrotropin-releasing hormone. ENDOCRINOLOGY 87:1015–1021, 1970.

Belanger, A.; Labrie, F.; Borgeat, P.; Savary, M.; Cote, J.; Drouin, J.; Schally, A.V.; Coy, D.H.; Coy, E.J.; Immer, H.; Sestanj, K.; Nelson, V.; Gotz, M. Inhibition of growth hormone and thyrotropin release by growth hormone-release inhibiting hormone. MOLECULAR AND CELLULAR ENDOCRINOLOGY 1:329–339, 1974.

Belchetz, P.; Dufy, B.; Knobil, E. Identification of

inhibitory and stimulatory control of prolactin secretion in rhesus monkeys. NEUROENDOCRINOLOGY 27:32-33, 1978.

Besser, M. Hyperprolactinemia: Effects on reproductive function in humans. Pp. 345-358 in NEUROENDOCRINE ASPECTS OF REPRODUCTION. R.L. Norman, ed. New York, Academic Press, 1983.

Besses, G.S.; Burrow, G.N.; Spaulding, S.W.; Donabedian, R.K. Dopamine infusion acutely inhibits the TSH and prolactin response to TRH. JOURNAL OF CLINICAL ENDOCRINOLOGY AND METABOLISM 41:985-988, 1975.

Bivens, C.H.; Lebovitz, H.E.; Feldman, J.M. Inhibition of hypoglycemia-induced growth hormone secretion by the serotonin antagonists cyproheptadine and methyserside. NEW ENGLAND JOURNAL OF MEDICINE 289:236-239, 1973.

Blackard, W.G.; Heidingsfelder, S.A. Adrenergic receptor control mechanism for growth hormone secretion. JOURNAL OF CLINICAL INVESTIGATION 47:1407-1414, 1968.

Boyar, R.; Finkelstein, J.; Roffwarg, H.; Kapen, S.; Weitzman, E.D.; Hellman, L. Synchronization of augmented luteinizing hormone secretion with sleep during puberty. NEW ENGLAND JOURNAL OF MEDICINE 287:582-586, 1972.

Boyar, R.M.; Wu, R.H.K.; Roffwarg, H,; Kapen, S,; Weitzman, E.D.; Hellman, L.; Finkelstein, J.W. Human puberty: 24-hour estradiol patterns in pubertal girls. JOURNAL OF CLINICAL ENDOCRINOLOGY AND METABOLISM 43:1418-1421, 1976.

Brazeau, P.; Vale, W.; Burgus, R.; Ling, N.; Butcher, M.; Rivier, J.; Guillemin, R. Hypothalamic polypeptide that inhibits the secretion of immunoreactive pituitary growth hormone. SCIENCE 179:77-79, 1973.

Brodish, A. Control of ACTH secretion by corticotropin-releasing factor(s). VITAMINS AND HORMONES 37:111-152, 1979.

Brown, G.M.; Seeman, P.; Lee, T. Dopamine/neuroleptic receptors in the basal hypothalamus and pituitary. ENDOCRINOLOGY 99:1407-1410, 1976.

Burgus, R.; Dunn, T.F.; Desiderio, D.; Vale, W.; Guillemin, R. Derives polypeptides de synthétase doués d'activité hypophysiotrope TRF. Nouvelles observations. COMPTES RENDUS HEBDOMADAIRES DES SEANCES DE L'ACADEMIE DES SCIENCES, SERIES D, SCIENCES NATURELLES 269:154-156, 1969.

Burgus, R.; Dunn, T.F.; Desiderio, D.; Ward, D.N.; Vale, W.; Guillemin, R. Characterization of ovine hypothalamic hypophysiotropic TSH-releasing factor. NATURE (LONDON) 226:321-325, 1970.

Butler, W.R.; Krey, L.C.; Espinosa-Campos, J.; Knobil, E. Surgical disconnection of the medial basal

hypothalamus and pituitary function in the rhesus monkey. III. Thyroxine secretion. ENDOCRINOLOGY 96:1094-1098, 1975.

Camanni, F.; Massara, F.; Molinatti, G.M. Propranolol enhancement of L-dopa induced growth hormone stimulation. BIOMEDICINE (EXPRESS) 21:241-231, 1974.

Carmel, P.W.; Araki, S.; Ferin, M. Pituitary stalk portal blood collection in rhesus monkeys: Evidence for pulsatile release of gonadotropin-releasing hormone (GnRH). ENDOCRINOLOGY 99:243-248, 1976.

Chambers, J.W.; Brown, G.M. Neurotransmitter regulation of growth hormone and ACTH in the rhesus monkey: Effects of biogenic amines. ENDOCRINOLOGY 98:420-428, 1976.

Chan, V.; Jones, A.; Liendo-Ch, P.; McNeilly, A.; Landon, J.; Besser, G.M. The relationship between circadian variations in circulating thyrotropin, thyroid hormones and prolactin. CLINICAL ENDOCRINOLOGY 9:337-349, 1978.

Chihara, K.; Kato, Y.; Maeda, K.; Matsukura, S.; Imura, H. Suppression by cyproheptadine of human growth hormone and cortisol secretion during sleep. JOURNAL OF CLINICAL INVESTIGATION 57:1393-1402, 1976.

Clarke, I.J.; Cummin, J.T. The temporal relationship between gonadotropin releasing hormone (GnRH) and luteinizing hormone secretion in ovariectomized ewes. ENDOCRINOLOGY 111:1737-1739, 1982.

Copinschi, G.; Littermite, M.; Golstein, J.; Leclercq, R.; Desir, D.; Vanhaelst, L.; Virasoro, E.; Robyn, C.; Van Cauter, E. Interrelations between circadian and ultradian variations of PRL, ACTH, cortisol, MSH and TSH in normal man. Pp. 165-172 in PROGRESS IN PROLACTIN PHYSIOLOGY AND PATHOLOGY. C. Robyn; M. Harter, eds. Amsterdam, Elsevier/North Holland, 1978.

Corner, G.W. THE HORMONES IN HUMAN REPRODUCTION. Princeton, NJ, Princeton University Press, 1943.

Cox, B.; Lomax, P. Pharmacologic control of temperature regulation. ANNUAL REVIEW OF PHARMACOLOGY AND TOXICOLOGY 17:341-353, 1977.

Critchlow, V.; Leibelt, R.A.; Bar-Sela, M.; Mountcastle, W.; Lipscomb, H.S. Sex difference in resting pituitary-adrenal function in the rat. AMERICAN JOURNAL OF PHYSIOLOGY 205:807-815, 1963.

Croxson, M.S.; Hall, T.D.; Kletzky, O.A.; Jaramillo, J.E.; Nicoloff, J.T. Decreased serum thyrotropin induced by fasting. JOURNAL OF CLINICAL ENDOCRINOLOGY AND METABOLISM 45:560-568, 1977.

Delitala, G. Dopamine and T.S.H. secretion in man. LANCET 2:760-761, 1977.

Delitala, G.; Devilla, L.; Arata, L. Opiate receptors

and anterior pituitary hormone secretion in man. Effect of naloxone infusion. ACTA ENDOCRINOLOGIA (COPENHAGEN) 97:150–156, 1981.

Diefenbach, W.P.; Carmel, P.W.; Frantz, A.G.; Ferin, M. Suppression of prolactin secretion by L-dopa in the stalk-sectioned rhesus monkey. JOURNAL OF CLINICAL ENDOCRINOLOGY AND METABOLISM 43:638–642, 1976.

Dierschke, D.J.; Bhattacharya, A.N.; Atkinson, L.E.; Knobil, E. Cichoral oscillations of plasma LH levels in the ovariectomized rhesus monkey. ENDOCRINOLOGY 87:850–853, 1970.

Eddy, R.L.; Gilliland, P.F.; Ibarra, J.D.; McMurray J.F. Jr.; Thompson, J.Q. Human-growth hormone release. Comparison of provocative test procedures. AMERICAN JOURNAL OF MEDICINE 56:179–185, 1974.

Ehara, Y.; Siler, T.; VandenBerg, G.; Sinha, Y.N.; Yen, S.C.C. Circulating prolactin levels during the menstrual cycle: Episodic release and diurnal variation. AMERICAN JOURNAL OF OBSTETRICS AND GYNECOLOGY 117:962–970, 1973.

Everett, J.W. Luteotropic function of the autographs of the rat hypophysis. ENDOCRINOLOGY 54:685–690, 1954.

Ferin, M.; Antunes, J.L.; Zimmerman, E.; Dyrenfurth, I.; Frantz, A.G.; Robinson, A.; Carmel, P.W. Endocrine function in female rhesus monkeys after hypothalamic disconnection. ENDOCRINOLOGY 101:1611–1620, 1977.

Ferin, M.; Van Vugt, D.; Chernick, A. Central nervous system peptides and reproductive function in primates. Pp. 69–92 in NEUROENDOCRINE ASPECTS OF REPRODUCTION. R.L. Norman, ed. New York, Academic Press, 1983.

Filicori, M.; Crowley, W.F. Jr. Hypothalamic regulation of gonadotropin secretion in women. Pp. 285–294 in NEUROENDOCRINE ASPECTS OF REPRODUCTION. R.L. Norman, ed. New York, Academic Press, 1983.

Finkelstein, J.W.; Anders, T.F.; Sachar, E.J.; Roffwarg, H.P.; Hellman, L.D. Behavioral state, sleep stage, and growth hormone levels in human infants. JOURNAL OF CLINICAL ENDOCRINOLOGY AND METABOLISM 32:368–371, 1971.

Finkelstein, J.W.; Roffwarg, H.P.; Boyar, R.M.; Kream, J.; Hellman, L. Age-related change in the twenty-four hour spontaneous secretion of growth hormone. JOURNAL OF CLINICAL ENDOCRINOLOGY AND METABOLISM 35:665–670, 1972.

Fisher, D.A.; Odell, W.D. Acute release of thyrotropin in the newborn. JOURNAL OF CLINICAL INVESTIGATION 48:1670–1677, 1969.

Folkers, K.; Enzmann, F.; Boler, M.; Bowers, C.Y.; Schally, A.V. Discovery of modification of the synthetic tripeptide-sequence of the thyrotropin releasing hormone having activity. BIOCHEMICAL AND BIOPHYSICAL RESEARCH COMMUNICATIONS 37:123–126, 1969.

Fortier, C. Nervous control of ACTH secretion. Pp. 195–234 in THE PITUITARY GLAND, Vol. 2. G.W. Harris; B.T. Donovan, eds. Berkeley, University of California Press, 1966.

Franks, R. Diurnal variation of plasma 17-hydroxycorticosteroids in children. JOURNAL OF CLINICAL ENDOCRINOLOGY AND METABOLISM 27:75–78, 1967.

Frantz, A.G.; Rhythms in prolactin secretion. Pp. 175–186 in ENDOCRINE RHYTHMS. D.T. Krieger, ed. New York, Raven, 1979.

Frantz, A.G.; Kleinberg, D.L. Prolactin: Evidence that it is separate from growth hormone in human blood. SCIENCE 170:745–747, 1970.

Frantz, A.G.; Kleinberg, D.L.; Noel, G.L. Studies on prolactin in man. RECENT PROGRESS IN HORMONE RESEARCH 28:527–573, 1972.

Frawley, L.S.; Mulchahey, J.J.; Neill, J.D. Nursing induces a biphasic release of prolactin in rhesus monkeys. ENDOCRINOLOGY 112:558–561, 1983.

Fuxe, K.; Hökfelt, T. Further evidence for the existence of tuberoinfundibular dopamine neurons. ACTA PHYSIOLOGICAL SCANDANAVICA 66:245–246, 1966.

Gallagher, T.F.; Yoshida, K.; Roffwarg, H.D.; Fukushima, D.K.; Weitzman, E.D.; Hellman, L. ACTH and cortisol secretory pattern in man. JOURNAL OF CLINICAL ENDOCRINOLOGY AND METABOLISM 36:1058–1068, 1973.

Glick, S.M.; Goldsmith, S. The physiology of growth hormone secretion. Pp. 84–88 in GROWTH HORMONE. A. Pecile; E.E. Muller, eds. Amsterdam, Excerpta Medica, 1968.

Glick, S.M.; Roth, J.; Yalow, R.S.; Berson, S.A. Secretion of human growth hormone secretion. RECENT PROGRESS IN HORMONE RESEARCH 21:241–283, 1965.

Goldenberg, I.S.; Rosenbaum, P.J.; White, C.; Hayes, M.A. The effect of operative trauma on the utilization of thyroid hormone. SURGERY, GYNECOLOGY AND OBSTETRICS 104:295–298, 1957.

Golstein-Golaire, J.; Vanhaelst, L.; Bruno, O.D.; Leclercq, R.; Copinschi, G. Acute effects of cold on blood levels of growth hormone, cortisol and thyrotropin in man. JOURNAL OF APPLIED PHYSIOLOGY 29:622–626, 1970.

Greer, M.A. The role of the hypothalamus in the control of thyroid function. JOURNAL OF CLINICAL ENDOCRINOLOGY AND METABOLISM 12:1259–1268, 1952.

Guillemin, R.; Rosenberg, B. Humoral hypothalamic control of anterior pituitary: A study with combined tissue cultures. ENDOCRINOLOGY 57:599–607, 1955.

Guillemin, R.; Brazeau, P.; Bohlen, P.; Esch, F.; Ling, N.; Wehrenberg, W.B. Growth hormone-releasing factor from a human pancreatic tumor that caused acromegaly. SCIENCE 218:585–587, 1982.

Hall, R.; Besser, G.M.; Schally, A.V.; Coy, D.H.; Evered, D.; Goldre, D.J.; Kastin, A.M.; McNeilly, A.L.; Mortimer, C.H.; Phenekos, C.; Turnbridge, W.M.G.; Weightman, D. Action of growth-hormone-release inhibitory hormone in healthy men and in acromegaly. LANCET 2:581–584, 1973

Hansen, A.P. The effect of adrenergic receptor blockade on the exercise-induced serum growth hormone rise in normals and juvenile diabetics. JOURNAL OF CLINICAL ENDOCRINOLOGY AND METABOLISM 33:807–812, 1971.

Harris, G.W. Neural control of the pituitary gland. PHYSIOLOGICAL REVIEWS 28:139–179, 1948.

Harrison, T.S.; Silver, D.M.; Zuideman, G.D. Thyroid and adrenal medullary function in chronic "executive" monkeys. ENDOCRINOLOGY 78:685–689, 1966.

Hayward, J.M. Functional and morphological aspects of hypothalamic neurons. PHYSIOLOGICAL REVIEWS 57:574–658, 1977.

Hershman, J.M.; Pittman, J.A. Jr. Response to synthetic thyrotropin-releasing hormone in man. JOURNAL OF CLINICAL ENDOCRINOLOGY AND METABOLISM 31:457–460, 1970.

Hess, D.L.; Plant, T.M. Neonatal ontogeny of diurnal hormone secretion by the adrenal gland and testis in the rhesus monkey *(Macaca mulatta).* ABSTRACTS OF THE ENDOCRINE SOCIETY (Abstract No. 137) 1981.

Hidaka, H. Fusaric acid, an inhibitor of dopamine-B-hydroxylase, affects serotonin and noradrenaline. NATURE (LONDON) 231:54–55, 1971.

Himsworth, R.L.; Carmel, P.W.; Frantz, A.G. The location of the chemoreceptor controlling growth hormone secretion during hypoglycemia in primates. ENDOCRINOLOGY 91:217–226, 1972.

Holaday, J.W.; Martinez, H.M.; Natelson, B.H. Synchronized ultradian cortisol rhythms in monkeys: Persistence during corticotropin infusion. SCIENCE 198:56–58, 1977.

Honda, Y.; Takahashi, K.; Takahashi, S.; Azumi, K.; Irie, M.; Sakuma, M.; Tsushima, T.; Shizume, K. Growth hormone secretion during nocturnal sleep: Electroencephalographic correlation. JOURNAL OF CLINICAL ENDOCRINOLOGY AND METABOLISM 29:871–874, 1969.

Imura, H.; Nakai, Y.; Yoshimi, T. Effect of 5-hydroxytryptophan (5-HTP) on growth hormone. Response to L-5-hydroxytryptophan (5-HTP) in man. ENDOCRINOLOGY AND METABOLISM 36:204–206, 1973.

Jacobs, L.S.; Snyder, P.J.; Wilber, J.F.; Utiger, R.D.; Daughaday, W.H. Increased serum prolactin after administration of synthetic thyrotropin releasing hormone (TRH) in man. JOURNAL OF CLINICAL ENDOCRINOLOGY AND METABOLISM 33:996–998, 1971.

Jacoby, J.H.; Greenstein, M.; Sassin, J.F.; Weitzman, E.D. The effect of monoamine precursors on the release of growth hormone in the rhesus monkey. NEUROENDOCRINOLOGY 14:95–102, 1974.

Jacoby, J.H.; Sassin, J.F.; Greenstein, M.; Weitzman, E.D. Patterns of spontaneous cortisol and growth hormone secretion in rhesus monkeys during the sleep-waking cycle. NEUROENDOCRINOLOGY 14:165–173, 1974.

Jaffe, R.B.; Keye, W.R. Jr. Estradiol augmentation of pituitary responsiveness to gonadotropin-releasing hormone in women. JOURNAL OF CLINICAL ENDOCRINOLOGY AND METABOLISM 39:850–855, 1974.

Judd, H.L. Biorhythms of gonadotropins and testicular hormone secretion. Pp. 299–324 in ENDOCRINE RHYTHMS. D.T. Krieger, ed. New York, Raven, 1979.

Kaplan, S.L.; Grumbach, M.M.; Friesen, H.G.; Costom, B.H. Thyrotropin-releasing factor (TRF) effect on secretion of human pituitary prolactin and thyrotropin in children and in idiopathic hypopituitary dwarfism: Further evidence for hypophysiotropic hormone deficiencies. JOURNAL OF CLINICAL ENDOCRINOLOGY AND METABOLISM 35:825–830, 1972.

Kapstein, E.M.; Kletzky, O.A.: Spencer, C.A.; Nicoloff, J.T. Effects of prolonged dopamine infusion on anterior pituitary function in normal males. JOURNAL OF CLINICAL ENDOCRINOLOGY AND METABOLISM 51:488–491, 1980.

Kehlet, H.; Klauber, P.V.; Weeke, M. Thyrotropin, free and total triiodothyronine and thyroxine in serum during surgery. CLINICAL ENDOCRINOLOGY 10:131–136, 1979.

Knobil, E. The neuroendocrine control of the menstrual cycle. RECENT PROGRESS IN HORMONE RESEARCH 36:53–88, 1980.

Krey, L.C.; Butler, W.R.; Knobil, E. Surgical disconnection of the medial basal hypothalamus and pituitary function in the rhesus monkey. I. Gonadotropin secretion. ENDOCRINOLOGY 96:1073–1087, 1975.

Krey, L.C.; Butler, W.R.; Weiss, G.; Weick, R.F.; Dierschke, D.J.; Knobil, E. Influences of endogenous and exogenous gonadal steroids on the actions of synthetic LRF in the rhesus monkey. Pp. 39–47 in HYPOTHALAMIC HYPOPHYSIOTROPIC HORMONES: PHYSIOLOGICAL AND CLINICAL STUDIES. C Gual; E. Rosenberg, eds. Amsterdam, Excerpta Medica, 1973.

Krey, L.C.; Hess, D.L.; Butler, W.R.; Espinosea-Campos, J.; Lu, K.H.; Piva, F.; Plant, T.M.; Knobil, E. Medial basal hypothalamic disconnection and the onset of puberty in the female rhesus monkey. ENDOCRINOLOGY 108:1944–1948, 1981.

Krey, L.C.; Lu, K.-H.; Butler, W.R.; Hotchkiss, J.; Piva, F.; Knobil, E. Surgical disconnection of the medial basal hypothalamus and pituitary function in the rhesus monkey. II. GH and cortisol secretion. ENDOCRINOLOGY 96:1088–1093, 1975.

Krieger, D.T. Pathophysiology of central nervous system regulation of anterior pituitary function. Pp. 351–408 in BIOLOGY OF BRAIN DYSFUNCTION, Vol II. G.E. Guall, ed. New York, Plenum, 1973.

Krieger, D.T. Factors influencing the circadian periodicity of plasma corticosteroid levels. CHRONOBIOLOGIA 1:195–216, 1974.

Krieger, D.T.; Allen, W.; Rizzo, F.; Krieger, H.P. Characterization of the normal temporal pattern of plasma corticosteroid levels. JOURNAL OF CLINICAL ENDOCRINOLOGY AND METABOLISM 32:266–284, 1971.

Krulich, L.; Fawcett, C.P.; Quijada, M.; McCann, S. Dual hypothalamic regulation of growth hormone secretion. Pp. 306–316 in GROWTH AND GROWTH HORMONE. A. Pecile; E.E. Muller, eds. Amsterdam, Excerpta Medica, 1971.

Lal, S.; De la Vega, C.E.; Sourkes, T.L.; Friesen, H.G. Effect of apomorphine on growth hormone, prolactin, luteinizing hormone and follicle-stimulating hormone levels in human serum. JOURNAL OF CLINICAL ENDOCRINOLOGY AND METABOLISM 37:719–724, 1973.

Lal, S.; Tolis, G.; Martin, J.B.; Brown, G.M.; Guyda, H. Effect of clonidine on growth hormone, prolactin, luteinizing hormone, follicle-stimulating hormone and thyroid-stimulating hormone in the serum of normal men. JOURNAL OF CLINICAL ENDOCRINOLOGY AND METABOLISM 41:827–832, 1975.

Lambers, B.-A.; Linnoila, M.; Fogelholm, R.; Olkinuora, M.; Kotilainen, P.; Saarinen, P. The effect of psychotropic drugs on the TH-response to thyroliberin (TRH). NEUROENDOCRINOLOGY 24:90–97, 1977.

Lancranian, I.; Marbach, P. New evidence for growth hormone modulation by the alpha-adrenergic system in man. METABOLISM 26:1225–1230, 1977.

Leebaw, W.F.; Lee, L.A.; Woolf, P.D. Dopamine affects basal and augmented pituitary hormone secretion. JOURNAL OF CLINICAL ENDOCRINOLOGY AND METABOLISM 47:480–487, 1978.

Leshner, A.I.; Toivola, P.T.K.; Terasawa, E. Circadian variations in cortisol concentrations in the plasma of female rhesus monkeys. JOURNAL OF ENDOCRINOLOGY 78:155–156, 1978.

Levi, L. STRESS AND DISTRESS IN RESPONSE TO PSYCHOSOCIAL STIMULI. Oxford, England, Pergamon, 1972.

Levine, J.E.; Pan, K.-Y.F.; Ramirez, V.P.; Jackson, G.L. Simultaneous measurement of luteinizing hormone-releasing hormone and luteinizing hormone-release in unanesthetized, ovariectomized sheep. ENDOCRINOLOGY 111:1489–1455, 1982.

Lucke, C.; Hoffken, B.; Von zur Muhlen, A. The effect of somatostatin on TSH levels in patients with primary hypothyroidism. JOURNAL OF CLINICAL ENDOCRINOLOGY AND METABOLISM 41:1082–1084, 1975.

MacLaren, N.K.; Taylor, G.E.; Raiti, S. Propranolol-augmented, exercise-induced human growth hormone release. PEDIATRICS 56:804–807, 1975.

MacLeod, RM.; Fontham, E.H.; Lehmeyer, J.E. Prolactin and growth hormone production as influenced by catecholamines and agents that affect brain catecholamines. NEUROENDOCRINOLOGY 6:283–294, 1970.

Marantz, R.; Sachar, E.J.; Weitzman, E.; Sassin, J. Cortisol and GH responses to D- and L-amphetamine in monkeys. ENDOCRINOLOGY 99:459–465, 1976.

Martin, J.B. Neural regulation of growth hormone secretion. NEW ENGLAND JOURNAL OF MEDICINE 288:1384–1393, 1973.

Martin, J.B. Brain regulation of growth hormone secretion. Pp. 129–168 in FRONTIERS IN NEUROENDOCRINOLOGY, Vol. 4. L. Martini; W.F. Ganong, eds. New York, Raven, 1976.

Martin, J.B.; Brazeau, P.; Tannenbaum, G.S.; Willoughby, J.O.; Epelbaum, J.; Terry, L.C.; Durand, D. Neuroendocrine organization of growth hormone regulation. Pp. 329–355 in THE HYPOTHALAMUS. S. Reichlin; R.J. Baldessarini; J.B. Martin, eds. New York, Raven, 1978.

Martin, J.B.; Reichlin, S.; Brown, G.M. Regulation of growth hormone and its disorders. Pp. 147–178 in CLINICAL NEUROENDOCRINOLOGY. Philadelphia, F.A. Davis, 1977a.

Martin, J.B.; Reichlin, S.; Brown, G.M. Regulation of TSH and its disorders. Pp. 201–228 in CLINICAL NEUROENDOCRINOLOGY. Philadelphia, F.A. Davis, 1977b.

Marut, E.L.; Williams, R.F.; Cowan, B.D.; Lynch, A.; Lerner, S.P.; Hodgen, G.D. Pulsatile pituitary gonadotropin secretion during maturation of the dominant follicle in monkeys: Estrogen positive feedback enhances the biological activity of LH. ENDOCRINOLOGY 109:2270–2272, 1981.

Mason, J.W.; Mougey, E.H.; Brady, J.V.; Tolliver, G.A. Thyroid (plasma butanol-extractable iodine) responses to 72-hr avoidance sessions in the monkey. PSYCHOSOMATIC MEDICINE 30:682–695, 1968.

Massara, F.; Camanni, F.; Vergano, V.; Belforte, L.; Molinatti, G.M. Inhibition of thyrotropin and prolactin secretion by dopamine in man. JOURNAL OF ENDOCRINOLOGICAL INVESTIGATION 1:25–30, 1978.

Matsuo, H.; Arimura, A.; Nair, R.M.G.; Schall, A.V. Synthesis of the porcine LH and FSH releasing hormone by the solid phase method. BIOCHEMICAL AND BIOPHYSICAL RESEARCH COMMUNICATIONS 45:822–827, 1971.

McHugh, P.R. Hypothalamic controls on feeding behavior as revealed by a "disconnection" method.

TRANSACTIONS OF THE AMERICAN NEU-ROLOGICAL ASSOCIATION 95:100–103, 1970.

McIntosh, T.; Lothrop, D.; Jackson, B.; Lee, A.; Piasecki, B.; Egdahl, R. Circadian variations in plasma cortisol concentrations of female baboons. HORMONE AND METABOLIC RESEARCH 13:125–126, 1981.

McWilliam, J.R.; Meldrum, B.S. Noradrenergic regulation of growth hormone secretion in the baboon. ENDOCRINOLOGY 112:254–259, 1983.

Melander, A. Aminergic regulation of thyroid activity: Importance of the sympathetic innervation and of the mast cells of the thyroid gland. ACTA MEDICA SCANDINAVICA 201:257–262, 1977.

Melander, A.; Sundler, F.; Westgren, U. Intrathyroidal amines and the synthesis of thyroid hormone. ENDOCRINOLOGY 93:193–200, 1973.

Meyer, J.V.; Knobil, E. Stimulation of growth hormone secretion by vasopressin in the rhesus monkey. ENDOCRINOLOGY 79:1016–1018, 1966.

Michael, R.P.; Setchell, K.D.R.; Plant, T.M. Diurnal changes in plasma testosterone and studies on plasma corticosteroids in non-anesthetized male rhesus monkeys (Macaca mulatta). JOURNAL OF ENDOCRINOLOGY 63:325–335, 1974.

Migeon, C.J.; Tyler, F.H.; Mahoney, J.P.; Florentin, A.A.; Castle, H.; Bliss, E.L.; Samuels, L.T. The diurnal variation of plasma levels and urinary excretion of 17-hydroxycorticosteroids in normal subjects, night workers and blind subjects. JOURNAL OF CLINICAL ENDOCRINOLOGY AND METABOLISM 16:622–633, 1956.

Moore, R.Y. Central neural control of circadian rhythms. Pp. 185–206 in FRONTIERS IN NEUROENDOCRINOLOGY, Vol. 5. W.F. Ganong; L. Martini, eds. New York, Raven, 1978.

Moore-Ede, M.C.; Sulzman, F.M.; Fuller, C.A. THE CLOCKS THAT TIME US: PHYSIOLOGY OF THE CIRCADIAN TIMING SYSTEM. Cambridge, MA, Harvard University Press, 1982.

Morley, J.E. Neuroendocrine control of thyrotropin secretion. ENDOCRINE REVIEWS 2:396–436, 1981.

Morley, J.E.; Raleigh, M.J.; Brammer, G.L.; Yuwiler, A.; Geller, E.; Flannery, J.; Hershman, J.M. Serotonergic and catecholaminergic influence on thyroid function in the vervet monkey. EUROPEAN JOURNAL OF PHARMACOLOGY 67:283–288, 1980.

Naftolin, F.; Yen, S.S.C.; Perlman, D.; Tsai, C.C.; Parker, D.C.; Vargo, T. Nocturnal patterns of serum gonadotropins during the menstrual cycle. JOURNAL OF CLINICAL ENDOCRINOLOGY AND METABOLISM 37:6–10, 1973.

Nair, R.M.G.; Barrett, J.F.; Bowers, C.Y.; Schally, A.V. Structure of porcine thyrotropin releasing hormone. BIOCHEMISTRY 9:1103–1106, 1970.

Nakai, Y.; Imura, H. Effect of adrenergic-blocking agents on plasma growth hormone. Response to 5-hydroxytryptophan (5-HTP) in man. ENDOCRINOLOGICA JAPONICA 21:493–497, 1974.

Nakayama, T.; Hammel, H.T.; Hardy, J.D.; Eisenman, J.S. Thermal stimulation of electrical activity of single unit of the preoptic region. AMERICAN JOURNAL OF PHYSIOLOGY 204:1122–1126, 1963.

Neill, J.D.; Patton, J.M.; Dailey, R.A.; Tsou, R.C.; Tindall, G.T. Luteinizing hormone releasing hormone (LHRH) in pituitary stalk blood of rhesus monkeys: Relationship to level of LH release. ENDOCRINOLOGY 101:430–434, 1977.

Norman, R.L.; Spies, H.G. Brain lesions in infant female rhesus monkeys: Effects on menarche and first ovulation and on diurnal rhythms of prolactin and cortisol. ENDOCRINOLOGY 108:1723–1729, 1981.

Norman, R.L.; Resko, J.A.; Spies, H.G. The anterior hypothalamus: How it effects gonadotropin secretion in the rhesus monkey. ENDOCRINOLOGY 99:59–71, 1976.

Norman, R.L.; Quadri, S.K.; Spies, H.G. Differential sensitivity of prolactin release to dopamine and thyrotropin-releasing hormone in intact and pituitary-stalk sectioned rhesus monkeys. JOURNAL OF ENDOCRINOLOGY 84:479–487, 1980.

Norman, R.L.; Ellinwood, W.E.; Spies, H.G. Episodic secretion of prolactin and luteinizing hormone are synchronized in ovariectomized rhesus monkeys. PROGRAM AND ABSTRACTS OF THE ENDOCRINE SOCIETY, 63RD ANNUAL MEETING, Abstract 43, p. 93, 1981.

Norman, R.L.; Gliessman, P.; Lindstrom, S.A.; Hill, J.; Spies, H.G. Reinitiation of ovulatory cycles in pituitary stalk-sectioned rhesus monkeys: Evidence for a specific hypothalamic message for the preovulatory release of luteinizing hormone. ENDOCRINOLOGY 111:1874–1882, 1982.

Norman, R.L.; Levine, J.E.; Spies, H.G. Control of gonadotropin secretion in primates: Observations in stalk-sectioned rhesus monkeys. Pp. 263–284 in NEUROENDOCRINE ASPECTS OF REPRODUCTION. R.L. Norman, ed. New York, Academic Press, 1983.

Norman, R.L.; Lindstrom, S.A.; Bangsberg, D.; Ellinwood, W.E.; Gliessman, P.; Spies, H.G. Pulsatile secretion of luteinizing hormone during the menstrual cycle of rhesus macaques. ENDOCRINOLOGY 115:261–266, 1984.

Oldendorf, W.H. Brain uptake of radiolabeled amino acids, amines, and hexoses after arterial injection. AMERICAN JOURNAL OF PHYSIOLOGY 221:1629–1639, 1971.

Oppenheimer, J.H.; Wise, H.M.; Lasley, D.A. The role of the thyroid gland in experimental traumatic shock. JOURNAL OF CLINICAL INVESTIGATON 37:380–388, 1958.

Parker, D.C.; Rossman, L.G. Physiology of human growth hormone release in sleep. Pp. 655–660 in ENDOCRINOLOGY. R.O. Scow, ed. Amsterdam, Excerpta Medica, 1973.

Parker, D.C.; Sassin, J.F.; Mace, J.W.; Gotlin, R.W.; Rossman, L.G. Human growth hormone release during sleep: Electroencephalographic correlation. JOURNAL OF CLINICAL ENDOCRINOLOGY AND METABOLISM 29:871–874, 1969.

Parker, D.C.; Morishima, M.; Koerker, D.J.; Gale, C.C.; Goodner, C.J. Pilot study of growth hormone release in sleep of the chair-adapted baboon: Potential as model of human sleep release. ENDOCRINOLOGY 91:1462–1467, 1972.

Parker, D.C.; Rossman, L.G.; VanderLaan, E.F. Sleep-related nyctohemeral and briefly episodic variation in human plasma prolactin concentrations. JOURNAL OF CLINICAL ENDOCRINOLOGY AND METABOLISM 36:1119–1124, 1973.

Parker, D.C.; Pekary, A.E.; Hershman, J.M. Effect of normal and reversed sleep-wake cycles upon nyctohemeral rhythmicity of plasma thyrotropin: Evidence suggestive of an inhibitory influence in sleep. JOURNAL OF CLINICAL ENDOCRINOLOGY AND METABOLISM 43:318–329, 1976.

Parker, D.C.; Rossman, L.G.; Kripke, D.F.; Gibson, W.; Wilson, K. Rhythmicities in human growth hormone concentrations in plasma. Pp. 143–173 in ENDOCRINE RHYTHMS. D.T. Krieger, ed. New York, Raven, 1979.

Patel, Y.C.; Baker, H.W.G.; Burger, H.G.; Johns, M.W.; Ledinek, J.E. Suppression of the thyrotrophin circadian rhythm by glucocorticoids. JOURNAL OF ENDOCRINOLOGY 62:421–422, 1974.

Perkoff, G.T.; Eik-Nes, K.; Nugent, C.A.; Fred, H.L.; Nimer, R.A.; Rush, L.; Samuels, L.T.; Tyler, F.H. Studies of the diurnal variation of plasma 17-hyroxycorticosteroids in man. JOURNAL OF CLINICAL ENDOCRINOLOGY AND METABOLISM 19:432–443, 1959.

Plant, T.M. Neuroendocrine basis of the diurnal variation of testicular testosterone secretion in the adult rhesus monkey (Macaca mulatta). Pp. 419–424 in TESTICULAR DEVELOPMENT, STRUCTURE AND FUNCTION. A. Steinberger; E. Steinberger, eds. New York, Raven, 1980.

Powell, E.D.U.; Frantz, A.G.; Rabkin, M.T.; Field, R.A. Growth hormone in relation to diabetic retinopathy. NEW ENGLAND JOURNAL OF MEDICINE 275:922–925, 1966.

Quabbe, H.-J.; Gregor, M.; Bumke-Vogt, C.; Eckhof, A.; Witt, I. Twenty-four hour pattern of growth hormone secretion in the rhesus monkey: Studies including alterations of the sleep/wake and sleep stage cycles. ENDOCRINOLOGY 109:513–522, 1981.

Quabbe, H.-J.; Gregor, M.; Bumke-Vogt, C.; Hardel, C. Pattern of plasma cortisol during the 24-hour sleep/wake cycle in the rhesus monkey. ENDOCRINOLOGY 110:1641–1646, 1982.

Quabbe, H.-J.; Schilling, E.; Helge, H. Pattern of growth hormone secretion during a 24-hour fast in normal adults. JOURNAL OF CLINICAL ENDO-

CRINOLOGY AND METABOLISM 26:1173–1177, 1966.

Quadri, S.K.; Spies, H.G. Cyclic and diurnal patterns of serum prolactin in the rhesus monkey. BIOLOGY OF REPRODUCTION 14:495–501, 1976.

Quadri, S.K.; Oyama, T.; Spies, H.G. Effects of 17β-estradiol on serum prolactin levels and on prolactin responses to thyrotropin-releasing hormone in female rhesus monkeys. ENDOCRINOLOGY 104:1649–1655, 1979.

Quigley, M.E.; Ropert, J.F.; Yen, S.S.C. Acute prolactin release triggered by feeding. JOURNAL OF CLINICAL ENDOCRINOLOGY AND METABOLISM 52:1043–1045, 1981.

Rasmussen, D.D.; Liu, J.H.; Wolf, P.L.; Yen, S.S.C. Endogenous opioid regulation of gonadotropin-releasing hormone release from the human fetal hypothalamus in vitro. JOURNAL OF CLINICAL ENDOCRINOLOGY AND METABOLISM 52:583–585, 1981.

Rebar, R.W.; Yen, S.S.C. Endocrine rhythms in gonadotropins and ovarian steroids with reference to reproductive processes. Pp. 259–298 in ENDOCRINE RHYTHMS. D.T. Krieger, ed. New York, Raven, 1979.

Refetoff, S.; Fang, V.S.; Rapaport, B.; Friesen, H.G. Interrelationships in the regulation of TSH and prolactin secretion in man: Effects of L-dopa, TRH and thyroid hormone in various combinations. JOURNAL OF CLINICAL ENDOCRINOLOGY AND METABOLISM 38:450–457, 1974.

Reichlin, S.; Baldessarini, R.J.; Martin, J.B., eds. THE HYPOTHALAMUS. New York, Raven, 1978.

Ropert, J.F.; Quigley, M.E.; Yen, S.S.C. Endogenous opiates modulate pulsatile luteinizing hormone release in humans. JOURNAL OF CLINICAL ENDOCRINOLOGY AND METABOLISM 52:583–585, 1981.

Roth, J.; Glick, S.M.; Yalow, R.S.; Berson, S.A. Secretion of human growth hormone: Physiologic and experimental modification. METABOLISM 12:577–579, 1963.

Saffran, M.; Schally, A.V. The release of corticotrophin by anterior pituitary tissue in vitro. CANADIAN JOURNAL OF BIOCHEMISTRY AND PHYSIOLOGY 33:408–415, 1955.

Santen, R.J.; Bardin, C.W. Episodic luteinizing hormone secretion in man. Pulse analysis, clinical interpretation, physiological mechanisms. JOURNAL OF CLINICAL INVESTIGATION 52:2617–2628, 1973.

Sassin, J.F.; Frantz, A.G.; Kapen, S.; Weitzman, E.D. The nocturnal rise of human prolactin is dependent on sleep. JOURNAL OF CLINICAL ENDOCRINOLOGY AND METABOLISM 37:436–440, 1973.

Sassin, J.F.; Frantz, A.G.; Weitzman, E.D.; Kapen, S. Human prolactin: 24-hour pattern with increased release during sleep. SCIENCE 177:1205–1207, 1972.

Scanlon, M.F.; Lewis, M.; Weightman, D.R.; Chan,

V.; Hall, R. The neuroregulation of human thyrotropin secretion. Pp. 333–380 in FRONTIERS IN NEUROENDOCRINOLOGY, Vol. 6. L. Martini; W.F. Ganong, eds. New York, Raven, 1978.

Schaub, C.; Delbarre, B.; Bluet-Pajot, M.; Casset-Senon, D.; Lornet-Videau, C.; Perger, A. Effect of beta adrenergic agonists and antagonists on growth hormone (GH) and prolactin (Prl) secretion in the monkey. NEUROENDOCRINOLOGY LETTERS (SUPPLEMENT 1) 2:45–46, 1980.

Shaywitz, B.; Finkelstein, J.; Hellman, L.; Weitzman, E.D. Growth hormone in infants during sleep-wake periods. PEDIATRICS 48:103–109, 1971.

Shintani, I.; Zervas, M.; Kuwayama, A.; Pallotta, J.; Spark, R. Transorbital pituitary stalk section in primates. JOURNAL OF NEUROSURGERY 37:601–605, 1972.

Short, R.V. Biological basis for the contraceptive effects of breast-feeding. Pp. 325–344 in NEUROENDOCRINE ASPECTS OF REPRODUCTION. R.L. Norman, ed. New York, Academic Press, 1983.

Siler, T.M.; Yen, S.S.C.; Valee, W.; Guillemin, R. Inhibition by somatostatin in the release of TSH induced in man by thyrotropin-releasing factor. JOURNAL OF CLINICAL ENDOCRINOLOGY AND METABOLISM 38:742–745, 1974.

Smyth, G.A.; Compton, P.J.; Lazarus, L. Serotonergic control of human growth hormone secretion: The action of L-dopa and 2-bromo-alpha-ergocryptine. Pp. 222–235 in GROWTH HORMONE AND RELATED PEPTIDES. A. Pecile; E.E. Muller, eds. Amsterdam, Excerpta Medica, 1976.

Spaulding, S.W.; Burrow, G.N.; Donabedian, R.; Van Woert, M. L-dopa suppression of thyrotropin releasing hormone response in man. JOURNAL OF CLINICAL ENDOCRINOLOGY AND METABOLISM 35:182–185, 1972.

Spies, H.G.; Norman, R.L.; Buhl, A.E. Twenty-four-hour patterns in serum prolactin and cortisol after partial and complete isolation of the hypothalamic-pituitary unit in rhesus monkeys. ENDOCRINOLOGY 105:1361–1368, 1979.

Spies, H.G.; Norman, R.L.; Chappel, S.C.; Pavasuthipaisit, K.; Hess, D.L. Neural control of pituitary hormone secretion in the rhesus macaque. Pp. 634–639 in ENDOCRINOLOGY 1980. I.A. Cumming; J.W. Funder; F.A.O. Mendelsohn, eds. Amsterdam, Elsevier/North Holland, 1980.

Spiess, J.; Rivier, J.; Rivier, C.; Vale, W. Primary structure of corticotropin-releasing factor from ovine hypothalamus. PROCEEDINGS OF THE NATIONAL ACADEMY OF SCIENCES U.S.A. 78:6517–6521, 1981.

Steiner, R.A.; Peterson, A.P.; Yu, J.Y.L.; Conner, M.; Gilbert, M.; terPenning, B.; Bremner, W.J. Ultradian luteinizing hormone and testosterone rhythms in the adult male monkey Macaca fascicularis. ENDOCRINOLOGY 107:1489–1493, 1980.

Steiner, R.A.; Stewart, J.K.; Barber, J.; Koerker, D.;

Goodner, C.J.; Brown, A.; Illner, P.; Gale, C.C. Somatostatin: A physiological role in the regulation of growth hormone secretion in the adolescent male baboon. ENDOCRINOLOGY 10:1587–1594, 1978.

Strauch, G.; Girault, D.; Rifai, M.; Bricaire, H. Alpha-MSH stimulation of growth-hormone release. JOURNAL OF CLINICAL ENDOCRINOLOGY AND METABOLISM 37:990–993, 1973.

Takahashi, Y.; Kipnis, D.M.; Daughaday, W.H. Growth hormone secretion during sleep. JOURNAL OF CLINICAL INVESTIGATION 47:2079–2090, 1968.

Tashjian A.H. Jr.; Barowsky, N.J.; Jensen, D.K. Thyrotropin releasing hormone: Direct evidence for stimulation of prolactin production by pituitary cells in culture. BIOCHEMICAL AND BIOPHYSICAL RESEARCH COMMUNICATIONS 43:516–523, 1971.

Toivola, P.T.K.; Gale, C.C. Stimulation of growth hormone release by microinjection of norepinephrine into the hypothalamus of baboons. ENDOCRINOLOGY 90:895–902, 1972.

Toivola, P.T.K.; Gale, C.C.; Goodner, C.J.; Werbach, J.H. Central α-adrenergic regulation of growth hormone and insulin. HORMONES 3:192–213, 1972.

Tuomisto, J.; Mannisto, P.; Lamberg, B.-A.; Linnoila, M. Effect of cold-exposure on serum thyrotrophin levels in man. ACTA ENDOCRINOLOGICA (COPENHAGEN) 83:522–527, 1976.

Tyson, J.E.; Friesen, H.G. Factors influencing the secretion of human prolactin and growth hormone in the menstrual cycle and gestational women. AMERICAN JOURNAL OF OBSTETRICS AND GYNECOLOGY 117:962–970, 1973.

Vale, W.; Rivier, C.; Brazeau, P.; Guillemin, R. Effects of somatostatin on the secretion of thyrotropin and prolactin. ENDOCRINOLOGY 95:968–977, 1974.

Vale, W.; Spiess, J.; Rivier, C.; Rivier, J. Characterization of a 41-residue ovine hypothalamic peptide that stimulates secretion of corticotropin and beta-endorphin. SCIENCE 213:1394–1397, 1981.

Vanhaelst, L.; Van Cauter, E.; Degaute, J.P.; Goldstein, J. Circadian variations of serum thyrotropin levels in man. JOURNAL OF CLINICAL ENDOCRINOLOGY AND METABOLISM 35:479–482, 1972.

Van Horn, R.N. Seasonal reproductive patterns in primates. Pp. 181–221 in PROGRESS IN REPRODUCTIVE BIOLOGY. P.O. Hubinont, ed. Basel, Karger, 1980.

Vaughan, L.; Carmel, P.W.; Dyrenfurth, I.; Frantz, A.G.; Antunes, J.L.; Ferin, M. Section of the pituitary stalk in the rhesus monkey. I. Endocrine studies. NEUROENDOCRINOLOGY 30:70–75, 1980.

Vekemans, M.; Delvoye, P.; L'Hermite, M.; Robyn, C. Serum prolactin levels during the menstrual cycle. JOURNAL OF CLINICAL ENDOCRINOLOGY AND METABOLISM 44:989–993, 1977.

Vigneri, R.; D'Agata, R. Growth hormone release during the first year of life in relation to sleep-wake periods. JOURNAL OF CLINICAL ENDOCRINOLOGY AND METABOLISM 33:561–563, 1971.

Vinik, A.I.; Kalk, W.J.; McLaren, H.; Hendricks, S.; Pimstone, B.L. Fasting blunts the TSH response to synthetic thyrotropin-releasing hormone (TRH). JOURNAL OF CLINICAL ENDOCRINOLOGY AND METABOLISM 40:509–511, 1975.

Weeke, J. Circadian variation of the serum thyrotropin level in normal subjects. SCANDINAVIAN JOURNAL OF CLINICAL LABORATORY INVESTIGATION 31:337–342, 1973.

Weeke, J.; Christensen, S.E.; Hanse, A.P.; Laurberg, P.; Lundbaek, K. Somatostatin and the 24 h levels of serum TSH, T_3, T_4 and reverse T_3 in normals, diabetics and patients treated for myxoedema. ACTA ENDOCRINOLOGICA (COPENHAGEN) 94:30–37, 1980.

Weeke, J.; Hanse, A.; Lundbaek, K. The inhibition by somatostatin of the thyrotropin response to thyrotropin-releasing hormone in normal subjects. SCANDINAVIAN JOURNAL OF CLINICAL LABORATORY INVESTIGATION 33:101–103, 1974.

Weeke, J.; Hanse, A.P.; Lundbaek, K. Inhibition by somatostatin of basal levels of serum thyrotropin (TSH) in normal men. JOURNAL OF CLINICAL ENDOCRINOLOGY AND METABOLISM 41:168–171, 1975.

Wehrenberg, W.B.; Ling, N.; Bohlen, P.; Esch, F.; Brazeau, P.; Guillemin, R. Physiological roles of somatocrinin and somatostatin in the regulation of growth hormone secretion. BIOCHEMICAL AND BIOPHYSICAL RESEARCH COMMUNICATIONS 109:562–567, 1982.

Weil-Malherbe, H.; Whitby, L.G.; Axelrod, J. The uptake of circulating (^{3}H)norepinephrine by the pituitary gland and various areas of the brain. JOURNAL OF NEUROCHEMISTRY 8:55–64, 1961.

Weiner, R.I.; Bethea, C.L. Hypothalamic control of prolactin secretion. Pp. 19–55 in PROLACTIN. R.B. Jaffe, ed. New York, Elsevier, 1981.

Weiner, R.I.; Ganong, W.F. Role of brain monoamines and histamine in regulation of anterior pituitary secretion. PHYSIOLOGICAL REVIEWS 58:905–976, 1978.

Weitzman, E.D.; Fukushima, D.; Nogeire, C.; Roffwarg, H.; Gallagher, T.F.; Hellman, L. Twenty-four hour pattern of the episodic secretion of cortisol in normal subjects. JOURNAL OF CLINICAL ENDOCRINOLOGY AND METABOLISM 33:14–22, 1971.

Weitzman, E.D.; Nogeire, C.; Perlow, M.; Fukushima, D.; Sassin, J.; McGregor, P.; Gallagher, T.F.; Hellman, L. Effect of a prolonged 3-hour sleep-wake cycle on sleep stages, plasma cortisol, growth hormone and body temperature in man. JOURNAL OF CLINICAL ENDOCRINOLOGY AND METABOLISM 38:1018–1030, 1974.

Wilbur, J.F.; Baum, D. Elevation of plasma TSH during surgical hypothermia. JOURNAL OF CLINICAL ENDOCRINOLOGY AND METABOLISM 31:372–375, 1970.

Woolf, P.D.; Lee, L. Effect of the serotonin precursor, tryptophan, on pituitary hormone secretion. JOURNAL OF CLINICAL ENDOCRINOLOGY AND METABOLISM 45:123–133, 1977.

Yasuda, N.; Greer, M.A. Distribution of CRF activity and immunoreactive ACTH within the hypothalamic-neurohypophyseal complex in various species. PROCEEDINGS OF THE SOCIETY FOR EXPERIMENTAL BIOLOGY AND MEDICINE 158:421–425, 1978.

Yasuda, N.; Greer, M.A.; Aizawa, T. Corticotropin-releasing factor. ENDOCRINE REVIEWS 3:123–140, 1982.

Yen, S.S.C. Chronic anovulation due to CNS-hypothalamic-pituitary dysfunction. Pp. 341–372 in REPRODUCTIVE ENDOCRINOLOGY, PHYSIOLOGY, PATHOPHYSIOLOGY AND CLINICAL MANAGEMENT. S.S.C. Yen; R.B. Jaffe, eds. Philadelphia, Saunders, 1978.

Yen, S.S.C.; Tsai, C.C.; Naftolin, F.; VandenBerg, G.; Ajabor, L. Pulsatile patterns of gonadotropin release in subjects with and without ovarian function. JOURNAL OF CLINICAL ENDOCRINOLOGY AND METABOLISM 34:671–675, 1972a.

Yen, S.S.C.; VandenBerg, G.; Rebar, R.; Ehara, Y. Variation of pituitary responsiveness to synthetic LRF during different phases of the menstrual cycle. JOURNAL OF CLINICAL ENDOCRINOLOGY AND METABOLISM 35:931–934, 1972b.

Zimmerman, E.A.; Carmel, P.W.; Husain, M.K.; Fein, M.; Tannenbaum, M.; Frantz, A.G.; Robinson, A.G. Vasopressin and neurophysin: High concentrations in monkey hypophyseal portal blood. SCIENCE 182:925–927, 1973.

Pituitary Gonadotropins and Prolactin

Michael S. Blank

Yerkes Regional Primate Research Center and Department of Anatomy, Emory University, Atlanta, Georgia 30322

INTRODUCTION AND OVERVIEW

Introduction

General History of Gonadotropins and Prolactin. Investigations of pituitary gonadotropins, substances that maintain or stimulate the normal functions of the gonads, began in the early part of this century with the finding that pituitary extirpation leads to gonadal regression (ie, atrophy) in the rat [Smith, 1926]. The ability of gonadotropins to stimulate the gonads [Fevold et al, 1931] and sexual precocity [Smith and Engle, 1927] and localization of these factors to the pars distalis of the pituitary soon followed Smith's findings.

The lactogenic action of prolactin was first to be recognized [Stricker and Grueter, 1928; Riddle and Braucher, 1931], with its gonadotropic effects in rodents being established later [Astwood, 1941].

History of Primate Gonadotropins and Prolactin. By 1928, when Ascheim and Zondeck first described a gonadotropic activity in the urine of pregnant women, it was clear that gonad-stimulating factors existed in primates. In 1930 Zondeck reported finding follicle-stimulating activity in urine from nonpregnant women. However, the relative insensitivity of existing gonadotropin bioassays [Fevold et al, 1931; Claus, 1931] hampered further studies. Investigations were facilitated when Steelman and Pohley [1953] improved the bioassay of follicle-stimulating hormone (FSH) by noting ovarian weight augmentation in immature rats injected with preparations of human chorionic gonadotropin (hCG), and later Reichert and Parlow [1963] published a bioassay for luteinizing hormone (LH) based on its ability to deplete ovarian ascorbic acid content. These assays, combined with collections of human pituitaries by the National Pituitary Agency of the National Institute of Arthritis, Metabolic and Digestive Disorders, beginning in the late 1950s, assisted in the final process of isolation and purification of human gonadotropins.

Parallel studies demonstrated that the sexual cycles of nonhuman [Ball and Hartman, 1935; Elder and Yerkes, 1936] and human primates were qualitatively similar. In fact the increase in copulations observed during the periovulatory period in rhesus monkey, baboon, and chimpanzee [Elder and Yerkes, 1936] suggested that hormones that regulated ovulation in humans might also be responsible for cyclic behavioral changes in nonhuman primates. Therefore, even before detailed biochemical analyses of primate gonadotropins were available it was clear that nonhuman primates would serve as valuable models for inquiries into human reproductive physiology.

The development of a sensitive bioassay for prolactin in the 1950s by Grosvenor and Turner [1958], who optimized the pigeon crop sac method of Riddle and Braucher [1931], opened the door for the pioneering studies of Nicoll et al [1970] and Friesen and Guyda [1971]. They established that the growth-hormone and prolactin activities of rhesus monkey pituitary glands were associated with separate molecular entities.

Overview

Human Versus Nonhuman Primate Gonadotropins. Similarities abound between human and nonhuman primate gonadotropins. The evidence is clear and distinct for a common genetic inheritance of pituitary hormones between primate species. Based on immunological cross-reaction data, the amino acid sequences of the gonadotropins and prolactin of the primate pituitary compare favorably across species. Not only are nonhuman and human primate gonadotropins chemically similar, but the cell types from which they are secreted are morphologically related. Tinctorial or immunocytochemical staining of nonhuman and human primate pituitaries reveals similar cell types for LH- and FSH-secreting cells (gonadotropes) or for prolactin-secreting cells (lactotropes).

Because of the close immunological similarities that exist for gonadotropins and prolactin within the order Primates, radioimmunoassays (RIAs) based on antibodies raised against human gonadotropins are valid for measuring gonadotropin levels in members of the family Pongidae as well as some species taxonomically classified outside the family Hominidae. In turn, it may be predicted from the "genetic distances" (see below for further discussion) within families or superfamilies that antibodies directed against gonadotropins of species within the same taxonomic class will cross-react with gonadotropins in that class.

The lack of species specificity of certain antibodies to mammalian gonadotropins makes it possible to monitor circulating levels in a variety of primate species without resorting to direct hormone purification. It is both unethical and unwise to obtain pituitaries simply for hormone extraction from animals whose numbers are rapidly dwindling. Indeed, using the techniques of RIA and bioassay (which, for the most part, also lacks species specificity), patterns of circulating gonadotropins are found that conform, with few exceptions, to patterns found in humans.

The regulation of pituitary hormone secretion by gonadal and central nervous system factors in man and nonhuman primate is so closely related as to designate the latter a surrogate for the former. Rhesus monkeys *(Macaca mulatta)* are used to great advantage in investigations of central regulation of gonadotropin secretion [Knobil, 1974, 1980].

Nonhuman primate gonadotropins stimulate gonadal steroidogenesis and steroid secretion in a manner identical to that of gonadotropins in the human. Exogenous human gonadotropins are used interchangeably with nonhuman primate gonadotropins to stimulate gonadal steroid secretion. However, in contrast to lower mammalian gonadotropin receptors, primate gonadal receptors appear to be order-specific: that is, nonprimate, mammalian gonadotropins compete less effectively than primate gonadotropins for gonadal membrane recognition sites [Davies et al, 1979a; Cameron and Stouffer, 1981].

Comparative Aspects of Nonhuman Primate Gonadotropins. Direct biochemical comparisons of primate gonadotropins are lacking. Most investigations draw indirect comparisons, relying on antibodies that recognize LH, FSH, or prolactin in several primate species. However, direct similarities exist in pituitary cell morphology and in patterns of circulating gonadotropins across many primate taxa.

A Note on Classification of Primates

The classification system of Goodman [1975], which is based on immunodiffusion data of blood protein, is used in this chapter. This system is chosen over a strictly taxonomic classification because of its greater relevancy to comparisons of nonhuman primate gonadotropins. One significant disparity which results is the movement of the great apes into the family Hominidae with *Homo sapiens*. Another difference is the placement of marmosets in the same superfamily (Ceboidea) with squirrel monkeys. For further details of this classification system see Table 4, page 228 of Goodman [1975].

MOLECULAR AND GENETIC HOMOLOGY AMONG PRIMATE GONADOTROPINS

Overview

Absence of Direct Comparisons. Excellent cross-reaction occurs between antibodies to human gonadotropins and serum, urine, or pituitary extracts from the African apes (chimpanzee and gorilla). This situation also exists between antibodies to human prolactin and serum or pituitary extracts of many species within the suborder Anthropoidea. However, a lack of purified hormone preparations from nonhuman primates hinders direct comparisons between species.

Inferences Based on Homologies of Gene Products

Blood Proteins. The chimpanzee and human are nearly identical in their blood protein biochemistry. The average human blood protein is more than 97% homologous in its amino acid composition with its counterpart in the chimpanzee [King and Wilson, 1975] and gorilla [Goodman, 1975]. An examination of percentage differences in amino acids from molecules such as α, β, γ, or δ hemoglobin, myoglobin, fibrinopeptides, cytochrome C, and portions of carbonic anhydrases I and II is shown in Table 1 [from Goodman, 1975, with permission]. By examining the "amino acid dis-

TABLE 1. The Amino Acid Difference Matrix for Primates

	Man	Chi	Gor	Ora[a]	Gib	Mac	Cer	Squ	Spi	Cap	Slo
Man		3/1127	3/463	12/432	12/505	31/799	20/547	29/330	20/317	24/317	36/317
Chimpanzee	0.27		2/463	11/432	12/505	31/684	19/432	30/330	20/317	24/317	36/317
Gorilla	0.65	0.43		7/322	10/352	16/312	16/317	X	20/317	24/317	36/317
Orang-utan[a]	2.78	2.54	2.17		X	X	X	X	X	X	X
Gibbon	2.38	2.38	2.84	X		23/354	X	28/330	X	X	X
Macaque	3.89	4.54	5.13	X	6.51		12/542	25/330	23/312	26/312	37/312
Cercopithecus	3.65	4.39	5.06	X	X	2.21		X	22/317	25/317	39/317
Squirrel monkey	8.78	9.08	X	X	8.49	7.58	X		11/323	X	X
Spider monkey	6.31	6.31	6.31	X	X	7.38	6.95	3.39		14/317	32/317
Capuchin monkey	7.56	7.56	7.56	X	X	8.35	7.86	X	4.41		35/317
Slow loris	11.36	11.36	11.36	X	X	11.85	12.28	X	10.08	11.04	

Upper half of matrix: number of differing amino acids per number of shared amino acid positions; lower half of matrix: percent of differing amino acids, the amino acid distance (AAD) values.

[a]The amino acid composition data of orang-utan α-Hb and β-Hb chains were used in the estimations of amino acid differences in the comparisons of the orang-utan to other hominoids but not in those of orang-utan to phylogenetically more distant primates, since amino acid composition data could only be expected to yield correct or nearly correct AAD values between closely related species.

X = comparisons not done because of insufficient data.

From Goodman [1975] with permission.

tances," as Goodman [1975] refers to them, one finds less distance between man and the African apes (chimpanzee and gorilla) than between man and the Asiatic apes (orang-utan and gibbon). Likewise, the African apes diverge less from one another than they do from the Asiatic apes. Therefore, it appears that the taxonomic grouping of man, gorilla, and chimpanzee into the subfamily Homininae makes sense from a biochemical (and probably genetic) standpoint. With increasing taxonomic distance from man (ie, as one moves into the superfamilies Cercopithecoidea [macaque and vervet], Ceboidea [squirrel, spider, and capuchin monkeys], and finally Lorisoidea [slow loris]), amino acid distances also increase (Table 1).

Gonadotropins and Prolactin. Primate gonadotropins and prolactin are compared by examining cross-reaction with antisera to human gonadotropins or prolactin. Little or no cross-reaction of purified rhesus LH and FSH preparations with antisera to human LH (hLH) and human FSH (hFSH) is detected [Neill et al, 1967]. However, circulating gonadotropins of the chimpanzee [Howland et al, 1971] and gorilla [Nadler et al, 1979; Nadler, 1980] show a high degree of cross-reaction with antibodies to human gonadotropins. We have taken advantage of the latter situation to monitor circulating and urinary levels of LH and FSH in the great apes. Figure 1 shows parallelism between human pituitary gonadotropin standard (LER 907) and dilutions of serum from a pygmy chimpanzee *(Pan paniscus)* in RIAs for hLH or hFSH. Since the FSH response to gonadotropin-releasing hormone injection is somewhat delayed when compared to the LH response [Rebar et al, 1973], the FSH inhibition curves for postinjection samples are more widely separated. In our hands, gorilla serum displays a similar parallelism with human gonadotropin preparations, whereas orang-utan serum shows less cross-reaction (Blank and Nadler, unpublished observation). Similarly, ethanol extracts of urine from chimpanzees and gorillas display parallelism with human gonadotropin urinary standard in a hLH RIA (Figs. 2, 3), with urine extracts obtained near midcycle (Fig. 2) exhibiting somewhat greater potency than those obtained during the follicular phase (Fig. 3) of the menstrual cycle. In our laboratory, chimpanzee urine usually displays a slightly higher potency than gorilla urine in the hLH RIA. This finding is in keeping with the amino acid homologies between the great ape blood proteins noted in the preceding section. While urinary LH in chimpanzees and gorillas cross-reacts favorably with hLH antibodies, LH-like activity of orang-utan urine shows poorer cross-reactivity, similar to the situation in blood. However, by assaying larger volumes of urine or serum, the midcycle surge of LH is detected in orang-utans [Nadler et al, 1980].

Experiments in which animals are passively or actively immunized to gonadotropins indicate homology between human (and also nonhuman mammalian) and nonhuman primate gonadotropins. Either passive or active immunization with gonadotropins compromises normal reproductive function. For example, passive immunization with antisera to ovine LH terminates pregnancy in bonnet monkeys (*Macaca radiata* [Moudgal et al,

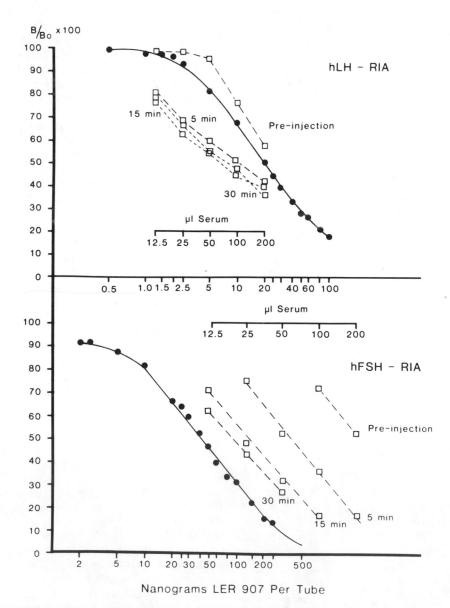

Fig. 1. Parallelism of dilutions of chimpanzee (*Pan paniscus*) serum with human pituitary gonadotropin reference preparation (LER-907) in a hLH (top) and hFSH (bottom) RIA. Separate blood samples were obtained before (preinjection) and 5, 15, and 30 min after an injection of 100 μg gonadotropin-releasing hormone.

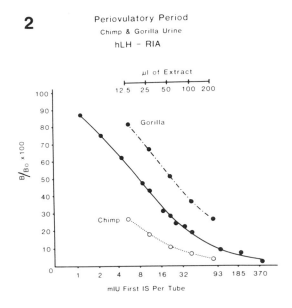

2

Periovulatory Period
Chimp & Gorilla Urine
hLH – RIA

μl of Extract

12.5 25 50 100 200

Gorilla

Chimp

B/Bo ×100

mIU First IS Per Tube

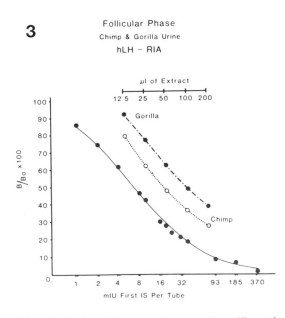

3

Follicular Phase
Chimp & Gorilla Urine
hLH – RIA

μl of Extract

12.5 25 50 100 200

Gorilla

Chimp

B/Bo ×100

mIU First IS Per Tube

Figs. 2, 3. Parallelism of dilutions of gorilla and chimpanzee urine extracts with human urinary gonadotropin reference preparation (First International Standard, IS) in a hLH RIA. Figure 2 depicts parallelism of periovulatory samples and Figure 3 of follicular phase samples. Each urine sample was extracted in duplicate 5-ml aliquots with the ethanol procedure described by Geiger [1971]; data points represent the mean of at least two determinations.

1978]) and is an effective contraceptive in rhesus monkeys (*Macaca mulatta* [Yamamoto et al, 1982]), whereas active immunization with the β subunit of ovine LH results in shortened luteal phases [Spinola et al, 1982]. Furthermore, the function of FSH in male rhesus and bonnet monkeys is deduced by active and passive immunization with ovine FSH [Wickings and Nieschlag, 1980; Moudgal, 1981]. Also, when rhesus monkeys are actively immunized with ovine LH β subunit, the antibodies generated show high cross-reaction with hLH and rhesus LH (rhLH) [Yamamoto et al, 1982]. Moreover, Ouchterlony double-diffusion studies [Moudgal et al, 1972] show that monkey pituitary extracts cross-react with human LH and that the actions of endogenous LH in rhesus monkeys are neutralized with an antiserum to human chorionic gonadotropin (hCG). This fact can be used to develop an RIA for rhesus LH based on an antiserum to hCG [Karsch et al, 1973a].

Greater interspecific homology appears to exist for prolactin (and perhaps growth hormone). Antibodies to human prolactin (hPRL) cross-react with prolactin from a wide range of primate species within the suborder Anthropoidea. These include the great apes, macaques, baboon, mangabey, patas monkey, and marmoset. By example, Figure 4 illustrates the parallelism between dilutions of rhesus monkey serum or pituitary extracts and human pituitary reference preparations in radioimmunoassays for human prolactin (upper panel) and human growth hormone (hGH) (lower panel). Each assay utilizes an antiserum raised against a purified human growth hormone. Rhesus monkey growth hormone diverges slightly from parallelism in the hGH RIA [Himsworth et al, 1972]. To avoid a potential problem when measuring rhesus GH in serum, our laboratory routinely assays ≤ 50 μl of serum. Taking this precaution for determinations of GH in serum, hGH and hPRL RIAs are appropriate for measuring circulating levels of these polypeptides in rhesus monkeys. By comparison, human gonadotropin RIAs are less useful for measuring circulating gonadotropins in primates outside the superfamily Hominoidea [Neill et al, 1967].

The foregoing discussion implies a greater conservation of amino acid sequences for prolactin than for the gonadotropins. Lewis [1975], in reviewing the chemistry of prolactin, points out that marked similarities exist between human and nonprimate prolactin. If prominent homologies exist between primate and even nonprimate prolactin, one could surmise, from immunological compari-

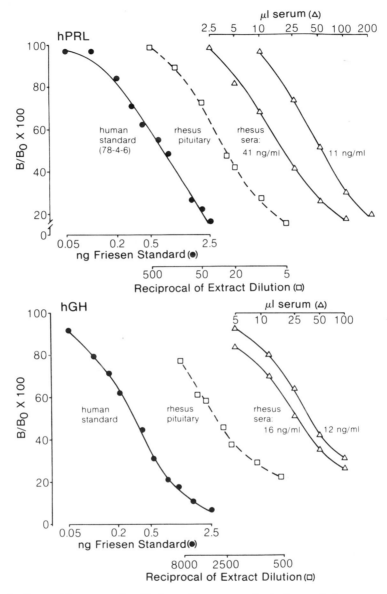

Fig. 4. Competition curves for dilutions of human standard, rhesus pituitary extracts, or rhesus sera in a human PRL (upper panel) or human GH (lower panel) RIA.

sons, that an even greater degree of conservation exists within the order Primates.

Comparisons of Gene Sequences

Sequences for Blood Proteins. The average human protein exhibits greater than 99% amino acid homology with its related protein in the chimpanzee. Proteins of the gorilla and human are also very closely related [King and Wilson, 1975]. There-

fore, it is likely that the genetic sequences that code for these products are also closely related.

Sequences for Gonadotropins and Prolactin. Nothing is known about nonhuman primate genes coding for gonadotropins or prolactin, and the only human gonadotropin genes currently under investigation code for chorionic gonadotropin [Boime et al, 1978]. Examination of differences in human, chimpanzee, and rhesus monkey DNA coding for GH and chorionic somatomammotropin shows no greater homology between man and chimpanzee than between man and rhesus monkey [Herd et al, 1982]. Although the technique of Herd et al [1982] (hybridizing restriction endonuclease digests to human chorionic somatomammotropin cDNA probe) does not resolve down to the level of nucleotide sequence, their findings suggest that differences in pituitary gene products among primates may reflect differential processing rather than genomic coding. However, since separate genes may code for the synthesis of the α and β subunits of human glycoprotein hormones [Boime et al, 1978], perhaps this also applies to glycoprotein genes from nonhuman primates.

PITUITARY GONADOTROPIN AND PROLACTIN CELL MORPHOLOGY

Overview

Gonadotropes. Tinctorial staining methods [Dawson, 1948; Fujita et al, 1959] or chemical reactions [Barrnett and Ladman, 1954] distinguish two morphological cell types—an LH cell and an FSH cell. However, immunocytochemical methods suggest a more subtle distinction between two gonadotropic hormone-secreting cells. Most current studies of nonhuman primate pituitaries agree that a population of adenohypophysial cells exists which contains both LH and FSH [Herbert, 1976; Girod et al, 1980a]. Specialized cells, containing only LH, appear in the pars tuberalis [Antunes et al, 1979; Herbert, 1978a; Girod et al, 1980a]. Another report describes parenchymal cells (associated with the median eminence) in the pars tuberalis which contain FSH [Baker et al, 1977]. Electron-microscopic studies [Tseng et al, 1974] demonstrate "castration" cells with dilated endoplasmic reticulum, prominent Golgi bodies, and lower numbers of secretory granules—changes that are reversed by estrogen administration [Tseng et al, 1974].

Gonadotropic cells are periodic acid-Schiff (PAS) reaction positive since this staining method is specific for the carbohydrates which comprise a portion of each LH and FSH molecule. PAS-positive cells are categorized as basophils from the staining of their granules with basic dyes, but the specificity of the PAS reaction for sugars simplifies their identification [Bloom and Fawcett, 1968]. Gonadotropes are fairly large (15–30 μ in diameter) and are found singly in a random and wide distribution

throughout the pars distalis [Herbert, 1976, 1978a]; they are capable of concentrating testosterone [Herbert et al, 1981].

Lactotropes. The growth hormone cells (somatotropes) and prolactin-secreting cells (lactotropes) of the adenohypophysis are termed *acidophilic* based on the tinctorial reaction of their granules with acid dyes [El Etreby et al, 1973]. The acidophils are subdivided into carminophils (dark red) and orangeophils (yellow-orange) based on the trichrome staining technique of Brooks [Herbert and Hayashida, 1970]. Two acidophilic cells types are identified tinctorially in the genus *Cebus* (capuchin), in *Macaca mulatta*, and *M. fascicularis*, and in all three species of great apes (chimpanzee, gorilla, orang-utan). When the trichrome technique is combined with immunocytochemistry, the carminophils are found to contain only prolactin [Herbert and Hayashida, 1970, 1974]. Typically, both small and large prolactin cells are found in the nonhuman primate pituitary, with both types seen in widely dispersed areas of the pars distalis and only the large cells found in clusters [Girod and Dubois, 1976a].

Immunocytochemical Localization

Gonadotropes. Investigators localize particular cell types within the adenohypophysis with labeled antisera to human or ovine LH and FSH. This method greatly enhances our ability to distinguish between gonadotropes and other glycoprotein-containing cell types. A fluorescent (usually fluorescein) or enzyme label is covalently linked to the antibody. The fluorescent tag must be read immediately under the microscope, whereas the enzyme-labeled antibody is more permanent. Although most evidence with β-subunit-specific antisera, which should localize individual glycoprotein hormones, suggests a single LH/FSH cell type [Herbert, 1976], some cells contain a majority of just one gonadotropin [Girod et al, 1981].

Family Cercopithecidae

Genus *Macaca*

Macaca mulatta. Using ovine LH-β antisera, single, randomly distributed PAS-positive cells are distinguished in pars distalis and numerous cells are detected in the inferior portion of pars tuberalis [Herbert, 1976, 1978a] (Fig. 5). Antisera to hLH-β and hFSH-β stain only the gonadotropes of rhesus monkey pituitaries [Halmi, 1981], but anti-

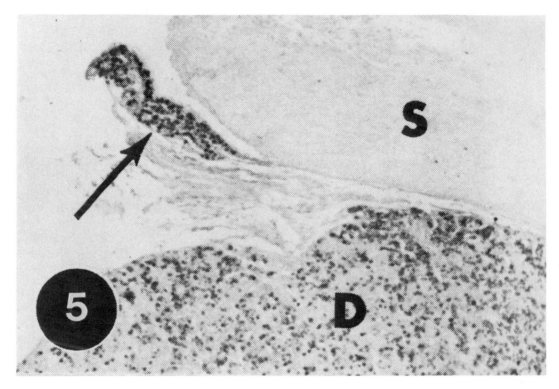

Fig. 5. LH cells (arrow), immunocytochemically stained, in the pars tuberalis of the adult rhesus monkey (*M. mulatta*). This is a sagittal section through the superior region of the pituitary gland. D—pars distalis; S—pituitary stalk (×36). From Herbert [1978] with permission.

hFSH-β also stains thyrotropes of human pituitaries. Although no sex- or age-dependent changes are found in the number of cells, a decrease is noted during pregnancy and lactation [Herbert, 1978a] (Fig. 6).

The immunocytochemical evidence for LH [Antunes et al, 1979] cells in the pars tuberalis is strengthened by the demonstration of large pituitary portal: peripheral blood ratios for LH of between 2 and 48:1 [Antunes et al, 1979].

Macaca fascicularis. A majority (85–90%) of adenohypophysial cells react with both hFSH and ovine LH antisera whereas some cells of the pars tuberalis are reactive for LH only [Girod et al, 1980b]. A "gonadotropic zone" is observed in the median area of female lateral lobes.

Genus *Papio* and *Cercopithecus*
P. hamadryas; C. aethiops. The majority (85%) of anterior pituitary cells of the baboon (*P. hama-*dryas) and vervet (*C. aethiops*) react with antisera to intact LH and FSH or their β subunits [Girod et al, 1981].

Lactotropes. Prolactin and growth hormone are biochemically separate entities [Nicoll et al, 1970; Friesen and Guyda, 1971]. Likewise, lactotropes are distinguished from somatotropes with combined immunocytochemical and tinctorial stains [Herbert and Hayashida, 1970].

Family Cercopithecidae
Genus *Macaca*
Macaca mulatta and *M. fascicularis.* A fluorescein-labeled antiovine prolactin serum is used to identify prolactin cells in these species [Pasteels et al, 1972; Herbert and Hayashida, 1974]. Females (especially pregnant or lactating) have more lactotropes than males, and the prolactin content of pituitary glands, as measured by radioimmunoassay, correlates with the histological findings. Lac-

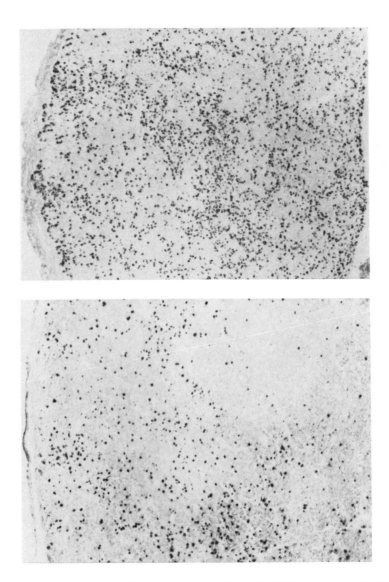

Fig. 6. LH cells, immunocytochemically stained with anti-oLHβ, in the pars distalis of a nonpregnant, nonlactating adult female rhesus monkey (*M. mulatta*) (top) and of a 3-week-old lactating monkey (bottom). From Herbert [1978] with permission.

totrope hyperplasia and higher prolactin content are related to estrogens since treatment of juveniles with estradiol benzoate increases pituitary prolactin content by sevenfold [Herbert and Hayashida, 1974].

The regional distribution of prolactin cells in the pituitary gland of a rhesus monkey is shown in Figure 7 [from Herbert and Hayashida, 1974]. Lactotropes localize in a broad, outer band on the rostral aspects of the adenohypophysis, with a heavier concentration of cells medially. In contrast, somatotropes are concentrated more caudally. Overlap between the two cell types occurs mostly in the ventrolateral aspects of the gland. The regional distribution of lactotropes is similar in the adult rhesus monkey, cynomolgus monkey, capuchin, gorilla, and juvenile orang-utan and chimpanzee. The rhesus and cynomolgus monkeys exhibit the largest numbers of cells [Herbert and Hayashida, 1974]. Two types of acidophils are tinctorially discerned in the cynomolgus monkey, indicating the probable existence of both somatotropes and lactotropes. Both small and large lactotropes are found dispersed throughout the pars distalis [Girod and Dubois, 1976a], with the large cells found in clusters. The pars tuberalis does not stain with antisera to human prolactin [Girod et al, 1980a]. Prolactin cells are identified with antisera to ovine prolactin in the following genuses of Cercopithecidae: *Papio hamadryas, Erythrocebus patas, Cercopithecus aethiops* [Girod and Dubois, 1976b].

Alterations in Cell Morphology

Overview. Lactotrope and gonadotrope dependency on hypothalamic input is clearly demonstrated after section of the pituitary stalk. In the rhesus monkey, stalk section engenders rapid increases in the number of lactotropes and marked decreases in gonadotropes [Antunes et al, 1980]. Remarkably, the gonadotropes of the pars tuberalis

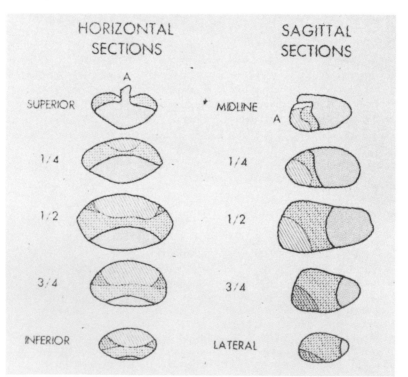

Fig. 7. Diagrammatic representation of the regional distribution of prolactin and growth hormone cells in the rhesus monkey pituitary as identified by immunocytochemistry. Diagonal lines represent areas where prolactin cells predominate, and broken lines areas rich in growth hormone cells. Where both diagonal and broken lines appear, intermixing of cell types occur. Stippled areas designate pars intermedia and neurohypophysis. A = anterior. From Herbert and Hayashida [1974] with permission.

appear unaffected [Antunes et al, 1980]. Circulating prolactin levels increase and LH levels decrease after stalk section in rhesus monkeys [Vaughan et al, 1980]. Therefore, morphological and physiological evidence clearly indicate that the brain exerts an inhibitory influence on the lactotrope and a sustaining influence on the gonadotrope.

Gonadotropes. "Chemical castration" with cadmium chloride injection into the testes results in increased vacuolation and granulation in gonadotropes of the langur (*Presbytis entellus entellus*) [David and Ramaswami, 1971]. This description of castration cells is in agreement with a report of dilated endoplasmic reticulum in electron micrographs of castrated rhesus monkey pituitary [Tseng et al, 1974].

Lactotropes. Several studies verify the stimulatory actions of estrogens, pregnancy [El Etreby et al, 1973; Herbert and Hayashida, 1974], and lactation [Pasteels et al, 1972] on the number of prolactin cells and the prolactin content of the rhesus monkey and human pituitary. The number of lactotropes usually correlates with the prolactin content of the gland [Pasteels et al, 1972; Herbert and Hayashida, 1974]. Figure 8 [El Etreby and Gunzel, 1974] illustrates pituitary lactotrope hyperplasia induced by estrogen treatment in rhesus monkeys. In human pregnancy when estrogen secretion is high, the lactotropes may comprise up to one-half of the total acidophils in the pituitary gland [Goluboff and Ezrin, 1969].

CHEMISTRY
Gonadotropins

As pointed out earlier, much of the detailed biochemistry of primate pituitary gonadotropins derives from purified human gonadotropins. Because of the abundant homologies which probably exist between human and nonhuman primate pituitary hormones, it is beneficial to review here the chemistry of human gonadotropins.

Human. The human glycoprotein hormones, LH, FSH, thyroid-stimulating hormone, and chorionic gonadotropin share a common α subunit consisting of between 89 and 96 amino acids with five disulfide bonds and a unique β subunit consisting of between 116 and 147 amino acids with six disulfide

linkages. The α and β subunits are linked by hydrophobic bonds [Aloj et al, 1973]. Carbohydrate moieties are located on both subunits. The α subunit contains a constant number (2) of carbohydrate groups linked presumably through an N-glycosamine linkage to asparagine residues which are separated by 26 intervening amino acids. Similar linkages with between one and five carbohydrate groups occur on asparagine residues 7 or 13 and 24 or 30 of the β subunit [Garnier, 1978; Saxena and Rathnam, 1978]. The branched carbohydrate side chains usually end in sialic acid [Vaitukaitis, 1978] which is usually N-acetylated [Saxena and Rathnam, 1978]. Glycoprotein hormones have varying proportions of carbohydrate and protein. Those with highest carbohydrate content also have the longest circulating half-life, such as hCG [Vaitukaitis, 1978]. The combined α and β subunits give mammalian gonadotropins a molecular weight of approximately 30,000 daltons [Papkoff, 1982].

Interestingly, although the isolated subunits lack intrinsic bioactivity, when α and β subunits from different glycoproteins or the same hormone of different species are recombined, the "hybrid" molecules are biologically active [Reichert et al, 1970].

Physically, human gonadotropins are fairly rigid molecules probably because there are disulfide bridges between the α and β subunits [Giudice and Pierce, 1978]. This rigidity is a requirement for full biological potency of the α subunit and could explain the inability of antisera to human LHα to detect LHα subunits of other species [Vaitukaitis, 1978].

Studies with bovine LH indicate that the α subunit of LH accounts for most of the receptor-binding activity of the molecule and that the β subunit specifies α subunit conformation [Cheng, 1976]. However, other investigators suggest the opposite is true: that the α subunit confers conformation on the β subunit [Giudice and Pierce, 1978]. The tyrosines at positions 92 and 93 of the α chain are essential for full bioactivity of LH, and the methionines at positions 51 and 71 of LHα are important for receptor interaction [Ward, 1978]. The molecular weight of the α subunit is approximately 14,000 [Catt and Pierce, 1978].

Physicochemical characterization of human FSH indicates a fairly acidic molecule (pI about 4.25) as are all glycoproteins owing to their sialic acid content [Reichert, 1971], with an average molecular weight (based on sedimentation equilibration) of

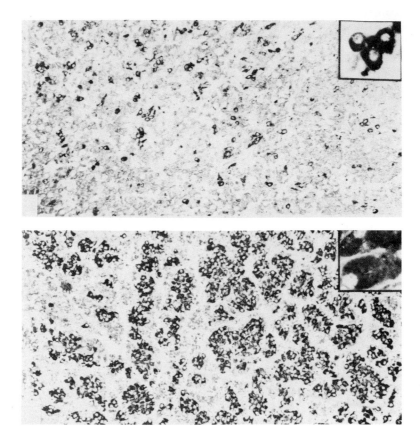

Fig. 8. Prolactin cells, immunocytochemically stained, in adenohypophysis of a nonpregnant, mature female (top) and estradiol-treated male (bottom) rhesus monkey. Note clusters of small prolactin cells in top panel and ability of estrogen to cause hyperplasia and hypertrophy. From El Etreby and Gunzel [1974] with permission.

31,000 daltons [Saxena and Rathnam, 1980]. Human FSH is over 20% carbohydrate, which consists of sialic acid, galactose, mannose, and glucosamine and two carbohydrate moieties on the β subunit. Human LH has a molecular weight of approximately 28,000 daltons, one carbohydrate moiety on the β subunit, and is 16% carbohydrate [Catt and Pierce, 1978]. Human LH has a pI between 5 and 6.

Gel filtration can result in overestimates of glycoprotein molecular weights [Reichert and Jiang, 1965]. For example, the molecular weight of human FSH is estimated to be 52,480 daltons by gel filtration [Reichert and Midgley, 1968]. Similarly, we find that mangabey LH and FSH elute from G-100 columns at positions equivalent to globular proteins of between 35,000 and 50,000 daltons

(Fig. 9), well above the molecular weights of other mammalian gonadotropins [Papkoff, 1982].

The tryptophan residue of hFSH-β may be responsible for recombination of subunits and/or biological activity. Sugar moieties are also essential to biological activity in vivo since treatment with neuraminidase or galactosidase results in loss of bioactivity [Saxena and Rathnam, 1978]. The loss of bioactivity probably results from decreased circulating half-life and intrinsic loss of molecular activity. The latter could result from loss of conformation which inhibits efficient binding of the molecule to its receptor sites.

Nonhuman Primate. Although gonadotropins of nonhuman primates are not well characterized biochemically, the limited studies performed argue for

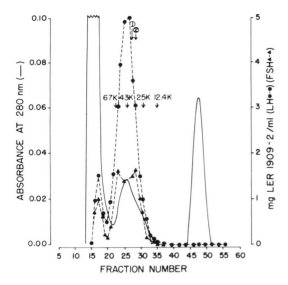

Fig. 9. Sephadex G-100 gel chromatography of an aqueous extract of female mangabey pituitary (128.3 mg). The column was eluted with 0.01 M PBS, pH 7.4, and each fraction contained 2.5 ml. The protein absorption peaks at 280 nm are shown by the continuous line and LH or FSH immunoactivity by the dashed lines. Arrows denote elution of various molecular-weight markers from the same column. The number 1 denotes peak immunoactive LH fraction for a rhesus pituitary extract, and 2 denotes peak of radioactivity when ^{125}I-oLH was run on the same column. Recovery of immunoactivity was 108% for LH and 79% for FSH. Estimated molecular weight of mangabey LH was 40,000–42,000 daltons. From Mann et al [1982] with permission.

a probable structural homology between nonhuman and human primate gonadotropins.

Family Cercopithecidae
Genus *Macaca*
  Macaca mulatta. Heterogeneous molecular forms of rhesus monkey pituitary FSH exist which are related to the gonadal steroid environment [Peckham et al, 1973]. The larger forms of FSH have enhanced biological activity in the Steelman-Pohley assay [Steelman and Pohley, 1953]. Furthermore, ovariectomy amplifies the overall FSH bioactivity of rhesus monkey serum or pituitaries and increases amounts of "large" FSH. Since FSH from ovariectomized rhesus monkeys is cleared more slowly from the circulation of test rats, it appears that altered metabolic clearance rather than

intrinsic attributes of the FSH molecule is the reason for enhanced bioactivity. Steroid-sensitive pleomorphism of FSH is also reported in humans [Wide, 1981].

A similar situation is found for pituitary LH in castrated male monkeys [Peckham and Knobil, 1976a]. However, pituitary LH from intact females is larger and cleared more slowly than either LH or FSH from male rhesus monkeys. The notion that increased sugar content of the gonadotropins is related to both larger size and slower metabolic clearance and thus to enhanced bioactivity is confirmed by treatment of pituitary extracts from ovariectomized rhesus monkeys with neuraminidase (to cleave sialic acid residues). After exposure to this enzyme, LH and FSH return to normal size and clearance [Peckham and Knobil, 1976b]. Interestingly, chronic treatment of female rhesus monkeys with estradiol reverses the effects of ovariectomy on gonadotropin size.

To isolate LH and FSH from rhesus pituitaries, purification methods for human gonadotropins prove successful [Monroe et al, 1970; Yamaji et al, 1973].

Genus *Papio*
  Papio hamadryas. Purification methods for human FSH and LH are applied to baboon pituitaries with tenfold purification of FSH and 50-fold of LH resulting [Shownkeen et al, 1973].

Genus *Cercocebus*
  Cercocebus atys. Partial purification of LH and FSH from mangabey pituitaries by G-100 column chromatography results in a 55-fold increase in LH purity (Fig. 9) [Mann et al, 1982]. Thus mangabey LH appears to lend itself more readily to purification than baboon LH, although the possibility of increased degradation due to the acidic ethanol precipitation in the latter case [Shownkeen et al, 1973] cannot be discounted.

In summary, little attention is directed toward the physicochemical characterization of nonhuman primate gonadotropins for at least two reasons: 1) an abundance of human pituitary glands collected by the National Pituitary Agency greatly eased the process of purification of human gonadotropins, and 2) an unwillingness to sacrifice the large numbers of nonhuman primates required for pituitary hormone purification especially in light of dwindling resources.

Thus far, investigations on nonhuman primate gonadotropins rely, to a large extent, on immunological similarities between primate gonadotropins and those of other mammals including humans. The results of most studies imply extensive structural homology among mammals. More thorough chemical characterization of gonadotropins within the order Primates is certainly needed. Such studies will undoubtedly uncover not only important similarities but also differences between closely related species.

Prolactin

Lactogenic activity is a well-known characteristic of the mammalian pituitary [Stricker and Grueter, 1928], but difficulties are encountered in separating lactogenic from growth-promoting properties of primate pituitaries [Guyda and Friesen, 1971; Nicoll et al, 1970]. The separation of primate prolactin from growth hormone activities is made difficult for two reasons: 1) primate growth hormone and prolactin are both lactogenic, and 2) the physicochemical properties of prolactin and growth hormone are quite similar [Niall et al, 1973].

Because the pigeon crop sac bioassay for prolactin [Riddle and Braucher, 1931] also detects primate growth hormone, claims appeared into the late 1960s [Solomon et al, 1969] of a single molecular identify for prolactin and growth hormone. However, pigeon crop sac bioassay and growth hormone RIA measurements show varying prolactin:growth hormone ratios in medium from pituitary cultures [Nicoll et al, 1970; Channing et al, 1970]. Definitive proof of their separate origins is obtained when extracts of rhesus monkey pituitary are affinity-purified with an antisera to human placental lactogen (hPL) [Guyda and Friesen, 1971]. Since hPL is closely related to human growth hormone immunologically [Friesen, 1965], little growth hormone immunoreactivity is found in the effluent from an anti-hPL column. However, practically all of the prolactin bioactivity is unabsorbed. Distinct growth hormone and prolactin fractions, which are pulse-labeled with ^{3}H-leucine, are immunoprecipitated with antisera to human growth hormone or to rhesus prolactin [Friesen and Guyda, 1971]. The binding of these tritium-labeled fractions to the appropriate antisera is specific since it is displaced with prolactin or growth hormone competitors [Friesen et al, 1971].

Although human and cynomolgus prolactins are polymorphic with respect to charge, they have similarities [Hummel et al, 1975]. Thus physico-chemically as well as immunologically primate polypeptide hormones (prolactin, growth hormone) show closer interspecific correspondence than the glycoprotein hormones (LH, FSH). Prolactin has a molecular weight of approximately 22,000 daltons [Lewis, 1975].

Prolactin biosynthesis in nonhuman primates is not well studied, but it is reasonable to assume that processing is analogous to that found in nonprimate mammalian systems such as the rodent pituitary [Maurer et al, 1978]. In the rodent, the initial translation product of prolactin messenger RNA (mRNA) is preprolactin which is a polypeptide chain of an additional 29 amino acids, preceding the prolactin sequence. Studies of prolactin biosynthesis in pituitaries requires extraction and purification of RNA to yield messenger-enriched mRNA. The latter often makes up 2% (or less) of total RNA. Thus, the requirement for large numbers of pituitaries makes it unlikely that work will progress rapidly unless recombinant DNA technology is applied to this area.

MEASUREMENT
Overview

Gonadotropins. Bioassays for gonadotropins (FSH [Steelman and Pohley, 1953], LH [Reichert and Parlow, 1963]) are valuable identification tools, and radioimmunoassays [Yalow and Berson, 1960] enable us to better understand the physiological roles of gonadotropins. The radioimmunoassays for human gonadotropins (LH [Midgley, 1966; Faiman and Ryan, 1967], FSH [Midgley, 1967; Faiman and Ryan, 1967]) do not readily recognize gonadotropins of nonhuman primates. Therefore rhesus monkey gonadotropins are purified to develop radioimmunoassay methods for these species (LH [Monroe et al, 1970], FSH [Yamaji et al, 1973]).

Despite the finding of Neill et al [1967] that purified nonhuman primate gonadotropins do not cross-react in radioimmunoassays for human gonadotropins, heterologous assays for rhesus monkey FSH are based on antisera to human FSH [Yamaji et al, 1973; Boorman et al, 1973; Faiman et al, 1975] or to ovine FSH [Hodgen et al, 1976]. However, antisera to human LH are not useful for measurement of macaque LH, compelling investigators either to purify macaque LH [Monroe et al, 1970] or to rely on cross-reaction with antisera to human chorionic gonadotropin [Karsch et al, 1973a; Faiman et al, 1975] or to ovine LH [Niswender et al, 1971; Hodgen et al, 1976]. The assay of Niswender et al [1971] employs an antiserum to ovine LH which cross-reacts with LH from a wide variety of species. Why rhesus monkey LH exhibits greater cross-reactivity with an antisera to a nonprimate gonadotropin (ovine LH) than with antisera to human LH remains an enigma.

Table 2 summarizes the various combinations of radiolabeled hormone and antiserum with which LH or FSH is measured in nonhuman primates.

To test the validity of nonhuman primate gonadotropin radioimmunoassays two criteria are deemed essential: 1) the inability to detect significant immunoreactivity in serum from hypophysectomized monkeys [Monroe et al, 1970; Yamaji et al, 1973; Boorman et al, 1973], and 2) parallel inhibition curves generated by dilutions of pituitary extracts, serum, or urine extracts from intact or castrated animals [Monroe et al, 1970; Hodgen et al, 1976].

Several problems arise with the use of heterologous radioimmunoassays for the measurement of primate gonadotropins. First, the lack of a standardized procedure leads to large differences in absolute values which are reported [Yamaji et al, 1973; Faiman et al, 1975]. Second, the heterologous radioimmunoassay for LH [Niswender et al, 1971] detects significant amount of LH-like substance in serum from hypophysectomized rhesus monkeys [Neill et al, 1977]. A highly sensitive and practical bioassay for gonadotropins, based on in vitro stimulation of testosterone production by dispersed rat interstitial (Leydig) cells [Dufau et al, 1976], detects discrepancies between bioactivity and immunoreactivity in the serum of hypophysectomized (bio:immuno, B:I ratio < 0.06), ovariectomized (B:I = 3.02), and prepubertal (B:I < 0.09–0.14) rhesus monkeys [Dufau et al, 1977; Neill et

al, 1977a]. Thus, the heterologous LH radioimmunoassay overestimates LH in prepubertal, hypophysectomized, and steroid-suppressed monkeys and underestimates LH in ovariectomized animals, despite giving similar potencies for purified gonadotropin preparations from rhesus pituitaries [Dufau et al, 1977; Neill et al, 1977a].

The homologous rhesus LH RIA developed by Monroe et al [1970] demonstrates a correlation between menstrual-cycle patterns of LH and progesterone and detects circhoral LH discharges [Atkinson et al, 1970; Dierschke et al, 1970]. However, reagents for this assay are not generally available. Thus, most investigations of rhesus monkey LH are undertaken with the heterologous ovine-ovine LH assay of Niswender et al [1971]. This assay utilizes a unique antisera to ovine LH (GDN-15) which cross-reacts with rhesus monkey LH in serum and pituitary. Now, reagents are available for an assay similar to the one first described by Karsch et al [1973a] through Dr. William Peckham and the Contraceptive Development Branch, Center for Population Research. This assay is based on an antiserum to hCG, cynomolgus monkey (*M. fascicularis*) LH for radioiodination, and a rhesus monkey pituitary gonadotropin standard. The general availability of this assay will undoubtedly facilitate future studies of nonhuman primate LH secretion.

Prolactin. Reagents prepared from rhesus monkey pituitaries can be used to immunoassay *human* prolactin [Hwang et al, 1971]. Monkey prolactin, separated from growth hormone by passing monkey pituitary fractions over an affinity column of anti-hPL serum, is used for tracer, and the antiserum is raised against either monkey or human

TABLE 2. Reagents for Radioimmunoassays of Nonhuman Primate Gonadotropins

Species	Gonadotropin	Antiserum to	Trace	Reference
Macaca mulatta	LH	Rhesus LH	Rhesus LH	Monroe et al [1970]
M. mulatta	LH	Ovine LH	Ovine LH	Niswender et al [1971]
M. mulatta	LH	Human CG	Rhesus LH	Karsch et al [1973]
M. mulatta	LH	Human CG	Ovine LH	Faiman et al [1975]
M. mulatta	FSH	Human FSH	Rat FSH	Boorman et al [1973]
M. mulatta	FSH	Rhesus or human FSH	Rhesus FSH	Yamaji et al [1973]
M. mulatta	FSH	Human FSH	Rat FSH	Faiman et al [1975]
M. mulatta and *M. fascicularis*	FSH	Ovine FSH	Human FSH	Hodgen et al [1976]
P. anubis	FSH	Human FSH	Human FSH	Tillson et al [1976]

prolactin. A radioimmunoassay for monkey prolactin is available [Guyda and Friesen, 1971], but limited supplies of reagents lead to a reliance on homologous human prolactin radioimmunoassays [Sinha et al, 1973]. These are readily validated for use in non-human primates [Quadri and Spies, 1976; Milmore, 1978].

Applications of Gonadotropin Assay Methodology

Radioimmunoassay. Table 3 lists radioimmunoassay methodologies that are employed for gonadotropin measurements in nonhuman primates under a variety of physiological circumstances. Although in most cases the heterologous radioimmunoassays for LH and FSH readily detect circulating gonadotropins in nonhuman primates, a few exceptions are worth noting. Among macaques, *M. arctoides* shows poor cross-reaction with antisera to ovine LH and FSH or to human FSH [Wilks, 1977; Wilks et al, 1980]. Mangabey (*Cercocebus atys*) gonadotropins show less cross-reaction with antisera to ovine LH and FSH than rhesus monkey gonadotropins, and mangabey FSH diverges immunologically from ovine and rhesus FSH [Mann et al, 1982]. In *Cercocebus atys lunulatus* circulating LH is undetectable with a radioimmunoassay for human LH [Aidara et al, 1981a]. The degree of cross-reaction of gonadotropins from *Pongo pygmaeus* with antisera to human gonadotropins is considerably less than that observed for other species in the family Hominidae [Nadler et al, 1980].

Bioassay. In vitro bioassays for gonadotropins expand our understanding of nonhuman primate reproduction. The indiscriminant response of rat [Dufau et al, 1976] or mouse [Van Damme et al, 1974] Leydig cells to gonadotropins from a wide variety of species greatly widens their applicability.

Family Cercopithecidae
Genus *Macaca*
    Macaca mulatta. The hCG-augmented mouse uterine weight bioassay detects elevated gonadotropin bioactivity in urine from ovariectomized animals [McArthur and Perley, 1969]. Circulating levels of bioactive LH in infant [Dufau et al, 1977; Neill et al, 1977; Frawley and Neill, 1979] or mature [Wickings et al, 1979] males and females [Marut et al, 1981] are examined with in vitro rat or mouse Leydig cell bioassays. In addition, cerebrospinal fluid from male rhesus monkeys contains bioactive LH [Puri et al, 1980].

Macaca fascicularis. The mouse Leydig cell bioassay is used to determine LH levels in adult [Steiner et al, 1980] and prepubertal [Steiner and Bremner, 1981] males.

Genus *Papio*
    Papio hamadryas. The mouse Leydig cell bioassay of Van Damme et al [1974] is used to establish circulating LH patterns during the menstrual cycle of the baboon [Goncharov et al, 1979].

Family Hominidae

LH bioactivity in urine can be characterized by RICT bioassay in the following species: *Gorilla gorilla*, *Pan troglodytes*, and *Pongo pygmaeus* [Lasley et al, 1980]. In addition, LH bioactivity is identified in urine from the douc langur (*Pygathrix nemaeus*) and capuchin monkey (*Cebus albifrons*) [Hodges et al, 1979; Lasley et al, 1980].

Radioreceptor Assay. Because of problems with serum interference, radioreceptor assays are applied only limitedly to the measurement of blood LH or FSH levels. However, blood [Sakai and Channing, 1979a] and follicular fluid [Sakai and Channing, 1979b] levels of LH are measurable with a radioreceptor assay for LH based on the binding of iodinated hCG to porcine granulosa cells. In species such as the orang-utan in which LH immunoassays are less useful, our laboratory uses radioreceptor assays to screen urine or blood for preovulatory LH surge levels.

Applications of Prolactin Assay Methodology

Radioimmunoassay. Tables 4a,b indicate species in which radioimmunoassays are used to quantitate prolactin levels in body fluids. Homologous human prolactin RIAs are appropriate for assessing prolactin secretion within the infraorder Catarrhini.

Bioassay. Rhesus monkey prolactin is indistinguishable from growth hormone with the pigeon crop sac bioassay for lactogens as modified by Grosvenor and Turner [1958] [Solomon et al, 1969; Nicoll et al, 1970; Channing et al, 1970; Gala, 1973]. Similarly, a newer bioassay method, in which the proliferation of Nb-2 lymphoma cells is augmented by prolactin [Tanaka et al, 1980], does not distinguish between the two primate molecules. To measure only primate prolactin with this bioassay the sample is assayed in the presence of antisera to hGH. The Nb-2 lymphoma cell bioassay for prolactin is extremely sensitive and suited to handle larger numbers of samples.

Radioreceptor Assay. Serum interference also occurs in radioreceptor assays for prolactin, thereby limiting their usefulness. However, radioreceptor methods are used to detect target tissues for prolactin in primates [Posner et al, 1974]. The potential use of the radioreceptor assay as a semiquantitative measure of biological activity in primates is largely ignored. However, this method might be used to examine the biological versus immunological activity of stored pituitary prolactin in nonhuman primates.

BODY FLUID LEVELS
Overview

Gonadotropins. Comparison of circulating gonadotropins across primate species is made difficult since techniques for the measurement of gonadotropins in blood are not standardized. Even in instances where similar assays are employed, specific reagents often differ. Therefore, discussions of absolute gonadotropin levels must first be qualified with relevant details about the assay, including reagents. Where this information is unavailable, only qualitative comparisons within a given physiological condition (eg, timing of midcycle elevation of LH in blood) are appropriate. The following description of gonadotropin levels under various physiological conditions attempts to draw qualitative comparisons across species.

Prolactin. Methods for the quantitation of prolactin levels in nonhuman primates are less variable than those used to detect gonadotropins. The homologous human prolactin RIA [Sinha et al, 1973] has been the method of choice for most species.

Comparisons of Gonadotropins Levels Across Species

During Pregnancy. The predominant circulating gonadotropin of primate pregnancy, chorionic gonadotropin (CG), originates from the placenta. Human chorionic gonadotropin (hCG) is secreted by the syncytiotrophoblastic layer of the placenta [Midgley and Pierce, 1962] and is detectable within 9 days of the midcycle peak of LH [Jaffe et al, 1969]. There is evidence for a CG also in rhesus monkeys, baboons, chimpanzees, gorillas, and orang-utans. Whereas hCG shows a steady increase to reach peak levels (80–100 IU/ml) by 90 days,

remaining elevated at somewhat reduced levels for the remainder of gestation, nonhuman primate CG increases early in pregnancy and then declines to undetectable levels [Winter et al, 1980]. Because of high levels of hCG during pregnancy and its chemical similarities to LH, circulating levels of LH are difficult to distinguish during this period. However, FSH [Talas et al, 1973] and LH [Reyes et al, 1976] levels fall to undetectable values during human pregnancy and LH is not an essential luteotropin of pregnancy in rhesus monkeys [Chandrashekar et al, 1978]. In the chimpanzee there is a simultaneous increase in LH/CG and a decrease in FSH beginning approximately 9–15 days after the midcycle LH peak [Reyes et al, 1975]. In the orang-utan a CG-like, bioactive substance is found in urine which peaks by the seventh week of pregnancy [Lasley et al, 1980].

Circulating gonadotropins are detectable in the nonhuman primate fetus. Female chimpanzee [Winter et al, 1980] and rhesus monkey [Ellinwood and Resko, 1980] fetuses have higher levels of LH than their male counterparts. This is especially true during the latter half of gestation.

During Sexual Maturation. Patterns of circulating gonadotropins observed during this time span are fairly consistent across species from the superfamilies Cercopithecidae and Hominoidea. In general, gonadotropin levels are elevated during the early neonatal period, after which they gradually decline to reach prepubertal values. This pattern is similar to that found in children where levels of FSH and LH rise to "castrate, adult" levels within 2–3 months of birth [Forest et al, 1974] and then decrease slowly over the next 2–3 years [Winter et al, 1975]. Corresponding changes occur in rhesus monkeys and chimpanzees but they are temporally advanced, taking place within the first year of life [Fuller et al, 1982].

Family Cercopithecidae
Genus *Macaca*
Macaca mulatta. Circulating, bioactive LH, as measured by rat interstitial cell testosterone (RICT) bioassay, is undetectable in rhesus monkey infants 6–20 months old [Dufau et al, 1977; Neill et al, 1977]. At earlier postnatal ages, elevations in LH are detected by bioassay [Frawley and Neill, 1979] and radioimmunoassay [Plant, 1980]. Testosterone is also elevated in males postnatally [Robinson and Bridson, 1978; Frawley and Neill, 1979]. These data indicate an early activation of the pituitary-

TABLE 3. Applications of Gonadotropin Radioimmunoassay Methodology in Nonhuman Primates

Gonado-tropin	Family (F.) or superfamily (S.)	Species	Tracer	Antisera	Reference[c] for assay	Physiological events	Reference
LH	F. Lemuridae	*Lemur catta*	ovine (o)LH	oLH	1	Surge; ovx; GnRH stimulation	Norman et al [1978]
LH	S. Ceboidea	*Callithrix jacchus*	oLH	oLH	1	Gonadectomy, estrogen	Hodges [1978]
LH, FSH	S. Ceboidea	*Saimiri sciureus*	human (h)LH, hFSH	hLH, hFSH[a]	2, 3	Midcycle surge	Barry and Croix [1978][a]; Ghosh et al [1982]
LH	F. Cercopithecidae	*Macaca mulatta*	rhesus (rh)LH	rhLH	4	Estrogen-induced surge	Yamaji et al [1971]
LH, FSH	F. Cercopithecidae	*Macaca mulatta*	oLH, rat (r)FSH	oLH, hFSH	1, 5	Menstrual cycle	Niswender and Spies [1973]
LH	F. Cercopithecidae	*Macaca mulatta*	rhLH	hCG	4[b]	Estrogen-positive feedback	Karsch et al [1973a]
LH, FSH	F. Cercopithecidae	*Macaca mulatta*	oLH, rFSH	oLH, hFSH	1, 5	Season, female	Dailey and Neill [1981]
LH, FSH	F. Cercopithecidae	*Macaca mulatta*	oLH, hFSH	oLH, oFSH	1, 6	Season, male	Beck and Wuttke [1979]
LH, FSH	F. Cercopithecidae	*Macaca mulatta*	oLH, hFSH	oLH, oFSH	1, 6	Maturation, female	Williams et al [1982]
LH	F. Cercopithecidae	*Macaca mulatta*	rhLH	hCG	7	Maturation, male	Plant [1982]
LH, FSH	F. Cercopithecidae	*M. fascicularis*	oLH, hFSH	oLH, oFSH	1, 6	Menstrual cycle	Mori et al [1973]; Goodman et al [1977]
LH, FSH	F. Cercopithecidae	*M. fascicularis*	oLH, hFSH	oLH, oFSH	1, 6	Postpartum	Goodman and Hodgen [1978]
LH	F. Cercopithecidae	*M. fascicularis*	oLH	oLH	1	Cultured pituicytes	Tang and Spies [1974]

	Family	Species					Reference
LH	F. Cercopithecidae	*M. fascicularis* and *M. radiata*	oLH	oLH	1	Menstrual cycle	Mori et al [1973]
LH, FSH	F. Cercopithecidae	*M. arctoides*	oLH, h and rFSH	oLH, o and hFSH	1, 5, 6	Menstrual cycle	Wilks [1977, 1980]
LH, FSH	F. Cercopithecidae	*Papio anubis*	oLH, hFSH	oLH, hFSH	1, 2, 3	Menstrual cycle	Tillson et al [1976]
LH	F. Cercopithecidae	*P. anubis*	rhLH	rhLH	1, 2, 3	Menstrual cycle	Stevens et al [1970]
LH	F. Cercopithecidae	*P. cynocephalus*	baboon LH	baboon LH	1, 2, 3	Menstrual cycle	Koyama et al [1977]
LH, FSH	F. Cercopithecidae	*P. cynocephalus*	oLH, hFSH	oLH, oFSH	1, 6	Menstrual cycle	Su et al [1980]
LH, FSH	F. Cercopithecidae	*Cercocebus atys*	oLH, hFSH	oLH, oFSH	1, 6	Response to GnRH	Mann et al [1983]
FSH	F. Cercopithecidae	*C. atys lunulatus*	hFSH	oFSH	6	Menstrual cycle	Aidara et al [1981a]
LH, FSH	F. Hominidae	*Gorilla gorilla*	hLH, hFSH	hLH, hFSH	2, 3	Menstrual cycle	Nadler et al [1979, 1980]
LH, FSH	F. Hominidae	*Pan troglodytes*	hLH, hFSH	hLH, hFSH	2, 3	Cycle; pregnancy; maturation	Howland et al [1971] Reyes et al [1975] Winter et al [1980] Fuller et al [1982]
LH, FSH	F. Hominidae	*Pan paniscus*	hLH, hFSH	hLH, hFSH	2, 3	Response to GnRH	Gould and Blank, unpublished
LH, FSH	F. Hominidae	*Pongo pygmaeus*	hLH, hFSH	hLH, hFSH	2, 3	Menstrual cycle (blood, urine)	Nadler et al [1980]

[a]Data are not convincing for use of antisera in species indicated.
[b]Modified for anti-hCG serum.
[c]References: 1) Niswender et al [1971]; 2) Midgley [1966, 1967]; 3) Faiman and Ryan [1967]; 4) Monroe et al [1970]; 5) Boorman et al [1973]; 6) Hodgen et al [1976]; 7) Karsch et al [1973a].

TABLE 4a. Application of Homologous Human Prolactin Radioimmunoassays in Rhesus Monkeys (*Macaca mulatta*)

Sex	Physiological end point	Reference
Female	Menstrual cycle[a]	Quadri and Spies [1976]
Female	Sexual maturation	Norman and Spies [1981]
Female	Pregnancy/lactation	Weiss et al [1976]; Williams and Hodgen [1980]; Blank et al [1983]; Frawley et al [1983]
Female	Diurnal rhythms	Quadri and Spies [1976]; Williams and Hodgen [1980]; Norman and Spies [1981]
Male	Diurnal rhythms	Quabbe et al [1982]; Perlow [1982]
Female, male	Circannual rhythms	Gala et al [1977]; Beck and Wuttke [1979]
Female	Cerebrospinal fluid	Belchetz et al [1982]
Male	Cerebrospinal fluid	Puri et al [1980]; Kalin et al [1981, 1982]; Perlow [1982]
—	Cord blood, fetus	Seron-Ferre et al [1979]

[a]Unless otherwise noted, peripheral blood levels of prolactin were measured.

TABLE 4b. Application of Prolactin Radioimmunoassay Methodology in Other Nonhuman Primates

Family (F.) or superfamily (S.)	Species	Physiological end point	Reference
S. Ceboidea	*Callithrix jacchus*	Lactation, drug stimulation	McNeilly et al [1981][a]
F. Cercopithecidae	*Papio anubis*	Mature males	Steiner et al [1978][b]
F. Cercopithecidae	*Papio cynocephalus*	Immature	Su [1981][b]
F. Cercopithecidae	*Cercocebus atys lunulatus*	Mature, immature; drug stimulation	Aidara et al [1981a][b]
F. Cercopithecidae	*Erythrocebus patas*	Mature, immature; drug stimulation	Aidara et al [1981b][b]
F. Hominidae	*Pan troglodytes*	Cycling, pregnant	Reyes et al [1975][b]
F. Hominidae	*Gorilla gorilla*	Cycling	Nadler [1980][b]

[a]Tracer = ovine prolactin; antisera = guinea pig antihuman prolactin.
[b]Homologous human prolactin radioimmunoassays.

gonadal axis of the rhesus monkey. The early increase in LH might be due to release of the pituitary from steroid-negative feedback, since males castrated at 1 week of age exhibit adultlike postcastration elevations in LH and FSH. However, even in the absence of the gonads, gonadotropin levels return to baseline by 8 months postnatally [Plant, 1980]. Thus the postnatal elevation in gonadotropin levels but not the decline is attributed to an activation of the hypothalamic-pituitary axis [Wildt et al, 1980]. The hypothalamic-gonadotrope unit is under inhibitory influence which renders it unresponsive to estradiol-positive feedback until 4–8 months after menarche [Dierschke et al, 1974]. The source of this inhibitory influence is unknown, but the pineal does not appear to be involved [Plant et al, 1981].

As in man and chimpanzee, sex differences exist in the magnitude of postnatal gonadotropin elevations in the rhesus monkey. Figure 10 shows the relatively higher FSH peak (12–20 μg /ml) in female rhesus monkeys [Fuller et al, 1982] between days 20 and 50 postnatally. Although differences in LH levels between males and females are not apparent (Fig. 11), the heterologous ovine-ovine LH radioimmunoassay used in this study [Fuller et al, 1982] may be less sensitive to fluctuations in LH levels [Williams et al, 1982].

A pulsatile pattern of LH secretion is observed in infant male rhesus monkeys by Plant [1982a]. This indicates a similar mode of gonadotropin secretion in infants and mature animals [Dierschke et al, 1970]. In male infants, the pulse pattern of LH

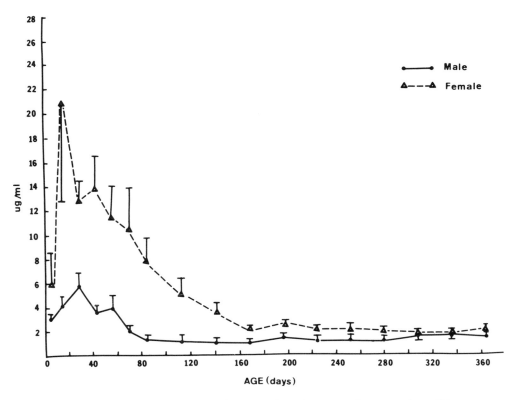

Fig. 10. Immunoactive FSH levels in serum from immature rhesus monkeys (*M. mulatta*). LER 1909-2 is the gonadotropin reference preparation. From Fuller et al [1982] with permission.

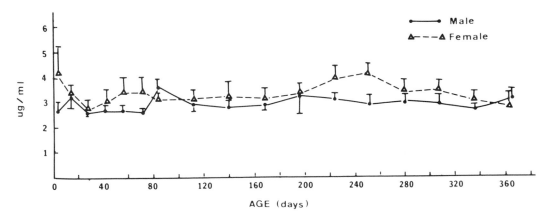

Fig. 11. Immunoactive LH levels in serum from immature rhesus monkeys (*M. mulatta*). LER 1909-2 is the gonadotropin reference preparation. From Fuller et al [1982] with permission.

secretion is reflected in a diurnal variation in testosterone [Plant, 1982b].

Once female rhesus monkeys reach sexual maturity, a period of shortened luteal phases ensues [Foster, 1977]. Williams et al [1982] find little bioactive LH but dynamic spikes of immunoreactive FSH in serum of prepubertal female rhesus monkeys. A lowered basal level of LH is found following preovulatory release in adolescents [Foster, 1977] and in adults with short luteal phases [Wilks et al, 1976]. The latter situation may indicate pituitary dysfunction.

The concept that the hypothalamus is rate-limiting in the onset of puberty in rhesus monkeys is strengthened by the finding that ovulatory menstrual cycles and normal patterns of gonadotropins are induced in prepubertal animals with intermittent infusions of gonadotropin-releasing hormone (GnRH) [Wildt et al, 1980]. The rhesus monkey does not exhibit adrenarche [Koritnik and Jaffe, 1980].

M. fascicularis. Steiner and Bremner [1981] find higher levels of LH bioactivity and testosterone in neonates and infants up to 8 months of age than in juveniles. Therefore, this species, like *M. mulatta*, exhibits depressed LH levels between 8 and 36 months of life. The inhibition of LH secretion may be related to an elevated pituitary threshold to GnRH [Steiner and Bremner, 1981].

Genus *Papio*

Papio cynocephalus. Peripubertal females show elevations in basal FSH immunoreactivity 7 months before menarche and in LH 1 month prior to menarche. Shortly before menarche, the FSH response to GnRH stimulation exceeds the LH response. This situation is reversed with the approach of sexual maturity [Su, 1981]. The first few menstrual cycles are characterized by lengthened follicular phases (possibly due to delayed elevation of FSH) and shortened luteal phases.

Genus *Cercocebus*

Cercocebus atys. The sooty mangabey exhibits elevated LH bioactivity before 6 months of age. The levels decline between 7 and 72 months of age [Mann et al, 1983].

Family Hominidae
Genus *Pan*

Pan troglodytes. As in other primate infants, the chimpanzee exhibits elevated circulating gonadotropins shortly after birth (within 2 or 3 weeks postnatally) which decline thereafter [Winter et al, 1975].

Sex differences in circulating levels of LH and FSH are present in the developing chimpanzee [Faiman et al, 1973; Fuller et al, 1982]. Figures 12 and 13 illustrate the augmented levels of serum FSH that are present in females (300–600 ng/ml) and of LH (60–100 ng/ml) found in males [Fuller et al, 1982]. The rise in blood gonadotropins in chimpanzees, as in macaques and humans, is thought to occur subsequent to the withdrawal of steroid suppression with expulsion of the placenta. However, the timing of the gonadotropin elevation is subject to considerable variation between individuals [Winter et al, 1980].

Menarche occurs between 7 and 10 years of age in the female chimpanzee and is followed by up to 2 years of adolescent sterility [Young and Yerkes, 1943]. The pituitary LH response of exogenous GnRH is magnified at puberty whereas there is only minimal release of FSH. FSH levels are lower in pubertal male chimpanzee than in pubertal boys [Winter et al, 1980]. Similar to humans [Grumbach et al, 1974], adrenarche may play a role in the sexual maturation and prepubertal gonadotropin secretion of the chimpanzee [Cutler et al, 1978].

During the Female Reproductive Cycle. Urinary LH and FSH bioactivity in adult female chimpanzees approximates levels found in the human female whereas little gonadotropin bioactivity is present in urine from rhesus monkeys, stump-tailed monkeys, and baboons [McArthur and Perley, 1969]. This suggests reduced gonadotropin secretion in lower primates. Although cycle length is approximately the same in species within the infraorder Catarrhini, cycle lengths below Catarrhini may be considerably shorter [Wolf et al, 1977; Ghosh et al, 1982]. Still, it appears that the overall qualitative relationships between pituitary gonadotropins and gonadal steroids are conserved in primate species studied thus far. However, some important differences exist, including postovulatory elevations in gonadotropins and variations in duration of the midcycle LH peak.

Superfamily Ceboidea
Genus *Saimiri*

Saimiri sciureus. Based on fluctuations in steroid hormone levels, the length of the reproductive cycle of the squirrel monkey is estimated to be about 9 days [Wolf et al, 1977]. Ghosh et al [1982]

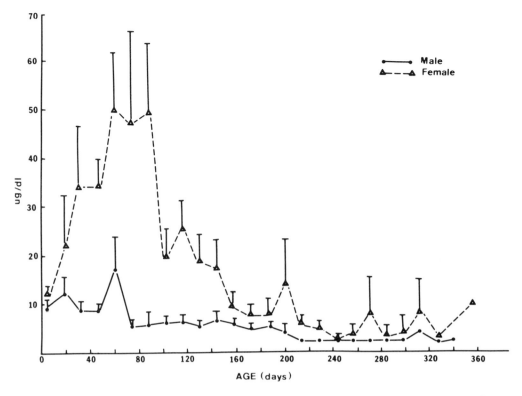

Fig. 12. Immunoactive FSH levels in serum from immature chimpanzees (*P. troglodytes*). LER 907 is the gonadotropin reference preparation. From Fuller et al [1982] with permission.

found that cyclic fluctuations in gonadal hormones correlate with changes in LH-like immunoreactivity. That is, a midcycle LH elevation of threefold (days 3–5) is followed by a rise in circulating progesterone between days 6 and 9. Higher LH and FSH levels are reported during the luteal phase with human LH and FSH RIAs, but documentation for the validity of the human FSH assay for measuring squirrel monkey gonadotropin is lacking [Barry and Croix, 1978]. In that regard, Ghosh et al [1982] do not find detectable cross-reactivity between squirrel monkey serum and antibodies to human FSH.

Family Cercopithecidae
Genus *Macaca*

Macaca mulatta. Menstrual cycle patterns of gonadotropins and ovarian steroids in the rhesus monkey closely resemble those observed in the human female [Monroe et al, 1970; Hotchkiss et al, 1971; Kirkton et al, 1970; Niswender et al,

1971]. More recent studies of the rhesus monkey cycle suggest that LH secreted during the preovulatory surge has enhanced bioactivity [Marut et al, 1981; Williams et al, 1982]. That is, circulating levels of immunoactive LH [Niswender et al, 1981] rise but at a slower rate than bioassayable LH [Marut et al, 1981]. However, circulating levels of LH radioreceptor activity are lower than values determined by radioimmunoassay [Niswender et al, 1971] during the preovulatory surge [Sakai and Channing, 1979a]. In contrast, the radioreceptor assay detects higher LH activity in animals with inadequate luteal phases [Sakai and Channing, 1979a]. These animals also exhibit decreased circulating LH bioactivity [Dailey and Neill, 1981]. In the latter case the radioreceptor assay appears to detect bioinactive forms of circulating LH.

Macaca arctoides. The serum LH and FSH pattern of cycling stump-tailed monkeys is, in general, similar to the rhesus monkey. However, two

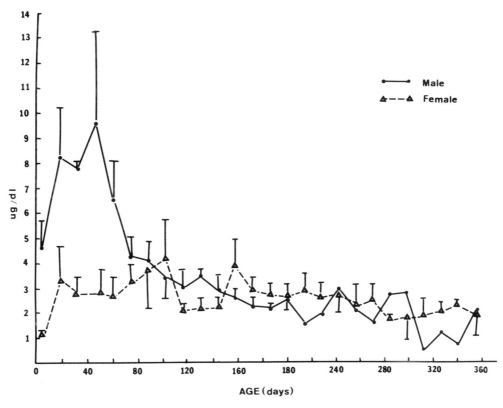

Fig. 13. Immunoactive LH levels in serum from immature chimpanzees (*P. troglodytes*). LER 907 is the gonadotropin reference preparation. From Fuller et al [1982] with permission.

differences are noted: 1) lower gonadotropin levels [Wilks, 1977], and 2) a secondary rise of FSH early in the luteal phase (2–3 days after the mid-cycle LH peak) [Wilks et al, 1980]. The lower levels of gonadotropins may reflect more a methodological than a physiological phenomenon. That is, ovine LH and FSH antisera show less cross-reaction with gonadotropins from *M. arctoides* [Wilks et al, 1980] and *Cercocebus atys* [Mann et al, 1982] than with rhesus monkey gonadotropins.

Macaca fascicularis. Like other macaques, the cynomolgus macaque exhibits a 1-day elevation in serum LH between days 10 and 13 of the reproductive cycle [Mori et al, 1973]. Patterns of FSH are comparable to those of the rhesus monkey and women [Goodman et al, 1977]. Luteal-phase discharges of LH occur in this species, and shortened cycle length is associated with follicular rather than luteal-phase variability [Mori et al, 1973]. During anovulatory cycles, LH secretion is absent and the return to normal cyclicity after lactation appears to result from a recovery of depressed gonadotropin secretion [Goodman and Hodgen, 1978], although some FSH activity is observed during the puerperium.

Macaca radiata. The bonnet monkey's cyclic gonadotropin patterns are similar to those of *M. fascicularis* [Mori et al, 1973].

Genus *Papio*

Papio anubis and *P. cynocephalus.* Levels of radioimmunoassayable LH and FSH are similar to those found in rhesus monkeys and women [Stevens et al, 1970; Su et al, 1980]. By bioassay, follicular and perimenstrual levels of LH are lower in baboons than in women and a luteal pattern of LH bursting is observed [Goncharov et al, 1979].

Genus *Cercocebus*

Cercocebus atys lunulatus. Studies in mangabeys confirm the close resemblance of their gonadotropic hormone pattern to those of other primates [Aidara et al, 1981a].

Family Hominidae
Genus *Pan*

Pan troglodytes. The midcycle surge of LH in the chimpanzee lasts for several days and is preceded by or coincident with a peak in serum estradiol [Reyes et al, 1975]. The chimpanzee's LH surge is of longer duration than the sharp 24-hour spike of LH observed in baboons and macaques [Mori et al, 1973; Goodman et al, 1977; Goncharov et al, 1979]. The chimpanzee exhibits both perimenstrual and periovulatory increases in circulating FSH [Howland et al, 1971]. Peak urinary LH bioactivity coincides with the decline in urinary estrogens and swelling of the sex skin [Lasley et al, 1980]. A secondary luteal rise in circulating estrogens is also observed [Hobson et al, 1976a].

Genus *Gorilla*

Gorilla gorilla. Including the secondary rise in estrogens during the luteal phase, the reproductive cycle of the female gorilla is essentially humanlike. Although cycle length varies between 23 and 48 days [Nadler et al, 1979], this variability may be caused by the frequent application of anesthesia which is required for blood collection. However, luteal-phase length is fairly constant (11–13 days). According to Nadler [1980], sex skin detumescence is temporally related to the postovulatory decline in LH and accompanying decline in estradiol and rise in progesterone levels. Peaks of bioactive LH in urine coincide with peak elevations of urinary estrogens [Lasley et al, 1980].

Genus *Pongo*

Pongo pygmaeus. The orang-utan is more closely related to lower primate species than it is to other great apes in its patterns of circulating LH during the menstrual cycle. Midcycle elevations of LH are followed by luteal-phase bursts in some animals [Nadler et al, 1984]. FSH levels have not been examined in this species.

In the Male. By comparison with data available for females, little is known about gonadotropins in male nonhuman primates. Since the male does not exhibit regular monthly fluctuations in gonadotropins, it has been of interest to examine diurnal variations. Significant daily fluctuations of circulating LH or FSH are not apparent in the bonnet monkey (*M. radiata*) [Mukku et al, 1981], but LH does vary diurnally in *M. fascicularis* [Steiner et al, 1980]. In the latter species, testosterone levels and pulse release are greater in the evening, each pulse of testosterone being preceded by a three- to tenfold increase in LH bioactivity [Steiner et al, 1980]. Basal levels of bioactive LH in male rhesus monkeys do not differ among laboratory-caged or free-ranging animals [Wickings et al, 1979]. Increments in serum LH amplitude and frequency are observed in males after GnRH stimulation or castration [Plant, 1982; Wickings et al, 1979].

Comparison of Prolactin Across Species

During Pregnancy. The pregnant rhesus monkey shows elevations in circulating prolactin only after the 155th day of gestation [Weiss et al, 1976]. During this period, fetal levels of prolactin in cord blood increase approximately fivefold [Seron-Ferre et al, 1979]. No differences between cord blood and fetal peripheral levels of prolactin are evident. As term approaches in the rhesus monkey, maternal serum prolactin concentrations remain somewhat elevated but do not exhibit a diurnal rhythm [Williams and Hodgen, 1980], as is the case in cycling animals [Quadri and Spies, 1976]. In the pregnant chimpanzee a prepartum elevation in prolactin levels is observed [Reyes et al, 1975].

During Lactation. Prolactin levels in indoor-housed [Williams and Hodgen, 1980] and outdoor-housed [Blank et al, 1983] lactating female rhesus monkeys are elevated and show large daily fluctuations during the first week postpartum. A slow and fast phase of prolactin secretion can be discerned in the rhesus monkey in response to suckling [Frawley et al, 1983]. A characteristic of lactation in the rhesus monkey and most other nonhuman primates is a marked inhibition of gonadotropin secretion and accompanying amenorrhea. In spite of prolactin's direct luteolytic action on the primate ovary [Balmaceda et al, 1981], lactational amenorrhea is apparently due more to the suckling stimulus than to hyperprolactinemia [Schallenberger and Knobil, 1980], since chemical suppression of prolactin levels in the presence of suckling does not disinhibit gonadotropin secretion. The marmoset (*Callithrix jacchus*), on the other hand, shows no signs of lactational amenorrhea. This is in spite of elevated levels of prolactin in suckled female marmosets [McNeilly et al, 1981].

During Sexual Maturation. In the maturing female rhesus monkey disconnection of the hypothalamus yields exaggerated diurnal rhythms of prolactin secretion [Norman and Spies, 1981]. No differences are found between prolactin levels in mature and immature male mangabey (*Cercocebus atys lunulatus*) or patas monkeys (*Erythrocebus patas*) [Aidara et al, 1981b].

During the Menstrual Cycle. Although basal circulating levels of prolactin are, in general, higher in females than males [Aidara et al, 1981b], no consistent patterns of prolactin are observed during the menstrual cycle of chimpanzees [Reyes et al, 1975], gorilla [Nadler et al, 1979], baboons [Steiner et al, 1978], rhesus monkeys [Quadri and Spies, 1976], or marmosets [McNeilly et al, 1981].

Endogenous Rhythms. Yearly rhythms in prolactin secretion are apparently absent in female humans and cynomolgus macaques [Gala et al, 1977]. However, significant variability between individuals could mask potential rhythms. Diurnal rhythms of prolactin in blood and cerebrospinal fluid are reported in male rhesus monkeys [Puri et al, 1980; Kalin et al, 1981, 1982; Quabbe et al, 1982]. In general, cerebrospinal fluid prolactin in rhesus monkeys is ten- to 15-fold lower than serum prolactin [Puri et al, 1980] and follows blood concentrations [Quadri and Spies, 1976; Norman and Spies, 1981; Kalin et al, 1982; Williams and Hodgen, 1980; Belchetz et al, 1982]. Prolactin levels in blood and cerebrospinal fluid are higher during periods of darkness [Puri et al, 1980; Kalin et al, 1981; Perlow, 1982; Quabbe et al, 1982], with levels rising approximately 2–6 hours after the lights are turned off and reaching a nadir 2–6 hours after the lights are turned on.

Summary

Although direct comparison of body-fluid levels of gonadotropins and prolactin are made impractical due to nonstandardized assay techniques, qualitative contrasts are instructive. Moreover, recent advances in availability of reagents for radioimmunoassay of LH and in bioassays for LH [Dufau et al, 1976; Van Damme et al, 1974] and prolactin [Tanaka et al, 1980] will ease future comparisons.

FACTORS INFLUENCING SECRETION
Overview

Secretion of pituitary gonadotropins and prolactin is subject to regulation by a multitude of physiological factors. The hypothalamic pituitary system provides the final common pathway through which these various modulatory factors exert their actions. Central nervous system regulation of the hypothalamic-pituitary axis is reviewed in this volume by R. Norman and has been extensively reviewed elsewhere [Knobil, 1980, 1981]. Therefore the following discussion will focus primarily on regulation by extraneuronal factors, such as the gonads.

Gonadal Effects

Family Cercopithecidae
Genus *Macaca*
Macaca mulatta. Since an abundance of information is available on steroid feedback influences on gonadotropin secretion in this species, work with other primates must ultimately be compared to work with the rhesus monkey.

The male rhesus monkey already shows signs of negative feedback sensitivity to gonadal hormones in utero since removal of the fetal testes results in tenfold elevations of LH bioactivity [Ellinwood et al, 1982] and increases in FSH immunoactivity [Reyes et al, 1980]. Interestingly, basal levels of LH and FSH are higher in female than male fetuses [Ellinwood and Resko, 1980], and these higher levels are suppressed in gonadectomized females but not males by treatment with testosterone [Ellinwood et al, 1982]. Therefore, the importance of gonadal steroids per se in fetal negative feedback sensitivity is unclear. Developmental alterations in brain steroid-metabolizing enzymes may be relevant in explaining these results.

The neonatal male rhesus monkey manifests a rise followed by a fall in circulating gonadotropins during the first year of life regardless of the animal's gonadal status [Plant, 1980]. Moreover, gonadectomy in the neonatal male or female rhesus monkey has no effect on estradiol-positive feedback on LH [Karsch et al, 1973b] which develops 4–8 months after menarche [Dierschke et al, 1974].

Estrogen may be required in combination with testosterone for complete negative feedback in the adult male [Resko et al, 1977, 1980], and the interval between castration and reexposure may be critical in assessing testosterone's negative feedback role in males [Plant et al, 1978].

In general, both sexes respond to large doses of estradiol with surge LH secretion [Karsch et al, 1973b; Steiner et al, 1976], but females appear more sensitive to estradiol's negative feedback effects [Yamaji et al, 1971; Steiner et al, 1976]. Both inhibition [Karsch et al, 1973c] and potentiation [Karsch et al, 1973a] of LH release by estradiol are sensitive to small changes in absolute amount and duration of exposure to steroid. Estradiol is clearly an important regulator of LH secretion during the menstrual cycle since active immunization to estradiol causes anovulation [Ferin et al, 1974]. Like women, rhesus monkeys respond to the antiestrogen, clomiphene, with elevations in circulating LH and FSH [Marut and Hodgen, 1982]. Episodic LH release occurs in ovariectomized female rhesus monkeys [Dierschke et al, 1970]. However, pulsatile LH release in ovariectomized monkeys is no longer thought to reflect a gonadotropin axis which is "free running" in the absence of estrogen-negative feedback [Knobil, 1981].

Estradiol's site of action on gonadotropin secretion in the rhesus monkey is claimed to be both hypothalamic and pituitary [Ferin et al, 1975; Krey et al, 1975; Pfaff et al, 1976; Hess et al, 1977; Neill et al, 1977b; Nakai et al, 1978; Plant et al, 1978; Attardi et al, 1980; Chappel et al, 1981; Zeleznik et al, 1981]. Previous work suggests a mainly pituitary site of estradiol action by demonstrating steroid-induced LH secretion in the absence of GnRH in rhesus monkeys bearing hypothalamic lesions [Wildt et al, 1981a]. In these studies gonadotropin-releasing hormone is thought to be permissive rather than necessary in estradiol-induced LH surges [Knobil et al, 1980]. However, the notion of a nonhypothalamic site of estradiol action is based on the destruction of all GnRH-producing areas of the hypothalamus [Wildt et al, 1981a]. In a recent study Norman et al [1982] shed further light on this issue by inserting barriers which were permeable or impermeable to GnRH between the hypothalamus and pituitary. Estradiol levels of between 200 and 300 pg/ml elicit LH surges in pituitary stalk-sectioned animals when a GnRH-permeable Silastic barrier is inserted but do not provoke LH release when an impermeable Teflon barrier is present. Although an estradiol-priming effect on the pituitary cannot be ruled out, it appears from this study that estradiol must act first on the hypothalamus to elicit the release of a small facilitative peptide, probably GnRH [Norman et al, 1982].

The physiological role of progesterone in regulating gonadotropin secretion in rhesus monkeys is confused somewhat by experiments in which pharmacological doses of progesterone are employed. However, most studies agree that increased levels of progesterone inhibit FSH secretion [Resko et al, 1981] and advance the onset of surge gonadotropin release [Clifton et al, 1975; Helmond et al, 1980]. The ability of progesterone to both stimulate [Resko et al, 1981] and inhibit [Wildt et al, 1981b; Pohl et al, 1982] LH secretion correlates either with the timing of its administration during the menstrual cycle [Resko et al, 1981] or with the gonadal [Terasawa et al, 1980; Jackson et al, 1981] and hypothalamic [Wildt et al, 1981b] status of the animal. Progesterone is clearly biphasic in its effects on estradiol-induced [Helmond et al, 1981] or spontaneous [Resko et al, 1981] LH surges.

A nonsteroidal, gonadal inhibitor of FSH secretion (inhibin) is hypothesized for the rhesus monkey since luteectomy does not effect LH or FSH patterns but advances the next ovulation [Goodman and Hodgen, 1977], and charcoal-stripped porcine follicular fluid specifically inhibits FSH secretion [Hodgen et al, 1980; Channing et al, 1981]. Since size and development of the dominant follicle are adversely affected by this selective inhibition of FSH, it is concluded that FSH is required to support the dominant follicle during the menstrual cycle of rhesus monkeys [DiZerega et al, 1981].

Genus *Papio*

Papio cynocephalus. Estrogen-positive feedback is operative in the baboon 1 month prior to menarche [Su et al, 1980], and postovulatory release of LH is also sensitive to estrogen feedback [Hagino, 1979].

Superfamily Ceboidea
Genus *Callithrix*

Callithrix jacchus. Both positive and negative feedback effects of estradiol are present in male and female marmoset monkeys [Hodges, 1978]. Gonadectomy increases LH levels in both sexes and episodic LH secretion is evident in chronically gonadectomized marmosets. Supraphysiological levels of estradiol (500–600 pg/ml) first augment and then inhibit LH secretion in gonadectomized animals. In contrast to male rhesus and pig-tailed macaques where only estrogen-primed, castrated subjects show LH responses to estrogen stimulation [Karsch et al, 1973c; Steiner et al, 1976, 1978], the intact male marmoset has the capacity to respond to estradiol without priming [Hodges and Hearn, 1978]. The marmoset is apparently different from rodents where males lose their ability to respond to estrogen-positive feedback [Hodges, 1980], and the responses of rhesus and pig-tailed macaques fall somewhere in between.

Sensitivity to Gonadotropin-Releasing Hormone (GnRH)

During Development

Family Cercopithecidae
Genus *Macaca*

Macaca mulatta. The rhesus monkey is relatively insensitive to the LH elevating effects of GnRH [Arimura et al, 1973]. Still, the species has been used to advantage in uncovering developmental changes in pituitary sensitivity to this neuropeptide. The fetal monkey responds to GnRH with increases in bioactive and immunoactive LH [Huhtaniemi et al, 1979; Norman and Spies, 1979]. The LH which is secreted in response to GnRH is capable of stimulating the fetal testes but not the ovaries [Norman and Spies, 1979]. Huhtaniemi et al [1979] report the greatest testosterone response to GnRH administration occurring between 18 and 89 days of age whereas Norman and Spies [1979] observe no significant increase in LH or testosterone in male infants. After 3 months of age LH and testosterone responses to GnRH become progressively smaller [Huhtaniemi et al, 1979]. Prepubertal and premenarcheal females exhibit LH responses to GnRH [Dierschke et al, 1974; Norman and Spies, 1979]. In summary, developing females of all ages are responsive to GnRH whereas males are responsive only during fetal life and as young infants.

In Mature Animals

Family Lemuroidea
Genus *Lemur*

Lemur catta. The ring-tailed lemur is quite sensitive to GnRH stimulation. Ovariectomized, estrogen-treated animals exhibit greater than tenfold elevations of serum LH [Norman et al, 1978].

Family Cercopithecoidea
Genus *Macaca*

Macaca mulatta. The gonadotropin response to exogenous GnRH is greatest at midcycle in female rhesus monkeys [Ferin et al, 1974]. If one removes the ovaries and then lesions GnRH-secreting areas of the hypothalamus, LH and FSH levels are markedly reduced [Wildt et al, 1981c]. Furthermore, pulse administration of GnRH (one 6-min pulse per hour) restores LH and FSH to normal levels. By altering the frequency or rate of pulse GnRH administration, varying ratios of LH and FSH secretion are obtained [Wildt et al, 1981c]. Thus GnRH alone may regulate both LH and FSH secretion. Although pituitary stalk section results in a transient facilitation of LH responses to GnRH administration [Frawley et al, 1981], the fact that stalk section ultimately reduces circulating LH to undetectable levels [Vaughan et al, 1980] is indirect evidence for the importance of the hypothalamus (and, probably, GnRH) for normal LH secretion. Active immunization to GnRH in males markedly reduces serum LH and testosterone [Chappel et al, 1980]. These phenomenona are ultimately mediated by changes in pituitary GnRH receptors [Adams et al, 1981]. Furthermore, pituitary portal blood levels of and pituitary receptors for GnRH are increased during LH discharges [Neill et al, 1977b; Adams et al, 1981].

Family Hominidae
Genus *Pan*

Pan troglodytes. LH and FSH responses to GnRH reach a zenith during the periovulatory period of the menstrual cycle [Hobson and Fuller, 1977]. The timing of this augmentation is similar to that found in rhesus monkeys but the magnitude of LH response is greater: a 115% increase in rhesus monkeys compared with increases of between 280% and 560% in chimpanzees during the follicular phase [Hobson and Fuller, 1977]. Antagonists of GnRH inhibit LH release in this species [Gosselin et al, 1979] as they do in macaques [Fraser et al, 1980] and baboons [Hagino et al, 1977]. In general, LH and FSH responses to GnRH stimulation in female chimpanzees and human females are similar [Graham et al, 1979].

Effects of Various Other Substances

Prostaglandins. These fatty-acid-derived substances may have a stimulatory role in surge secretion of LH in nonhuman primates. Administration of prostaglandin E_2 or $F_{2\alpha}$ augments LH and FSH release [Kimball et al, 1979], and indomethacin, a prostaglandin synthesis inhibitor, reduces estradiol-induced LH surges in female rhesus monkeys [Carlson et al, 1977]. These substances are thought to act centrally.

Aspartate. This putative excitatory neurotransmitter evokes large and rapid elevations in LH and FSH in female rhesus monkeys but its site of action is undetermined [Wilson and Knobil, 1982].

Opiates. Morphine decreases LH and FSH in ovariectomized rhesus monkeys but has no effect on estradiol-induced or GnRH-induced (in stalk-sectioned animals) gonadotropin secretion. Thus a suprahypophyseal site of morphine action has been hypothesized [Ferin et al, 1982]. Although naloxone, an opiate antagonist, elevates LH levels in rodents, chimpanzees, and women [Blank et al, 1979; Quigley and Yen; 1980, Gosselin et al, 1983; Blank and Nadler, unpublished observations], it is not readily effective in rhesus monkeys [Spies et al, 1980] (Blank and Gordon, unpublished observation). This may partly result from the insensitivity of rhesus monkeys to GnRH. Despite the presence of elevated levels of β-endorphin in portal blood of *M. nemestrina* [Wardlaw et al, 1980a] which decline to undetectable levels after ovariectomy [Wehrenberg et al, 1982], questions remain regarding the physiological role of endogenous opiates in regulating LH secretion in nonhuman primates.

Anesthetics. A problem in obtaining blood samples for gonadotropin analyses from many species of nonhuman primates is the necessity for anesthetizing the animals. Phencyclidine and ketamine are commonly used for this purpose. Phencyclidine interferes with LH secretion [Ferin et al, 1976], but ketamine does not influence bioactive LH [Puri et al, 1981] in adult rhesus monkeys.

Effects of Other Factors

Suckling. The LH response to GnRH stimulation is reduced in nursing bonnet monkeys (*M. radiata*) but not in nonsuckled animals [Maneckjee et al, 1976]. Estradiol-positive feedback is absent in nursing or foster rhesus monkeys or in ovariectomized talapoin monkeys with drug-induced hyperprolactinemia [Bowman et al, 1978]. Thus lactational amenorrhea is a direct result of the nursing act rather than other factors occurring near or after the puerperium.

Season and Behavior. Rhesus monkeys exhibit seasonally related patterns of sexual behavior and gonadotropin secretion. This phenomenon is more pronounced in the outdoor environment [Wilson et al, 1984] but also occurs in laboratory-housed animals [Beck and Wuttke, 1979; Dailey and Neill, 1981]. Summer anovulation, which is a hallmark of this species, may be the result of insufficient estrogen secretion for LH surges [Dailey and Neill, 1981] or a resetting of the hypothalamic gonadostat to estradiol-negative feedback [Foster et al, 1981]. The rhesus monkey, similar to the ewe, may receive cues from the external environment which modulate gonadotropin secretion. However, unlike the ewe, the socially living rhesus monkey does not appear to exhibit seasonal changes in feedback sensitivity to estradiol [Herndon et al, 1985].

Dominant but not subordinate female talapoin monkeys are responsive to estradiol-positive feedback on LH secretion [Bowman et al, 1978].

Direct Effects on the Pituitary. Release of gonadotropins from the nonhuman primate pituitary does not depend on cyclic adenosine monophosphate as a second messenger [Tang and Spies, 1974]. However, elevations in LH levels appear to correlate with increases in pituitary receptor sites for GnRH [Adams et al, 1981]. Thus GnRH action on the gonadotrope appears to be a final determinant of gonadotropin release [Knobil et al, 1980]. Direct modulation of the pituitary by factors such as steroids [Wildt et al, 1981a] or peptides [Wardlaw et al, 1980a] also may be involved.

Factors Influencing Prolactin Secretion

Steroids. Ovariectomy of rhesus monkeys decreases circulating levels of prolactin and estradiol treatment reestablishes these levels [Milmore, 1978; Quadri et al, 1979]. Estradiol treatment results in elevations of prolactin in long-term ovariectomized [Quadri et al, 1979] or in stalk-sectioned ovariectomized [Diefenbach et al, 1980; Frawley and Neill, 1980] monkeys. However, in animals with intact pituitary stalks, inhibitory hypothalamic input (probably via dopamine) [Neill et al, 1981] is dominant and is not overcome by estrogens in the physiological range [Diefenbach et al, 1980]. Supraphysiological levels of estradiol cause prolactin levels to fall in cycling rhesus monkeys [Williams et al, 1981]. Progesterone itself does not influence prolactin secretion in rhesus monkeys [Jackson et al, 1981], but a progesteronelike drug, cyproterone acetate, increases prolactin levels [Herbert et al, 1977]. Prolactin secretion in immature male rhesus monkeys is stimulated by testosterone administration [Herbert, 1978b] but adrenal glucocorticoids can inhibit prolactin release [Steger et al, 1981].

Thus it appears that prolactin secretion is sensitive to steroids, but changes in its pattern of secretion are related to the dose of steroid.

Suckling. The infant's suckling on the mother's breast is a well-known stimulus for prolactin secretion in mammals, and the nonhuman primate is no exception to this maxim. Treatment of lactating rhesus monkeys with dopamine agonists reduces postpartum elevations in prolactin [Schallenberger et al, 1981], but recent evidence suggests that more than one control mechanism may be involved in suckling-induced prolactin release [Frawley et al, 1983].

Stress and Behavior. Immobilization [Quadri et al, 1978], capture [Blank et al, 1983], and cage-restraint [Puri et al, 1981] stress in rhesus monkeys elevate prolactin levels; copulation is without effect [Quadri et al, 1977]. Elevations in serum prolactin return to basal values 90 to 120 minutes later [Quadri et al, 1978] despite repeated venipuncture [Blank et al, 1983]. Male talapoins (*Miopithecus talapoin*) that are subordinate in the dominance hierarchy of a social group have higher prolactin levels [Eberhart and Keverne, 1979] as do male marmosets (*Callithrix jacchus*) that are carrying their offspring [Dixson and George, 1982].

Peptides and Transmitters. Several compounds are active releasers of prolactin in macaques. They include: β-endorphin, thyrotropin-releasing hormone, and vasoactive intestinal polypeptide [Spies et al, 1980; Gala and Jaques, 1975; Frawley and Neill, 1981]. Current thought is focused on thyrotropin-releasing hormone as a physiological prolactin-releasing factor and dopamine as an inhibiting factor. Dopamine receptors are found in the anterior pituitary of *M. fascicularis* and the number of dopamine-binding sites correlates with circulating prolactin levels [Cronin and Koritnik, 1983]. The endogenous opioid, β-endorphin, acts to increase prolactin levels by interfering with dopamine input in *M. mulatta* and *M. nemestrina* [Wardlaw et al, 1980b; Wehrenberg et al, 1981].

Other Factors. The possibility that prolactin secretion in rhesus monkeys is regulated by a circhoral clock similar to that regulating GnRH is suggested by the episodic secretion of prolactin which is found after pentobarbital anesthesia [Belchetz et al, 1978]. Phencyclidine and ketamine anesthesia interfere with prolactin secretion [Ferin et al, 1976; Puri et al, 1981] in rhesus monkeys.

ACTIONS OF GONADOTROPINS AND PROLACTIN
Gonadotropins

Ovaries. In the rhesus monkey (*Macaca mulatta*), gonadotropins cause luteinization of granulosa cells of mature follicles (days 7–10 of the menstrual cycle) [Channing, 1970] and stimulate progesterone secretion during the luteal phase [Macdonald and Greep, 1972]. The continued presence of LH is needed for luteinization to occur [Channing, 1974]. Gonadotropin administration increases the number of vesicles of the outer layer of the zone pellucida [Maruffo, 1967]. During the luteal phase, cells obtained from the corpus luteum of the rhesus monkey exhibit selectivity for LH over FSH and sensitivity to LH decreases with age of the corpus luteum [Stouffer et al, 1977]. The layer of granulosa cells must be exposed to a midcycle surge of LH if full luteinization is to occur [Channing, 1980].

Binding sites for hLH and hCG are demonstrated in ovaries from rhesus and cynomolgus monkeys [DiZerega and Hodgen, 1980; Zeleznik et al, 1981; Cameron and Stouffer, 1981]. Enhanced gonadotropin binding in the thecal layer during the midfollicular phase [DiZerega and Hodgen, 1980] and increased vascularization with concomitant increased gonadotropin uptake [Sakai and Channing, 1979b; Zeleznik et al, 1981] help select the dominant follicle which is destined for ovulation. The prepubertal ovary exhibits little or none of the hLH/hCG binding exhibited by the corpus luteum of the midluteal phase [Cameron and Stouffer, 1982]. Interestingly, corpus luteum gonadotropin receptors from rhesus monkey show marked selectivity for primate gonadotropins [Cameron and Stouffer, 1981, 1982] but otherwise possess binding affinities and capacities similar to those found in other mammalian species. Other (nongonadotropic) hormones may synergize with LH to maintain corpus luteum function in rhesus monkeys [Gulyas et al, 1980]. Considering the specific actions of LH on the primate ovary, it is not surprising that restriction of breeding to shortly after the midcycle

LH surge significantly enhances fertility rates [Hobson et al, 1976b]. Although gonadotropins are implicated in the regulation of gene expression in mammals [Jungmann and Hunzicker-Dunn, 1978; McKerns, 1978], similar actions are not yet confirmed in the primate corpus luteum.

FSH is important to the primate menstrual cycle for normal follicular growth [Clark et al, 1979], for the production of estrogen during the follicular phase, and for luteal cell response to LH [Stouffer and Hodgen, 1980]. The rise of FSH that occurs before the midfollicular phase may have a role in determining the quality of the luteal phase [DiZerega et al, 1981].

Testes. The Sertoli cell is thought to be FSH's main target in male mammals [Steinberger et al, 1978]. In the mature male, FSH may be important for spermatogenesis since administration of antiserum to ovine FSH results in decreases in testicular volumes and seminiferous tubular diameters in rhesus monkeys [Wickings et al, 1980]. LH receptors from rhesus monkey testes are similar to human receptors in that they are of high affinity ($K_a = 1$–$2 \times 10^{10} \, M^{-1}$), low capacity (23–146 fmol hCG/g), and are primate-specific [Davies et al, 1979a]. The biological action of LH on the rhesus monkey testis is dependent on the β subunit [Davies et al, 1979a]. Similar to testicular LH receptors in other species, the rhesus monkey receptor exhibits desensitization after hCG administration [Davies et al, 1979b].

Prolactin

Pituitary Prolactin. The stimulation of milk secretion is a well-known action of prolactin in mammals. Prolactin stimulates α-lactalbumin (a major milk protein) production in mammary tissue from mature and immature rhesus monkeys [Kleinberg et al, 1979] and monkey prolactin displaces other prolactins from receptor sites on rabbit mammary glands [Shiu et al, 1973]. Roles for prolactin in both rescuing the corpus luteum of lactation [Weiss et al, 1973] and lysing the corpus luteum of the menstrual cycle [Balmaceda et al, 1981] are proposed for rhesus monkeys. However, prolactin does not appear to have an effect on the prostate of the chacma baboon [Schoonees et al, 1970]. Prolactin binds to fetal tissues of the rhesus monkey including placenta, liver, lung, and myocardium during the latter half of gestation [Josimovich et al, 1977]. Prolactin exhibits very low specific binding to heart and ovary receptors of rhesus monkeys and less to liver, kidney, uterus, placenta, adrenal, mammary,

and testis [Posner et al, 1974]. The reason for the relative inability of rhesus monkey tissues to bind prolactin in vitro is unclear especially since these tissues do not possess an inhibitor of binding [Posner et al, 1974]. When studying biological actions of prolactin in primates, one must consider that primate growth hormone possesses considerable prolactinlike (especially lactogenic) activity [Rivera et al, 1967; Peckham et al, 1968; Kleinberg and Todd, 1980].

Amniotic Fluid Prolactin. Large amounts of prolactin are found in amniotic fluid of rhesus monkeys, and the source seems to be the maternal circulation [Josimovich et al, 1974], although recent reports suggest that the human chorion is capable of synthesizing prolactin [Clements et al, 1983]. Amniotic fluid prolactin may influence fluid and electrolyte balance and thereby maintain homeostasis across the amniotic membrane [Josimovich et al, 1977].

CONCLUSIONS

The history of gonadotropin research, as in other areas of endocrinology, parallels advances in our ability to first detect and then, later, quantitate these substances. Primate gonadotropin research lags behind work in other mammalian species because of limited animal resources. In addition, a national program for the collection of human pituitaries in the United States provides a rich resource for the chemical characterization of human gonadotropins. Since, in general, radioimmunoassays based on human gonadotropins can detect nonhuman primate gonadotropins, there is less incentive to purify the latter. An exception is macaque LH which is not detected with antibodies to human LH and therefore is the most thoroughly characterized nonhuman primate gonadotropin. Other nonhuman primate gonadotropins are studied from an indirect immunological standpoint alone. Still, recent standardization of reagents for radioimmunoassay and the development of highly sensitive in vitro bioassays for gonadotropins and prolactin hold great promise in facilitating cross-species comparisons. Moreover, the use of monoclonal antibodies to specific gonadotropins will also yield interesting new information in this area.

Detailed elucidation of the chemistry of nonhuman primate gonadotropins will await further advances in our ability to extract minute quantities of mRNA from pituitary tissue. Once again, limited animal resources dictate the necessity for this approach. In the meantime, human cDNA probes hold out promise for comparisons of genes that code for nonhuman primate gonadotropins.

Great strides have been made in uncovering the physiological mechanisms that regulate gonadotropin/prolactin secretion in nonhuman primates. However, we are now just scratching the surface of the basis for central nervous system regulation of gonadotropin and prolactin secretion: interneuronal communication.

Gonadotropin and prolactin actions in nonhuman primates appear to be closely related to those found in humans. In vitro stimulation of cultured nonhuman primate gonadal cells will provide future answers to many of the remaining questions regarding how the information contained in gonadotropin and prolactin molecules is transmitted to and decoded by their target cells. Moreover, these techniques will also allow the closer examination of intracellular alterations induced by gonadotropins and prolactin.

ACKNOWLEDGMENTS

The author thanks Drs. Kenneth Gould, Ronald Nadler, Tom Gordon, Mark Wilson, and Harold McClure of the Yerkes Primate Center for providing samples for analysis, and Drs. John S. Parks, Emory University, Ione A. Kourides, Memorial Sloan-Kettering Cancer Center, and Maria L. Dufau, NICHD, National Institutes of Health, for helpful discussion. Special thanks go to Mrs. Jean Torbit for manuscript preparation, Mr. Frank Kiernan for photography, and Mr. James Murphy for preparing the list of references. This investigation was supported by PHS research grants RR00165 (Yerkes Center) and HD15073 (M.S.B.) from NIH.

REFERENCES

Adams, T.E.; Norman, R.L.; Spies, H.G. Gonadotropin-releasing hormone receptor binding characteristics and pituitary responsiveness in estradiol-primed monkeys. SCIENCE 213:1388–1390, 1981.

Aidara, D.; Badawi, M.; Tahiri-Zagret, C.; Robyn, C. Changes in concentrations of serum prolactin, FSH, oestradiol and progesterone and of the sex skin during the menstrual cycle in the mangabey monkey (Cercocebus atys lunulatis). JOURNAL OF REPRODUCTION AND FERTILITY 62:475–481, 1981a.

Aidara, D.; Tahiri-Zagret, C.; Robyn, C. Serum prolactin concentrations in mangabey (Cercocebus atys lunulatus) and patas (Erythrocebus patas) monkeys in response to stress, ketamine, TRH, sulpiride, and levodopa, JOURNAL OF REPRODUCTION AND FERTILITY 62:165–172, 1981b.

Aloj, S.M.; Edelhoch, H.; Ingham, K.C.; Morgan, F.J.; Canfield, R.E.; Ross, G.T. The rates of dissociation and reassociation of the subunits of human chorionic gonadotropin. ARCHIVES OF BIOCHEMISTRY AND BIOPHYSICS 159:497–504, 1973.

Antunes, J.L.; Carmel, P.W.; Zimmerman, E.A.; Ferin, M. The pars tuberalis of the rhesus monkey secretes luteinizing hormone. BRAIN RESEARCH 166:49–55, 1979.

Antunes, J.L.; Louis, K.; Cogen, P.; Zimmerman, E.A.; Ferin, M. Section of the pituitary stalk in the rhesus monkey. II. Morphological studies. NEUROENDOCRINOLOGY 30:76–82, 1980.

Arimura, A.; Spies, H.G.; Schally, A.V. Relative insensitivity of rhesus monkeys to the LH-releasing hormone (LH-RH). JOURNAL OF CLINICAL ENDOCRINOLOGY AND METABOLISM 36:372–374, 1973.

Ascheim, S.; Zondeck, B. Die schwangerschafts Diagnose aus Darn durch Nachweis des hypophysenvordenlappen Hormons. KLINISCHE WOCHENSCHRIFT 7:1404–1411, 1928.

Astwood, E.B. The regulation of corpus luteum function by hypophysial luteotrophin. ENDOCRINOLOGY 28:309–312, 1941.

Atkinson, L.E.; Bhatlacharya, A.N.; Monroe, S.E.; Dierschke, D.J.; Knobil, E. Effects of gonadectomy on plasma LH concentrations in the rhesus monkey. ENDOCRINOLOGY 87:847–849, 1970.

Attardi, B.; Hotchkiss, J.; Knobil, E. Monkey pituitary oestrogen receptors and the biphasic action of oestradiol on gonadotropin secretion. NATURE 285:252–254, 1980.

Baker, B.L.; Karsch, F.J.; Hoffman, D.L.; Beckman, W.C. The presence of gonadotropic and thyrotropic cells in the pituitary pars tuberalis of the monkey (Macaca mulatta). BIOLOGY OF REPRODUCTION 17:232–240, 1977.

Ball, J.; Hartman, G.G. Sexual excitability as related to the menstrual cycle in the monkey. AMERICAN JOURNAL OF OBSTETRICS AND GYNECOLOGY 29:117–119, 1935.

Balmaceda, J.P.; Eddy, C.A.; Smith, C.G.; Asch, R.H. The effects of hyperprolactinemia on the luteal phase of the rhesus monkey; evidence for a direct prolactin effect on the ovary. FERTILITY AND STERILITY 36:431–432, 1981 (abstract).

Barrnett, R.; Ladman, A.J. Histochemical demonstration of protein-bound sulfhydryl and disulfide groups in cells of the anterior pituitary. ENDOCRINO-LOGY 54:355-359, 1954.

Barry, J.; Croix, D. Immunofluorescence study of the hypothalomo-infundibular LRH tract and serum gonadotropin levels in the female squirrel monkey during the estrous cycle. CELL AND TISSUE RESEARCH 192:215-226, 1978.

Beck, W.; Wuttke, W. Annual rhythms of luteinizing hormone, follicle-stimulating hormone, prolactin and testosterone in the serum of male rhesus monkeys. JOURNAL OF ENDOCRINOLOGY 83:131-139, 1979.

Belchetz, P.; Dufy, B.; Knobil, E. Identification of inhibitory and stimulatory control of prolactin secretion in the rhesus monkey. NEUROENDOCRINOLOGY 27:32-38, 1978.

Belchetz, D.E.; Ridley, R.M.; Baker, H.F. Studies on the accessibility of prolactin and growth hormone to brain: Effect of opiate agonists on hormone levels in serial, simultaneous plasma and cerebrospinal fluid samples in the rhesus monkey. BRAIN RESEARCH 239:310-314, 1982.

Blank, M.S.; Panerai, A.E.; Friesen, H.G. Opioid peptides modulate luteinizing hormone secretion during sexual maturation. SCIENCE 202:1129-1131, 1979.

Blank, M.S.; Gordon, T.P.; Wilson, M.E. Effects of capture and venipuncture on serum levels of prolactin, growth hormone and cortisol in outdoor, compound-housed female rhesus monkeys (Macaca mulatta). ACTA ENDOCRINOLOGICA 102:190-195, 1983.

Bloom, W.; Fawcett, D.W. A TEXTBOOK OF HISTOLOGY. Philadelphia, W.B. Saunders, 1968.

Boime, I.; Landefeld, T.; McQueen, S.; McWilliams, D. The biosynthesis of chorionic gonadotropin and placental lactogen in first- and third-trimester human placenta. Pp. 235-257 in STRUCTURE AND FUNCTION OF THE GONADOTROPINS. K.W. McKerns, ed. New York, Academic Press, 1978.

Boorman, G.A.; Niswender, G.D.; Goy, V.L.; Reichert, L.E. Jr.; Midgley, A.R. Jr. Radioimmunoassay for follicle stimulating hormone in the rhesus monkey using an anti-human FSH serum and rat FSH [131]I. ENDOCRINOLOGY 92:618-623, 1973.

Bowman, L.A.; Dilley, S.R.; Keverne, E.B. Suppression of oestrogen-induced LH surges by social subordination in talapoin monkeys. NATURE 275:56-58, 1978.

Cameron, J.L.; Stouffer, R.L. Comparison of the species specificity of gonadotropin binding to primate and nonprimate corpora lutea. BIOLOGY OF REPRODUCTION 25:568-572, 1981.

Cameron, J.L.; Stouffer, R.L. Gonadotropin receptors of the primate corpus luteum. I. Characterization of the ^{125}I-labeled human luteinizing hormone and human chorionic gonadotropin binding to luteal membranes from the rhesus monkey. ENDOCRINOLOGY 110:1905-1913, 1982.

Carlson, J.C.; Wong, A.P.; Perrin, D.G. Luteinizing hormone secretion in the rhesus monkey and a possible role for the prostaglandins. BIOLOGY OF REPRODUCTION 16:474-478, 1977.

Catt, K.J.; Pierce, J.G. Gonadotropic hormones of the adenohypophysis (FSH, LH and prolactin). Pp. 34-62 in REPRODUCTIVE ENDOCRINOLOGY. S.S.C. Yen; R.B. Jaffe, eds. Philadelphia, W.B. Saunders, 1978.

Chandrashekar, V.; Meyer, R.K.; Bridson, W.E.; Wolf, R.C. Circulating levels of chorionic gonadotropin and progesterone in the rhesus monkey treated with LH antiserum during early gestation. BIOLOGY OF REPRODUCTION 20:889-895, 1979.

Channing, C.P. Effects of stage of the menstrual cycle and gonadotropins on luteinization of rhesus monkey granulosa cells in culture. ENDOCRINOLGOY 87:49-60, 1970.

Channing, C.P. Temporal effects of LH, hCG, FSH and dibutyryl cyclic 3',5'-AMP upon luteinization of rhesus monkey granulosa cells in culture. ENDOCRINOLOGY 94:1215-1223, 1974.

Channing, C.P. Progesterone and estrogen secretion by cultured monkey ovarian cell types: Influences of follicular size, serum luteinizing hormone levels, and follicular fluid estrogen levels. ENDOCRINOLOGY 107:342-352, 1980.

Channing, C.P.; Taylor, M.; Knobil, E.; Nicoll, C.S.; Nichols, C.W. Jr. Secretion of prolactin and growth hormone by cultures of adult simian pituitaries. PROCEEDINGS OF THE SOCIETY FOR EXPERIMENTAL BIOLOGY AND MEDICINE 135:540-542, 1970.

Channing, C.P.; Anderson, L.D.; Hoover, D.J.; Gagliano, P.; Hodgen, G. Inhibitory effects of porcine follicular fluid on monkey serum FSH levels and follicular maturation. BIOLOGY OF REPRODUCTION 25:885-903, 1981.

Chappel, S.C.; Ellinwood, W.E.; Huckins, C.; Herbert, D.C.; Spies, H.G. Active immunization of male rhesus monkeys against luteinizing hormone releasing hormone. BIOLOGY OF REPRODUCTION 22:333-342, 1980.

Chappel, S.C.; Resko, J.A.; Norman, R.L.; Spies, H.G. Studies in rhesus monkeys on the site where estrogen inhibits gonadotropins: Delivery of 17 beta-estradiol to the hypothalamus and pituitary gland. JOURNAL OF CLINICAL ENDOCRINOLOGY AND METABOLISM 52:1-8, 1981.

Cheng, K.W. A radioreceptor assay for follicle-stimulating hormone. JOURNAL OF CLINICAL ENDOCRINOLOGY AND METABOLISM 41:581-589, 1975.

Clark, J.R.; Dierschke, D.J.; Meller, P.A.; Wolf, R.C.

Hormonal regulation of ovarian folliculogenesis in rhesus monkeys. II. Serum concentrations of estradiol-17beta and follicle stimulating hormone associated with growth and identification of the preovulatory follicle. BIOLOGY OF REPRODUCTION 21:497-503, 1979.

Claus, P.E. Separation of anterior lobe substances and study of their individual effects. PHYSIOLOGICAL ZOOLOGY 4:36-57, 1931.

Clements, J.; Whitfield, P.; Corke, N.; Healy, D.; Matheson, B.; Shine, J.; Funder, J. Expression of the prolactin gene in human decidua-chorion. ENDOCRINOLOGY 112:1133-1134, 1983.

Clifton, D.K.; Steiner, R.A.; Resko, J.A.; Spies, H.G. Estrogen-induced gonadotropin release in ovariectomized rhesus monkeys and its advancement by progesterone. BIOLOGY OF REPRODUCTION 13:190-194, 1975.

Cronin, M.J.; Koritnik, D.R. Dopamine receptors of the monkey anterior pituitary in various endocrine states. ENDOCRINOLOGY 112:618-623, 1983.

Cutler, G.B.; Glen, M.; Bush, M.; Hodgen, G.D.; Graham, C.E.; Loriaux, D.L. Adrenarche: A survey of rodents, domestic animals and primates. ENDOCRINOLOGY 103:2112-2118, 1978.

Dailey, R.A.; Neill, J.D. Seasonal variation in reproductive hormones of rhesus monkeys: Anovulatory and short luteal phase menstrual cycles. BIOLOGY OF REPRODUCTION 25:560-567, 1981.

David, G.F.; Ramaswami, L.S. Changes observed in the FSH and LH cells of the adenohypophysis of *Presbytis entellus entellus* following cadium induced testicular necrosis. EXPERIENTIA. 27:342-343, 1971.

Davies, T.F.; Walsh, P.C.; Hodgen, G.D.; Dufau, M.L.; Catt, K.J. Characterization of the primate luteinizing hormone receptor in testis homogenates and Leydig cells. JOURNAL OF CLINICAL ENDOCRINOLOGY AND METABOLISM 48:680-685, 1979a.

Davies, T.F.; Hodgen, G.D.; Dufau, M.L.; Catt, K.J. Regulation of primate testicular luteinizing hormone receptors and steroidogenesis. JOURNAL OF CLINICAL INVESTIGATION 64: 1070-1073, 1979b.

Dawson, A.B. The relationship of pars tuberalis to pars distalis in the hypophysis of the rhesus monkey. ANATOMICAL RECORD 102:103-121, 1948.

Diefenbach, W.P.; Dennison, A.; Rosenblatt, H.; Vaughan, L.; Frantz, A.G.; Ferin, M. Effect of estrogen on thyrotropin-releasing hormone-induced release of prolactin in intact, ovariectomized and stalk-sectioned female rhesus monkeys. ENDOCRINOLOGY 107:183-186, 1980.

Dierschke, D.J.; Battacharya, A.N.; Atkinson, L.E.; Knobil, E. Circhoral oscillations of plasma LH levels in the ovariectomized rhesus monkey. ENDO-CRINOLOGY 87:850-853, 1970.

Dierschke, D.J.; Weiss, G.; Knobil, E. Sexual maturation in the female rhesus monkey and the development of estrogen-induced gonadotropic hormone release. ENDOCRINOLOGY 94:198-206, 1974.

Dixson, A.F.; George, L. Prolactin and parental behavior in a male New World primate. NATURE 299:551-553, 1982.

DiZerega, G.S.; Hodgen, G.D. The primate ovarian cycle: Suppression of human menopausal gonadotropin-induced follicular growth in the presence of the dominant follicle. JOURNAL OF CLINICAL ENDOCRINOLOGY AND METABOLISM 50: 819-825, 1980.

DiZerega, G.S.; Turner, C.K.; Stouffer, R.L.; Anderson, L.D.; Channing, C.P.; Hodgen, G.D. Suppression of follicle-stimulating hormone-dependent folliculogenesis during the primate ovarian cycle. JOURNAL OF CLINICAL ENDOCRINOLOGY AND METABOLISM 52:451-456, 1981.

Dufau, M.L.; Pock, R.; Neubauer, A.; Catt, K.J. In vitro bioassay of LH in human serum: The rat interstitial cell testosterone (RICT) assay. JOURNAL OF CLINICAL ENDOCRINOLOGY AND METABOLISM 42:958-969, 1976.

Dufau, M.L.; Hodgen, G.D.; Goodman, A.L.; Catt, K.J. Bioassay of circulating luteinizing hormone in the rhesus monkey: Comparison with radioimmunoassay during physiological changes. ENDOCRINOLOGY 100:1557-1565, 1977.

Eberhart, J.A.; Keverne, E.B. Influences of the dominance hierarchy on luteinizing hormone, testosterone, and prolactin in male talapoin monkeys. JOURNAL OF ENDOCRINOLOGY 83:42P-43P, 1979.

El Etreby, M.F.; Gunzel, P. Sex hormones—effects on prolactin cells. ACTA ENDOCRINOLOGICA 189:1-15, 1974.

El Etreby, M.F.; Richter, K.D.; Gunzel, P. Sexual hormones and prolactin cells in rat, dog, monkey and man. Pp. 65-69 in HUMAN PROLACTIN. J.L. Pasteels; C. Robyn; F.J.G. Ebling, eds. Amsterdam, American Elsevier, 1973.

Elder, J.H.; Yerkes, R.M. The sexual cycle of the chimpanzee. ANATOMICAL RECORD 67:119-143, 1936.

Ellinwood, W.E.; Resko, J.A. Sex differences in biologically active and immunoreactive gonadotropins in the fetal circulation of rhesus monkeys. ENDOCRINOLOGY 107:902-907, 1980.

Ellinwood, W.E.; Baugham, W.L.; Resko, J.A. The effects of gonadectomy and testosterone treatment on luteinizing hormone secretion in fetal rhesus monkeys. ENDOCRINOLOGY 110:183-189, 1982.

Evans, H.M.; Simpson, M.E.; Lyons, W.R.; Turpeinen, K. Anterior pituitary hormones which favor the production of the traumatic uterine placentoma. EN-

DOCRINOLOGY 28:933–945, 1941.

Faiman, C.; Ryan, R.J. Radioimmunoassay for human follicle stimulating and luteinizing hormones in plasma. JOURNAL OF CLINICAL ENDOCRINOLOGY 27:441–447, 1967.

Faiman, C.; Winter, J.C.; Grotts, D. Gonadotropins in the infant chimpanzee: A sex difference. PROCEEDINGS OF THE SOCIETY FOR EXPERIMENTAL BIOLOGY AND MEDICINE 144:952–955, 1973.

Faiman, C.; Stearns, E.L.; Winter, J.S.; Reyes, F.I.; Hobson, W.C. Radioimmunoassay for rhesus monkey gonadotropins. PROCEEDINGS OF THE SOCIETY FOR EXPERIMENTAL BIOLOGY AND MEDICINE 149:670–676, 1975.

Ferin, M.; Warren, M.; Dryenfurth, I.; Vande Wiele, R.L.; White, W.F. Response of rhesus monkeys to LRH throughout the ovarian cycle. JOURNAL OF CLINICAL ENDOCRINOLOGY AND METABOLISM 38:231–237, 1974.

Ferin, M.; Carmel, P.W.; Zimmerman, E.A.; Warren, M.; Perez, R.; Vande Wiele, R.L. Location of intrahypothalamic estrogen responsive sites influencing LH secretion in the female rhesus monkey. ENDOCRINOLOGY 95:1059–1068, 1975.

Ferin, M.; Carmel, P.W.; Warren, M.P.; Himsworth, R.L.; Frantz, A.G.; Nocenti, M.R. Phencyclidine sedation as a technique for handling rhesus monkeys: Effects on LH, GH, and prolactin secretion. PROCEEDINGS OF THE SOCIETY FOR EXPERIMENTAL BIOLOGY AND MEDICINE 151:428–433, 1976.

Ferin, M.; Wehrenberg, W.B.; Lam, N.Y.; Alston, E.J.; Vande Wiele, R.L. Effects and site of action of morphine on gonadotropin secretion in the female rhesus monkey. ENDOCRINOLOGY 111:1652–1656, 1982.

Fevold, H.L.; Hisaw, F.L.; Leonard, S.L. The gonad stimulating and luteinizing hormones of the anterior lobe of the hypophesis. AMERICAN JOURNAL OF PHYSIOLOGY 97:291–301, 1931.

Forest, M.G.; Sizonenko, P.C.; Cathiard, A.M.; Bertrand, J. Hypophysio-gonadal function in humans during the first year of life. 1. Evidence for testicular activity in early infancy. JOURNAL OF CLINICAL INVESTIGATION 53:819–828, 1974.

Foster, D.L. Luteinizing hormone and progesterone secretion during sexual maturation of the rhesus monkey: Short luteal phases during the initial menstrual cycles. BIOLOGY OF REPRODUCTION 17:584–590, 1977.

Foster, D.L.; Ropisarda, J.J.; Bergman, K.S. Decrease in responsiveness to estradiol inhibition of gonadotropin secretion in the postmenarchial rhesus monkey. PROCEEDINGS OF THE 63RD ANNUAL MEETING OF THE ENDOCRINE SOCIETY, Abstract 490, 1981.

Fraser, H.M.; Laird, N.C.; Blakely, D.M. Decreased pituitary responsiveness and inhibition of the luteinizing hormone surge and ovulation in the stumptailed monkey (Macaca arctoides) by chronic treatment with an agonist of luteinizing hormone-releasing hormone. ENDOCRINOLOGY 106:452–457, 1980.

Frawley, L.S.; Neill, J.D. Age related changes in serum levels of gonadotropins and testosterone in infantile male rhesus monkeys. BIOLOGY OF REPRODUCTION 20:1147–1151, 1979.

Frawley, L.S.; Neill, J.D. Effect of estrogen on serum prolactin levels in rhesus monkeys after hypophyseal stalk transection. BIOLOGY OF REPRODUCTION 22:1089–1093, 1980.

Frawley, L.S.; Neill, J.D. Stimulation of prolactin secretion in rhesus monkeys by vasoactive intestinal polypeptide. NEUROENDOCRINOLOGY 33:79–83, 1981.

Frawley, L.S.; Daily, R.A.; Tindall, G.T.; Neill, J.D. Increased LH secretory response to LHRH after hypophyseal stalk-transection of monkeys. NEUROENDOCRINOLOGY 32:14–18, 1981.

Frawley, L.S.; Mulcahey, J.J.; Neill, J.D. Nursing induces a biphasic release of prolactin in rhesus monkeys. ENDOCRINOLOGY 112:558–561, 1983.

Friesen, H. Purification of a placental factor with immunological and chemical similarity to human growth hormone. ENDOCRINOLOGY 76:369–381, 1965.

Friesen, H.G.; Guyda, H. Biosynthesis of monkey growth hormone and prolactin in vitro. ENDOCRINOLOGY 88:1353–1362, 1971.

Friesen, H.; Guyda, H.; Hwang, P. Prolactin synthesis in primates. NATURE 232:19–20, 1971.

Fujita, H.; Hirakawa, Y.; Oka, M. Histological observations on the hypothalamo-hypophysial system of a chimpanzee (one case report). ARCHIVUM HISTOLOGICUM JAPONICUM 16:273–288, 1959.

Fuller, G.B.; Faiman, C.; Winter, J.S.D.; Reyes, F.I.; Hobson, W.C. Sex-dependent gonadotropin concentrations in infant chimpanzees and rhesus monkeys. PROCEEDINGS OF THE SOCIETY FOR EXPERIMENTAL BIOLOGY AND MEDICINE 169:494–500, 1982.

Gala, R.R. Prolactin production by monkey (Macaca mulatta) anterior pituitaries cultured in vitro. HORMONE RESEARCH 4:157–168, 1973.

Gala, R.R.; Jaques, S. Jr. The influence of 2br-alpha-ergocryptine (CB-154) and apomorphine on induced prolactin secretion in the crab eating monkey (Macaca fascicularis). ENDOCRINE RESEARCH COMMUNICATIONS 2:95–108, 1975.

Gala, R.R.; Van de Walle, C.; Hoffman, W.H.; Lawson, D.M.; Pieper, D.R.; Smith, S.W.; Subramanian, M.G. Lack of a circannual cycle of daytime serum prolactin in man and monkey. ACTA EN-

DOCRINOLOGICA 86:257–262, 1977.

Garnier, G. Molecular aspects of the subunit assembly of glycoprotein hormones. Pp. 381–413 in STRUCTURE AND FUNCTION OF THE GONADOTROPINS. K.W. McKerns, ed. New York, Plenum, 1978.

Geiger, W. Extraction and concentration of hormones from physiological fluids. Discussion: B. Extraction from urine. Pp. 524–526 in RADIOIMMUNOASSAY METHODS. K.E. Kirkham; W.M. Hunter, eds. Edinburgh and London, Churchill Livingstone, 1971.

Ghosh, M.; Hutz, R.J.; Dukelow, W.R. Serum estradiol 17β, progesterone and relative LH levels in *Saimiri sciureus*: Cyclic variations and the effect of laparoscopy and follicular aspiration. JOURNAL OF MEDICAL PRIMATOLOGY, 11:312–318, 1982.

Girod, C.; Dubois, M.P. Immunofluorescent identification of somatotropic and prolactin cells in the anterior lobe of the hypophysis (pars distalis) of the monkey, *Macacus irus*. CELL AND TISSUE RESEARCH 172:145–148, 1976a.

Girod, C.; Dubois, M.P. Demonstration by immunofluorescence of somatotropic cells and prolactin cells in monkeys *Erythrocebus patas*, *Cercopithecus aethiops* and *Papio hamadryas*. COMPTES RENDUS DES SEANCES DE LA SOCIETE DE BIOLOGIE ET DES SES FILIALES (PARIS) 170:1214–1218, 1976b.

Girod, C.; Dubois, M.P.; Trouillas, J. Immunohistochemical study of the pars tuberalis of the adenohypophysis in the monkey, *Macaca irus*. CELL AND TISSUE RESEARCH 210:191–203, 1980a.

Girod, C.; Dubois, M.P.; Trouillas, J. Demonstration of gonadotropic cells in the adenohypophysis (pars distalis and pars tuberalis) of the monkey *Macaca irus*. Immunofluorescence study using human anti-beta-FSH and ovine anti-beta-LH antibodies. COMPTES RENDUS DES SEANCES DE LA SOCIETE DE BIOLOGIE ET DES SES FILIALES (PARIS) 174:304–313, 1980b.

Girod, C.; Dubois, M.P.; Trouillas, J. Immunohistochemical localization of FSH and LH in the pars distalis of the vervet (*Cercopithecus aethiops*) and baboon (*Papio hamadryas*) pituitaries. CELL AND TISSUE RESEARCH 217:245–257, 1981.

Giudice, L.C.; Pierce, J.G. Glycoprotein hormones: Some aspects of studies of secondary and tertiary structure. Pp. 81–109 in STRUCTURE AND FUNCTION OF THE GONADOTROPINS. K.W. McKerns, ed. New York, Plenum, 1978.

Goluboff, L.G.; Ezrin, C. Effect of pregnancy on the somatotroph and prolactin cell of the human adenohypophysis. JOURNAL OF CLINICAL ENDOCRINOLOGY AND METABOLISM 29:1533–1538, 1969.

Goncharov, N.; Antonichev, A.V.; Gorluschkin, V.M.;

Chachundocova, L.; Robertson, D.M.; Diczfalusy, E. Luteinizing hormone levels during the menstrual cycle of the baboon (*Papio hamadryas*). ACTA ENDOCRINOLOGICA 91:49–58, 1979.

Goodman, A.L.; Hodgen, G.D. Systemic versus intraovarian progesterone replacement after luteectomy in rhesus monkeys: Differential patterns of gonadotropins and follicle growth. JOURNAL OF CLINICAL ENDOCRINOLOGY AND METABOLISM 45:837–840, 1977.

Goodman, A.L.; Hodgen, G.D. Postpartum patterns of circulating FSH, LH, prolactin, estradiol, and progesterone in nonsuckling cynomolgus monkeys. STEROIDS 31:731–744, 1978.

Goodman, M. Protein sequence and immunological specificity. Their role in phylogenetic studies of the primates. Pp. 219–248 in PHYLOGENY OF THE PRIMATES. W.P. Luckett; J.S. Szalay, eds. New York, Plenum, 1975.

Goodman, A.L.; Descalzi, C.D.; Johnson, D.K.; Hodgen, G.D. Composite pattern of circulating LH, FSH, estradiol, and progesterone during the menstrual cycle in cynomolgus monkeys. PROCEEDINGS OF THE SOCIETY FOR EXPERIMENTAL BIOLOGY AND MEDICINE 155:479–481, 1977.

Gosselin, R.E.; Blankstein, J.; Dent, D.W.; Hobson, W.C.; Fuller, G.B.; Reyes, F.I.; Winter, J.S.D.; Faiman, C. Effects of naloxine and an enkephalin analog on serum prolactin, cortisol, and gonadotropins in the chimpanzee. ENDOCRINOLOGY 112:2168–2173, 1983.

Gosselin, R.E.; Fuller, G.B.; Coy, D.H.; Schally, A.V.; Hobson, W.C. Inhibition of gonadotropin release in chimpanzees by the LH-RH antagonist (D-Phe^2,D-Trp^3,D-Phe^6)-LH-RH. PROCEEDINGS OF THE SOCIETY FOR EXPERIMENTAL BIOLOGY AND MEDICINE 16:21–24, 1979.

Graham, C.E.; Gould, K.G.; Collins, D.C.; Preedy, J.R.K. Regulation of gonadotropin release by luteinizing hormone-releasing hormone and estrogen in chimpanzees. ENDOCRINOLOGY 105:269–275, 1979.

Grosvenor, C.E.; Turner, C.W. Assay of lactogenic hormones. ENDOCRINOLOGY 63:530–534, 1958.

Grumbach, M.M.; Roth, J.C.; Kaplan, S.L.; Kelch, R. Hypothalamic-pituitary regulation of puberty in man: Evidence and concepts derived from clinical research. Pp. 115–166 in THE CONTROL OF THE ONSET OF PUBERTY. M.M. Grumbach; G.D. Grave; F.E. Mayer, eds. New York, Wiley, 1974.

Gulyas, B.J.; Yuan, L.C.; Hodgen, G.D. Synthesis of progesterone and estradiol by monkey luteal cells in culture: Effects of insulin, thyroxine, cortisol and cholesterol with and without hCG. BIOLOGY OF REPRODUCTION 23:21–28, 1980.

Guyda, H.J.; Friesen, H.G. The separation of monkey prolactin from monkey growth hormone by affinity chromatography. BIOCHEMICAL AND BIO-PHYSICAL RESEARCH COMMUNICATIONS 42:342–343, 1971.

Hagino, H. Effect of estrogen on postovulatory LH surge in baboons. HORMONE AND METABOLIC RESEARCH 11:481–484, 1979.

Hagino, N.; Coy, D.H.; Schally, A.V.; Arimura, A. Inhibition of LH release in the baboon by inhibitory analogs of luteinizing hormone releasing hormone. HORMONE AND METABOLIC RESEARCH 9:247–248, 1977.

Halmi, N.S. Immunoperoxidase staining of primate pituitaries with antibodies against the beta subunits of human pituitary glycoprotein hormones. JOURNAL OF HISTOCHEMISTRY AND CYTOCHEMISTRY 29:837–843, 1981.

Helmond, F.A.; Simons, P.A.; Hein, P.R. The effects of progesterone on estrogen-induced luteinizing hormone and follicle-stimulating hormone release in the female rhesus monkey. ENDOCRINOLOGY 107:478–485, 1980.

Helmond, F.A.; Simons, P.A.; Hein, P.R. Strength and duration characteristics of the facilitory and inhibitory effects of progesterone on the estrogen-induced gonadotropin surge in the female rhesus monkey. ENDOCRINOLOGY 108:1837–1842, 1981.

Herbert, D.C. Immunocytochemical evidence that luteinizing hormone (LH) and follicle-stimulating hormone (FSH) are present in the same cell type in the rhesus monkey pituitary gland. ENDOCRINOLOGY 98:1554–1557, 1976.

Herbert, D.C. Identification of the LH and FSH-secreting cells in the pituitary gland of the rhesus monkey. CELL AND TISSUE RESEARCH 190:151–161, 1978a.

Herbert, D.C. Stimulation of prolactin secretion by testosterone in juvenile male rhesus monkeys. BIOLOGY OF REPRODUCTION 18:448–453, 1978b.

Herbert, D.C.; Hyashida, T. Prolactin localization in the primate pituitary by immunofluorescence. SCIENCE 169:378–379, 1970.

Herbert, D.C.; Hayashida, T. Histologic identification and immunochemical studies of prolactin and growth hormone in the primate pituitary gland. GENERAL AND COMPARATIVE ENDOCRINOLOGY 50:381–397, 1974.

Herbert, D.C.; Schuppler, J.; Poggel, A.; Gunnzel, P.; El Etreby, M.F. Effect of cyproterone acetate on prolactin secretion in the female rhesus monkey. CELL AND TISSUE RESEARCH 183:51–60, 1977.

Herbert, D.C.; Weaker, F.J.; Sheridan, P.J. Localization of ^{3}H-dihydrotestosterone in the pituitary gland of the rhesus monkey. CELL AND TISSUE RESEARCH 215:499–504, 1981.

Herd, J.E.; Parks, J.S.; Harris, H. Non-human primates have multiple genes for growth hormone and chorionic somatomammotropin. PROCEEDINGS OF THE 64TH ANNUAL MEETING OF THE ENDOCRINE SOCIETY, Abstract 76, 1982.

Herndon, J.G., Blank, M.S.; Mann, D.R.; Collins, D.C.; Turner, J.J. Negative feedback effects of estradiol-17β on luteinizing hormone in female rhesus monkeys under different seasonal conditions. ACTA ENDOCRINOLOGICA, 108:31–35, 1985.

Hess, D.L.; Wilkins, R.H.; Moossy, J.; Chang, J.L.; Plant, T.M.; McCormack, J.T.; Nakai, Y.; Knobil, E. Estrogen-induced gonadotropin surges in decerebrated female rhesus monkeys with medial basal hypothalamic peninsulae. ENDOCRINOLOGY 101:1264–1271, 1977.

Himsworth, R.L.; Carmel, P.W.; Frantz, A.G. The location of the chemoreceptor controlling growth hormone secretion during hypoglycemia in primates. ENDOCRINOLOGY 91:217–226, 1972.

Hobson, W.; Fuller, G.B. LH-RH induced gonadotropin release in chimpanzees. BIOLOGY OF REPRODUCTION 17:294–297, 1977.

Hobson, W.; Coulston, F.; Faiman, C.; Winter, J.S.D.; Reyes, F. Reproductive endocrinology of female chimpanzees: A suitable model of humans. JOURNAL OF TOXICOLOGY AND ENVIRONMENTAL HEALTH 1:657–668, 1976a.

Hobson, W.; Dougherty, W.; Lowry, J.; Fuller, G.; Coulston, F. Increased fertility in rhesus monkeys by breeding after the preovulatory LH surge. LABORATORY ANIMAL SCIENCE 26:63–65, 1976b.

Hodgen, G.D.; Wilks, J.W.; Vaitukaitus, J.L.; Chen, H.C.; Papkoff, H.; Ross, G.T. A new radioimmunoassay for follicle-stimulating hormone in macaques: Ovulatory menstrual cycles. ENDOCRINOLOGY 99:137–145, 1976.

Hodgen, G.; Channing, C.; Anderson, L.; Gagliano, P.; Turner, C.; Stouffer, R. On the regulation of FSH secretion in the primate hypothalamic-pituitary-ovarian system. Pp. 263–266 in ENDOCRINOLOGY: PROCEEDINGS OF THE VIth INTERNATIONAL CONGRESS OF ENDOCRINOLOGY. I.A. Cumming; J.W. Funder; F.A.O. Mendelsohn, eds. Amsterdam, Elsevier/North Holland, 1980.

Hodges, J.K. Effects of gonadectomy and oestradiol treatment on plasma luteinizing hormone concentrations in the marmoset monkey, *Callithrix jacchus*. JOURNAL OF ENDOCRINOLOGY 76:271–281, 1978.

Hodges, J.K. Regulation of oestrogen-induced LH in the male and female marmoset monkey (*Callithrix jacchus*). JOURNAL OF REPRODUCTION AND FERTILITY 60:389–398, 1980.

Hodges, J.K.; Hearn, J.P. A positive feedback effect of oestradiol on LH release in the male marmoset monkey, *Callithrix jacchus*. JOURNAL OF REPRODUCTION AND FERTILITY 52:83–86, 1978.

Hodges, J.K.; Szakala, N.M.; Lasley, B.L. Estrogen

and luteinizing hormone secretion in diverse primate species from simplified urinary analysis. JOURNAL OF MEDICAL PRIMATOLOGY 8:349–364, 1979.

Hotchkiss, J.; Atkinson, L.E.; Knobil, E. Time course of serum estrogen and luteinizing hormone (LH) concentrations during the menstrual cycle of the rhesus monkey. ENDOCRINOLOGY 89:177–183, 1971.

Howland, B.E.; Faiman, C.; Butler, T.M. Serum levels of FSH and LH during the menstrual cycle of the chimpanzee. BIOLOGY OF REPRODUCTION 4:101–105, 1971.

Huhtaniemi, I.T.; Koritnik, D.R.; Korenbrot, C.C.; Mennin, S.; Foster, D.B.; Jaffe, R.B. Stimulation of pituitary-testicular function with gonadotropin releasing hormone in fetal and infant monkeys. ENDOCRINOLOGY 105:109–114, 1979.

Hummel, B.C.; Brown, G.M.; Hwang, P.; Friesen, H.G. Human and monkey prolactin and growth hormone: Separation of polymorphic forms by isoelectric focusing. ENDOCRINOLOGY 97:855–867, 1975.

Hwang, P.; Guyda, H.; Friesen, H. A radioimmunoassay for human prolactin. PROCEEDINGS OF THE NATIONAL ACADEMY OF SCIENCES U.S.A. 68:1902–1906, 1971.

Jackson, G.L.; Norman, R.L.; Norton, H.W.; Spies, H.G. Estrogen and progesterone affect electrically induced release of luteinizing hormone and prolactin in macaques. PROCEEDINGS OF THE SOCIETY FOR EXPERIMENTAL BIOLOGY AND MEDICINE 167:194–200, 1981.

Jaffe, R.B.; Lee, P.A.; Midgley, A.R. Jr. Serum gonadotropins before, at the inception of, and following human pregnancy. JOURNAL OF CLINICAL ENDOCRINOLOGY AND METABOLISM 29:1281–1283, 1969.

Josimovich, J.B.; Weiss, G.; Hutchinson, D.L. Sources and disposition of pituitary prolactin in maternal circulation, amniotic fluid, fetus and placenta in the pregnant rhesus monkey. ENDOCRINOLOGY 94:1364–1371, 1974.

Josimovich, J.B.; Merisko, K.; Boccella, L.; Tobon, H. Binding of prolactin by fetal rhesus cell membrane fractions. ENDOCRINOLOGY 100:506–512, 1977.

Jungmann, R.A.; Hunzicker-Dunn, M. Mechanism of action of gonadotropins and the regulation of gene expression. Pp. 1–29 in STRUCTURE AND FUNCTION OF THE GONADOTROPINS. K.W. McKerns, ed. New York, Plenum, 1978.

Kalin, N.H.; Burns, R.S.; Risch, S.C.; Cosgrove, S.A.; Warden, D.; Murphy, D.L. The relationship between blood and cerebrospinal fluid prolactin in nonhuman primates. LIFE SCIENCES 31:159–163, 1982.

Kalin, N.H.; Insel, T.R.; Cohen, R.M.; Risch, S.C.;

Murphy, D.L. Diurnal variation in cerebrospinal fluid prolactin concentration of the rhesus monkey. JOURNAL OF CLINICAL ENDOCRINOLOGY AND METABOLISM 52:857–858, 1981.

Karsch, F.J.; Weick, R.F.; Butler, W.R.; Dierschke, D.J.; Krey, L.C.; Weiss, G.; Hotchkiss, J.; Yamaji, T.; Knobil, E. Induced LH surges in the rhesus monkey: Strength-duration characteristics of the estrogen stimulus. ENDOCRINOLOGY 92:1740–1747, 1973a.

Karsch, F.J.; Dierschke, D.J.; Knobil, E. Sexual differentiation of pituitary function: Apparent differences between primates and rodents. SCIENCE 179:484–486, 1973b.

Karsch, F.J.; Weick, R.F.; Hotchkiss, J.; Dierschke, D.J.; Knobil, E. An analysis of the negative feedback control of gonadotropin secretion utilizing chronic implantation of ovarian steroids in ovariectomized rhesus monkeys. ENDOCRINOLOGY 93:478–486, 1973c.

Kimball, F.A.; Kirkton, K.T.; Forbes, A.D.; Frielink, R.D.; Porteus, S.E.; Wilks, J.W.; Mohberg, N.R.; Turner, L.F. Serum FSH, LH and testosterone in the male rhesus following prostaglandin injection. PROSTAGLANDINS 18:117–126, 1979.

King, M.C.; Wilson, A.C. Evolution at two levels in humans and chimpanzee. SCIENCE 188:107–116, 1975.

Kirkton, K.T.; Niswender, G.G.; Midgley, A.R. Jr.; Jaffe, R.B.; Forbes, A.D. Serum luteinizing hormone and progesterone concentrations during the menstrual cycle of the rhesus monkey. JOURNAL OF CLINICAL ENDOCRINOLOGY AND METABOLISM 30:105–110, 1970.

Kleinberg, D.L.; Todd, J. Evidence that human growth hormone is a potent lactogen in primates. JOURNAL OF CLINICAL ENDOCRINOLOGY AND METABOLISM 51:1009–1013, 1980.

Kleinberg, D.L.; Todd, J.; Niemann, W. Evidence that prolactin stimulates alpha-lactalbumin production in mammary tissues from premenarcheal rhesus monkeys. ENDOCRINOLOGY 104:50–52, 1979.

Knobil, E. On the control of gonadotropin secretion in the rhesus monkey. RECENT PROGRESS IN HORMONE RESEARCH 30:1–46, 1974.

Knobil, E. The neuroendocrine control of the menstrual cycle. RECENT PROGRESS IN HORMONE RESEARCH 36:53–88, 1980.

Knobil, E. Patterns of hypophysiotropic signals and gonadotropin secretion in the rhesus monkey. BIOLOGY OF REPRODUCTION 24:44–49, 1981.

Knobil, E.; Plant, T.M.; Wildt, L.; Belchetz, P.E.; Marshall, G. Control of the rhesus monkey menstrual cycle: Permissive role of hypothalamic gonadotropin-releasing hormone. SCIENCE 207:1371–1373, 1980.

Koritnik, D.R.; Jaffe, R.B. Evidence for the absence of

adrenal androgen influence on the hypothalamo-pituitary-testicular axis of the neonatal and the infant rhesus monkey. Pp. 155–166 in ADRENAL ANDROGENS. A.R. Genazzani; J.H.H. Thijssen; P.K. Siiteri, eds. New York, Raven, 1980.

Koyama, T.; de la Pena, A.; Hagino, N. Plasma estrogen, progestin and luteinizing hormone during the normal menstrual cycle in baboons: role of luteinizing hormone. AMERICAN JOURNAL OF OBSTETRICS AND GYNECOLOGY 127:67–72, 1977.

Krey, L.C.; Butler, W.R.; Knobil, E. Surgical disconnections of the medial basal hypothalamus and pituitary function in the rhesus monkey. I. Gonadotropin secretion. ENDOCRINOLOGY 96:1073–1087, 1975.

Lasley, B.L.; Hodges, J.K.; Szekala, N.M. Monitoring the female reproductive cycle of great apes and other primate species by determination of oestrogen and LH in small volumes of urine. JOURNAL OF REPRODUCTION AND FERTILITY, SUPPLEMENT 28:121–129, 1980.

Lewis, U.J. Chemistry of prolactin. PHARMACOLOGY AND THERAPEUTICS, PART B 1:423–435, 1975.

Macdonald, G.J.; Greep, R.O. Ability of luteinizing hormone (LH) to acutely increase serum progesterone levels during the secretory phase of the rhesus menstrual cycle. FERTILITY AND STERILITY 23:466–470, 1972.

McArthur, J.W.; Perley, R. Urinary gonadotropin excretion by infrahuman primates. ENDOCRINOLOGY 84:508–513, 1969.

McKerns, K.W. Regulation of gene expression in the nucleus by gonadotropin. Pp. 315–338 in STRUCTURE AND FUNCTION OF THE GONADOTROPINS. K.W. McKerns, ed. New York, Plenum, 1978.

McNeilly, A.S.; Abbott, D.H.; Lunn, S.F.; Chambers, P.C.; Hearn, J.P. Plasma prolactin concentrations during the ovarian cycle and lactation and their relationship to the return of fertility post partum in the common marmoset (Callithrix jacchus). JOURNAL OF REPRODUCTION AND FERTILITY 62:353–360, 1981.

Maneckjee, R.; Srinath, B.R.; Moudgal, N.R. Prolactin suppresses release of luteinizing hormone during lactation in the monkey. NATURE 262:507–508, 1976.

Mann, D.R.; Blank, M.S.; Gould, K.G.; Collins, D.C. Validation of radioimmunoassays for LH and FSH in the sooty mangabey (Cercocebus atys): Characterization of LH and the response to GnRH. AMERICAN JOURNAL OF PRIMATOLOGY 2:275–283, 1982.

Mann, D.R.; Castracane, V.D.; McLaughlin, F.; Gould, K.G.; Collins, D.C. Developmental patterns of serum luteinizing hormone, gonadal and adrenal

steroids in the sooty mangabey (Cercocebus atys). BIOLOGY OF REPRODUCTION 28:279–284, 1983.

Maruffo, C.A. Zona pellucida of rhesus monkey ovum after gonadotropin stimulation. SCIENCE 157:1313–1314, 1967.

Marut, E.L.; Hodgen, G.D. Antiestrogenic action of high-dose clomiphene in primates: Pituitary augmentation but with ovarian attenuation. FERTILITY AND STERILITY 38:100–104, 1982.

Marut, E.L.; Williams, R.F.; Cowan, B.D.; Lynch, A.; Lerner, S.P.; Hodgen, G.D. Pulsatile pituitary gonadotropin secretion during maturation of the dominant follicle in monkeys. Estrogen positive feedback enhances the biological activity of LH. ENDOCRINOLOGY 109: 2270–2272, 1981.

Maurer, R.A.; Stone, R.T.; Gorski, J. The biosynthesis of prolactin. Pp. 213–234 in STRUCTURE AND FUNCTION OF THE GONADOTROPINS. K.W. McKerns, ed. New York, Plenum, 1978.

Midgley, A.R. Jr. Radioimmunoassay: A method for human chorionic gonadotropin and human luteinizing hormone. ENDOCRINOLOGY 79:10–18, 1966.

Midgley, A.R. Jr. Radioimmunoassay for human follicle stimulating hormone. JOURNAL OF CLINICAL ENDOCRINOLOGY AND METABOLISM 27:295–299, 1967.

Midgley, A.R. Jr.; Pierce, G.B. Jr. Immunohistochemical localization of human chorionic gonadotropin. JOURNAL OF EXPERIMENTAL MEDICINE 115:289–294, 1962.

Milmore, J.E. Influence of ovarian hormones on prolactin release in the rhesus monkey. BIOLOGY OF REPRODUCTION 19:593–596, 1978.

Monroe, S.E.; Peckham, W.D.; Neill, J.D.; Knobil, E. A radioimmunoassay for rhesus monkey luteinizing hormone (RhLH). ENDOCRINOLOGY 86:1012–1018, 1970.

Mori, J.; Hafez, E.S.; Jaszczak, S.; Kanagawa, H. Serum LH during ovulatory and anovulatory menstrual cycles in macaques. ACTA ENDOCRINOLOGICA 73:751–758, 1973.

Moudgal, N.R. A need for FSH in maintaining fertility of adult male subhuman primates. ARCHIVES OF ANDROLOGY 7:117–125, 1981.

Moudgal, N.R.; MacDonald, G.J.; Greep, R.O. Role of endogenous primate LH in maintaining corpus luteum function in the monkey. JOURNAL OF CLINICAL ENDOCRINOLOGY AND METABOLISM 35:113–116, 1972.

Moudgal, R.N.; Mukku, V.R.; Prahalada, S.; Murty, G.S.; Li, C.H. Passive immunization with an antibody to the beta-subunit of ovine luteinizing hormone as a method of early abortion—a feasibility study in monkeys (Macaca radiata). FERTILITY AND STERILITY 30:223–239, 1978.

Mukku, V.R.; Murty, G.S.; Srinath, B.R.; Ramasharma, K.; Kotagi, S.G.; Moudgal, N.R. Regulation of testosterone rhythmicity by gonadotropins in bonnet monkeys (*Macaca radiata*). BIOLOGY OF REPRODUCTION 24:814–819, 1981.

Nadler, R.D. Reproductive physiology and behaviour of gorillas. JOURNAL OF REPRODUCTION AND FERTILITY, SUPPLEMENT 28:79–89, 1980.

Nadler, R.D.; Graham, C.E.; Collins, D.C.; Gould, K.G. Plasma gonadotropins, prolactin, gonadal steroids and genital swelling during the menstrual cycle of lowland gorillas. ENDOCRINOLOGY 105:290–296, 1979.

Nadler, R.D.; Collins, D.C.; Blank, M.S. Luteinizing hormone and gonadal steroid levels during the menstrual cycle of orang-utans. JOURNAL OF MEDICAL PRIMATOLOGY, 13:305–318, 1984.

Nakai, Y.; Plant, T.M.; Hess, D.L.; Keogh, E.J.; Knobil, E. On the sites of the negative and positive feedback actions of estradiol in the control of gonadotropin secretion in the rhesus monkey. ENDOCRINOLOGY 102:1008–1014, 1978.

Neill, J.D.; Peckham, W.D.; Knobil, E. Apparent absence of immunological cross-reactivity between human and simian gonadotropic hormones as determined by radioimmunoassay. NATURE 213:1014–1015, 1967.

Neill, J.D.; Dailey, R.A.; Tsou, R.C.; Reichert, L.E. Jr. Immunoreactive LH-like substances in serum of hypophysectomized and prepubertal monkeys: Inactive in an in vitro LH bioassay. ENDOCRINOLOGY 100:856–861, 1977a.

Neill, J.D.; Patton, J.M.; Dailey, R.A.; Tsou, R.C.; Tindall, G.T. Luteinizing hormone releasing hormone (LHRH) in pituitary stalk blood of rhesus monkeys: Relationship to level of LH release. ENDOCRINOLOGY 101:430–434, 1977b.

Neill, J.D.; Frawley, L.S.; Plotsky, P.M.; Tindall, G.T. Dopamine in hypophyseal stalk blood of the rhesus monkey and its role in regulating prolactin secretion. ENDOCRINOLOGY 108:489–494, 1981.

Niall, H.D.; Hogan, M.L.; Tregear, G.W.; Segre, G.V.; Hwang, P.; Friesen, H. The chemistry of growth hormone and the lactogenic hormones. RECENT PROGRESS IN HORMONE RESEARCH 29:387–416, 1973.

Nicoll, C.W.; Parsons, J.A.; Fiorindo, R.P.; Nichols, C.W. Jr.; Sakuma, M. Evidence of independent secretion of prolactin and growth hormone in vitro by adenohypophyses of rhesus monkeys. JOURNAL OF CLINICAL ENDOCRINOLOGY AND METABOLISM 30:512–519, 1970.

Niswender, G.D.; Spies, H.G. Serum levels of luteinizing hormone, follicle-stimulating hormone and progesterone throughout the menstrual cycle of rhesus monkeys. JOURNAL OF CLINICAL ENDOCRINOLOGY AND METABOLISM 37:326–328, 1973.

Niswender, G.D.; Monroe, S.E.; Peckham, W.D.; Midgley, A.R. Jr.; Knobil, E.; Reichert, L.E. Jr. Radioimmunoassay for rhesus monkey luteinizing hormone (LH) with anti-ovine LH serum and ovine LH-^{131}I. ENDOCRINOLOGY 88:1327–1331, 1971.

Norman, R.L.; Spies, H.G. Effect of luteinizing hormone-releasing hormone on the pituitary-gonadal axis in fetal and infant rhesus monkeys. ENDOCRINOLOGY 105:655–659, 1979.

Norman, R.L.; Spies, H.G. Brain lesions in infant female rhesus monkeys: Effects on menarche and first ovulation and on diurnal rhythms of prolactin and cortisol. ENDOCRINOLOGY 108:1723–1729, 1981.

Norman, R.L.; Brandt, H.; Van Horn, R.N. Radioimmunoassay for luteinizing hormone (LH) in the ring-tailed lemur (*Lemur catta*) with antiovine LH and ovine ^{125}I-LH. BIOLOGY OF REPRODUCTION 19:1119–1124, 1978.

Norman, R.L.; Gliessman, P.; Lindstrom, S.A.; Hill, J.; Spies, H.G. Reinitiation of ovulatory cycles in pituitary stalk-sectioned rhesus monkeys: Evidence for a specific hypothalamic message for the preovulatory release of luteinizing hormone. ENDOCRINOLOGY 111:1874–1882, 1982.

Papkoff, H. A comparative view of the chemistry and function of the anterior pituitary hormones. Pp. 16–30 in PITUITARY HORMONES AND RELATED PEPTIDES. M. Motta; M. Zanisi; F. Piva, eds. New York, Academic Press, 1982.

Pasteels, J.L.; Gausset, P.; Danguy, A.; Ectors, P.; Nicoll, C.S.; Varavudhi, P. Morphology of the lactotropes and somatotropes of man and rhesus monkeys. JOURNAL OF CLINICAL ENDOCRINOLOGY AND METABOLISM 34:959–967, 1972.

Peckham, W.D.; Knobil, E. Qualitative changes in the pituitary gonadotropins of the male rhesus monkey following castration. ENDOCRINOLOGY 98:1061–1064, 1976a.

Peckham, W.D.; Knobil, E. The effects of ovariectomy, estrogen replacement, and neuraminidase treatment on the properties of the adenohypophysial glycoprotein hormones of the rhesus monkey. ENDOCRINOLOGY 98:1054–1060, 1976b.

Peckham, W.D.; Hotchkiss, J.; Knobil, E.; Nicoll, C.S. Prolactin activity of homogeneous primate growth hormone preparations. ENDOCRINOLOGY 68:1247–1248, 1968.

Peckham, W.D.; Yamaji, T.; Dierschke, D.J.; Knobil, E. Gonadal function and the biological and physiochemical properties of follicle stimulating hormone. ENDOCRINOLOGY 92:1652–1659, 1973.

Perlow, M.J. Cerebrospinal fluid prolactin: A daily rhythm and response to an acute perturbation. BRAIN RESEARCH 15:382–385, 1982.

Pfaff, D.W.; Gerlach, G.L.; McEwen, B.S.; Ferin, M.; Carmel, P.; Zimmerman, E.A. Autoradiographic localization of hormone-concentrating cells in the brain of the female rhesus monkey. JOURNAL OF COMPARATIVE NEUROLOGY 170: 279–294, 1976.

Plant, T.M. The effects of neonatal orchidectomy on the developmental pattern of gonadotropin secretion in the male rhesus monkey (Macaca mulatta). ENDOCRINOLOGY 106:1451–1454, 1980.

Plant, T.M. Pulsatile luteinizing hormone secretion in the neonatal male rhesus monkey. JOURNAL OF ENDOCRINOLOGY 93:71–74, 1982a.

Plant, T.M. A striking diurnal variation in plasma testosterone concentrations in infantile male rhesus monkeys (Macaca mulatta). NEUROENDOCRINOLOGY 35:370–373, 1982b.

Plant, T.M.; Nakai, Y.; Belchetz, P.; Keogh, E.; Knobil, E. The sites of action of estradiol and phentolamine in the inhibition of the pulsatile, circhoral discharges of LH in the rhesus monkey (Macaca mulatta). ENDOCRINOLOGY 102:1015–1018,1978.

Plant, T.M.; Zonub, D.S.; Moossy, J. Effects of pinealectomy on the developmental pattern of gonadotropin secretion in the rhesus monkey (Macaca mulatta). FEDERATION PROCEEDINGS 40:389, 1981.

Pohl, C.R.; Richardson, D.W.; Marshall, G.; Knobil, E. Mode of action of progesterone in the blockade of gonadotropin surges in the rhesus monkey. ENDOCRINOLOGY 110:1454–1455, 1982.

Posner, B.I.; Kelly, P.A.; Shiu, R.P.C.; Friesen, H.G. Studies of insulin, growth hormone and prolactin binding: Tissue distribution, species variation and characterization. ENDOCRINOLOGY 95:521–531, 1974.

Puri, C.P.; Puri, V.; David, G.F.; Kumar, T.C. Testosterone, cortisol, prolactin, and bioactive luteinizing hormone in day and night samples of cerebrospinal fluid and serum of male rhesus monkeys. BRAIN RESEARCH 208:377–387, 1980.

Puri, C.P.; Puri, V.; Anand Kumar, T.C.A. Serum levels of testosterone, cortisol, prolactin and bioactive luteinizing hormone in adult male rhesus monkeys following cage-restraint or anaesthetizing with ketamine hydrochloride. ACTA ENDOCRINOLOGICA 97:118–124, 1981.

Quabbe, H.-J.; Bumke-Vogt, C.B.; Gregor, M.; Stolz, B.; Witt, I. 24-Hour pattern of plasma prolactin in the male rhesus monkey and its relation to the sleep/wake cycle. ENDOCRINOLOGY 110:969–975, 1982.

Quadri, S.K.; Spies, H.G. Cyclic and diurnal patterns of serum prolactin in the rhesus monkey. BIOLOGY OF REPRODUCTION 14:495–501, 1976.

Quadri, S.K.; Pierson, C.; Spies, H.G. Failure of copulation to affect serum prolactin, LH and estrogen levels in female rhesus monkeys. PROCEEDINGS OF THE SOCIETY FOR EXPERIMENTAL BIOLOGY AND MEDICINE 155:247–251, 1977.

Quadri, S.K.; Pierson, C.; Spies, H.G. Effects of centrally active drugs on serum prolactin levels in rhesus monkeys. NEUROENDOCRINOLOGY 27:136–147, 1978.

Quadri, S.K.; Oyama, T.; Spies, H.G. Effects of 17beta-estradiol on serum prolactin levels and on prolactin responses to thyrotropin-releasing hormone in female rhesus monkeys. ENDOCRINOLOGY 104: 1649–1655, 1979.

Quigley, M.E.; Yen, S.S.C. The role of endogenous opiates on LH secretion during the menstrual cycle. JOURNAL OF CLINICAL ENDOCRINOLOGY AND METABOLISM 51:179–181, 1980.

Rebar, R.W.; Yen, S.S.C.; VandenBerg, G.; Naftolin, F.; Ehara, Y.; Engblom, S.; Ryan, K.J.; Rivier, J.; Amoss, M.; Guillemin, R. Gonadotropin responses to synthetic LRF: Dose-response relationship in men. JOURNAL OF CLINICAL ENDOCRINOLOGY AND METABOLISM 36:10–16, 1973.

Reichert, L.E. Jr. Electrophoretic properties of pituitary gonadotropins as studied by electrofocusing. ENDOCRINOLOGY 88:1029–1044, 1971.

Reichert, L.E. Jr.; Jiang, N.S. Comparative gel filtration and density gradient centrifugation studies on heterologous pituitary luteinizing hormones. ENDOCRINOLOGY 77:78–86, 1965.

Reichert, L.E.; Midgley, A.R. Jr. Preliminary studies of the effects of urea and chymotrypsin on the molecular biological and immunological properties of human follicle-stimulating hormone and luteinizing hormone. Pp. 25–31 in GONADOTROPINS. E. Rosemberg, ed. Los Altos, CA, Geron-X, 1968.

Reichert, L.E. Jr.; Parlow, A.F. Preparation of ovine luteinizing hormone (LH, ICSH) having high biological activity. ENDOCRINOLOGY 73:285–293, 1963.

Reichert, L.E. Jr.; Midgley, A.R. Jr.; Niswender, G.D.; Ward, D.N. Formation of a hybrid molecule from subunits of human and bovine luteinizing hormone. ENDOCRINOLOGY 87:534–541, 1970.

Resko, J.A.; Quadri, S.K.; Spies, H.G. Negative feedback control of gonadotropins in male rhesus monkeys: Effects of time after castration and interactions of testosterone and estradiol-17beta. ENDOCRINOLOGY 101:215–224, 1977.

Resko, J.A.; Jackson, G.L.; Huckins, C.; Stadelman, H.; Spies, H.G. Cryptorchid rhesus macaques: Longterm studies on changes in gonadotropins and gonadal steroids. ENDOCRINOLOGY 107:677–683, 1980.

Resko, J.A.; Ellinwood, W.E.; Knobil, E. Differential effects of progesterone on secretion of gonadotropic hormones in the rhesus monkey. AMERICAN JOURNAL OF PHYSIOLOGY 240:489–492, 1981.

Reyes, F.I.; Hobson, W.C.; Fuller, G.; Winter, J.S.D.; Faiman, C. Effect of fetal castration in utero upon serum FSH levels in rhesus monkeys. PROCEED-

INGS OF THE 62nd ANNUAL MEETING OF THE ENDOCRINE SOCIETY, Abstract 630, 1980.

Reyes, F.I.; Winter, J.S.D.; Faiman, C.; Hobson, W.C. Serial serum levels of gonadotropins, prolactin and sex steroids in the nonpregnant and pregnant chimpanzee. ENDOCRINOLOGY 96:1447–1455, 1975.

Reyes, F.I.; Winter, J.S.D.; Faiman, C. Pituitary gonadotropin function during human pregnancy: Serum FSH and LH levels before and after LHRH administration. JOURNAL OF CLINICAL ENDOCRINOLOGY AND METABOLISM 42:590–592, 1976.

Riddle, O.; Braucher, P.F. Studies on the physiology of reproduction in birds; control of special secretion of the crop-gland in pigeons by anterior pituitary hormone. AMERICAN JOURNAL OF PHYSIOLOGY 97:617–625, 1931.

Rivera, E.M.; Forsyth, I.A.; Folley, S.I. Lactogenic activity of mammalian growth hormones in vitro. PROCEEDINGS OF THE SOCIETY FOR EXPERIMENTAL BIOLOGY AND MEDICINE 124:859–865, 1967.

Robinson, J.A.; Bridson, W.E. Neonatal hormone patterns in the macaque. 1. Steroids. BIOLOGY OF REPRODUCTION 19:773–778, 1978.

Sakai, C.N.; Channing, C.P. Evidence for alterations in luteinizing hormone secreted in rhesus monkeys with normal and inadequate luteal phases using radioreceptor and radioimmunoassay. ENDOCRINOLOGY 104:1217–1225, 1979a.

Sakai, C.N.; Channing, C.P. Uptake of luteinizing hormone by the preovulatory monkey follicle in vivo. ENDOCRINOLOGY 104:1226–1232, 1979b.

Saxena, B.B.; Rathnam, P. The structure and function of follicle-stimulating hormone. Pp. 183–212 in STRUCTURE AND FUNCTION OF THE GONADOTROPINS. K.W. McKerns, ed. New York, Plenum, 1978.

Schallenberger, E.; Knobil, E. Suppression of suckling-induced hyperprolactinemia and puerperal amenorrhea in the rhesus monkey. ACTA ENDOCRINOLOGICA, SUPPLEMENT 234:12–13, 1980.

Schallenberger, E.; Richardson, D.W.; Knobil, E. Role of prolactin in the lactational amenorrhea of the rhesus monkey (Macaca mulatta). BIOLOGY OF REPRODUCTION 25:370–374, 1981.

Schoonees, R.; de Klerk, J.N.; Murphy, G.P. The effect of prolactin on organ weights and zinc-65 uptake in male baboons. JOURNAL OF SURGICAL ONCOLOGY 2:103–106, 1970.

Seron-Ferre, M.; Monroe, S.E.; Hess, D.; Parer, J.T.; Jaffe, R.B. Prolactin concentrations in the monkey fetus in the last third of gestation. ENDOCRINOLOGY 104:1243–1246, 1979.

Shiu, R.P.; Kelly, P.A.; Friesen, H.G. Radioreceptor assay for prolactin and other lactogenic hormones. SCIENCE 180:968–971, 1973.

Shownkeen, R.C.; Thomas, M.B.; Hartree, A.S.; Ste-

vens, V.C. A note on the purification of follicle-stimulating and luteinizing hormones from baboon pituitaries. JOURNAL OF ENDOCRINOLOGY 59:659–660, 1973.

Sinha, Y.N.; Selby, F.W.; Lewis, U.J.; Vanderlaan, W.P. A homologous radioimmunoassay for human prolactin. JOURNAL OF CLINICAL ENDOCRINOLOGY AND METABOLISM 36:509–516, 1973.

Smith, P.E. Hastening development of female genital system by daily homoplastic pituitary transplants. PROCEEDINGS OF THE SOCIETY FOR EXPERIMENTAL BIOLOGY AND MEDICINE 24:131–132, 1926.

Smith, P.E.; Engle, E.T. Precocious sexual maturity in the mouse following pituitary transplants. ANATOMICAL RECORD 35:22, 1927.

Solomon, I.L.; Grant, D.B.; Burr, I.M.; Kaplan, S.L.; Grumbach, M.M. Correlation between immunoreactive growth hormone and prolactin activity in human and simian pituitary cell cultures. PROCEEDINGS OF THE SOCIETY FOR EXPERIMENTAL BIOLOGY AND MEDICINE 132:505–508, 1969.

Spies, H.G.; Quadri, S.F.; Chappel, S.C.; Norman, R.L. Dopaminergic and opioid compounds. Effects on prolactin and LH release after electrical stimulation of the hypothalamus in ovariectomized rhesus monkeys. NEUROENDOCRINOLOGY 30:249–256, 1980.

Spinola, P.G.; Seidman, L.S.; Sundaram, K.; Thau, R.B. Impaired steroidogenesis in the luteal phase of the reproductive cycle and during pregnancy in rhesus monkeys immunized with the β-subunit of ovine luteinizing hormone. JOURNAL OF STEROID BIOCHEMISTRY 16:151–156, 1982.

Steelman, S.L.; Pohley, F.M. Assay of the follicle stimulating hormone based on the augmentation with human chorionic gonadotropin. ENDOCRINOLOGY 53:604–616, 1953.

Steger, R.W.; Silverman, A.Y.; Asch, R.H. Glucocorticoid suppression of pituitary prolactin release in the nonhuman primate. JOURNAL OF CLINICAL ENDOCRINOLOGY AND METABOLISM 53:1167–1170, 1981.

Steinberger, A.; Sanborn, B.M.; Steinberger, E. FSH and the Sertoli cell. Pp. 517–551 in STRUCTURE AND FUNCTION OF THE GONADOTROPINS. K.W. McKerns, ed. New York, Plenum, 1978.

Steiner, R.A.; Bremner, W.J. Endocrine correlates of sexual development in the male monkey, Macaca fascicularis. ENDOCRINOLOGY 109:914–919, 1981.

Steiner, R.A.; Clifton, D.K.; Spies, M.G.; Resko, J.A. Sexual differentiation and feedback control of luteinizing hormone secretion in the rhesus monkey. BIOLOGY OF REPRODUCTION 76:291–296, 1976.

Steiner, R.A.; Schiller, H.S.; Barber, J.; Gale, C.C.

Luteinizing hormone regulation in the monkey (*Macaca nemestrina*): failure of testosterone and dihydrotestosterone to block the estrogen-induced gonadotropin surge. BIOLOGY OF REPRODUCTION 19:51–56, 1978.

Steiner, R.A.; Peterson, A.P.; Yu, J.Y.; Conner, H.; Gilbert, M.; ter Penning, B.; Bremner, W.J. Ultradian luteinizing hormone and testosterone rhythms in the adult male monkey, *Macaca fascicularis*. ENDOCRINOLOGY 107:1489–1493, 1980.

Stevens, V.C.; Sparks, S.J.; Powell, J.E. Levels of estrogens, progestogens and luteinizing hormone during the menstrual cycle of the baboon. ENDOCRINOLOGY 87:658–666, 1970.

Stouffer, R.L.; Hodgen, G.D. Induction of luteal phase defects in rhesus monkeys by follicular fluid administration at the onset of the menstrual cycle. JOURNAL OF CLINICAL ENDOCRINOLOGY AND METABOLISM 51:669–671, 1980.

Stouffer, R.L.; Nixon, W.E.; Gulyas, B.J.; Hodgen, G.D. Gonadotropin-sensitive progesterone production by rhesus monkey luteal cells in vitro: A function of age of the corpus luteum during the menstrual cycle. ENDOCRINOLOGY 100:506–512, 1977.

Stricker, P.; Grueter, R. Action du lobe anterieur de l'hypophyse sur la montee laiteuse. COMPTES RENDUS, SOCIETY DE BIOLOGIE 99:1978–1980, 1928.

Su, J.-H. Change of hypothalamic-pituitary-ovarian function during peripubertal period in female baboons (*Papio cynocephalus*). FOLIA ENDOCRINOLOGICA JAPONICA 57:779–794, 1981.

Su, J.-H.; Aso, T.; Motohashi, T.; Aochi, H.; Matsuora, M.; Horie, K.; Nishimura, T. Radioimmunoassay method for baboon plasma gonadotropins. ENDOCRINOLOGICA JAPONICA 27:513–520, 1980.

Talas, M.A.; Midgley, A.R. Jr.; Jaffe, R.B. Regulation of human gonadotropins. XIV. Gel filtration and electrophoretic analysis of endogenous and extracted immunoreactive human follicle-stimulating hormone of pituitary, serum and urinary origin. JOURNAL OF CLINICAL ENDOCRINOLOGY AND METABOLISM 36:817–825, 1973.

Tanaka, T.; Shiu, R.P.C.; Gout, P.W.; Beer, C.T.; Noble, R.L.; Friesen, H.G. A new sensitive and specific bioassay for lactogenic hormones: Measurement of prolactin and growth hormone in human serum. JOURNAL OF CLINICAL ENDOCRINOLOGY AND METABOLISM 51:1058–1063, 1980.

Tang, L.K.; Spies, H.G. Effect of synthetic LH-releasing factor (LRF) on LH secretion in monolayer cultures of the anterior pituitary cells of cynomolgus monkeys. ENDOCRINOLOGY 94:1016–1021, 1974.

Terasawa, E.; Rodriguez-Sierra, J.F.; Dierschke, D.J.; Bridson, W.E.; Goy, R.W. Positive feedback effect of progesterone on luteinizing hormone (LH) release in cyclic female rhesus monkeys: LH response occurs in two phases. JOURNAL OF CLINICAL ENDOCRINOLOGY AND METABOLISM 51:1245–1250, 1980.

Tillson, S.A.; Swisher, D.A.; Pharriss, B.B.; Erickson, R.E.; Neill, J.D. Interrelationship between pituitary gonadotropins and ovarian steroids in baboons during continuous intrauterine progesterone treatment. BIOLOGY OF REPRODUCTION 15:291–296, 1976.

Tseng, M.T.; Kittinger, G.W.; Spies, H.G. An ultrastructural study of the gonadotropins in oophorectomized rhesus (*Macaca mulatta*) adults treated with estrogen. PROCEEDINGS OF THE SOCIETY FOR EXPERIMENTAL BIOLOGY AND MEDICINE 147:412–417, 1974.

Vaitukaitis, J.L. Glycoprotein hormones and their subunits—immunological and biochemical characterization. Pp. 339–360 in STRUCTURE AND FUNCTION OF THE GONADOTROPINS. K.W. McKerns, ed. New York, Plenum, 1978.

Van Damme, M.P.; Robertson, D.M.; Diczfalusy, E. An improved in vitro bioassay method for measuring luteinizing hormone (LH) activity using mouse Leydig cell preparations. ACTA ENDOCRINOLOGICA 77:655–671, 1974.

Vaughan, L.; Carmel, P.W.; Dyrenfurth, I.; Frantz, A.G.; Antunes, J.L.; Ferin, M. Section of the pituitary stalk in the rhesus monkey. I. Endocrine studies. NEUROENDOCRINOLOGY 30:70–75, 1980.

Ward, D.N. Chemical approaches to the structure-function relationships of luteinizing hormone (lutropin). Pp. 31–45 in STRUCTURE AND FUNCTION OF THE GONADOTROPINS. K.W. McKerns, ed. New York, Plenum, 1978.

Wardlaw, S.L.; Wehrenberg, W.B.; Ferin, M.; Carmel, P.W.; Frantz, A.G. High levels of β-endorphin in hypophyseal portal blood. ENDOCRINOLOGY 106:1323–1326, 1980a.

Wardlaw, S.L.; Wehrenberg, W.B.; Ferin, M.; Frantz, A.G. Failure of beta-endorphin to stimulate prolactin release in the pituitary stalk-sectioned monkey. ENDOCRINOLOGY 107:1663–1666, 1980b.

Wehrenberg, W.B.; McNichol, D.; Wardlaw, S.L.; Frantz, A.G.; Ferin, M. Dopaminergic and serotonergic involvement in opiate-induced prolactin release in monkeys. ENDOCRINOLOGY 109:544–547, 1981.

Wehrenberg, W.B.; Wardlaw, S.L.; Frantz, A.G.; Ferin, M. β-Endorphin in hypophyseal portal blood: Variations throughout the menstrual cycle. ENDOCRINOLOGY 111:897–881, 1982.

Weiss, G.; Dierschke, D.J.; Karsch, F.J.; Hotchkiss, J.; Butler, W.R.; Knobil, E. The influence of lactation on luteal function in the rhesus monkey. ENDOCRINOLOGY 93:954–959, 1973.

Weiss, G.; Butler, W.R.; Hotchkiss, J.; Dierschke, D.J.; Knobil, E. Periparturitional serum concentrations of prolactin, the gonadotropins and the gonadal hormones in the rhesus monkey. PROCEEDINGS OF THE SOCIETY FOR EXPERIMENTAL BIOLOGY AND MEDICINE 151:113–116, 1976.

Wickings, E.J.; Nieschlag, E. Suppression of spermatogenesis over two years in rhesus monkeys actively immunized with follicle-stimulating hormone. FERTILITY AND STERILITY 34:269–274, 1980.

Wickings, E.J.; Qazi, M.H.; Nieschlag, E. Determination of biologically active LH in the serum of male rhesus monkeys (Macaca mulatta). JOURNAL OF REPRODUCTION AND FERTILITY 57:497–504, 1979.

Wickings, E.J.; Usadel, K.H.; Dathe, G.; Nieschlag, E. The role of follicle stimulating hormone in testicular function of the male rhesus monkey. ACTA ENDOCRINOLOGICA 95:117–128, 1980.

Wide, L. Male and female forms of human follicle-stimulating hormone in serum. JOURNAL OF CLINICAL ENDOCRINOLOGY AND METABOLISM 55:682–688, 1981.

Wildt, L.; Marshall, G.; Knobil, E. Experimental induction of puberty in the infantile female rhesus monkey. SCIENCE 207:1373–1375, 1980.

Wildt, L.; Hausler, A.; Hutchison, J.S.; Marshall, G.; Knobil, E. Estradiol as a gonadotropin-releasing hormone in the rhesus monkey. ENDOCRINOLOGY 108:2011–2013, 1981a.

Wildt, L.; Hutchison, J.S.; Marshall, G.; Pohl, C.R.; Knobil, E. On the site of action of progesterone in the blockade of the estradiol-induced gonadotropin discharge in the rhesus monkey. ENDOCRINOLOGY 109:1293–1294, 1981b.

Wildt, L.; Hausler, A.; Marshall, G.; Hutchison, J.S.; Plant, T.M.; Belchetz, P.E.; Knobil, E. Frequency and amplitude of gonadotropin-releasing hormone stimulation and gonadotropin secretion in the rhesus monkey. ENDOCRINOLOGY 109:544–557, 1981c.

Wilks, J.W. Endocrine characterization of the menstrual cycle of the stumptailed monkey (Macaca arctoides). BIOLOGY OF REPRODUCTION 16:474–478, 1977.

Wilks, J.W.; Hodgen, G.D.; Ross, G.T. Luteal phase defects in the rhesus monkey: The significance of serum FSH:LH ratios. JOURNAL OF CLINICAL ENDOCRINOLOGY AND METABOLISM 43:1261–1267, 1976.

Wilks, J.W.; Hodgen, G.D.; Ross, G.T. Anovulatory menstrual cycles in the rhesus monkey: The significance of serum follicle-stimulating/hormone-luteinizing hormone ratios. FERTILITY AND STERILITY 28:1094–1100, 1977.

Wilks, J.W.; Marciniak, R.D.; Hildebrand, D.L.; Hod-

gen, G.D. Periovulatory endocrine events in the stumptailed monkey (Macaca arctoides). ENDOCRINOLOGY 107:237–244, 1980.

Williams, R.F.; Hodgen, G.D. Reinitiation of the diurnal rhythm of prolactin secretion in postpartum rhesus monkeys. BIOLOGY OF REPRODUCTION 23:276–280, 1980.

Williams, R.F.; Barber, D.L.; Cowan, B.D.; Lynch, A.; Marut, E.L.; Hodgen, G.D. Hyperprolactinemia in monkeys: Induction by an estrogen-progesterone synergy. STEROIDS 38:321–331, 1981.

Williams, R.F.; Turner, C.K.; Hodgen, G.D. The late pubertal cascade in perimenarchial monkeys: Onset of assymetrical ovarian estradiol secretion and bioassayable luteinizing hormone release. JOURNAL OF CLINICAL ENDOCRINOLOGY AND METABOLISM 55:660–665, 1982.

Wilson, M.E.; Gordon, T.P.; Blank, M.S.; Collins, D.C. Timing of sexual maturity in female rhesus monkeys (Macaca mulatta) housed outdoors. JOURNAL OF REPRODUCTION AND FERTILITY, 70:625–633, 1984.

Wilson, R.C.; Knobil, E. Acute effects of N-methyl-DL-aspartate on the release of pituitary gonadotropins and prolactin in the adult female rhesus monkey. BRAIN RESEARCH 248:177–179, 1982.

Winter, J.S.D.; Faiman, C.; Hobson, W.C.; Prasad, A.V.; Reyes, F.I. Pituitary-gonadal relations in infancy. I. Patterns of serum gonadotropin concentrations from birth to four years of age in man and chimpanzee. JOURNAL OF CLINICAL ENDOCRINOLOGY AND METABOLISM 40:545–551, 1975.

Winter, J.S.D.; Faiman, C.; Hobson, W.C.; Reyes, F.I. The endocrine basis of sexual development in the chimpanzee. JOURNAL OF REPRODUCTION AND FERTILITY, SUPPLEMENT 28:131–138, 1980.

Wolf, R.C.; O'Connor, R.F.; Robinson, J.A. Cyclic changes in plasma progestins and estrogens in squirrel monkey. BIOLOGY OF REPRODUCTION 17:228–231, 1977.

Yalow, R.S.; Berson, S.A. Immunoassay of endogenous plasma insulin in man. JOURNAL OF CLINICAL INVESTIGATION 39:1157–1174, 1960.

Yamaji, T.; Dierschke, D.J.; Hotchkiss, J.; Bhatlacharya, A.N.; Surue, A.H.; Knobil, E. Estrogen induction of LH release in the rhesus monkey. ENDOCRINOLOGY 89:1034–1041, 1971.

Yamaji, T.; Peckham, W.D.; Atkinson, L.E.; Dierschke, D.J.; Knobil, E. Radioimmunoassay of rhesus monkey follicle stimulating hormone (RhFSH). ENDOCRINOLOGY 92:1652–1659, 1973.

Yamamoto, Y.; Gurasalus, G.L.; Sundarum, K.; Thau, R.B. Characterization of anti-oLH beta-antibodies acting as contraceptives in rhesus monkeys. JOURNAL OF REPRODUCTIVE IMMUNOLOGY 111:1652–1656, 1982.

Young, W.C.; Yerkes, R.M. Factors influencing the reproductive cycle in the chimpanzee; the period of adolescent sterility and related problems. ENDOCRINOLOGY 33:121–154, 1943.

Zeleznik, A.J. Premature elevation of systemic estradiol reduces levels of follicle-stimulating hormone and lengthens follicular phase of the menstrual cycle in rhesus monkeys. ENDOCRINOLOGY 109:352–355, 1981.

Zeleznik, A.J.; Schuler, H.M.; Reichert, L.E. Gonadotropin-binding sites in the rhesus monkey ovary: Role of the vasculature in the selective distribution of human chorionic gonadotropin to the preovulatory follicles. ENDOCRINOLOGY 109:356–362, 1981.

Zondeck, B. Uber die Hormone des Hypophysenvorderlappens. KLINISCHE WOCHENSCHRIFT 9:245–248, 1930.

Steroid Hormones and the Ovarian Cycle

Jerry A. Robinson and Robert W. Goy

University of Wisconsin Regional Primate Research Center, Madison, Wisconsin 53706

INTRODUCTION: THE OVULATORY CYCLE

Our knowledge about the anatomy of the ovary justifies the general view of the organ as presenting one of the most dynamic and changing morphological pictures available for study. The general outlines of this changing morphology are represented in all adult mammals regardless of whether they are monotocous or polytocous, seasonal or nonseasonal breeders, spontaneous or reflex ovulators, and whether or not the postovulatory transformation of the follicle into a corpus luteum is spontaneous or induced. Viewed anatomically, the following general characteristics are true of all mammals: eggs are not shed continuously from the ovary, but recurrently and at species-specific intervals; within the ovary, eggs are ensheathed in a protective and nuturant layer or layers of cells which gradually increase in number and eventually form a fluid-filled sphere or follicle; as many follicles exist within the ovary as there are eggs, but these exist simultaneously in a wide range of sizes; mechanisms involved in the increase in size of follicles act only on a very small proportion of the total number of follicles at any one time; of the small proportion stimulated to increase in size, only one or a few will reach the species-specific size that may be regarded as maximum and that is associated with rupture and the release of the egg from the ovary; following release of the egg, the cells constituting the follicle are suddenly and rapidly transformed anatomically, and the fluid of the follicle itself is replaced by cells so that the previously hollow structure is soon a solid mass of cells known as the corpus luteum; the anatomic and microscopic appearance of the corpus luteum in turn changes dynamically in a manner that can be described as a waxing and waning, a growth and decline, which determines a definite and species-specific life-span.

In the normal mammalian female, if fertilization of the released egg does not occur, all of the anatomical changes in size, shape, and cellular detail outlined above recur in the same order and are repeated in exquisite detail.

Gross anatomical inspection alone of the ovary made it possible to divide these recurrent or cyclical events into two phases—one dominated by growing follicles (the follicular phase) and the other dominated by the corpus luteum (the luteal phase). Microscopic study made possible the further subdivision of these phases into stages differing in rates of follicular growth or stages of corpus luteum growth, decline, and demise. The follicular phase can be generally subdivided into periods or stages characterized by slow, medium, and rapid and/or terminal growth rates of those follicles stimulated into growth during any given cycle. Characterization of stages of the follicular phase based on other criteria also has been carried out successfully (eg, the stage of selection or recruitment of the follicle[s] destined to ovulate, the stage of maximum wasting of follicles by atresia, or the stage of ovulation or follicular rupture). When stages are based on differing criteria, correspondence between them is either vague or totally invalid. In the subdivision of the luteal phase into stages, the microscopic anatomical criteria generally permit establishment of early, mature, and senescent stages. Anatomical criteria alone have not permitted accurate estimates of the age in hours of the early corpus luteum.

Probably the best indicators of ovarian developmental stages are measurements of circulating steroid concentrations. As the follicle(s) develop in maturity and increase in size to the terminal stages, the ovary secretes estrogen (predominantly estradiol) in ever increasing quantities. In most primate species studied thus far, there is a dramatic increase in estrogen secretion (commonly referred to as the "estrogen surge") during the terminal preovulatory stage. Ovulation then follows the estrogen surge within a more or less predictable period. Whether or not this interval differs or is constant among primate species is not now known with certainty. Subsequently, during what is referred to as the luteal phase, certain ovarian tissues begin secreting steroids of a second type, referred to generally as the progestins. Progesterone appears to be the major progestin secreted at this time and is both the most potent and the most common progestagenic component.

Many different tissues undergo profound changes in response to these estrogenic and progestogenic steroids. Cells that selectively concentrate these steroids are referred to as target tissue, most of which are involved in the various aspects of the reproductive process. Once concentrated within specific tissues, dynamic changes occur, frequently involving cellular morphology and gene activation—ie, DNA, RNA, and protein synthesis. These intracellular biosynthetic processes in turn lead to changes in membrane potential and/or secretory activity of the cells of the target tissues.

Actions of Estrogens

The word estrogen is derived from two Greek words, estrus meaning "mad desire or frenzy" and gen meaning "produce." Copulatory activity of many female mammals in fact occurs most frequently or intensely during those periods when estrogen concentrations are markedly elevated, just prior to ovulation, and it is the consequence of the estrogen stimulating certain target areas within the brain.

Estrogen also has a dramatic effect on the uterus. It stimulates the growth of the endometrium and the myometrium by inducing protein and carbohydrate synthesis and causing changes in membrane permeability resulting in a hyperemic effect. In the vagina, estrogen may effect patency as well as changes in the appearance of the epithelial cells. Estrogen also influences the consistency of the cervical mucus secretion. The mucus serves as a barrier by preventing bacteria and other infectious materials from entering the uterus and upper portions of the reproductive tract and body cavity. Estrogen, however, probably through permeability

and ion exchange, alters the consistency of the mucus thus allowing passage of sperm. These alterations in the tract secretions are also beneficial by enhancing sperm capacitation.

Estrogen also causes a thickening of collagen bundles in skin and may cause edema, presumably by increasing sodium retention. Many nonhuman primate species have distinct changes in the perineal sex skin with cyclic variations in swelling and color intensity. The increases in these two parameters parallel the increase in circulating concentrations of estrogen.

Many other tissues such as the mammary bodies, bone, and other connective tissue as well as the anterior pituitary gland respond to the presence or absence of estrogens. For example, estrogen stimulates the release of the midcycle surge in the gonadotropins, LH and FSH, which is responsible for the final maturation and ovulation of the developing follicle(s). Prolactin synthesis by the anterior pituitary is the result of estrogen feedback. Loss of estrogen after the menopause results in significant bone loss. Thus estrogens are important not only for reproduction but also for the physiological functioning of many other tissues.

Actions of Progestins

Progesterone is the major steroid secreted during the latter portion of an ovulatory cycle, and most of its physiological effects result from its interaction with the estrogens. The secretion pattern of this steroid appears as the inverse of the estrogen secretion pattern, suggesting possible antagonist actions of the two types of steroids. This is true in some cases; however, in many situations the compounds work synergistically on many target tissues. For example, estrogen is believed to be the active component for eliciting sexual behavior, but, under many test conditions, estrogen treatment followed by progesterone results in greater sexual activity. Whereas this appears to be a synergistic action, antagonistic interactions are exemplified in the prevention of sexual activity by administering progesterone prior to estrogen. In the vagina, progesterone inhibits the estrogen-induced cornification of the epithelial cells. Thus, when vaginal cytology changes throughout the cycle, it does so in accord with the steroid that is the predominant one in the circulation.

In the uterus, initial estrogen stimulation induces glandular growth and proliferation and then progesterone stimulates these hyperplastic and hypertrophied cells into secretory activity. Thus, estrogen priming begins the uterine preparation, and progesterone adds the finishing touches in anticipation of conception and implantation. Progesterone also inhibits spontaneous myometrial contractions by somehow decreasing the electrical coupling between the myometrial cells—thus, the importance of elevated progesterone throughout gestation.

Many other tissues can be used to demonstrate the synergistic and/or antagonistic effects of estrogen and progesterone such as mammary tissue, connective tissue, etc. The sex skin of nonhuman primates, which swells and increases in color intensity under the influence of estrogen, rapidly loses both coloration and swelling in conjunction with increasing concentrations of progesterone. Cervical mucus also changes dramatically under the influence of progesterone.

Thus, during the ovarian cycle, estrogens are secreted early, initiating the preparation of the reproductive tract for the about-to-be-released ova as well as preparing for the impending sperm deposit. At the height of the estrogen secretion, the events are synchronized by inducing the female to receive the male at the time when the final signal is given for releasing the ova. Once these climactic events are passed, progesterone secretion is enhanced, which in turn overrides the estrogen-induced activities and quietly finishes the preparations for an enriched environment conducive for optimal fetal development.

Target Tissues as Monitors of the Ovarian Cycle

Many different types of studies have been conducted to define and determine stages of the two major phases of the ovarian cycle, particularly attempts to determine the time of ovulation. For the most part, nonintervention methods have been developed to alleviate the need for removal of the ovary so that a single cycle can be studied with repeated observations and measurements. Samples of vaginal epithelium have been used to study changes in vaginal cytology throughout the cycle. Although the vaginal cytology of primates does change in a cyclical fashion, distinct changes like those commonly found in rodents do not occur on a day-to-day basis in primates. Rather, the cytological changes appear to be gradual transitions in epithelial cell types. Thus, a specific criterion for identifying the precise time of ovulation cannot be derived from vaginal-smear studies.

Daily collections of cervical mucus also have been utilized with limited success. Investigators aspirate the mucus from the cervical canal and place the contents on a glass slide. Analysis of the mucus can be undertaken in two ways. The first is to take spinnbarkheit measurements which are obtained by measuring the elasticity of mucus. Another glass object, such as the head of a syringe plunger, is brought into contact with the mucus and then drawn upward, stretching the mucus until it breaks. When done beside a ruler placed vertically, an approximate measurement of the height at which the strand of mucus breaks can be obtained. As ovulation approaches, the elasticity of the mucus increases but after ovulation the mucus becomes watery and loses its elasticity. A second method of estimating cycle stage by studying the daily mucus samples is to dry the mucus on a slide. As ovulation approaches, the dried materials assume a characteristic "ferning" pattern which disappears after ovulation has taken place. Neither of these methods provides accurate predictions of ovulation. In addition, both frequently involve handling or restraining the animal which if true, a blood sample is probably just as easily obtained and steroid determinations carried out. Change in mucus consistency does appear to parallel estrogen secretion during the cycle, but again, the changes are more gradual over a few days, and sharp delineations in the mucus consistency are not observed.

In some women the basal body temperature has been used to determine the time of ovulation, but this estimate can only be used by women who have regular menstrual cycles and thus is of questionable reliability. A few attempts have been made in nonhuman primate species with very little success. In women, it is recommended that they take their temperature the very first thing upon awakening and before arising from bed and prior to coitus. Resting body temperature determinations in animals are next to impossible to obtain except through sophisticated telemetric measurements. Thus, a drop in basal body temperature at the time of ovulation in nonhuman primates remains to be adequately studied.

Many primate species do have external cues which can be used as indicators for stages of the cycle. Many species of primates go through alterations in sex skin coloration and/or swelling of specific perineal areas. By observing an animal on a daily basis, a trained observer can follow the changes in color intensity or perineal tumescence as an animal approaches ovulation. After ovulation, color breakdown or perineal detumescence occurs signifying that ovulation has occurred. Unfortunately for those investigators wanting timed matings or interested in specific preovulatory events, the visual cues of detumescence occur too late to be of benefit. Furthermore, the signals obtained from observing these changes in the sex skin can occur in the absence of ovulation—eg, by the demise of a follicle because of atresia. Two target tissue systems respond to the ovarian hormones by externally observable episodic manifestations. One of these episodic responses, characteristic primarily of Old World primates, is menstruation. The other, an increase in sexual behavior, varies in complex ways among mammals and defines the estrous cycle.

Sexual behavior can often be used as an indicator of cycle stage in many species. In nonprimate mammals, estrous behavior, including copulation, is limited in duration and is most generally displayed in the few hours or days preceding ovulation. In rodents especially, estrous behavior has a unique advantage over other external markers of the ovarian cycle. Its characteristic display requires the synergistic actions of sequential stimulation by estrogen and progesterone, the latter hormone being secreted by the preovulatory follicle concurrently with the discharge of ovulatory amounts of pituitary gonadotropin. Hence in these species it is the most sensitive and reliable predictor that ovulation is about to occur. However, many primate species copulate throughout the ovarian cycle, and there are perhaps only subtle differences in copulatory frequency during the periovulatory period. Since copulatory behavior in primates most likely serves purposes other than procreation, in most cases it cannot serve as an indicator of impending ovulation with the same degree of precision as that characteristic of the nonprimate estrus. Nevertheless, even among higher Old World primates, methods for assessing sexual behavior of the female have been developed that increase the usefulness of this indicator for defining an estrous cycle. These methods generally involve some system for permitting the female, rather than the male, to exercise control over the initiation of pairing. Under these circumstances, copulation is much more restricted to that time in the ovarian cycle when the follicle with the potential to ovulate has been selected. The waxing and waning of sexual behavior is a valuable indicator of ovarian activity for those primate species that lack other external indicators.

The menstrual cycle, defined as the temporal interval between successive episodic recurrences of menstruation, is dependent upon ovarian conditions that are completely different from those associated with estrus. The latter occurs generally at the time of maximum follicular growth and estrogen production, whereas the former occurs in association with corpus luteum senescence. Day 1 of a menstrual cycle is usually designated as that day when blood is observed either flowing from the vagina or in a vaginal lavage. This bleeding is the result of the breakdown and sloughing of uterine tissues at the end of a ovarian cycle in the absence of fertilization. If the uterus has not received a fertilized ovum and no longer receives appropriate hormone stimulation, then the hypertrophied endometrial tissue and accompanying vasculature are sloughed and discharged through the vagina. This menstruation period lasts several days, the precise length of time depending on the species and individual animal. Shortly after the end of this discharge, a new wave of follicles begin developing and low levels of estrogen are secreted. Estrogen stimulation of the uterine endometrium promotes another developmental stage as the uterus again prepares for a possible pregnancy. Ovulation occurs at some point between menstrual periods, but not necessarily at midcycle. The periods of folliculogenesis and luteal function are not always equal, but the length of time for the latter is ordinarily very consistent. The length of the menstrual cycle is thus designated as that period from the onset of menses of one cycle to the onset of the ensuing menses which then determines the beginning point for the next cycle. Menstruation occurs during a period when there is little or no ovarian hormone secretion.

Steroid Hormone Changes in Normal Ovulatory Cycles

The past two decades have been marked by a resurgence of comparative interest in descriptive endocrinology of the ovarian cycle. In part this renewed interest has come about because of technical achievements enabling greater sensitivity and precision of steroid hormone measurement. In addition, however, the new focus on nonhuman primates has been stimulated by two considerations: 1) the search for animal models with greater correspondence to the human being, and 2) concern for the declining reproductive success of primates in the world and the related need to enhance their reproductive success in captivity. The burgeoning of descriptive information that has resulted from the impact of these factors is amply illustrated in the following paragraphs which describe the steroid hormone cycles for 25 different taxonomic units of primates including the human being. Despite progress in the fund of information the developing picture is still unbalanced, and 19 of these taxa involve Old World primates whereas only six of them pertain to New World monkeys.

STEROID MEASUREMENTS

To evaluate the functional status of an endocrine gland or endocrine tissue, hormonal levels can be estimated in different body fluids, specifically blood and urine. Whereas the collection of routine blood samples will most likely result in some degree of trauma, especially to an experimental animal subject, the collection of urine specimens can be relatively innocuous. However, the excretion of steroids in the urine represents only a small and variable fraction of the original compound and its metabolites. The steroids found in urine are usually found in conjugated form or have been significantly altered structurally to another form. Measurements of the metabolites can be biased by the fact that other less pertinent steroids (ie, of adrenal cortex origin) may also be shunted to the same metabolite, thus complicating the data. Metabolite and conjugated forms also appear somewhat later and thus are slightly out of phase with respect to specific endocrine activity. Thus, urinary assays do not reflect the true secretory activity of specific endocrine tissues although the measurement of hormones in urine samples does bear some proportionality to the total hormone secretion during a specified collection period.

Regular blood sampling, on the other hand, represents a more proximal estimate of potential endocrine activity. However, hormones disappear quickly from the blood. Thus, the information obtained represents only that condition at the particular moment the blood sample was taken. It must be emphasized that a hormonal concentration in the blood is proportional to the secretion rate only if the rate of removal is constant. And as is the case in urine samples, studies on the hormonal activity can be complicated by hormone contributions from other sources. Thus, a clearer picture of the secretory activity of a specific endocrine tissue is rendered more likely by measuring the hormones in both types of bodily fluids.

Steroid hormones are secreted in relatively small quantities, and sophisticated techniques for measuring these compounds have been developed rel-

atively recently. Early measurement procedures involved colorimetric and fluorescent techniques which were relatively insensitive. These techniques at best had sensitivities of 0.1 or with some 0.01 gm of steroid. Since the ovarian steroids circulate in nanogram (ng) (10^{-9} gm) and picogram (pg) (10^{-12} gm) concentrations, large volumes of blood had to be processed to obtain enough steroid for measurement. These techniques were more advantageous for measuring steroid content in urine samples collected over a sustained period of time where they were more concentrated. These early measurements of urinary steroid levels were further complicated (as is still the case for urine samples) by the arduous chemical steps necessary to extract and purify the steroids. The hostile environment of the urine necessitates the refrigeration and/or preservation of the samples during collection to prevent substantial degradation of the steroids. Acid hydrolysis or enzyme digestion to free the conjugate is a time-consuming but necessary step prior to measurement. Some chromatographic steps are also needed to remove possible interfering substances in the colorimetric or fluorimetric reaction.

The advent of gas-liquid chromatography (GLC) combined the chromatographic and measurement steps into one and increased the sensitivity by 100- to 1,000-fold. The greater resolution of these instruments provided a quantum leap over the conventional chromatographic techniques. However, the complexity and amount of effort required to prepare the samples prior to GLC measurement made the procedure unsuitable for routine clinical measurements as well as for measurement of large numbers of samples. Frequently, steroids could not be detected in the GLC without first chemically altering the compound (ie, acetylation).

The use of the body's own protein materials which specifically bound certain steroids provided another significant advancement, competitive protein-binding (CPB) assays. Not only were these protein materials readily available and considerably cheaper than a GLC instrument, but also the chemical alteration of the steroid was unnecessary. However, these proteins (most of which circulate in the blood of various species — CBG, cortisol-binding globulin; SHBG, sex-hormone-binding globulin; PBG, pregnancy-binding globulin) usually bound several steroids — ie, CBG, cortisol and progesterone; SHBG, testosterone, dihydrotestosterone, and estradiol. Thus, chromatographic separation was needed prior to assay. Radiolabeled steroids were used to compete for the binding sites, and the amount of radioactive steroid bound was inversely related to the amount of unlabeled steroid extracted from the sample. Of course, this requires some instrumentation for the detection of the radioactivity [for review see Chattoraj and Wotiz, 1975].

The most sensitive of these methods (and the procedure by which the majority of the results reported in this publication have been derived) for measuring steroid concentrations in body fluids is the development of radioimmunoassay (RIA) techniques. Steroid quantities as low as a few picograms can be measured using antibodies produced against the specific steroid in question. As was mentioned in the CPB assays, the antibodies are incubated with radiolabeled and unlabeled (unknown) quantities of the steroid. Thus, the amount of radioactivity bound to the antibody is inversely related to the amount of unlabeled steroid which competes for the limited number of binding sites available in the antibodies. Many of the antibodies produced are very specific and will only bind the steroid molecule that was used to stimulate its production. Thus, many RIA measurements require only simple extraction prior to assay, and chromatographic separation is unnecessary owing to the antibody specificity. Some investigators report direct assay of diluted urine and serum samples without extraction, but extreme caution is needed especially with serum samples and the presence of the body's own binding proteins. Competition for the steroid between the binding proteins and the antibody in use may give spurious results.

In the following discussions on the steroid measurements within the various species, disagreements between laboratories can frequently be attributed to differences in assay sensitivities and procedures used for measurement. The authors have tried to establish where such differences are obvious and refer the reader to the specific references for in-depth comparisons.

Human Being

Much information has been obtained on the reproductive cycle of various nonhuman primate species as investigators have attempted to develop animal models to study problems associated with reproduction in the human. Many of the macaque species have menstrual cycle lengths which ap-

proximate the length seen in women. Based on intermenstrual intervals, the following means and standard deviations have been reported for women: 28.7 ± 4.31 days, n = 10,000 cycles [Gunn et al, 1937] and 29.4 ± 3.27 days, n = 2,136 cycles [Chiazze et al, 1968]. The luteal phase is usually consistent and approximately 15 days in length [Johansson, 1969; Mishell et al, 1971; Abraham et al, 1972]. The follicular phase is generally more variable.

Circulating estrogen concentrations throughout the cycle have been described [Mishell et al, 1971; Edquist and Johansson, 1972; Lundy et al, 1974; Lehman et al, 1976; Guerrero et al, 1976]. Estradiol levels between 50 and 75 pg/ml are observed in the early follicular phase. Six days prior to the luteinizing hormone (LH) peak, estradiol levels begin to increase and reach peak concentrations of about 350 pg/ml on the day before or the day of the LH peak. A rapid decline occurs during the next couple of days before increasing to a luteal-phase plateau of about 150 pg/ml (Fig. 1). Circulating levels of estrone follow a pattern similar to that of estradiol but at lower concentrations. Early follicular-phase concentrations were between 50 and 60 pg/ml. Peak concentrations of about 180 pg/ml were attained on the day of the LH peak. Luteal-phase levels of around 100 pg/ml were maintained before the estrone levels declined to about 50–60 pg/ml at the time of menses.

During menses and throughout the follicular phase, progesterone concentrations were found to be less than 1.0 ng/ml (Fig. 1). Progesterone levels began to increase slightly two days before the LH peak but did not exceed 1.0 ng/ml until the day of the LH peak. Progesterone concentrations continued to rise for 5–8 days after the LH peak, reaching concentrations of 5–20 ng/ml [Ross et al, 1970; Johansson et al, 1971; Black et al, 1972; Israel et al, 1972; Lundy et al, 1974; Guerrero et al, 1976]. Other progestin compounds have been measured throughout the menstrual cycle [Bermudez et al, 1970; Abraham et al, 1971, 1972, 1973; Thorneycroft et al, 1971; DiPietro et al, 1972; McKenna and Brown, 1974; Wu et al, 1974; Guerrero et al, 1976]. Of these compounds, only 17β-hydroxypregnenolone did not show a cyclic fluctuation. Pregnenolone was significantly higher in the luteal phase in some cycles but not all. Average concentrations for these steroids are approximately 1–3 ng/ml. The pattern of circulating 20α-dihydroprogesterone concentrations follows closely the

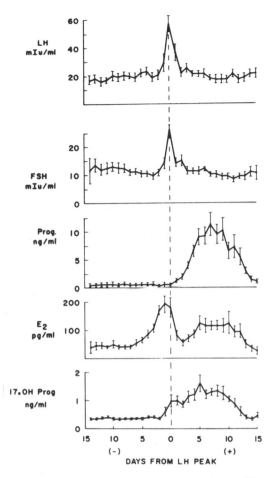

Fig. 1. LH, FSH, progesterone, estradiol, and 17α-OH progesterone concentrations in serum samples collected daily in ovulatory menstrual cycles from nine women. Means ± SEM [Reproduced from Thorneycroft et al, 1971, with permission.]

pattern seen for progesterone and is positively correlated. Follicular-phase concentrations are nearly identical to progesterone (< 0.3 ng/ml) with slight increases the day before and day of the LH peak. The highest concentrations of 20α-dihydroprogesterone were reached during the fifth through eighth day after LH peak but the highest was 5.0 ng/ml, which was substantially lower than that of progesterone. Perhaps the most interesting progestin during the menstrual cycle is 17α-hydroxyprogesterone. This steroid circulates in concentrations approximately equal to progesterone during the follicular phase. However, 17α-hydroxyproges-

terone increases rapidly one day before the LH peak and surges to 1–3 ng/ml on the day of the LH peak. Levels decline slightly for a couple of days before returning to levels of 1–3 ng/ml for the majority of the luteal phase. One possible hypothesis is that it is the rise in 17α-hydroxyprogesterone that is responsible for triggering the LH surge necessary for ovulation. At any rate, the dynamic changes in estrogens and progestins during this periovulatory period represent that division in the cycle between the end of the follicular phase and the onset of the luteal phase.

Several investigators [Judd and Yen, 1973; Abraham et al, 1974; Goebelsmann et al, 1974; Guerrero et al, 1976] have reported significant increases in testosterone at the time of the LH peak, but others [Dupon et al, 1973; Tyler et al, 1975] failed to observe any statistically significant changes during the menstrual cycle. The level of this steroid in the circulation never appears to exceed 1.0 ng/ml with ranges of 300–500 pg/ml being the norm. The data suggest that follicular-phase levels are slightly higher than luteal-phase concentrations. Dihydrotestosterone concentrations, on the other hand, appear not to change throughout the cycle [Abraham et al, 1974; Dawood and Saxena, 1976; Guerrero et al, 1976]. Circulating concentrations (100–300 pg/ml) are less than those observed for testosterone. Dihydrotestosterone is most likely derived from the peripheral conversion of testosterone. Androstenedione, unlike testosterone, is significantly higher in the luteal phase than in the follicular phase [Guerrero et al, 1976]. In addition, a significant midcycle rise has been reported for androstenedione which appears to occur on the day of the LH peak [Judd and Yen, 1973; Abraham et al, 1974; Guerrero et al, 1976]. The circulating concentration of this steroid is much higher than that of testosterone with levels of 2–3 ng/ml generally being found. Only the adrenal androgen, dehydroepiandrostione, circulates in higher concentrations than androstenedione during the menstrual cycle, but it does not fluctuate throughout the cycle [Guerrero et al, 1976]. Whereas testosterone appears to be mainly secreted by the ovaries, androstenedione appears to be derived from both the ovaries and adrenals.

Galago

Most of the information thus far reported on these animals has been on the greater bush baby,

Galago crassicaudatus. Estrous cycle lengths are approximately 40 days in length [Eaton et al, 1973; Dixon and Van Horn, 1977; Hendrickx and Newman, 1978], but mean cycle lengths of 50.3 days were reported by Valerio et al [1972]. *Galago senegalensis senegalensis* appears to have a shorter estrous cycle; the mean of 168 cycles from 11 animals was calculated to be 32.9 days [Darney and Franklin, 1982]. The criteria used in the studies on the galago cycle length were based on changes in vaginal cytology and by gross examinations of the external membrane that covers the vulvar orifice. As the animal approaches estrus, the vulvar area becomes hyperemic and the external membrane regresses.

The only report of steroid concentrations during the estrous cycle was by Eaton et al [1973]. From their estradiol and progesterone measurements, they observed a mean cycle length of 44 days with a luteal phase lasting at least 24 days. The mean concentration of estradiol at the midcycle peak was 519 pg/ml. High circulating concentrations of estradiol appeared to be maintained for at least 5 days and were correlated with fully cornified cells in the vaginal smears. The estradiol peak also correlated with the period of sexual receptivity which lasted about 6 days and presumably encompassed the time of ovulation. Progesterone concentrations were elevated throughout the luteal phase with a mean peak concentration of 8.6 ng/ml being attained.

Potto

Another prosimian that has received little attention is the potto. The estrous cycle of one species, *Perodicticus potto*, has been estimated by Ioannou [1966]. Two animals were studied for a total of 36 cycles and mean cycle lengths of 38.8 and 37.0 days were calculated, which were based entirely on changes in vaginal cytology. The changes that occurred in vaginal cytology appeared to be very similar to changes observed in the vaginal cytology of laboratory rodents but obviously on a much expanded scale. No measurements of ovarian hormone secretory patterns have thus far been published.

Lemur

Using changes in vaginal cytology as the criteria, a mean cycle length of 39.3 days was calculated for the ring-tailed lemur, *Lemur catta* [Evans and Goy, 1968]. The ruffed lemur, *L. variegatus*,

has a similar cycle length of 40 days [Bogart et al, 1977a, b]; however, a third species, *L. macaco*, has a somewhat shorter cycle, 33 days [Bogart et al, 1977b]. The shorter cycle length in this latter species was attributed to a shorter proestrous phase. The proestrous phase (follicular phase) was determined by low progesterone concentrations (< 2.0 ng/ml) and was estimated to be 14 days long in *L. catta* and *L. variegatus* but only 5 days in *L. macaco*.

From circulating concentrations of progesterone, luteal phases of 24–25 days have been determined for *L. catta* and *L. variegatus* [Bogart et al, 1977b; Van Horn and Resko, 1977] whereas a luteal phase of 28 days was found for *L. macaco* [Bogart et al, 1977b]. Bogart et al [1977b] reported peak progesterone concentrations (12–48 ng/ml) at approximately 5 days after estrus whereas Van Horn and Resko [1977] found peak concentrations of 92.5 ng/ml at 26 days after the estradiol peak. In the latter study, high concentrations of progesterone were maintained from the tenth day until about the 30th day after the estradiol peak.

In the Bogart et al [1977b] study, blood samples were only obtained every fifth day. A few peaks of estrogen (300–420 pg/ml) were observed during estrus. Usually, however, total immunoreactive estrogen concentrations were less than 200 pg/ml. Van Horn and Resko [1977] obtained samples daily throughout proestrus and estrus and estimated basal estradiol concentrations to be 10–20 pg/ml. The circulating level increased to 120 pg/ml and was coincident with the first day a cornified vaginal smear was obtained. Sexual receptivity was generally seen the first day after the estradiol peak and lasted about 24 hours.

Marmoset

Reports on the lengths of the estrous cycle for the common marmoset, *Callithrix jacchus*, have been inconsistent. Hearn and Lunn [1975] and McNeilly et al [1981] estimated cycle lengths of about 17 days whereas mean cycle lengths of 30.1 and 28.6 days have been reported more recently by Harding et al [1982] and Hearn [1982], respectively. In the McNeilly et al [1981] report, it was stated that their studies were conducted "during the ovarian cycle (approximately 17 days)"; the progesterone data presented indicate that this steroid is elevated (> 20 ng/ml) for 18–20 days with concentrations of about 5.0 ng/ml being maintained for approximately seven days. Thus, the apparent luteal phase alone was longer than 17 days and their figure suggests cycle lengths of greater than 25 days. On the other hand, Hearn and Lunn [1975] based their estimates on the interval between LH and/or estradiol peaks. However, Hearn [1982] later reported cycle lengths of 28 days. In the earlier study the authors were in the early stages of establishing their colony, whereas the latter study appeared to have been conducted on perhaps a somewhat more stable group of animals.

Separating the estrous cycle into follicular and luteal phases has been based naturally on circulating progesterone concentrations. The criterion for a luteal phase used by Hearn [1982] and Harding et al [1982] was when progesterone levels were greater than 10.0 ng/ml. Both studies found concentrations of progesterone to be above this criterion for 18–20 days. Peak concentrations of around 100 ng/ml have been reported and are reached somewhere between the fifth and 11th day following the LH surge. In the earlier study, Hearn and Lunn [1975] found that progesterone levels were maintained at about 60 ng/ml from the first to the eighth day following the LH surge and that progesterone values throughout the luteal phase rarely fell below 50 ng/ml. On the other hand, basal progesterone concentrations during the follicular phase appeared to be maintained around 5.0 ng/ml. Using circulating progesterone levels of less than 10 ng/ml as the criterion, mean follicular-phase lengths of 8.3 and 8.9 were calculated [Hearn, 1982; Harding et al, 1982].

Estradiol appears to be the major estrogen circulating in this species and becomes elevated in conjunction with the LH surge [Hearn and Lunn, 1975]. Since most of the studies obtained blood samples only every other or every third day, it is difficult to determine if an estradiol surge precedes or accompanies the LH surge. The data suggest that the estradiol and LH peaks occur on the same day, but it is very likely that the estradiol peak occurs at least some hours before the LH peak. Basal estradiol concentrations of 200–400 pg/ml have been reported, and peak concentrations of approximately 1,000 pg/ml are attained in a period of 2–4 days [Hearn and Lunn, 1975; Chambers and Hearn, 1979].

Tamarin

The cycle length of the tamarin, like that of the common marmoset, has yet to be completely established although the differences reported are not as great as reported in the marmoset. From the interval between peaks in circulating estrogen concentrations, Preslock et al [1973] calculated cycle lengths of 15.5 days. The later studies of Katz and Epple [1979] and Epple and Katz [1982] closely agreed with Preslock et al with mean cycle lengths of 17.8 and 17.3 days respectively. Both of these later studies based their calculations on the number of days between estrogen peaks. One set of these measurements was obtained from daily urine samples, and the other was based on blood plus urine measurements. However, longer cycle lengths for this species were estimated in two other studies which also used estrogen measurements in urine samples. A mean cycle length of 22.7 days was published by Brand [1981] using daily urine collections, and a mean cycle length of 23.6 days was calculated by French et al [1984] also from urine samples. Both of these studies measured the urinary estrogen content during the cycle and based the cycle length estimates on the intervals between estrogen peaks. Whether these discrepancies are the result of species, subspecies, or environmental differences remains to be resolved.

Although estrone is found in greater concentration in both plasma and urine, estradiol also fluctuates significantly. Peak concentrations of plasma estradiol reached levels of 1,700 pg/ml in the Epple and Katz [1982] study and 6,200 pg/ml in the Preslock et al [1973] report. The large discrepancy may be due to chromatographic separation prior to measurement in the former study, whereas in the latter study, samples were assayed without chromatography. The lowest estradiol concentrations reported in these studies were 350 and 2,300 pg/ml. Contrary to the observations reported for urinary concentrations, circulating estrone levels did not fluctuate significantly during the cycle [Epple and Katz, 1982]. These authors further reported that even though ovariectomy reduced estradiol concentrations to zero, estrone levels dropped only 20%. This strongly suggests that significant amounts of estrone are derived from nonovarian sources, perhaps the adrenal cortex. However, urinary estrone concentrations do fluctuate in a cylic fashion, with peak concentrations occurring every 22–23 days. French et al [1984] reported peak concentrations of 10.0 μg/mg creatinine in urine samples with the nadir being 3.83 μg/mg creatinine. Estradiol excretion followed a similar pattern but at much lower levels, 0.302 and 0.059 μg/mg creatinine respectively. Estrogen concentrations of 22.0 and 3.5 μg/mg creatinine were reported by Brand [1981] for peak and nadir levels respectively. The greater values obtained for the peak in this study could possibly be attributed to the lack of chromatographic separation prior to assay and the utilization of a nonspecific antibody in the assays. Since both laboratories pretreated the urine samples with β-glucuronidase to hydrolyze the conjugated steroids, differences in enzyme lots and digestive efficiencies could have been a contributing factor for the reported differences. A final contributing factor may have been the use of feral animals [Brand, 1981] versus laboratory-born animals [French et al, 1984], especially since it appears that the majority of the estrone is adrenal in origin. The adaptation of the feral animals to laboratory conditions may not have been as successful as for those animals reared under laboratory conditions. Thus, undue stress and hence adrenal activity may be prominent factors in the feral animals.

Progestin measurements from these primates have only been obtained in plasma samples. Epple and Katz [1982] reported mean progesterone concentrations of 28.8 ng/ml but did not show cyclic fluctuations in their publication. However, Preslock et al [1983] found basal progestin concentrations of 140 ng/ml which rose to peak levels of 272 ng/ml during a five-day period. These authors stated that the progestins remained elevated for about 9.0 days, possibly a luteal phase. Through their preliminary studies they indicted that progesterone was a component of the progestins measured. The extremely high values obtained in these latter studies may be attributed to the utilization of a relatively nonspecific assay system, competitive protein-binding, rather than a specific radioimmunoassay, as well as the lack of a chromatographic separation prior to assay.

Androgen measurements have been made during the cycle of only a few of the lower primate species. Epple and Katz [1982] did measure testosterone and androstenedione concentrations in several intact females but did not report the data with respect to the ovulatory cycle. Mean plasma concentrations of 15.33 and 4.87 ng/ml were observed for androstenedione and testosterone respectively. Ovariectomy resulted in significant reductions of 75–80% of these two androgens. Thus, the major source of these steroids appears not to be adrenal in origin. Furthermore, the relatively high estrone levels maintained in ovariectomized animals indicate a direct secretion of estrone by the adrenal rather than a peripheral aromatization of androstenedione to estrone.

Capuchin

From daily vaginal swabs, Wright and Bush [1977] calculated a mean cycle length of 21.1 days for *Cebus apella*. Cycle lengths of 21 days were reported by Nagle et al [1979] and of 18–19 days by Hodges et al [1979] based on plasma and urinary hormone measurements respectively. The slightly shorter cycle length by the latter authors was on another species, *Cebus albifrons*, and was based upon only three cycles in a single animal.

In this group of animals, early follicular-phase estrogens were maintained at 70–100 pg/ml of plasma. Circulating levels of estrogen quickly increased, reaching peak values of approximately 500 pg/ml on day 7, 8, or 9 of the cycle. Luteal-phase concentrations were slightly lower than the early follicular-phase concentrations, with a mean concentration of 53.6 pg/ml reported by Nagle et al [1979]. Although the authors did not chromatograph the samples prior to assay, the specificity of the antibody used indicated that nearly all of the estrogen measured was estradiol. Hodges et al [1979] measured the total estrogen excreted in the urine from one animal during three consecutive cycles. Peak concentrations were 25–30 μg/mg creatinine and either preceeded by 24 hours or occurred on the same day as the LH peak. Early foillicular-phase concentrations were less than 5.0 μg/mg creatinine before the periovulatory surge. However, luteal-phase concentrations remained somewhat elevated, 10–15μg/mg creatinine, and remained elevated for 13–14 days.

As had been noted in other New World monkeys, high circulating concentrations of progesterone have been noted in *Cebus* monkeys also. Basal levels of 3–10 ng/ml were found during the follicular phase of the cycle. Six days after the estradiol peak, a mean concentration of 66.9 ng/ml was determined for progesterone. Basal levels again returned about six days after the peak, indicating that the luteal phase in this species lasts approximately 12 days.

Owl Monkey

Since there is no evidence of menses in the owl monkey, *Aotus trivirgatus*, estimates of cycle lengths have been based on the intervals between the peaks and troughs of reproductive steroid secretory patterns. The steroid measurements have been performed on plasma as well as urine samples and have been accomplished by radioimmunoassay as well as gas chromatograph–mass spectrometric analysis. Bonney et al [1979, 1980] and Bonney and Setchell [1980] have studied this species extensively and report cycle lengths of 15–16 days. They have estimated that the follicular phase lasts about 6 days with a luteal-phase approximation of 10 days.

Although estrone appears to be the major circulating estrogen, the estradiol fluctuations seem to be more dramatic. The lowest concentrations observed for estrone were 700–900 pg/ml and gradually rose to 3,000–4,000 pg/ml. Plasma levels of estradiol were less than 100 pg/ml but reached peak concentrations of 600–700 pg/ml within a surge of 2–3 days. However, these high estradiol levels were maintained for a period of 4–5 days. Even though estrone follows a similar pattern, it appears to lag behind the estradiol surge by 1–2 days with the changes being more gradual [Bonney et al, 1980a,b].

Plasma progesterone concentrations begin to increase on the first day of the estradiol peak, rising from a low concentration of 14.2 ng/ml to an average peak concentration of 277.8 ng/ml. This peak was attained in 4–6 days and gradually declined throughout the rest of the luteal phase [Bonney et al, 1980a,b]. These extremely high concentrations are typical of New World monkeys, and the progesterone, in particular, may be secreted in such large quantities because of the activity of the very large mass of luteal tissue found in this species. The corpus luteum is indistinguishable from the interstitial masses, and large amounts of luteinized interstitial tissue are found in the ovarian medulla [Hertig et al, 1976].

Testosterone also circulates in high concentrations in this species, up to 10 ng/ml, and appears to fluctuate in a pattern similar to estrone [Bonney et al, 1980a,b]. Despite these high levels, no testosterone was found in urine samples. The major urinary steroid is estrone and it is excreted in a cyclic manner, paralleling that observed in plasma. During the peak, a mean concentration of 49.2 μg/mg creatinine was excreted. Whereas pregnanediol 3-glucuronide is the major progesterone metabolite and progesterone circulates in much greater quantities, still only 19.8 μg/mg creatinine of pregnanediol is excreted, less than half of the estrone levels being excreted [Bonney et al, 1979]. Very likely, the higher rate of excretion of estrone is due to the aromatization of the circulating testosterone to estrogen, although direct aromatization of testosterone would lead to estradiol and an additional step would be necessary to convert to estrone. Androstenedione, although not reported for this species, probably circulates in high concentrations, and much of it is very likely metabolized to estrone.

Squirrel Monkey

Based on steroid measurements in *Saimiri sciureus*, a cycle length of 8–9 days has been calculated [Wilson, 1977; Wolf et al, 1977], which agrees with a previous estimate based on vaginal cytology and estrous behavior [Rosenblum et al, 1967]. But other reports, also using changes in vaginal cytology, gave cycle lengths with greater variability, ranging from 7 to 13 days [Castellanos and McCombs, 1968; Hutchinson, 1970; Jarosz et al, 1977; Mendoza et al, 1978]. The inconsistencies may be due to a variety of factors. This species displays a definite seasonality in reproductive function which could contribute to the reported variability.

The one systematic attempt to analyze the cycle in terms of endocrine parameters supports the hypothesis of a cycle of 8–9 days [Wolf et al, 1977]. The authors reported estradiol peaks of 500+ pg/ml with a mean interval between peaks of 9.4 days. Mendoza et al [1978] also reported high estrogen concentrations with levels recorded as high as 1,200 pg/ml. Basal estradiol concentrations ranged from 100 to 200 pg/ml before becoming elevated usually during a 3-day period [Wolf et al, 1977]. These authors also measured progestin concentrations in the same blood samples and reported a mean interval of 8.4 days between successive peaks. The mean concentration of progestin at the peaks was found to be 399 ng/ml, 82% of which was progesterone, based on the authors' estimates with and without chromatographic separation. The lowest concentrations noted were still very high at 70 ng/ml when compared with those reported for Old World primates. Even though ovulation was not confirmed in these studies, the rise in progestins following the estradiol surge suggests that ovulation had indeed occurred and the corpus luteum was functioning as would be expected in a normal ovulatory but nonfertile cycle. Increased progestin output was observed for about a 6-day period, which suggests that this is the length of the luteal phase for this species.

Mangabey

Although external menses is rarely seen in the mangabey, *Cercocebus*, red blood cells can be detected in vaginal lavages at the appropriate stage of the cycle. The stage of the cycle can also be determined by visual inspection of the perineal area. Physical changes in the sex skin have been categorized as follows: 1) *flat*, which is coincident with menses; 2) *inflating stage I*, which occurs during an approximate 10-day period; 3) *inflating stage II*, a more rapid growth period that occurs in about 5 days and is that stage of the cycle when copulatory activity first begins; 4) *swollen*, during which maximum copulatory activity is observed; and 5) *deflating*, which is a gradual detumescence over about a 15-day period [Rowell and Chalmers, 1970; Chalmers and Rowell, 1971]. From these studies plus reproductive steroid hormone measurements, total cycle lengths of 30-34 days have been calculated [Rowell and Chalmers, 1970; Chalmers and Rowell, 1971; Stabenfeldt and Hendrickx, 1973a; Aidura et al, 1981].

From the reports of these authors, a follicular phase of 15-19 days can be estimated. Serum estradiol concentrations reported by Aidura et al [1981] are around 150 pg/ml during the first 5-7 days of the cycle. A gradual increase to 200+ pg/ml was observed during the next several days followed by a rapid 3- to 4-day surge, culminating in a mean peak concentration of 647 pg/ml. After the surge, these authors found that high estradiol concentrations (approximately 200 pg/ml) were maintained throughout most of the luteal phase.

Based on serum progesterone measurements, a mean luteal phase of 15.2 days was determined in *C. atys* by Stabenfeldt and Hendrickx [1973a] and confirmed by Aidura et al [1981], which agrees with the 15-day deflating period described above. The luteal phase was defined in both reports as that period when progesterone concentrations in the serum exceeded 1.0 ng/ml. Progesterone levels began rising on the day of the estradiol peak [Aidura et al, 1981], suggesting that the LH peak occurred on the same day as the estradiol peak. Peak levels of about 5-7 ng/ml were given in both reports, declining to less than 1.0 ng/ml at the time of menses. Progesterone values remained below 1.0 ng/ml throughout the follicular phase although Stabenfeldt and Hendrickx [1973a] reported intermittent spikes up to 2.0 ng/ml in those animals having long cycles.

Green Monkey (Vervet)

Menstrual cycle lengths of 30-31 days have been established for the African green monkey (*Cerco-*

pithecus aethiops based on vaginal lavages [Rowell, 1970; Johnson et al, 1973; Hess et al, 1979] and steroid hormone measurements [Hess et al, 1979; Setchell et al, 1980]. However, these cycle length estimations eliminated all menstrual intervals longer than 50 days as they were considered to be periods of amenorrhea. The number of such intervals were less than 10% of the total. External menses is usually seen for only 1-2 days but can be detected in the vaginal lavages for 4 days on average.

Hess et al's [1979] is the only study published thus far that provides information on serum concentrations of estradiol and progesterone. In that report, estradiol increased from levels below 100 pg/ml early in the cycle to 150-200 pg/ml which was maintained for 3-4 days before a rapid elevation occurred. A mean estradiol peak of 450 pg/ml was attained between the sixth and 14th day of the cycle. The estradiol peak occurred on the day before the LH peak in this species, which is similar to the estradiol-LH sequence in the human but unlike that in the rhesus where the hormone surges occur on the same day. During the luteal phase, estradiol concentrations of 100-150 pg/ml were maintained.

These same investigators also defined the luteal phase as the period when serum progesterone levels exceeded 1.0 ng/ml. They first observed progesterone concentrations above 1.0 ng/ml on the day following the estradiol surge but coincident with the LH surge. The average peak concentration of progesterone was 7.75 ng/ml and occurred approximately 9 days after the estradiol peak. The mean length for the luteal phase was determined to be 17.9 days.

Several urinary metabolites also have been identified but only from a single animal [Setchell et al, 1980]. Pregnanediol-3-glucuronide measurements provided an estimate of a 30-day interval between peak concentrations. During the 40-day study period, one estrogen peak of estrone-3-glucuronide and estradiol-3-glucuronide was observed but the authors did not establish cyclic correlations. Other major metabolites identified were androsterone, aetiocholanolone, and their 11β-hydroxylate counterparts. Again daily fluctuations were noted but no relationships to cyclicity were established.

Patas Monkey

The patas monkey, *Erythrocebus patas*, has not been extensively studied with respect to its reproductive physiology. No reproductive hormonal data are currently available. However, reproductive cycle lengths of 30-33 days have been reported based on intervals between menses (although external menses is rare) and attempts have been made to identify cycle stages through changes in vaginal cytology [Loy et al, 1978; Rowell and Hartwell, 1978; Sly et al, 1983].

observed an estradiol peak on day 9 and a mean cycle length of 26.8 days, the normal luteal phase for his animals would appear to be 17 days in length.

Langur

External menses is obvious in the langur, *Presbytis* sp., and menstrual cycle lengths of 24–27 days have been reported for one species, *P. entellus* [David and Ramaswami, 1969; David and Rao, 1969; Chowdhury et al, 1980]. In addition, ovulation in this species, as confirmed by laparoscopic examination of the ovary, has been correlated with maximum vaginal cornification and a drop in vaginal temperature [David and Ramaswami, 1969; David and Rao, 1969]. Females become receptive to males for 5–7 days, midway between the menstrual periods, a time when the female also actively initiates sexual interactions [Jay, 1965].

The only report on plasma estradiol concentrations [Chowdhury et al, 1980] indicates that estradiol levels peak at the time when females are receptive. During days 11–14 of the menstrual cycle, peak estradiol concentrations reached levels of 2,200 pmole/liter (nearly 600 pg/ml). On day 5 of the cycle, estradiol concentrations were already quite high at 1,100 pmole/liter (about 300 pg/ml) before reaching the peak several days later. Luteal phase levels also appeared to be elevated with concentrations around 400 pmole/liter (over 100 pg/ml). Previous reports had demonstrated a similar pattern in the secretion of estrogens through the identification of the estrogen metabolites in urine [Ramaswami, 1975; Shadilya et al, 1976]. The major urinary estrogen was estrone but estradiol was also detectable. Both were conjugated with glucuronides. Peak levels were detected on day 9 of the cycle, with conjugate estrone and estradiol excretion rates of 4.45 and 2.5 μg/day being determined.

Peak concentrations of progesterone in the plasma [Chowdhury et al, 1980] and of urinary pregnanediol [Ramaswami, 1975] were observed on day 17 of the menstrual cycle. Plasma progesterone levels rose from 2–6 nmole/liter (0.6–1.9 ng/ml) during the first 12 days to a peak of about 18 nmole/liter (5.7 ng/ml) before returning to basal levels on day 23. Based on the authors' estimate of a mean cycle length of 24 days, this suggests a luteal phase of about 12 days. However, the measurements of urinary pregnanediol in the study by Ramaswami [1975] suggest a longer luteal phase. Pregnanediol was first detectable in the urine on day 10 before rising to a peak excretion rate of 240 μg/day on day 17. Since Ramaswami [1975]

Baboon

Most of the reproductive studies in the baboon have been conducted on *Papio cynocephalus* although a few have been performed on *P. anubis*, *P. hamadryas*, and *P. ursinus*. The length of the menstrual cycles in these species is 30–35 days [Stevens et al, 1970; Goncharov et al, 1976; Wildt et al, 1977; Howard-Tripp and Bielert, 1978; Kling and Westfahl, 1978; Shaikh et al, 1982]. The cycle appears to be equally divided into follicular and luteal phases. Based on hormone profiles, Shaikh et al [1982] calculated the mean follicular phase to be 15.7 days and the mean luteal phase of 15.6 days. Kling and Westfahl [1978] also determined the luteal phase to be 15.8 days, but with a mean cycle length of 35.4 days, the follicular phase estimate has to be slightly longer.

Plasma estradiol concentrations of about 50 pg/ml were found in the early follicular phase. During a 3- to 4-day period in the late follicular phase, estradiol levels rose very rapidly, reaching peak concentrations of 250–350 pg/ml. Luteal-phase levels of estradiol were again about 50 pg/ml, and unlike in the human, a secondary rise during this period was not observed [Goldzeiher and Axelrod, 1969; Goncharov et al, 1976; Kling and Westfahl, 1978; Pauerstein et al, 1978; Shaikh et al, 1982]. Koyuma et al [1977] reported a similar pattern during the cycle, but their estimates of estradiol concentrations were substantially higher than other investigators reported, possibly a consequence of their measuring the steroid by radioimmunoassay *without* prior chromatographic separation.

Kling and Westfahl [1978] as well as Pauerstein et al [1978] ran comparative studies on baboon and human menstrual cycles. Both groups reported similar estrogen secretory patterns between the two species, but estradiol concentrations were higher in humans and a secondary rise in estradiol was observed in the human luteal phases which did not occur in the baboon. Estrone also was found to be higher in humans. In the baboon, estrone rose from 50 pg/ml early in the follicular phase to a peak level of about 100 pg/ml which was coincident with the estradiol peak. Luteal-phase concentrations also were only about 50 pg/ml [Goncharov et al, 1976; Kling and Westfahl, 1978].

The peak in circulating concentrations of the estrogens appears to occur approximately 24 hours before peak concentrations of LH are reached, which is similar to the relationship in humans [Goncharov et al, 1976; Shaikh et al, 1982]. However, Koyuma et al [1977] reported that plasma estradiol and LH peaks occurred on the same day in 60% of the cycles studied, and Stevens et al [1970] also reported that peak levels of estradiol and LH occurred on the same day in their measurements of urine samples. Obviously, for the time courses of the secretion of these two hormones to be resolved, sampling schedules of greater frequency than once a day will have to be followed.

A positive correlation has likewise been reported between estradiol changes and the perineal skin fluctuations. Tumescence occurs during the time that estradiol levels are beginning to rise, with tumescence occurring around the time of the estradiol peak [Stevens et al, 1970]. Detumescence then occurs during the luteal phase, when estrogen levels are reduced and progesterone is elevated.

Nearly all reports indicate that circulating progesterone concentrations during the follicular phase remain below 1.0 ng/ml. Concentrations of progesterone appear to increase initially *not before* but in concert with increasing preovulatory LH levels. Peak concentrations of 4–8 ng/ml are found on day 7 or 8 after the LH surge [Stevens et al, 1970; Goncharov et al, 1976; Koyuma et al, 1977; Pauerstein et al, 1978; Shaikh et al, 1982]. Kling and Westfahl [1978] reported that the initial increase of plasma progesterone concentration as reported by other workers did not occur until 3 days after the LH peak. The initial rise may be 17α-hydroxyprogesterone which does increase from 0.5 to 1.3 ng/ml, coincident with the increase in LH [Goncharov et al, 1976; Kling and Westfahl, 1978]. These discrepancies could possibly be attributed to the different techniques used in measuring progesterone and progestins. As indicated in a previous section, some radioimmunoassays utilize specific antibodies for progesterone, thus eliminating problems attributable to cross reactivity with other steroids. However, many investigators have used serum-binding proteins in their assays and these binding proteins have strong affinities for certain other steroids in addition to progesterone. Thus, without chromatographic separation, the preovulatory rise in progestins could be attributed to 17 α-hydroxyprogesterone or even some other steroid. In fact, Stevens et al [1970] compared progesterone measurements with and without chromatography and observed a significant rise in progestins on the day of the LH peak but did not find a progesterone elevation until 4 days after the LH peak. Since the estimate for the time interval between the LH peak and ovulation is about 18 hours [Pauerstein et al, 1978; Shaikh et al, 1982], the transition to a fully functional corpus luteum must take at least another 48 hours which is unlike the transition in the human being [Kling and Westfahl, 1978]. The initial rise could most likely be attributed to increases in 17α-hydroxyprogesterone and/or 20α-hydroxyprogesterone.

Two androgens, testosterone and androstenedione, have been measured during the baboon menstrual cycle. In one report on *P. hamadryas* [Goncharov et al, 1976], circulating testosterone concentrations were significantly higher in the follicular phase (0.3–0.4 ng/ml) than in the luteal phase (0.15–0.25 ng/ml), but there was only a suggestion of a midcycle peak. On the other hand, Kling and Westfahl [1978] found significant periovulatory peaks of testosterone (0.4 ng/ml) and androstenedione (0.7–0.8 ng/ml) in *P. cynocephalus*, and these androgen peaks were coincident with the estrogen peaks. The authors did not compare follicular- and luteal-phase concentrations, but follicular-phase testosterone levels appear to be greater than luteal-phase testosterone levels. Follicular- and luteal-phase concentrations of androstenedione appeared not to be different. Goncharov et al [1976] did not find any difference in androstenedione levels throughout the cycle in *P. hamadryas*. Thus, these slight differences in androgen secretory patterns may simply be a species difference.

Macaque

All species of macaque thus far studied have menstrual cycles although the degree of menstrual flow varies extensively. The cycle lengths in the macaques are similar to those of the human, being approximately 28 days in duration. Average cycle lengths for the rhesus monkey (*Macaca mulatta*) range from 25.5 to 29.5 days [Hartman, 1932; Neill et al, 1967; Kirton et al, 1970; Spies and Niswender, 1971, 1972; Bosu et al, 1972, 1973a; Hess and Resko, 1973; Niswender and Spies, 1973; Wilks et al, 1976; Czaja et al, 1977; Johnson and Phoenix, 1978]. Average menstrual cycle lengths recorded for the other macaque species are listed below.

M. arctoides: stump-tailed macaque, 28–29 days [Wilks, 1977; Slob et al, 1978; Brüggemann and Dukelow, 1980].

M. assamensis: Assamese monkey, 32 days [Wehrenberg et al, 1980].

M. cyclopsis: Formosan rock monkey, 29 days [Peng et al, 1973].

M. fascicularis: cynomolgus monkey, 28–32 days [Jewett and Dukelow, 1972; Nawar and Hafez, 1972; Saldarini et al, 1972; Stabenfeldt and Hendrickx, 1973b; Dukelow, 1977; Goodman et al, 1977; Shaikh et al, 1978; Goodman and Hodgen, 1979].

M. fuscata: Japanese macaque, 26–28 days [Nigi, 1975; Aso et al, 1976; Oshima et al, 1977; Enomoto et al, 1979].

M. nemestrina: pig-tailed macaque, 29–32 days [Blakley et al, 1972, 1981; Bullock et al, 1972; White et al, 1973; Blaine et al, 1975].

M. nigra: black ape of Celebes, 33 days [Dixson, 1977].

M. radiata: bonnet monkey, 25–30 days [McArthur et al, 1972; Stabenfeldt and Hendrickx, 1972; Lasley et al, 1974; Parkin and Hendrickx, 1975; Kholkute et al, 1981].

Menstrual cycle characterizations for these macaque species have been developed using a wide variety of methods. The most common has simply been to examine the animals daily for menstrual flow, which in some species can be completed without physically handling the animals. However, other species have minimal menstrual flow and menstruation may be detected only through daily swabbing of the vagina. Many investigators have attempted to determine the various stages of the menstrual cycle through microscopic examinations of vaginal smears obtained on a daily basis. Thus, the menstrual period would be determined by the presence of red blood cells in the smears. Menses also may be established through the detection of blood in urine samples. Such measurements serve only to identify the onset of each cycle and provide a marker to establish cycle lengths.

Cytological changes seen in vaginal smears provide crude estimates of ovarian physiology but the changes from one stage to the next are frequently very subtle and do not provide clear indices of ovarian activity. In some species (the black ape of Celebes, the pig-tailed macaque, the Formosan rock monkey, and the rhesus monkey), distinct changes in perineal skin coloration and/or swelling occur during the cycle and can be used as indicators of ovarian activity. The increase in color intensity and/or tumescence in these macaque species is in response to estrogen stimulation and thus parallels the increase in circulating estrogen con-

centrations. The decline in color intensity and/or detumescence seen in the latter part of the cycle is due to a reduction in estrogen stimulation by 1) a reduction in estrogen secretion and/or 2) antagonism of estrogen's action by the major luteal-phase steroid, progesterone. Therefore, daily examination of sex skin changes can provide a rough estimate of ovarian activity in some macaque species.

Although these methods adequately describe the cycle retrospectively, day-by-day changes in ovarian activity, especially during the periovulatory period, cannot be ascertained. Hormonal analyses, from either blood or urine samples, provide the most accurate indicators of ovarian activity and specific reproductive functionality. For many of the macaque species, the menstrual cycle has been further characterized by measuring these hormones on a daily basis and correlating the changes in these hormones with the specific stage of the ovarian cycle. With the advent of very sensitive assay procedures such as radioimmunoassay, the measurement of many of the hormones which by previous methodology were not detectable became possible, and hence the cyclic changes that occur in their secretion patterns could then be determined.

As the rhesus monkey is the most frequently used nonhuman primate research animal, it is not surprising that more is known about rhesus reproductive physiology than any other nonhuman primate species (Fig. 2). The first description of circulating estrogen levels throughout the menstrual cycle was provided by Hotchkiss et al [1971] and has been confirmed by many other laboratories during the past decade [Bosu et al, 1973b; Hess and Resko, 1973; Weick et al, 1973; Resko et al, 1974; Hodgen et al, 1976; Czaja et al, 1977; Johnson and Phoenix, 1978]. During the early follicular phase, estradiol concentrations of 50–100 pg/ml have been reported. As the follicle matures, circulating estradiol concentrations increase to 150–200 pg/ml before reaching peak concentrations of approximately 350 pg/ml. Based on one-a-day sampling, it was reported that estradiol and LH reach peak concentrations in the rhesus monkey on the same day [Hotchkiss et al, 1971], unlike in the human in which estradiol peaks on the day before the LH peak. However, the peak in circulating estradiol levels in the rhesus is actually reached 9–15 hours before the LH peak and at least 36 hours prior to ovulation [Weick et al, 1973]. Also unlike in the human, a secondary rise during the luteal phase is not routinely observed in

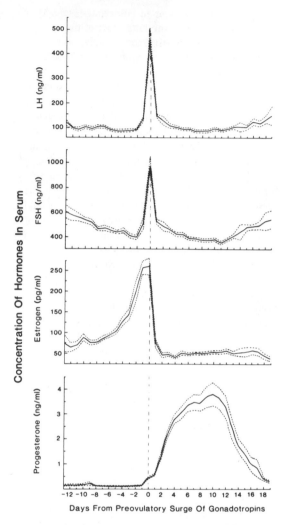

Fig. 2. LH, FSH, estrogen (estradiol 17-β), and progesterone in serum samples from rhesus monkeys during ovulatory cycles. (Unpublished data from the laboratories of Donald Dierschke, Jerry Robinson, and William E. Bridson of the Wisconsin Regional Primate Research Center.)

consistent in length, 14–17 days [Johansson et al, 1968; Kirton et al, 1970; Monroe et al, 1970; Bosu et al, 1972; Niswender and Spies, 1973; Wilks et al, 1976; Czaja et al, 1977]. Progesterone is the major gonadal steroid secreted throughout the luteal phase in the rhesus monkey. Neill et al [1967] first described the progesterone secretory pattern throughout the menstrual cycle of the rhesus monkey, a pattern that has been substantiated by many investigators [Johansson et al, 1968; Neill et al, 1969; Hopper and Tullner, 1970; Kirton et al, 1970; Monroe et al, 1970; Bosu et al, 1972; Hess and Resko, 1973; Niswender and Spies, 1973; Weick et al, 1973; Spies et al, 1974; Hodgen et al, 1976; Czaja et al, 1977; Johnson and Phoenix, 1978]. During the follicular phase, minimal progesterone levels (< 0.5 ng/ml) are found in the peripheral circulation. About 1 or 2 days before ovulation occurs, progesterone concentrations begin to increase. Although progesterone concentrations begin to rise before ovulation, it appears to plateau or even decline slightly on the day of ovulation. Some investigators have used this plateau as an indicator for the day of ovulation [Monroe et al, 1970; Bosu et al, 1972]. Maximum concentrations of 4–6 ng/ml are reached on about the 15th day of the cycle and remain relatively constant for approximately 7 days before gradually declining to follicular-phase levels before menstruation. The secretion pattern for progesterone during the menstrual cycle of the rhesus is nearly identical to that of the human, but quantitatively the circulating concentrations in the human are 3–4 times higher.

It has been hypothesized that the preovulatory rise in progesterone is responsible for the LH surge necessary for ovulation. However, experiments by Knobil and colleagues dispute such a preovulatory role [see for review Knobil, 1974, 1980]. Two other progestins (17α-hydroxyprogesterone and 20α-hydroxyprogesterone), like progesterone, begin to rise prior to ovulation [Johansson et al, 1968; Bosu et al, 1972; Resko et al, 1975]. Concentrations of these steroids appear to rise in conjunction with the initial elevation of LH and may represent the earliest response of the ovarian tissues to the increasing LH levels. During the luteal phase, significant quantities of 17α-hydroxyprogesterone are secreted in a pattern similar to progesterone but in lesser quantities [Bosu et al, 1972].

Testosterone concentrations have also been measured throughout the rhesus menstrual cycle [Hess

the rhesus female. Luteal-phase estradiol concentrations of < 60 pg/ml have been reported, but, other than the secondary increase during the luteal phase, estradiol concentrations in the rhesus monkey appear to be secreted throughout the menstrual cycle in a manner very similar to the human.

The duration of the luteal phase in the rhesus monkey also is like the human female and very and Resko, 1973; Johnson and Phoenix, 1978; Goy and Robinson, unpublished]. The three laboratories agree that there is a midcycle elevation in testosterone and that luteal-phase concentrations are significantly lower than those found during the follicular phase. The midcycle elevation appears to peak coincident with the estradiol peak. The only disagreement between laboratories is that the concentrations reported by Hess and Resko [1973] are 2–3 times greater than levels found by the other investigators. Except for the midcycle levels reported by the former authors, the testosterone levels during the menstrual cycle are less than 1.0 ng/ml.

The other macaque species appear to secrete estradiol in a very similar fashion to the rhesus monkey. The stump-tailed macaque, *M. arctoides*, has early follicular-phase concentrations of 50–125 pg/ml before rapidly increasing to peak concentrations of 300–500 pg/ml [Wilks, 1977; Slob et al, 1978]. In this species, the estradiol peak precedes the LH peak by approximately 24 hours [Wilks et al, 1980]. Luteal-phase estradiol concentrations are maintained at a significantly higher level in the stumptail (75–100+ pg/ml) than the rhesus, and a secondary rise in estradiol was observed during the luteal phase [Wilks, 1977; Slob et al, 1978].

The cynomolgus monkey, *M. fascicularis*, has follicular-phase estradiol concentrations of 50–150 pg/ml which rapidly increase to a midcycle peak of 200–350 pg/ml before declining to luteal-phase concentrations of 30–50 pg/ml [Goodman et al, 1977; Shaikh et al, 1978; Goodman and Hodgen, 1979]. However, an earlier report by Saldarini et al [1972] gave much higher values with an average estrogen peak level of 850 pg/ml on day 11 or 12 of the cycle. These investigators used a uterine cytosol receptor which apparently bound other estrogens in significant quantities and could be the reason for the higher values reported. Only one report examined the time sequence between the estradiol and LH peaks [Goodman et al, 1977], and in five of seven cycles the estradiol peak occurred one day before the LH peak, which is similar to the cycle of the rhesus. The peaks were observed on the same day in the other two cycles.

The estradiol-LH relationship has not been studied thus far in the Japanese macaque, *Macaca fuscata*. However, the secretion patterns of estradiol throughout the menstrual cycle suggest that daily concentrations are similar but slightly higher than those found in the rhesus. Follicular-phase

concentrations greater than 100 pg/ml have been reported for this species with midcycle peaks of around 500 pg/ml [Aso et al, 1976; Enomoto et al, 1979; Enomoto, 1980]. Luteal-phase levels from these reports gave circulating estradiol concentrations of 100–150 pg/ml, which is much higher than that in the rhesus. Ando et al [1976] also measured total urinary estrogen excretion and noted that the average peak rate of 10 μg/24 hours was attained in ten cycles. Serial laparoscopies also were performed on three animals during the urine collection period, and the estrogen peaks were found 0–2 days before ovulation. This study, however, may have been compromised by 1) the lack of refrigeration or chemical preservatives used during the 24-hour urine collection and 2) the somewhat insensitive fluorometric measurement technique (Kober-Ihrich procedure) used to measure the steroid concentrations.

The pig-tailed macaque, *Macaca nemestrina*, also has slightly higher circulating levels of estradiol than those found for the rhesus [Eaton and Resko, 1974; Steiner et al, 1977]. Follicular-phase concentrations approximate those of the rhesus with levels of 50–100 pg/ml, but peak levels of about 450 pg/ml are higher. This higher peak attained in *M. nemestrina* may be due to the longer follicular phase in this species, which is a few days longer than that of the rhesus. The longer follicular phase would provide an extended period of estrogen secretion and accumulation. Luteal-phase estradiol concentrations are also slightly higher than in the rhesus. A secondary rise in estradiol occurs about day 6–8 of the luteal phase. In this particular species, the changes in sex skin swelling follow the changes in estradiol very closely and are an excellent indicator of endocrine status. In addition, Steiner et al [1977] measured LH levels during the menstrual cycle and found in six females that the estradiol peak occurred the day before the LH peak in three animals and coincident with the LH peak in the other three. Thus, it appears likely that in this species the actual peaks of estradiol and LH are most likely separated by just several hours and not by a day or more.

The bonnet monkey, *Macaca radiata*, has menstrual cycle characteristics nearly identical to those of the rhesus monkey. Early follicular-phase concentrations of estradiol, like in the rhesus, were 75–125 pg/ml and increased to around 200 pg/ml during the late follicular phase. Peak concentrations of 400–450 pg/ml were reached on days 7–

11 and were slightly higher than in the rhesus as were the luteal-phase levels of 50–125 pg/ml [Lasley et al, 1974; Kholkute et al, 1981]. Parkin and Hendrickx [1975] reported a very similar pattern when they measured total estrogens. Urinary estrogens also peak during days 8–11 of the cycle at 6–8 µg/day while follicular- and luteal-phase excretion rates are 1–3 µg/day [Ovadio et al, 1971; McArthur et al, 1972].

Macaca assamensis is the only other macaque species for which steroid data are available. This species has a slightly longer follicular phase than the rhesus. Estradiol concentrations increase from basal values of 90–160 pg/ml to average peak levels of 416 pg/ml. Luteal-phase concentrations of 100–150 pg/ml are then maintained. The peak in this species is coincident with the LH peak which is identical to the relationship as described for the human female [Wehrenberg et al, 1980].

Whereas the follicular-phase lengths reported for the macaque species varied slightly, the luteal-phase lengths for these animals are for all practical purposes the same, 14–17 days. Progesterone is the major luteal-phase steroid in all species thus far studied. However, circulating concentrations throughout the luteal phase do appear to be different among the species although assay techniques might be responsible for the major discrepancies.

The progesterone profile in the stump-tailed macaque, *M. arctoides*, is very similar to that of the rhesus [MacDonald et al, 1973; Wilks, 1977; Slob et al, 1978]. During the follicular phase, progesterone measurements are routinely less than 1.0 ng/ml and usually less than 0.1 ng/ml. Progesterone begins to rise in concert with the increases in LH. This initial increase does not precede the LH rise, and the concentration is still less than 1.0 ng/ml at the time of ovulation. Progesterone rapidly rises after ovulation to peak concentrations of 5–7 ng/ml and remains elevated for approximately 11 days before declining to less than 1.0 ng/ml prior to menses.

Slightly higher progesterone peaks were attained in the cynomolgus monkey, *M. fascicularis*, during the luteal phase [Saldarini et al, 1972; Stabenfeldt and Hendrickx, 1973b; Goodman et al, 1977; Shaikh et al, 1978; Goodman and Hodgen, 1979]. Peak values of 7–10 ng/ml were reported to be attained about the middle of the 15- to 16-day luteal phase. However, Saldarini et al [1972] reported concentrations of 24 ng/ml, but these high values are undoubtedly due to the use of competitive protein-binding assay without prior chromatographic separation for their estimations. These

peaks were reached approximately one week after the estradiol and LH peaks. A preovulatory elevation of over 3.0 ng/ml was reported by Saldarini et al [1972], but Goodman et al [1977] indicated that there was no evidence for a preovulatory progesterone increase. The former authors may have been detecting a preovulatory rise in other progestins such as 17α-hydroxyprogesterone. Follicular-phase concentrations of progesterone in all other reports were less than 1.0 ng/ml.

Progesterone concentrations are also low (< 1.0 ng/ml) during the follicular phase of the Japanese macaque, *Macaca fuscata*. As in other species, the initial rise in progesterone follows the rise in LH and reaches peak concentrations of about 5.0 ng/ml in 9–10 days [Aso et al, 1976; Oshima et al, 1977; Enomoto et al, 1979; Enomoto, 1980]. Oshima et al [1977] did report a preovulatory increase in progesterone during cycle days 9–11. Since a competitive protein-binding method was used which is somewhat nonspecific, this early elevation could possibly be attributed to an increased secretion of 17α-hydroxyprogesterone or another progestin compound. However, no measurements of other progestins have yet been made in this species.

A progesterone metabolite has been measured in the pig-tailed macaque, *Macaca nemestrina*. Jeffery [1966] identified 3,6-dihydroxypregnan-20-one in urine samples of this species. Although this is probably not the major metabolite of progesterone, 6-oxygenated metabolites of progesterone are well known in man. Like in other macaque species, the follicular phase progesterone concentrations in the pig-tailed monkey are less than 1.0 ng/ml [Bullock et al, 1972; Blaine et al, 1975; Eaton and Resko, 1974; Steiner et al, 1977]. Peak concentrations of 5–10 ng/ml were attained 3–7 days after ovulation although Bullock et al [1972] reported levels of 15–20 ng/ml. As noted previously, these measurements were obtained with a relatively nonspecific method, a competitive protein-binding procedure without chromatography. This methodology also may have contributed to the confusion regarding the preovulatory increase in progesterone. Blaine et al [1975] reported a progesterone rise as much as 3 days prior to ovulation whereas Steiner et al [1977] showed that progesterone began to increase on the day of the LH peak. Eaton and Resko [1974], on the other hand, found no evidence of a preovulatory progesterone rise, and Bullock et al [1972] observed that the increase in progesterone coincided with the onset of detumescence, the presumed time of ovulation. These discrepancies are obviously related to the differences in assay sensitivities and specificities.

No evidence thus far exists for a preovulatory rise in circulating progesterone concentrations for the bonnet monkey, *Macaca radiata* [Stabenfeldt and Hendrickx, 1972; Lasley et al, 1974; Kholkute et al, 1981]. Follicular-phase levels of progesterone are less than 1.0 ng/ml and begin to rise 24–48 hours after the estradiol peak (and most likely coincident with the LH peak), although Lasley et al [1974] did observe a large progestin increase the day of the estradiol peak. Since 17α-hydroxyprogesterone was eluted with progesterone in their chromatography system, the observed increase at the time of the estradiol peak is most likely due to increased secretion of 17α-hydroxyprogesterone prior to ovulation, which has been observed in women [Abraham et al, 1972].

A preovulatory rise in progesterone levels was noted in *Macaca assamensis* [Wehrenberg et al, 1980]. Progesterone concentrations were less than 0.5 ng/ml during the follicular phase and began to increase at the time of the LH surge. Maximum concentrations were observed during the days 8–13 of the luteal phase, attaining levels typical of the macaques of 3–5 ng/ml. By the 19th day after the LH surge, and just prior to menses, progesterone concentrations had returned to less than 0.5 ng/ml.

Orang-utan

What little is known about the reproductive cycle or the orang-utan (*Pongo pygmaeus*) has been derived from studies on only a few animals which were housed at the Yerkes Primate Center. Cycle lengths of 24–32 days with a median of 30.5 days have been reported based on intermenstrual intervals [Collins et al, 1975; Graham, 1981; Nadler, 1982]. These data appear to have been derived from seven animals at most, which emphasizes the need for a greater amount of information regarding the reproductive physiology of this great ape.

Data on hormonal patterns during the menstrual cycle are even more scarce. Collins et al [1975] attempted to determine cyclic hormonal characteristics in *two* orang-utans by measuring the steroid excretory products in daily urine samples. Estrone and estradiol were the major estrogens found in the urine. Between 1 and 8 μg of each steroid was excreted each day in the first half of the cycle. During the second half, estradiol excretory rates

remained relatively constant; however, rates for estrone fluctuated between 3 and 21 μg/day. A midcycle peak of estrone was observed in one animal followed by a secondary rise near the end of the cycle. The second animal showed a similar pattern although the secondary rise occurred several days earlier. Estradiol was excreted in lesser amounts, and a definite pattern could not be established for the cycle. Rates for estradiol ranged from 0.5 to 6.0 μg/day in the first half and 2 to 10 μg/day in the second.

Pregnanediol, a major metabolite of progesterone, was found to be elevated during the latter half of the cycle. Rates of excretion of 56–840 μg/day were observed during the latter half. In contrast, rates of 20–200 μg/day were noted in the first half of the cycle. These rates are comparable to those found in humans and chimpanzees. However, that the amount of pregnanediol did *not* remain elevated for more than 10 days suggests that this species may have a shorter luteal phase than those measured in other higher primates.

Another urinary steroid measured by Collins et al [1975] was androsterone. The pattern of excretion was similar to that observed for pregnanediol, but amounts were slightly greater. Although this suggests that this steroid may also be a metabolite of progesterone, the authors point out that this metabolite could be derived from a number of other steroids.

Gorilla

Menses in the lowland gorilla (*Gorilla gorilla*) is difficult to detect but can be determined by examining urine samples for blood. Intermenstrual intervals determined by this method plus cyclic variability in hormone secretions have been used to estimate average cycle lengths of 31–33 days [Hodges et al, 1979; Nadler, 1980; Nadler et al, 1979; Lasley et al, 1982]. As in most species, the luteal phase appears to be of consistent duration, with a mean length of 11.2 days [Lasley et al, 1982] and 11–13 days [Nadler et al, 1979]. Lasley et al [1982] indicated that the follicular phase (average length 21.5 days) had much greater variability than the luteal phase.

In three female gorillas, plasma estradiol concentrations were found to be less than 100 pg/ml during the follicular phase but increased sharply at midcycle to peak levels of 200–500 pg/ml. A secondary rise to values greater than 100 pg/ml also was observed during the luteal phase [Nadler et al, 1979]. Despite the inability to obtain daily samples throughout the menstrual cycle, it appears that estradiol secretion during the cycle in the gorilla occurs in very similar fashion to that observed for the human.

Urinary estrogens as well as LH have been measured throughout the gorilla's menstrual cycle [Hodges et al, 1979; Lasley et al, 1982]. Peak concentrations of estrogens and LH were found in urine samples on the same day [Hodges et al, 1979]; however, Nadler et al [1979] noted coincident peaks in only one animal whereas the estradiol peak preceded the LH peak by 1 and 4 days in two other animals. Obviously, more frequent sampling is needed to ferret out the exact relationship between these two hormones, but most likely estrogen secretion peaks several hours before LH in this species as is the case in most other species.

Plasma progesterone concentrations begin to increase either coincident with or the day after the LH peak and remain elevated for up to 10 days following the LH peak. Peak concentrations of 10–12 ng/ml were reached on the sixth or seventh day, with an overall mean of 6.1 ng/ml for the entire luteal phase. Follicular-phase levels were always less than 0.5 ng/ml [Nadler et al, 1979]. Minimal secretion of progesterone during the follicular phase was confirmed by the measurement of a progesterone metabolite, pregnanediol-3-glucuronide, in urine samples [Lasley et al, 1982]. Very low levels (0–0.3 μg/ng creatinine) were obtained during this phase whereas 1.0–2.3 μg/mg creatinine was found in the luteal phase. The first indicated rise in urinary pregnanediol-3-glucuronide coincided with the urinary peak of LH.

Chimpanzee

The average length of the menstrual cycle in chimpanzees (*Pan troglodytes*) has been reported to be 31 days [McArthur et al, 1981], 34 days [Reyes et al, 1975], and 36.7 days [Coe et al, 1979]. Cyclic changes in perineal swelling provide general indications of ovarian condition although strict and specific relationships between circulating steroid concentrations and perineal skin condition are not discernible. At the time of menses, there is no evidence of swelling. However, early tumescence is associated with the proliferation of the uterine endometrium [Graham, 1973] which occurs in response to an increase in circulating estrogen concentrations. Tumescence continues throughout the early part of the cycle and parallels the increase in estrogen secretion. Maximum swelling is attained before the estrogen peak oc-

curs and is maintained for a few days after estrogen levels begin to decline [Reyes et al, 1975]. The LH surge usually occurs during the last two days of maximum swelling [Reyes et al, 1975; Graham, 1982]. The first appearance of secretory activity in the uterine endometrial glands, which is typically brought on through progesterone stimulation, is associated with the onset of detumescence of the sex skin [Graham et al, 1972; Graham, 1973]. Detumescence continues gradually throughout the latter part of the menstrual cycle, reaching a totally unstimulated or "flat" condition just prior to the next menses [Elder and Yerkes, 1936; Clark and Birch, 1948; Graham et al, 1969]. However, a premenstrual swelling has been observed in about 10% of cycles [Elder and Yerkes, 1936; Clark and Birch, 1948], presumably related to a premenstrual rise in estrogen. The number of days in which detumescence was noted plus measurements of progesterone and/or a metabolite have provided a basis for calculating the luteal phase which in this species is relatively consistent, 12–16 days [Reyes et al, 1975; McArthur et al, 1981].

Concentrations of estradiol in the peripheral circulation throughout the chimpanzee menstrual cycle have been reported by Reyes et al [1975] and Graham [1976]. During the early follicular phase, plasma estradiol concentrations were found to be less than 50 pg/ml. Estradiol levels gradually increased throughout the follicular phase with a surge being observed just prior to ovulation. Reyes et al [1975] reported peak concentrations of 350 pg/ml whereas Graham [1976] indicated that the estradiol peak reached only about 120 pg/ml. Since blood samples were obtained on a rather infrequent basis in the latter study, peak estradiol levels may have been missed in some animals. After the peak, estradiol concentrations drop precipitously before showing a secondary rise during the luteal phase of approximately 80 pg/ml [Graham 1976] and 100–180 pg/ml [Reyes et al, 1975]. The time of this secondary rise appears to be extremely variable. However, the relationship between the pre-ovulatory estradiol peak and the LH peak did not vary substantially. The LH surge occurred coincident with or within 24 hours after the estradiol surge [Reyes et al, 1975; McArthur et al, 1981], which is similar to the relationship observed in women.

Circulating levels of estrone were also measured by Graham [1976], who reported concentrations of 60–100 pg/ml during the cycle but with no apparent cyclic variation. Estrone plus estradiol and estriol also were measured in urine samples obtained from this species [Graham et al, 1972, 1977; McArthur et al, 1981]. The major urinary estrogen proved to be estrone. Excretion rates of less than 10 μg/day were measured during the follicular phase with a significant increase to 20–30 μg/day at midcycle followed by a secondary elevation of nearly the same magnitude during the luteal phase. Estradiol appears to be excreted in a similar pattern, but the corresponding peaks were not clearly defined. Excretion rates for estradiol never exceeded 10 μg/day. Since estrone appears to be secreted in a more or less constant fashion during the chimpanzee menstrual cycle [Graham, 1976], it would appear that the cyclical variation in urinary estrone values arises from the conversion of estradiol, the major estrogen in the blood. Conversion of steroids to estriol also occurs in these animals but appears to be minor inasmuch as excretion rates of only 2.5 μg/day were determined [Graham et al, 1972].

Progesterone secretion in the chimpanzee follows the typical pattern observed in other primate menstrual cycles. Circulating concentrations of this steroid are consistently low (< 1.0 ng/ml) during the follicular phase but begin to rise after the LH peak. Progesterone reaches peak concentrations of 5–15 ng/ml about the sixth day of the detumescence phase of the cycle [Graham et al, 1972, 1976; Reyes et al, 1975]. Progesterone concentrations remain above 1.0 ng/ml for nearly all of the 12- to 16-day luteal phase. Corpus luteum activity has also been estimated by examining steroid excretion in urine samples. YoungLai et al [1975] determined through studies using radiolabeled progesterone that most of the progesterone is metabolized and excreted as pregnanediol. Thus, several investigators have measured the urinary concentrations of this metabolite and used the measurements to evaluate ovarian physiology [Graham et al, 1972, 1977; McArthur et al, 1981]. As is expected, pregnanediol excretion rates are low (< 200 μg/day) during the follicular phase. Significant increases were noted approximately 5 days after the peak urinary level of estrone was reached, but this rise in pregnanediol excretion did not precede the LH surge. By the 8th day over 1,000 and as much as 1,800 μg/day are being excreted, but the rate then declines significantly to follicular-phase levels by the 11th day.

CONCLUDING COMMENTS

Informed readers may be amused by any listing of commonplace caveats regarding misuses and misinterpretation of data describing the hormonal changes associated with the ovarian cycle. Nevertheless, some guidelines to interpretation of these data are needed, especially when they are presented in a seemingly comparative context. Because of this context, it seems appropriate that our first word of caution paraphrases Yates's searching concern [1979] by asking the following: Comparative endocrinology, compared to what? Although in the present work we can avoid, as Yates would have us do, a comparison of alligators with aardvarks merely because both are there, we cannot press the data reported into formal analyses of similarities based on mass, length, and time. For comparative purposes we are somewhere in between these two extremes without knowing exactly where.

It may not be an overstatement to assert that the data reported reveal nothing about the quantitative hormonal requirements of any of the target systems for any species. Attempts to interpret the data in these terms fail to recognize that a variety of biochemical factors modify or otherwise limit the actions of the steroid hormones present in the circulation. These include factors like the serum-binding proteins which are known to differ widely among species. Thus, species will surely differ with respect to the amount of any given steroid hormone present in blood that is available for biological interaction with the target systems. Much less is known about these steroid-binding proteins in various nonhuman primate species than in more common laboratory species. Based on the growing fund of information from whatever source, however, it is clear that the physiological state of the organism per se can also influence the proportions of steroid that are bound and free in the blood by altering either production rate or metabolism of the steroid being measured [Burke and Anderson, 1972].

Even if we knew for each primate species the amount of hormone available to the cells of the target tissue, interpretation would be made complicated by the circumstance that species differ with respect to the cellular machinery for utilizing the hormone. For any given target system, species may differ with respect to the requirement for biotransformation of the hormone obtained from the blood, or in the nature, amount, or compartmentalization of the intracellular receptor proteins for the hormone [Plapinger et al, 1977]. Finally it should be pointed out emphatically that our measurement of steroid hormones is restricted to relatively few steroids of those present in the circulation. These few steroids do not act in a vacuum, independently of other steroids also present. Interactions among steroids occur at many levels (eg, competition for binding sites in the serum as well as other intracellular receptor proteins). Moreover, their interactions with respect to target systems can be subtle and complex, varying according to conditions from synergistic to antagonistic.

Interpretation of hormones measured in urine does not escape these limitations imposed upon the blood-borne hormones. Indeed, if anything, the urinary hormones are even more remote indicators or predictors of hormonal actions. If the amounts of hormone present in blood are poor predictors of the amount of hormone the target tissue might "see," then the amount of hormone present in urine has to be regarded as an equally poor predictor of the amount the target system might "have seen."

If, because of the limitations listed, we cannot use the data to predict the response of target systems, we are equally disadvantaged in any attempt to use the data to predict the secretory activity of the ovary. The amount of any steroid hormone present in the blood or urine is a measure of the amount produced by all sources, not the ovary alone. Furthermore, the amount of any given steroid present in blood or urine has been modified in accord with species-specific vagaries of metabolism and clearance, rendering it useless as a predictor of the amount originally secreted. Finally, secretory activity in many instances is known to be pulsatile in form. The specifics of the pulsatile release of hormone may be important to the target system response, and species may well differ in fundamental parameters of pulse amplitude, duration, and frequency. Although the momentary concentration of a steroid in blood may be affected by these parameters of secretion, the quantity of steroid measured in blood at only one instant in time does not reflect these parameters above.

From what has been said so far it should be obvious that any comparison of species based on the quantity of any given steroid hormone present in blood or urine has very limited meaning or interpretation. Even if the comparison were confined to an exactly comparable instant in the sequence of ovarian events, the utility to science of any identified species similarity or difference would be moot and its resolution likely unrewarding.

There are, of course, valid comparisons among species that the hormonal data permit. These comparisons are not new, but the new methods of hormone measurement provide bases for the comparisons with greater precision and confidence than was formerly possible. We refer, of course, to the ways we have already tried to make comparative use of the endocrine data—namely, by identifying similarities and differences between taxa with regard to the lengths of the follicular and luteal phases. In this regard, the new hormonal measures permit comparisons among primates that do not have external markers of the ovarian cycle (such as estrus, menstruation, changes in vaginal epithelium, or sex skin specializations), plus they also permit these same comparisons among these with and without such external markers. The advantages of the new hormonal methods for the delineation of these cyclic phases over older methods are obvious; they involve less intervention, they permit day-by-day (or even closer) monitoring of the same subject, they generate quantitative data which are more amenable to statistical treatment, and they provide for a high degree of objectivity. If our identification of species similarities and differences with respect to these uses of the endocrine data is to accomplish more than to amaze us, then the next step of using these species to test hypotheses still needs to be taken.

If comparative uses of the cyclic hormonal profiles remain mildly disappointing or even frustrating, what, then, is the bright light provided by such data that has inspired so many investigators to work so assiduously to obtain so much information on so many species? There is, of course, not a single answer. Of the many answers, some are species-specific and relate to the need to conserve an exotic animal in captivity, or the need to increase reproductive efficiency in commercial species. Others concern the need to identify a useful "model" for experimental analyses that law, morality, custom, or cost otherwise prohibits. Such measurements also provide investigators with unprecedented guidelines for replacement regimens following ablation of endocrine organs. Both understimulation and overstimulation can be avoided because of them. By far the most important need for such information, however, arises from its value to research in the direct assessment of factors that influence the ovarian events themselves. Despite prior caveats about the inadequacy of blood or urinary steroid measures and indices of ovarian secretory activity, the hormonal measures are used quite effectively in this manner when appropriate conditions are maintained. Thus, intraspecific uses of the hormonal data are abundant and scientifically meaningful, so much so that a continuing search for improved methods of measurement deserves encouragement. Optimistically, we should conclude this chapter by an expression of confidence that improved methods will permit even greater detection and resolution of the most intimate details of ovarian events heretofore only known to us through anatomical analysis.

ACKNOWLEDGMENTS

Publication number 23-015 of the University of Wisconsin Regional Primate Research Center supported by NIH grants RR00167 and AG-01612.

The authors wish to thank Ms. Jackie Kinney, Mary Schatz, and Carolyn De Luna for the secretarial and clerical services provided.

REFERENCES

Abraham, G.E.; Buster, J.E.; Kyle, F.W.; Corrales, P.C.; Teller, R.C. Radioimmunoassay of plasma pregnenolone, 17-hydroxypregnenolone and dehydroepiandrosterone under various physiological conditions. JOURNAL OF CLINICAL ENDOCRINOLOGY 37:140, 1973.

Abraham, G.E.; Maroulis, G.B.; Marshall, J.R. Evaluation of ovulation and corpus luteum function using measurements of plasma progesterone. OBSTETRICS AND GYNECOLOGY 44:522, 1974.

Abraham, G.E.; Odell, W.D.; Swerdloff, R.S.; Hopper, K. Simultaneous radioimmunoassay of plasma FSH, LH, progesterone, 17-hydroxyprogesterone and oestradiol-17 during the menstrual cycle. JOURNAL OF CLINICAL ENDOCRINOLOGY 34:312, 1972.

Abraham, G.E.; Swerdloff, R.S.; Tulchinsky, D.; Hopper, K.; Odell, W.D. Radioimmunoassay of plasma 17-hydroxyprogesterone. JOURNAL OF CLINICAL ENDOCRINOLOGY 33:42, 1971.

Aidura, D.; Badaivi, M; Tahiri-Zagret, C.; Robyn, C. Changes in concentrations of serum prolactin FSH, oestradiol and progesterone and of the sex skin during the menstrual cycle in the mangabey monkey (Cercocebus atys lunulatus). JOURNAL OF REPRODUCTION AND FERTILITY 62:475–481, 1981.

Ando, A.; Nigi, H.; Tanaka, T.; Ohsawa, N. Routine measurement of urinary total estrogens of the female Japanese monkey as an index for estimating the time of ovulation. PRIMATES 17:89–94, 1976.

Aso, T.; Tominago, T.; Oshima, K.; Matsuboyaski, K. Seasonal changes of plasma estradiol and progesterone in the Japanese monkey (Macaca fuscata fuscata). ENDOCRINOLOGY 100:745–750, 1976.

Bermudez, J.A.; Doerr, P.; Lipsett, M.B. Measurement of pregnenolone in blood. STEROIDS 16:505, 1970.

Black, W.P.; Martin, B.T.; Whyte, W.G. Plasma progesterone concentration as an index of ovulation and corpus luteum function on normal and gonadotrophin-stimulated menstrual cycle. JOURNAL OF OBSTETRICS AND GYNAECOLOGIA BRITISH COMMONWEALTH 79:363, 1972.

Blaine, C.R.; White, R.J.; Blakley, G.A.; Ross, W.F. CONTEMPORARY PRIMATOLOGY. S. Kondo; M. Kawai; A. Ehara; Inuyama, eds. Basel, Karger, 1975.

Blakley, G.A.; Morton, W.R.; Smith, O.A. PROCEEDINGS OF THE 3RD CONFERENCE OF EXPERIMENTAL MEDICINE AND SURGERY IN PRIMATES. Basel, Karger, 1972.

Blakley, G.B.; Beamer, T.W.; Dukelow, W.R. Characteristics of the menstrual cycle in nonhuman primates. IV. Timed mating in Macaca nemestrina. LABORATORY ANIMALS 15:351–353, 1981.

Bogart, M.H.; Cooper, R.W.; Benirschke, K. Reproductive studies of black and ruffed lemurs. INTERNATIONAL ZOO YEARBOOK 17:177–182, 1977a.

Bogart, M.H.; Kumamoto, A.T.; Lasley, B.L. A comparison of the reproductive cycle of three species of Lemur. FOLIA PRIMATOLOGICA 28:134–143, 1977b.

Bonney, R.C.; Dixson, A.F.; Fleming, D. Cyclic changes in the circulating and urinary levels of ovarian steroids in the adult female owl monkey (Aotus trivirgatus). JOURNAL OF REPRODUCTION AND FERTILITY 56:271–280, 1979.

Bonney, R.C.; Dixson, A.F.; Fleming, D. Plasma concentrations of oestradiol-17β, oestrone, progesterone and testosterone during the ovarian cycle of the owl monkey (Aotus trivirgatus). JOURNAL OF REPRODUCTION AND FERTILITY 60:101–107, 1980.

Bonney, R.C.; Setchell, K.D.R. The excretion of gonadal steroids during the reproductive cycle of the owl monkey (Aotus trivirgatus). JOURNAL OF STEROID BIOCHEMISTRY 12:417–421, 1980.

Bosu, W.T.K.; Holmdahl, T.H.; Johansson, E.D.B.; Gemzell, C. Peripheral plasma levels of oestrogens, progesterone and 17α-hydroxyprogesterone during the menstrual cycle of the rhesus monkey. ACTA ENDOCRINOLOGICA 71:755–764, 1972.

Bosu, W.T.K.; Johansson, E.D.B.; Gemzell, C. Ovarian steroid patterns in peripheral plasma during the menstrual cycle in the rhesus monkey. FOLIA PRIMATOLOGICA 19:218–234, 1973a.

Bosu, W.T.K.; Johansson, E.D.B.; Gemzell, C. Peripheral plasma levels of oestrone, oestradiol-17β and progesterone during ovulatory menstrual cycles in the rhesus monkey with special reference to the onset of menstruation. ACTA ENDOCRINOLOGICA (KBH) 74:732–42, 1973b.

Brand, H.M. Urinary oestrogen excretion in the female cotton-topped tamarin (*Saguinus oedipus oedipus*). JOURNAL OF REPRODUCTION AND FERTILITY 62:467–473, 1981.

Brüggemann, S.; Dukelow, W.R. Characteristics of the menstrual cycle in nonhuman primates. III. Tuned mating in *Macaca arctoides*. JOURNAL OF MEDICAL PRIMATOLOGY 9:213–221, 1980.

Bullock, D.W.; Paris, C.A.; Goy, R.W. Sexual behavior, swelling of the sex skin and plasma progesterone in the pigtailed macaque. JOURNAL OF REPRODUCTION AND FERTILITY 31:225–236, 1972.

Burke, C.W.; Anderson, D.C. Sex-hormone-binding globulin is an oestrogen amplifier. NATURE 240:38, 1972.

Castellanos, H.; McCombs, H.L. The reproductive cycle of the new world monkey. FERTILITY AND STERILITY 19:213–227, 1968.

Chalmers, N.R.; Rowell, T.E. Behavior and female reproductive cycles in a captive group of mangabeys. FOLIA PRIMATOLOGICA 14:1–14, 1971.

Chambers, P.L.; Hearn, J.P. Peripheral plasma levels of progesterone, oestradiol-17β, oestrone, testosterone, androstenedione and chorionic gonadotropin during pregnancy in the marmoset monkey, *Callithrix jacchus*. JOURNAL OF REPRODUCTION AND FERTILITY 56:23–32, 1979.

Chattoraj, S.C.; Wotiz, H.H. Estrogens. Pp. 1–49 in METHODS IN INVESTIGATIVE AND DIAGNOSTIC ENDOCRINOLOGY, Vol. 3. STEROID HORMONES. R.I. Dorfman, ed. S.A. Berson; R.S. Yalow, general eds. Amsterdam, North-Holland; New York, American Elsevier, 1975.

Chiazze, L.; Brayer, F.T.; Macisco, J.J. Jr.; Parker, M.P.; Duffy, B.J. The length and variability of the human menstrual cycle. JOURNAL OF THE AMERICAN MEDICAL ASSOCIATION 203:377–380, 1968.

Chowdhury, S.R.; Saran, R.K.; Harish, C. Plasma levels of estradiol and progesterone during normal menstrual cycle in langur monkey (*Presbytis entellus*) INDIAN JOURNAL OF PHYSIOLOGY AND PHARMACOLOGY 24(4):364–366, 1980.

Clark, G.; Birch, H.G. Observations on the sex skin and sex cycle in the chimpanzee. ENDOCRINOLOGY 43:218-231, 1948.

Coe, C.L.; Connolly, A.C.; Kraemer, H.C.; Levine, S. Reproductive development and behavior of captive female chimpanzees. PRIMATES 20(4):571–582, 1979.

Collins, D.C.; Graham, C.E.; Preedy, J.R.K. Identification and measurement of urinary estrone, estradiol

17β, estriol, pregnanediol and androsterone during the menstrual cycle of the orangutan. ENDOCRINOLOGY 96:93–101, 1975.

Czaja, J.A.; Robinson, J.A.; Eisele, S.G.; Scheffler, G.; Goy, R.W. Relationship between sexual skin colors of female rhesus monkeys and mid-cycle plasma levels of estradiol and progesterone. JOURNAL OF REPRODUCTION AND FERTILITY 49:147–150, 1977.

Darney, K.J. Jr.; Franklin, L.E. Analysis of the estrous cycle of the laboratory-housed Senegal galago (*Galago senegalensis senegalensis*): Natural and induced cycles. FOLIA PRIMATOLOGICA 37:106–126, 1982.

David, G.F.X.; Ramaswami, L.S. Studies on menstrual cycles and other related phenomena in the langur (*Presbytis entellus entellus*). FOLIA PRIMATOLOGICA 11:300–316, 1969.

David, G.F.X.; Rao, C.A.P. Ovulation and the serum protein changes during ovulation in *Presbytis entellus entellus* Dufresne. GENERAL AND COMPARATIVE ENDOCRINOLOGY, SUPPLEMENT 2:197–202, 1969.

Dawood, M.Y.; Saxena, B.B. Plasma testosterone and dihydrotestosterone in ovulatory and anovulatory cycles. AMERICAN JOURNAL OF OBSTETRICS AND GYNECOLOGY 35:729, 1976.

DiPietro, D.L.; Brown, R.D.; Strott, C.A. Pregnenolone radioimmunoassay utilizing a new fractionation technique for sheep antiserum. JOURNAL OF CLINICAL ENDOCRINOLOGY 35:729, 1972.

Dixson, A. Observations on the displays, menstrual cycles and sexual behavior of the "black ape" of Celebes (*Macaca nigra*). JOURNAL OF ZOOLOGY (LONDON) 182:63–84, 1977.

Dixson, A.F.; Van Horn, R.N. Comparative studies of morphology and reproduction in two subspecies of the greater bushbaby, *Galago crassicaudatus crassicaudatus* and *G.c. orgentatus*. JOURNAL OF ZOOLOGY (LONDON) 183:517–526, 1977.

Dukelow, W.R. Ovulatory cycle characteristics in *Macaca fascicularis*. JOURNAL OF MEDICAL PRIMATOLOGY 6:33–42, 1977.

Dupon, C.; Rosenfields, R.L.; Cleary, R.E. Sequential changes in total and free testosterone and androstenedione in plasma during spontaneous and clomid induced ovulatory cycles. AMERICAN JOURNAL OF OBSTETRICS AND GYNECOLOGY 115:478, 1973.

Eaton, G.G.; Resko, J.A. Ovarian hormones and sexual behavior in *Macaca nemestrina*. JOURNAL OF COMPARATIVE AND PHYSIOLOGICAL PSYCHOLOGY 86:919–925, 1974.

Eaton, G.G.; Slob, A.; Resko, J.A. Cycles of mating behaviour, oestrogen and progesterone in the thick-tailed bushbaby (*Galago crassicaudatus crassicaudatus*) under laboratory conditions. ANIMAL BEHAVIOUR 21:309–315, 1973.

Edquist, L.-E.; Johansson, E.D.B. Radioimmunoassay

of oestrone and oestradiol in human and bovine peripheral plasma. ACTA ENDOCRINOLOGICA (KBH) 71:716, 1972.

Elder, J.H.; Yerkes, R.M. The sexual cycle of the chimpanzee. ANATOMICAL RECORD 67:119–143, 1936.

Enomoto, T. Correlation between fluctuations of testosterone levels in systemic circulation and sexual behavior in intact female Japanese monkeys in the laboratory condition. JOURNAL OF THE ANTHROPOLOGICAL SOCIETY OF NIPPON 88:239–248, 1980.

Enomoto, T.; Seiki, K.; Haruki, Y. On the correlation between sexual behavior and ovarian hormone level during the menstrual cycle in Japanese monkeys. PRIMATES 20:563–570, 1979.

Epple, G.; Katz, Y. REPRODUCTION IN NEW WORLD PRIMATES. J.P. Hearn, ed. Lancaster, England, MTP Press, 1982.

Evans, C.S.; Goy, R.W. Social behavior and reproductive cycles in captive ring-tailed lemurs (Lemur catta). JOURNAL OF ZOOLOGY (LONDON) 156:181–197, 1968.

French, J.A.; Abbott, D.H.; Scheffler, G.; Robinson, J.A.; Goy, R.W. Cyclic excretion of urinary oestrogens in female tamarins (Saguinus oedipus). JOURNAL OF REPRODUCTION AND FERTILITY, 68:177–184, 1984.

Goebelsmann, U.; Arce, J.J.; Thorneycroft, I.H.; Mishell, D.R. Jr. Serum testosterone concentrations in women throughout the menstrual cycle and following HCG administration. AMERICAN JOURNAL OF OBSTETRICS AND GYNECOLOGY 119:445, 1974.

Goldzeiher, J.W.; Axelrod, L.R. Urinary metabolites of 4-^{14}C-progesterone in the baboon (Papio spp.). GENERAL AND COMPARATIVE ENDOCRINOLOGY 13:201–205, 1969.

Goncharov, N.; Aso, T.; Cekan, Z.; Pachalia, N.; Diczfalusy, E. Hormonal changes during the menstrual cycle of the baboon (Papio hamadryas). ACTA ENDOCRINOLOGICA (COPENHAGEN) 82:396–412, 1976.

Goodman, A.L.; Descalzi, C.D.; Johnson, D.K.; Hodgen, G.D. Composite pattern of circulating LH, FSH, estradiol and progesterone during the menstrual cycle in cynomolgus monkeys. PROCEEDINGS OF THE SOCIETY OF EXPERIMENTAL BIOLOGY AND MEDICINE 155:479–481, 1977.

Goodman, A.L.; Hodgen, G.D. Menstrual cycle characteristics in chronically hemiovariectomized cynomolgus monkeys (Macaca fascicularis). JOURNAL OF CLINICAL ENDOCRINOLOGY AND METABOLISM 48:345–347, 1979.

Graham, C.E. Chimpanzee endometrium and sexual swelling during menstrual cycle or hormone administration. FOLIA PRIMATOLOGICA 19:458–468, 1973.

Graham, C.E. THE LABORATORY ANIMAL IN THE STUDY OF REPRODUCTION. S. Ericksen; A. Spiegal, eds. New York, 1976.

Graham, C.E. Ovulation time: A factor in ape fertility assessment. AMERCIAN JOURNAL OF PRIMATOLOGY SUPPLEMENT 1:51–55, 1982.

Graham, C.E. REPRODUCTIVE BIOLOGY OF THE GREAT APES. New York, Academic Press, 1981.

Graham, C.E.; Collins, D.C.; Robinson, H.; Preedy, J.R.K. Urinary levels of estrogens and pregnanediol and plasma levels of progesterone during the menstrual cycle of the chimpanzee: Relationship to the sexual swelling. ENDOCRINOLOGY 91:13–24, 1972.

Graham, C.E.; Guilloud, N.; McArthur, J.W. PROCEEDINGS OF THE SECOND INTERNATIONAL CONGRESS OF PRIMATOLOGY. Basel, Karger, 1969.

Graham, C.E.; Warner, H.; Misener, J.; Collins, D.C.; Preedy, J.R.K. The association between basal body temperature, sexual swelling and urinary gonadal hormone levels in the menstrual cycle of the chimpanzee. JOURNAL OF REPRODUCTION AND FERTILITY 50:23–28, 1977.

Guerrero, R.; Aso, T.; Brenner, P.F.; Cekan, Z.; Landgren, B.-M.; Hagenfeldt, K.; Diczfalusy, E. Studies on the pattern of circulating steroids in the normal menstrual cycle. 1. Simultaneous assays of progesterone, pregnenolone, dehydroepiandrosterone, testosterone, dihydrotestosterone, androstenedione, oestradiol and oestrone. ACTA ENDOCRINOLOGICA 81:133, 1976.

Gunn, D.L.; Jenkin, P.M.; Gunn, A.L. Menstrual periodicity; Statistical observations on a large sample of normal cases. JOURNAL OF OBSTETRICS AND GYNAECOLOGY BRITISH EMPIRE 44:839–879, 1937.

Harding, R.D.; Hulme, M.J.; Lunn, S.F.; Henderson, C.; Aitken, R.J. Plasma progesterone levels throughout the ovarian cycle of the common marmoset (Callithrix jacchus). JOURNAL OF MEDICAL PRIMATOLOGY 11:43–51, 1982.

Hartman, C.G. Studies in the reproduction of the monkey Macacus (Pithecus) rhesus, with special reference to menstruation and pregnancy. CONTRIBUTIONS TO EMBRYOLOGY CARNEGIE INSTITUTE 33:81–101, 1932.

Hearn, J.P. REPRODUCTION IN NEW WORLD PRIMATES. Lancaster, England, MTP Press, 1982.

Hearn, J.P.; Lunn, S.F. The reproductive biology of the marmoset monkey, Callithrix jacchus. LABORATORY ANIMAL HANDBOOK 6:191–202, 1975.

Hendrickx, A.G.; Newman, L.M. Reproduction of the greater bushbaby (Galago crassicaudatus panganiensis) under laboratory conditions. JOURNAL OF MEDICAL PRIMATOLOGY 7:26–43, 1978.

Hertig, A.T.; Barton, B.R.; Mackey, J.J. The female genital tract of the owl monkey (Aotus trivirgatus) with special reference to the ovary. LABORATORY

ANIMAL SCIENCE 26:1041–1067, 1976.

Hess, D.L.; Resko, J.A. The effects of progesterone on the patterns of testosterone and estradiol concentrations in the systemic plasma of the female rhesus monkey during the intermenstrual period. ENDO-CRINOLOGY 92:446, 1973.

Hess, D.L.; Hendrickx, A.G.; Stabenfeldt, G.H. Reproductive and hormonal patterns in the African green monkey (Cercopithecus aethiops). JOURNAL OF MEDICAL PRIMATOLOGY 8:273–281, 1979.

Hodgen, G.D.; Wilks, J.W.; Vaitukaitis, J.L.; Chen, H.-C.; Papkoff, H.; Ross, G.T. A new radioimmunoassay for follicle stimulating hormone in macaques: Ovulatory menstrual cycles. ENDOCRINOLOGY 99:137, 1976.

Hodges, J.K.; Czekala, N.M.; Lasley, B.L. Estrogen and luteinizing hormone secretion in diverse species from simplified urinary analysis. JOURNAL OF MEDICAL PRIMATOLOGY 8:349–364, 1979.

Hopper, B.; Tullner, W.W. Urinary estrone and plasma progesterone levels during the menstrual cycle of the rhesus monkey. ENDOCRINOLOGY 86:1225–1230, 1970.

Hotchkiss, J.; Atkinson, L.E.; Knobil, E. Time course of serum estrogen and luteinizing hormone (LH) concentrations during the menstrual cycle of the rhesus monkey. ENDOCRINOLOGY 89:177–182, 1971.

Howard-Tripp, M.E.; Bielert, C. Social contact influences on the menstrual cycle of the female chacma baboon (Papio ursinus). JOURNAL OF SOUTH AFRICAN VETERINARY ASSOCIATION. 49:191–192, 1978.

Hutchinson, T.C. Vaginal cytology and reproduction in the squirrel monkey (Saimiri sciureus). FOLIA PRIMATOLOGICA 12:212–223, 1970.

Ioannou, J.M. The oestrous cycle of the potto. JOURNAL OF REPRODUCTION AND FERTILITY 11:455–457, 1966.

Israel, R.; Mishell, D.R. Jr.; Stone, S.C.; Thorneycroft, I.H.; Moyer, D.L. Single luteal phase serum progesterone assay as an indicator of ovulation. AMERICAN JOURNAL OF OBSTETRICS AND GYNECOLOGY 112:1043, 1972.

Jarosz, S.J.; Kuehl, T.J.; Dukelow, W.R. Vaginal cytology, induced ovulation and gestation in the squirrel monkey (Saimiri sciureus). BIOLOGY OF REPRODUCTION 16:97–103, 1977.

Jay, P. PRIMATE BEHAVIOR: FIELD STUDIES OF MONKEY AND APES. New York, Holt, Rinehart and Winston, 1965.

Jeffery, J. d'A. A polar progesterone metabolite in the pigtail monkey. JOURNAL OF ENDOCRINOLOGY 36:93–94, 1966.

Jewett, D.A.; Dukelow, W.R. Cyclicity and gestation length of Macaca fascicularis. PRIMATES 13:327–330, 1972.

Johansson, E.D.B.; Neill, J.D.; Knobil, E. Periovulaplasma during the luteal phase of the normal human menstrual cycle measured by a rapid competitive protein binding technique. ACTA ENDOCRINOLOGICA (KBH) 61:592. 1969.

Johansson, E.D.B.; Neill, J.D.; Knobil, E. Periovulatory progesterone concentration in the perirpheral plasma of the rhesus monkey, with a methodologic note on the detection of ovulation. ENDOCRINOLOGY 82:143–148, 1968.

Johansson, E.D.B.; Wide, L.; Gemzell, C. Luteinizing hormone (LH) and progesterone in plasma and LH and oestrogens in urine during 42 normal menstrual cycles. ACTA ENDOCRINOLOGICA (KBH) 68:502, 1971.

Johnson, D.F.; Phoenix, C.H. Sexual behavior and hormone levels during the menstrual cycle of rhesus monkeys. HORMONES AND BEHAVIOR 11:160–174, 1978.

Johnson, P.T.; Valerio, D.A.; Thompson, G.E. Breeding the African green monkey, Cercopithecus aethiops, in a laboratory environment. LABORATORY ANIMAL SCIENCE 23:355–359, 1973.

Judd, H.L.; Yen, S.S.C. Serum androstenedione and testosterone levels during the menstrual cycle. JOURNAL OF CLINICAL ENDOCRINOLOGY 36:475, 1973.

Katz, Y.; Epple, G. The coming of age in female Saguinus (marmoset monkeys). ENDOCRINOLOGY 104: Suppl 259, Abstract 745, 1979.

Katz, Y.; Epple, G. The ontogeny of plasma steroids in marmoset monkeys (Saguinus fuscicollis). BIOLOGY OF REPRODUCTION 24: Suppl 132A, Abstract 219, 1981.

Kholkute, S.D.; Joseph, R.; Joshi, U.M.; Maushi, S.R. Some characteristics of the normal menstrual cycle of the bonnet monkey (M. radiata). PRIMATES 22:399–403, 1981.

Kirton, K.T.; Niswender, G.G.; Midgley, A.R. Jr.; Jaffe, R.B.; Forbes, A.D. Serum luteinizing hormone and progesterone concentration during the menstrual cycle of the rhesus monkey. JOURNAL OF CLINICAL ENDOCRINOLOGY AND METABOLISM 30:105, 1970.

Kling, O.R.; Westfahl, P.K. Steroid changes during the menstrual cycle of the baboon (Papio cycnocephalus) and human. BIOLOGY OF REPRODUCTION 18:392–400, 1978.

Knobil, E. On the control of gonadotropin secretion in the rhesus monkey. RECENT PROGESTERONE HORMONE RESEARCH 30:1–46, 1974.

Knobil, E. The neuroendocrine control of the menstrual cycle. RECENT PROGESTERONE HORMONE RESEARCH 36:53–88, 1980.

Koyuma, T.; de la Pena, A.; Hagino, N. Plasma estrogen, progestin, and luteinizing hormone during the normal menstrual cycle in baboons: role of luteiniz-

ing hormone. AMERICAN JOURNAL OF OB-
STETRICS AND GYNECOLOGY 127:67–72,
1977.

Lasley, B.; Hendrickx, A.G.; Stabenfeldt, G.H. Estradiol levels near the time of ovulation in the bonnet
monkey (Macaca radiata). BIOLOGY OF REPRO-
DUCTION. 11:237–244, 1974.

Lasley, B.L.; Czekala, N.M.; Presley, S. A practical
approach to evaluation of fertility in the female gorilla. AMERICAN JOURNAL OF PRIMATOL-
OGY, SUPPLEMENT 1:45–50, 1982.

Lehman, F.; Just-Nastansky, I.; Czygan, P.J.; Betten-
dorf, G. Effects of 17α-ethinyl-19-nortestosterone
(ENT) on corpus luteum function. EUROPEAN
JOURNAL OF OBSTETRICS, GYNECOLOGY
AND REPRODUCTIVE BIOLOGY 6:219, 1976.

Loy, J.; Head, M.; Loy, K. Reproductive cycles of
captive patas monkeys. LABORATORY PRIMATE
NEWSLETTER 17(1):9–12, 1978.

Lundy, L.E.; Lee, S.G.; Levy, W.; Woodruf, J.D.;
Wu, C.-H.; Abdalla, M. The ovulatory cycle—a
histologic, thermal, steroid and gonadotrophin correlation. OBSTETRICS AND GYNECOLOGY
44:14, 1974.

Lunn, S.F. THE BIOLOGY OF THE CALLITRICHI-
DAE. J.P. Hearn; H. Rothe; H.J. Wolters, eds.
University of Gottingen, 1978.

MacDonald, G.J.; Demurs, L.M.; Greep, R.O. Peripheral serum progesterone and correlated endometrial
glycogen levels during the menstrual cycle of Macaca arctoides. FERTILITY AND STERILITY
24:98–103, 1973.

McArthur, J.W.; Beitins, I.Z.; Gorman, A.; Collins,
D.C.; Preedy, J.R.K.; Graham, C.E. The interrelationships between sex skin swelling and the urinary
excretion of gonadotropins, estrone and pregnanediol by the cycling female chimpanzee. AMERI-
CAN JOURNAL OF PRIMATOLOGY 1:265–270,
1981.

McArthur, J.W.; Ovadia, J.; Smith, O.W.; Bashiz-Far-
ahmand, J.G. The menstrual cycle of the bonnet
monkey (Macaca radiata). FOLIA PRIMATOLO-
GICA 17:107–121, 1972.

McKenna, T.J.; Brown, R.D. Pregnenolone in man:
Plasma levels in states of normal and abnormal ste-
roidogenesis. JOURNAL OF CLINICAL ENDO-
CRINOLOGY 38:480, 1974.

McNeilly, A.S.; Abbott, D.H.; Lunn, S.F.; Chambers,
P.C.; Hearn, J.P. Plasma prolactin concentrations
during the ovarian cycle and lactation and their relationship to return of fertility postpartum in the
common marmoset (Callithrix jacchus). JOURNAL
OF REPRODUCTION AND FERTILITY 62:353–
360, 1981.

Mendoza, S.P.; Lowe, E.L.; Resko, J.A.; Levine, S.
Seasonal variations in gonadal hormones and social
behavior in squirrel monkeys. PHYSIOLOGY AND
BEHAVIOR 20:515–522, 1978.

Mishell, D.R. Jr.; Nakamura, R.M.; Crosignani, P.G.;
Stone, S.; Kharma, K.; Nagata, Y.; Thorneycroft,
I.H. Serum gonadotrophin and steroid patterns dur-
ing the normal menstrual cycle. AMERICAN
JOURNAL OF OBSTETRICS AND GYNECOL-
OGY 111:60, 1971.

Monroe, S.E.; Atkinson, L.E.; Knobil, E. Patterns of
circulating luteinizing hormone and their relation to
plasma progesterone levels during the menstrual
cycle of the rhesus monkey. ENDOCRINOLOGY
87:453, 1970.

Nadler, R.D. Reproductive physiology and behavior of
gorillas (hormonal regulation). JOURNAL OF RE-
PRODUCTIVE FERTILITY, SUPPLEMENT
28:79–89, 1980.

Nadler, R.D. THE ORANGUTAN. ITS BIOLOGY
AND CONSERVATION. L.E.M. de Boer, ed. Boston, 1982.

Nadler, R.D.; Graham, C.E.; Collins, D.C.; Gould,
K.G. Plasma gonadotropins, prolactin, gonadal steroids and genital swellings during the menstrual
cycle of lowland gorillas. ENDOCRINOLOGY
105(1):290–296, 1979.

Nagle, C.A.; Denari, J.H.; Quiroga, S.; Riarte, A.;
Merlo, A.; Gernino, N.I.; Gomez-Argara, F.; Rosner, J.M. The plasma pattern of ovarian steroids
during the menstrual cycle in capuchin monkeys
(Cebus apella). BIOLOGY OF REPRODUCTION
21:979–983, 1979.

Nawar, M.M.; Hafez, E.S.E. The reproductive cycle
of the crab-eating macaque (Macaca fascicularis).
PRIMATES 13:43–56, 1972.

Neill, J.D.; Johansson, E.D.B.; Knobil, E. Levels of
progesterone in peripheral plasma during the menstrual cycle of the rhesus monkey. ENDOCRINOL-
OGY 81:1161, 1967.

Neill, J.D.; Johansson, E.D.B.; Knobil, E. Patterns of
circulating progesterone concentrations during the
fertile menstrual cycle and the remainder of gestation in the rhesus monkey. ENDOCRINOLOGY
84:45–48, 1969.

Nigi, H. Menstrual cycle and some other related aspects
of Japanese monkeys (Macaca fuscata). PRIMATES
16:207–216, 1975.

Niswender, G.D.; Spies, H.G. Serum levels of luteinizing hormone, follicle-stimulating hormone and
progesterone throughout the menstrual cycle of rhesus monkeys. JOURNAL OF CLINICAL ENDO-
CRINOLOGY AND METABOLISM 37:326–328,
1973.

Oshima, K.; Hayashi, M.; Matsubayashi, K. Progesterone levels in the Japanese monkey (Macaca fuscata
fuscata). during the breeding and nonbreeding season and pregnancy. JOURNAL OF MEDICAL PRI-
MATOLOGY 6:99–107, 1977.

Ovadia, J.; McArthur, J.W.; Kopito, L.; Ulfelder, H.

The cervical mucus secretion of the bonnet monkey (*M. radiata*): Anatomical basis and physiological regulation. BIOLOGY OF REPRODUCTION 5:127–145, 1971.

Parkin, R.F.; Hendrickx, A.G. The temporal relationship between the preovulatory estrogen peak and the optimal mating period in rhesus and bonnet monkeys. BIOLOGY OF REPRODUCTION 13:610–616, 1975.

Pauerstein, C.J.; Eddy, C.A.; Croxatto, H.D.; Hess, R.; Siler-Khodr, T.M.; Croxatto, H.B. Temporal relationships of estrogen, progesterone and luteinizing hormone levels to ovulation in women and infrahuman primates. AMERICAN JOURNAL OF OBSTETRICS AND GYNECOLOGY 130:876–886, 1978.

Peng, M.-T.; Lai, Y.-L.; Yang, C.-S.; Chiang, H.S.; New, A.E.; Chiang, C.-P. Reproductive parameters of the Taiwan monkey (*Macaca cyclopis*). PRIMATES 14:201–213, 1973.

Plapinger, L.; McEwen, B.S.; Landau, I.T.; Feder, H.H. Characteristics of estradiol binding macromolecules in fetal and adult guinea pig brain cytosols. BIOLOGY OF REPRODUCTION 16:586–599, 1977.

Preslock, J.P.; Hampton, S.H.; Hampton, J.K. Jr. Cyclic variations of serum progestins and immunoreactive estrogens in marmosets. ENDOCRINOLOGY 92:1096–1101, 1973.

Ramaswami, L.S. Some aspects of the reproductive biology of the langur monkey *Presbytis entellus entellus* Dufresne. PROCEDINGS OF THE INDIAN NATIONAL SCIENCE ACADEMY 41 (Part B): 1–30, 1975.

Resko, J.A.; Koering, M.J.; Goy, R.W.; Phoenix, C.H. Preovulatory progestins: Observations on their source in the rhesus monkey. JOURNAL OF CLINICAL ENDOCRINOLOGY AND METABOLISM 41:120–125, 1975.

Resko, J.A.; Norman, R.L.; Niswender, G.D.; Spies, H.G. The relationship between progestins and gonadotropins during the late luteal phase of the menstrual cycle in rhesus monkeys. ENDOCRINOLOGY 94:128–135, 1974.

Reyes, F.I.; Winter, J.S.D.; Faiman, C.; Hobson, W.C. Serial serum levels of gonadotropins, prolactin, and sex steroids in the nonpregnant and pregnant chimpanzee. ENDOCRINOLOGY 96:1447–1455, 1975.

Rosenblum, L.A.; Nathan, T.; Nelson, J.; Kaufman, I.C. Vaginal cornification cycles in the squirrel monkey (*Saimiri sciureus*). FOLIA PRIMATOLOGICA 6:83–91, 1967.

Ross, G.T.; Cargille, C.M.; Lipsett, M.B.; Rayford, P.L.; Marshall, J.R.; Strott, C.A.; Rodbard, D. Pituitary and gonadal hormones in women during spontaneous and induced ovulatory cycles. RECENT PROGRESS IN HORMONE RESEARCH 26:1, 1970.

Rowell, T.E. Reproductive cycles of two *Cercopithecus* monkeys. JOURNAL OF REPRODUCTION AND FERTILITY 22:321–338, 1970.

Rowell, T.E.; Chalmers, N.R. Reproductive cycles of the mangabey (*Cercocebus albigena*). FOLIA PRIMATOLOGICA 12:264–272, 1970.

Rowell, T.E.; Hartwell, K.M. The interaction of behavior and reproductive cycles in patas monkeys. BEHAVIORAL BIOLOGY 24:141–167, 1978.

Saldarini, R.J.; Spieler, J.M.; Coppola, J.A. Plasma estrogens, progestins and Spinnbarkeit characteristics during selected portions of the menstrual cycle of the cynomolgus monkey (*Macaca fascicularis*). BIOLOGY OF REPRODUCTION 7:347–355, 1972.

Setchell, K.D.R.; Bull, R.; Adlercreutz, H. Steroid excretion during the reproductive cycle and in pregnancy of the vervet monkey (*Cercopitheous aethiops pygerythrus*). JOURNAL OF STEROID BIOCHEMISTRY 12:375–384, 1980.

Setchell, K.D.R.; Chua, K.-S.; Heinsworth, R.L. Urinary steroid excretion by the squirrel monkey (*Saimiri sciureus*). JOURNAL OF ENDOCRINOLOGY 73:365–375, 1977.

Shaikh, A.A.; Celaya, C.L.; Gomez, I.; Shaikh, S.A. Temporal relationship of hormonal peaks to ovulation and sex skin deturgescence in the baboon. PRIMATES 23:444–452, 1982.

Shaikh, A.A.; Naqui, R.H.; Shaikh, S.A. Concentrations of estradiol-17β and progesterone in the peripheral plasma of the cynomolgus monkey (*Macaca fascicularis*) in relation to the length of the menstrual cycle and its component phases. JOURNAL OF ENDOCRINOLOGY 79:1–7, 1978.

Shandilya, L.N.; Ramaswami, L.S.; Shandilya, N. Oestrogen metabolites in urine during the menstrual cycle, pregnancy and puerperium in the Indian hanuman langur (*Presbytis entellus entellus*). JOURNAL OF REPRODUCTION AND FERTILITY 47:7–11, 1976.

Slob, A.K.; Wiegand, S.J.; Goy, R.W.; Robinson, J.A. Heterosexual interactions in laboratory-housed stumptail macaques (*Macaca arctoides*): Observations during the menstrual cycle and after ovariectomy. HORMONES AND BEHAVIOR 10:193–211, 1978.

Sly, D.L.; Harbaugh, S.W.; London, W.T.; Rice, J.M. Reproductive performance of a laboratory breeding colony of patas monkeys (*Erythrocebus patas*). AMERICAN JOURNAL OF PRIMATOLOGY 4:23–32, 1983.

Spies, H.G.; Niswender, G.D. Blockage of the surge of preovulatory serum luteinizing hormone and ovulation with exogenous progesterone in cycling rhesus (*Macaca mulatta*) monkeys. JOURNAL OF CLINICAL ENDOCRINOLOGY AND METABOLISM 32:309–316, 1971.

Spies, H.G.; Niswender, G.D. Effect of progesterone and estradiol on LH release and ovulation in rhesus monkeys. ENDOCRINOLOGY 90:257–261, 1972.

Spies, H.G.; Mahoney, C.J.; Norman, R.L.; Clifton, D.K.; Resko, J.A. Evidence for a diurnal rhythm in ovarian steroids. JOURNAL OF CLINICAL ENDOCRINOLOGY AND METABOLISM 39:347–351, 1974.

Stabenfeldt, G.H.; Hendrickx, A.G. Progesterone levels in the bonnet monkey (*Macaca radiata*) during the menstrual cycle and pregnancy. ENDOCRINOLOGY 91:614–619, 1972.

Stabenfeldt, G.H.; Hendrickx, A.G. Progesterone levels in the sooty mangabey (*Cercocebus atys*) during the menstrual cycle, pregnancy and parturition. JOURNAL OF MEDICAL PRIMATOLOGY. 2:1–10, 1973a.

Stabenfeldt, G.H.; Hendrickx, A.G. Progesterone studies in the *Macaca fascicularis*. ENDOCRINOLOGY 92:1296–1300, 1973b.

Steiner, R.A.; Schiller, H.S.; Illner, P.; Blandau, R.; Gale, C.C. Sex hormones correlated with sex skin swelling and rectal temperature during the menstrual cycle of the pigtail macaque (*Macaca nemestrina*). LABORATORY ANIMAL SCIENCE 27:217–221, 1977.

Stevens, V.C.; Sparks, S.J.; Powell, J.E. Levels of estrogens, progestogens and luteinizing hormone during the menstrual cycle of the baboon. ENDOCRINOLOGY 87:658–666, 1970.

Thorneycroft, I.H.; Mishell, D.R. Jr.; Stone, S.C.; Kharma, K.M.; Nakamura, R.M. The relation of serum 17-hydroxyprogesterone and estradiol-17β levels during the human menstrual cycle. AMERICAN JOURNAL OF OBSTETRICS AND GYNECOLOGY 111:947, 1971.

Tyler, J.P.P.; Newton, J.R.; Collins, W.P. Variations in the concentration of testosterone in peripheral venous plasma from healthy women, ACTA ENDOCRINOLOGICA (KBH) 80:542, 1975.

Valerio, D.A.; Johnson, P.T.; Thompson, G.E. Breeding the greater bushbaby, *Galago crassicaudatus*, in a laboratory environment. LABORATORY ANIMAL SCIENCE 22:203–206, 1972.

Van Horn, R.N.; Resko, J.A. The reproductive cycle of the ring-tailed lemur (*Lemur catta*): Sex steroid levels and sexual receptivity under controlled photoperiods. ENDOCRINOLOGY 101:1579–1586, 1977.

Wehrenberg, W.B.; Dyrenfurth, I; Ferin, M. Endocrine characteristics of the menstrual cycle in the Assamese monkey (*Macaca assamensis*). BIOLOGY OF REPRODUCTION 23:522–525, 1980.

Weick, P.F.; Dierschke, D.J.; Karsch, F.J.; Butler, W.R.; Hotchkiss, J.; Knobil, E. Periovulatory time courses of circulating gonadotropic and ovarian hormones in the rhesus monkey. ENDOCRINOLOGY 93:1140–1147, 1973.

White, R.J.; Blaine, C.R.; Blakley, G.A. Detecting ovulation in *Macaca nemestrina* by correlation of vaginal cytology, body temperature and perineal tumescence with laparoscopy. AMERICAN JOURNAL OF PHYSICAL ANTHROPOLOGY 38:189–194, 1973.

Wildt, D.E.; Doyle, L.L.; Stone, S.; Harrison, R. Correlation of perineal swelling with serum ovarian hormone levels, vaginal cytology and ovarian follicular development during the baboon reproductive cycle. PRIMATES 18:261–270, 1977.

Wilks, J.W. Endocrine characterization of the menstrual cycle of the stumptail monkey (*Macaca arctoides*). BIOLOGY OF REPRODUCTION 16:474–478, 1977.

Wilks, J.W.; Hodgen, G.D.; Ross, G.T. Luteal phase defects in the rhesus monkey: The significance of serum FSH:LH ratios. JOURNAL OF CLINICAL ENDOCRINOLOGY AND METABOLISM 43:1261–1267, 1976.

Wilks, J.W.; Marciniak, R.D.; Hildebrand, D.L.; Hodgen, G.D. Periovulatory endocrine events in the stumptail monkey (*Macaca arctoides*). ENDOCRINOLOGY 107:237–244, 1980.

Wilson, M.I. Characterization of the oestrous cycle and mating season of squirrel monkeys from copulatory behaviour. JOURNAL OF REPRODUCTION AND FERTILITY 51:57–63, 1977.

Wolf, R.C.; O'Connor, R.E.; Robinson, J.A. Cyclic changes in plasma progestins and estrogens in squirrel monkeys. BIOLOGY OF REPRODUCTION 17:228–231, 1977.

Wright, E.M. Jr.; Bush, D.E. The reproductive cycle of the capuchin (*Cebus apella*). LABORATORY ANIMAL SCIENCE 27:651–654, 1977.

Wu, C.-H.; Prazak, L.; Flickinger, G.L.; Mikhail, G. Plasma 20α-hydroxypregn-4-en-3-one in the normal menstrual cycle. JOURNAL OF CLINICAL ENDOCRINOLOGY 39:536, 1974.

Yates, F.E. Comparative physiology: compared to what? AMERICAN JOURNAL OF PHYSIOLOGY: REGULATORY, INTEGRATIVE AND COMPARATIVE PHYSIOLOGY 237(6):R1–2, 1979.

YoungLai, E.V.; Graham, C.E.; Collins, D.C. Metabolism of 4^{14}C-progesterone in the adult female chimpanzee. STEROIDS 25:465–476, 1975.

Endocrinology of Reproductive Senescence

Charles E. Graham

Primate Research Institute, New Mexico State University, Holloman AFB, New Mexico 88330

INTRODUCTION

Aging of the Reproductive System: Content and Scope

Aging may be considered from a variety of points of view and on different levels. To some, aging begins at birth, or even at conception. Indeed there is considerable literature dealing with aging of the gametes and consequences for fertility and teratology. The problem of gamete aging may be viewed as a specialized problem at the cellular level, and since comparative data at the nonhuman primate level are lacking the reader is referred to the review by Kram and Schneider [1978] on this subject.

In this chapter aging is approached from the standpoint of the progressive deterioration of the reproductive system after maturity.

It is difficult to separate the endocrinology of aging of the reproductive system from aging of the endocrine system in general, especially since the hypothalamic-pituitary axis controls a number of different endocrine subsystems, of which the reproductive system is one. There are interactions at many levels between these subsystems that make any attempt to describe reproductive endocrine senescence in isolation somewhat hazardous. A related aspect to bear in mind is that some environmental factors and aging processes are body-wide effects (eg, mutations, stress, cardiovascular changes), and this can affect the central neuroendocrine regulation of a variety of endocrine systems as well as affect the subsystems and their target organs and cells at every level. An important review of these integrative aspects of aging has been published by Everitt and Burgess [1976]; however, most of the data are either human or nonprimate, making a comparative primate review difficult. Nevertheless this review and the work by Schneider [1978] would be important sources for

primatologists who seek inspiration to extend the limited knowledge of comparative biology of primate endocrine senescence that is reviewed here.

Only in the last decade has there been any significant effort to investigate the endocrine correlates of reproductive aging in nonhuman primates, stimulated in part by the establishment of the National Institute on Aging. The majority of work has been oriented toward the female reproductive axis as a result of early impressions that menopause is a uniquely human phenomenon. Interest in the evolution of menopause and lack of understanding of its development led to repeated attempts to demonstrate menopause or its antecedents in nonhuman primates. Thus, the emphasis of this chapter of necessity is the endocrinology of reproductive senescence in the female.

Life-Span Data on Primates

Since there has been little interest in aging in nonhuman primates until recent years, there has been little effort to preserve aged specimens or to document age of older animals. Thus, although obviously aged specimens can be located, their actual age is usually in doubt. This situation stems in part from the practice in earlier years of importing wild-caught primates: unless the animals were received as juvenile specimens and their stage of development recorded, not even an approximately reliable estimate of age can usually be derived. Little use has been made of modern methods of age estimation [Harding and Dilley, 1976; Helfman and Bada, 1976]. As breeding colonies were slowly established, so more animals of known birth date were acquired, but useful numbers of such animals have survived to old age in only two instances — the rhesus (*Macaca mulatta*) colony of Gertrude van Wagenen, and the chimpanzee (*Pan troglodytes*) colony founded by Robert Yerkes.

Comparative Primate Biology, Volume 3: Reproduction and Development, pages 93–99

Another problem is life-span in captivity in relation to that in the wild. Do captive animals have a shorter life because of unnatural conditions and the stresses of research? Or do they live longer because they are assured regular, balanced nutrition, veterinary care in sickness, and protection from predators?

As time passes, longer life-spans in captivity for many species are being documented. Increased captive life-span of nonhuman primates increases the potential of discovering useful models of human endocrine senescence, but the new life-span data are of uncertain significance for understanding the natural history of wild populations.

The maximum longevity records for a variety of primate species are given by Bowden and Jones [1979]. They show that chimpanzees and orangutans (*Pongo pygmaeus*) may survive into the fifth decade, gorillas (*Gorilla gorilla*) in excess of 50 years, macaques (*Macaca* sp.) and baboons (*Papio* sp.) in excess of 35 years, and other Old World species 20–30 years. Among New World species, capuchins (*Cebus* sp.) have survived to 40–45 years, spider monkeys to 30–35 years, and other species 10–20 years. Longer life-spans are anticipated in the less commonly studied species as experience accumulates.

Survey of Species Studied

The only significant studies of endocrine senescence in nonhuman primates have been performed in chimpanzees, rhesus monkeys, and pig-tailed and crab-eating macaques (*M. nemestrina* and *M. fascicularis*). There have, in addition, been some incidental reports of waning reproductive capacity in older animals of various species.

Because of the paucity of comparative data, the main thrust of this chapter will be to compare the scanty nonhuman primate data with the more complete information derived from man. This will enable the reader to determine to what extent nonhuman primates resemble man in the endocrinology of aging and may so serve as research models. It will become evident that much additional research is required before the spectrum of aging patterns characteristic of primates can be defined.

FEMALE REPRODUCTIVE SENESCENCE
Menopause: Definitions and Characteristics

Menopause is the final cessation of menses characteristic of the human being in the fifth decade of life. Strictly speaking, it can only be recognized in

retrospect as it is discovered that no further menstrual cycles occur and as other correlates of the postmenopausal state appear.

Reproductive senescence in the human female may be divided into two distinct phases, pre- and postmenopausal. The premenopausal events are a moderately well characterized association of endocrine and endocrine-dependent changes that are associated with gradual ovarian failure.

The postmenopausal state is characterized not only by loss of menstrual cyclicity, but by a characteristic hypogonadal and hypergonadotropic syndrome associated with involutional changes relating to estrogen lack, affecting not only the reproductive organs, but also other systems, notably the skeletal system.

Among nonhuman primates, the only species in which menopause has been systematically demonstrated is the rhesus monkey, with isolated cases in pig-tailed monkeys and chimpanzees.

Until recently menopause was thought to be a uniquely human phenomenon, perhaps only revealed as the evolution of human cultures reached a stage that prolonged life-span became possible. It is unknown if menopause in laboratory animals is an artifact of an unnaturally extended life-span: resolution of this issue must await suitable field studies and additional information on the incidence of menopause in aging primates in the laboratory, correlated with an assessment of the general extent of aging in the menopausal primate compared with menopausal women.

Going strictly by definition of menopause, menopause cannot occur in nonmenstruating species of primates, such as the New World species seem to be. Consideration of this fact forces one to the recognition that menopause is a highly dramatic correlate of a more fundamental event, namely cessation of cyclicity. It will be interesting to see whether the nonmenstruating species of primate do show loss of cyclicity in old age.

Premenopausal Changes in Cyclicity

In women, approaching menopause is usually heralded by a decreasing frequency and regularity of menstrual bleeding. A similar pattern was noted in rhesus monkeys during the third decade of life [van Wagenen, 1972; Hodgen et al, 1977]. In one group of eight aged animals described by Hodgen et al [1977], intervals between successive menses ranged from 11 to 157 days.

Cyclicity in seven chimpanzees aged 35–48 years was compared with cyclicity in the same animals when aged 15–25 years [Graham, 1979]. In four individuals there was no significant change in cycle length whereas three individuals aged 40–47 at the time of analysis showed a significant increase in cycle length over the normal duration of 33 days [Graham, 1981]. This increased variability did not compare with the extreme variability noted by Hodgen et al [1977] in the rhesus monkeys.

Although reduction of fertility precedes menopause in women, a systematic study of fertility loss in aging nonhuman primates has not been published, except in chimpanzees. Conception rate (conception frequency per mated cycles) in chimpanzees aged 35–48 years was 3.85%. Conception rate in the same animals when aged 15–25 was 20%. Only three pregnancies were observed among chimpanzees aged 35–38: one of these animals and her infant died at birth as a result of dystocia associated with a cervical leiomyoma; a second at age 38 produced a normal term infant; the third produced a premature stillbirth at estimated age 40 [Graham, 1979].

Cessation of menstrual cyclicity has been documented in a pygmy chimpanzee (*Pan paniscus*) that showed evidence of old age and whose ovaries showed a menopausal histological pattern [Gould et al, 1981].

A loss of fertility in Japanese macaques (*Macaca fuscata*) aged over 22 years has recently been noted [Wolfe and Noyes, 1981]. A series of aged rhesus monkeys that had ceased cycling were demonstrated to be in a perimenopausal or menopausal condition [Hodgen et al, 1977].

Endocrine Relationships in Aging Primates

In women, impending menopause is characterized by gradually increasing follicle-stimulating hormone (FSH) levels [Sherman et al, 1976]. Ovarian steroid levels tend to fall, however, owing to gradual ovarian failure: the resulting loss of negative feedback inhibition by estrogens results in gonadotropin elevation. Although low levels of estrogen are characteristic of the postmenopausal state, some women continue to secrete sufficient estrone to temporarily prevent complete involution of the estrogen-dependent secondary sex organs. Although absolute estrogen levels fall, the pre- and postmenopausal state is characterized by a relative increase in circulating estrone; this is because ovarian secretion of estradiol ceases, whereas estrone synthesis continues as a result of peripheral anomatization of circulating androstenediol secreted by the adrenal gland or conversion of ovarian steroids [Grodin et al, 1971].

Exaggerated luteinizing hormone (LH) and FSH surges were noted by Hodgen et al [1977] in the last menstrual cycle of an apparently menopausal rhesus monkey, and there was an increase in FSH concentration toward the end of the luteal phase to about four times higher than the earlier baseline level, whereas LH remained in the normal range and estradiol and progesterone were basal.

In several aged rhesus monkeys that had ceased cycling, similar relationships prevailed: estradiol and progesterone levels were basal, and LH and FSH were elevated to 3–5 times above basal levels in normal monkeys, resembling the human pattern [Hodgen et al, 1977; Sherman et al, 1976].

An exhaustive analysis of circulating steroid hormones and LH in approximately 10- and 20-year-old *M. nemestrina* exhibited no significant age-related changes. The one evidently postmenopausal subject (probably well over 20 years old) showed elevated, fluctuating LH levels, normal estrone levels, and considerably depressed estradiol-17β levels.

Follow-up of the two oldest living chimpanzees in a group previously reported by Graham [1979] revealed more interesting endocrine data [Gould et al, 1981]. These animals were approximately 48 and 50 years old in 1980. Most strikingly, these aged subjects revealed polyphasic urinary LH peaks in three of four cycles studied. The urinary FSH levels of one subject were considerably elevated in one of two cycles depicted, consistent with observation in perimenopausal women [Sherman et al, 1976].

A postmenopausal *Pan paniscus* showed depressed circulating estradiol levels and elevated gonadotropin levels [Gould et al, 1981].

Gonadotropin-releasing hormone (GnRH) challenge experiments with the two *Pan troglodytes* did not reveal a response different from younger animals, but the *Pan paniscus* showed greatly exaggerated responses, particularly by FSH.

MORPHOLOGICAL CORRELATES OF FEMALE SENESCENCE
Adenohypophysis

Morphology of the aging adenohypophysis has been studied only in *M. nemestrina* and *M. fascicularis* among nonhuman primates [Aschenbrenner, 1979]. In these species an increase in degenerative changes in the ultrastructure of the gonadotropes was noted. Typical characteristics were hypertrophy, loss of cellular contour, nuclear pleomorphism, cytoplasmic vacuolization, and enlarged, dilated endoplasmic reticulum. These changes were most marked in two animals that had consistently elevated LH levels. Two such animals also exhibited degranulated gonadotropes. Such changes are characteristic also of castrated animals, which resemble the menopausal state in the loss of feedback inhibition of gonadotropin secretion; comparable changes have been reported in senescent humans.

Multivesiculated structures containing crystalline inclusions were frequently observed in the gonadotropes of aged *M. fascicularis* and have also been noted in spayed young rhesus monkeys primed with estrogen [Aschenbrenner, 1979].

Ovary

Aging of the ovary is a complex process because the ovary functions both as a repository of gametes and as an endocrine organ. A comparative review of this subject has been provided by Talbert [1978].

Aging of the primate ovary is associated with follicular depletion. Degeneration of human oocytes (atresia) begins even before birth and continues throughout life, accounting for far more of the loss of the original stock of 250,000 oocytes than does normal ovulation. By the time menopause occurs, few if any oocytes are left; it is therefore tempting to speculate that menopause is actually a result of the loss of the last oocytes. However, some apparently normal oocytes can be found in human postmenopausal ovaries [Costoff and Mahesh, 1975]. It is possible that although morphologically normal, postmenopausal oocytes are functionally deficient: this is suggested by their quiescence in the face of greatly elevated gonadotropin levels. An alternative explanation would be that some other unknown requirement for follicle maturation becomes deficient in older females.

Follicular depletion is associated with aging in the nonhuman primates that have been studied. One *M. nemestrina* that was apparently postmenopausal and four animals at least 20 years old showed varying degrees of follicular depletion [Graham et al, 1979]. Moderate to extreme follicular depletion was also noted in a group of *Pan troglodytes* aged 35–48 years, although menopause had not commenced in any of the subjects [Graham, 1979].

Extreme follicular depletion was noted in one pygmy chimpanzee (*P. paniscus*) that showed all the physical appearance of old age, had become acyclic during the last year of life, and had low circulating levels of estradiol and elevated gonadotropic levels: this animal was concluded to be menopausal [Gould et al, 1981].

Other characteristics of human ovarian aging also occur in nonhuman primates [Bigelow, 1958; Kuppe et al, 1976; Lang and Aponte, 1967]. Among the *M. nemestrina* the predominant features were weight reduction, cortical fibrosis, thickening of blood vessel walls, and coiling vessels; extensive ceroid deposition also occurred. Some of these changes were already developing in a group of 10-year-old monkeys. Ovarian changes reported in human females that did not occur in *M. nemestrina* included folding of the ovarian surface, extracellular pigmentation, and calcification of the medical coat of arteries [Graham et al, 1979].

The histopathology of the ovaries of two rhesus monkeys aged over 23 years was described by van Wagenen and Simpson [1965]. These ovaries showed follicular depletion, absence of corpora lutea, and cortical fibrosis.

Aging changes in *Pan troglodytes* ovaries resembled those of the human more closely than did those of *M. nemestrina*. Characteristic germinal ingrowths, arteriolar sclerosis, pigment deposition, and extensive thecal hypertrophy were noted. Cortical changes were not marked, in contrast to *M. nemestrina* and man [Graham, 1979].

A postmenopausal *Pan paniscus* ovary exhibited a scanty, fibrotic cortex, and large and thick-walled medullary vessels [Gould et al, 1981].

Accessory Genital Organs

A variety of involutional changes have been described in the reproductive tract of aging women [Bigelow, 1958; Kuppe et al, 1976; Lang and Aponte, 1967]. Such changes have been observed to a lesser extent among nonhuman primates. A pig-tailed monkey with evidence of menopause showed an involuted uterine corpus and cervix, and other animals showed atrophy of endometrium and myometrium, extracellular pigment deposition in the endometrium, hyalinization and vascular changes in the endometrium, reduced epithelial activity in the cervix, and regressed vaginal epithelum with lecuocytic infiltration [Graham et al, 1979].

In aged chimpanzees, adenomyosis and obliterative sclerosis of the myometrium has been noted. The endometrium was atrophic in one of five animals studied [Graham et al, 1979].

Breast

Senescent changes in breast have been studied only in two nonhuman primate species, *M. nemestrina* and *M. fascicularis* [Warner, 1979]. Large numbers of mammary dysplasias were detected in both 10- and 20-year-old female monkeys at 15–20 times the incidence of 6-year-old controls. The frequency was not significantly different between the 10- and 20-year-old groups, however. A sex difference was detected in that male M. fascicularis and M. nemestrina lacked dysplasias at age 10 but demonstrated mammary dysplasias at age 20.

Although frequency of dysplasia did not differ between the 10- and 20-year-old females, the character of the dysplasias did. In the younger animals, the lesions were characterized by leukocytic infiltration and hyperplasia of periductal connective tissue. By contrast, in the 20-year-old group, proliferative and metaplastic changes predominated. No malignant tumors were found; however, it is tempting to speculate that the M. nemestrina breast has a high carcinogenic potential that might be expressed in older animals. In this connection it is very interesting that there was a strong correlation between the frequency of dysplasias and the level of circulating androgens and triiodothyronine [Warner, 1979].

It has been noted that responsivity of breast to prolactin secretion decreases with age, using as an end point the quantity of α-lactalbumin secreted in organ culture. Two of three 4-year-old M. nemestrina produced 600–1,350 ng/ml medium of α-lactalbumin, whereas 10-year-old animals produced 25–250 ng/ml and 20-year-old animals produced less than 76 ng/ml [Kleinberg et al, 1979]. These authors noted that even a subject presumed to be postmenopausal was capable of responding to prolactin by a small amount of α-lactalbumin production, a function previously thought to be dormant in aged females.

Neoplasms

A variety of neoplasms were observed in the reproductive tract of five aged chimpanzees. One animal had large bilateral ovarian fibrothecomas, and a second had two fibrothecomas in one ovary and a small, highly differentiated Sertoli-Leydig cell tumor in the contralateral ovary. The latter was associated with adenomatous endometrial hyperplasia and frequent atretic follicles with thecal hyperplasia [Graham and McClure, 1976; Graham, 1979].

One chimpanzee had a large leiomyoma in the uterine corpus [Graham, 1979; Siebold and Wolf, 1973]. Another subject had extensive adenomatous hyperplasia of the endometrium with polyp formation. Epidermization of the endocervical glands occurred in one subject. The uterine cervix and upper vagina of a 35-year-old pregnant chimpanzee contained a leiomyoma measuring 14 × 17 cm [Graham and Bradley, 1972; Graham, 1979]. Three of four animals examined had slight to moderate replacement of the fimbrial columnar epithelium by stratified squamous epithelium.

Evidence of an association of ovarian thecal cell hyperplasia, excessive estrogen production, and endometrial hyperplasia has been noted in postmenopausal women and old chimpanzees [Graham, 1979]. However, Graham [1979] also noted some of these changes in younger animals.

MALE REPRODUCTIVE SENESCENCE

It is an unfortunate fact that there has been no systematic effort to investigate reproductive senescence in male nonhuman primates. Perhaps this lack of interest relates to the insidious progression of reproductive aging in males, contrasted with the dramatic climacteric in human females.

There is little point in reiterating the existing information on reproductive senescence in human males. Instead the reader is referred to existing reviews [eg, Brandes and Garcia-Brunel, 1978; Harman, 1978].

Information on aging in male nonhuman primates is needed to satisfy two general goals. First, knowledge of decline in fertility with age in male primates would be helpful in management of captive breeding programs. Such information could indeed be crucial for management of species such as apes where import from the wild is difficult or impossible, the sexual ability of colony-born animals is questionable because of deficiencies in sociosexual development, and the captive stock of productive, wild-born males is rapidly decreasing. Second, important male human problems exist where primate aging models could be invaluable. The most important age-related reproductive conditions in human males are benign prostatic hypertrophy (BPH) and prostatic cancer. BPH rarely occurs before 50 years of age, but affects most human males who reach the eighth decade of life; its chief effect is urinary obstruction, which can lead to life-threatening complications.

Prostatic cancer shows a similar age dependence and distribution to BPH; although it often remains local to the gland, it accounts for 10% of all male cancer deaths.

There are a number of ways in which age-related hormonal changes might affect male accessory organs and specifically BPH and prostate cancer

[Brandes and Garcia-Brunel, 1978]: 1) decrease in circulating testosterone, due to decreased testicular secretion; 2) decrease in specific binding of androgens by aging target organs; 3) altered steroid metabolism in target organs; and 4) altered response of aged target organs response to androgens.

Studies of these possibilities have been very limited. A decrease in specific binding of testosterone by plasma protein was correlated with increasing age in chimpanzees [McCormack, 1971]. There is an obvious opportunity to develop primate models to investigate such problems, targeted at understanding the etiology and prevention of BPH and prostate cancer.

Studies in reproductive senescence of nonhuman male primates may also be of importance in relation to human sociosexual problems. In this context the work of Phoenix and his colleagues represents a beginning. They found that a fall in sexual performance among aging rhesus monkeys was unrelated to serum levels of bound or free testosterone [Phoenix and Chambers, 1982]. The well-characterized sexual interaction of macaque monkeys and the ability to objectively quantitate many aspects of sexual performance should make these animals suitable for examining the relationships between many behavioral, anatomical, and physiological correlates of aging.

CONCLUSIONS

The primary bar to progress in a comparative primate biology of reproductive senescence has been the unavailability of aged animals of documented birth date and history. Considering the longevity of primates and the relatively recent interest in geriatric medicine, this problem is not surprising. A strong impetus to meticulous record keeping and electronic data-management systems would greatly promote the availability of suitable animals in the future. Better use should also be made of advances in age estimating techniques for older, but undocumented animals.

I have noted that the virtual nonexistence of male data hampers breeding management and research into such problems as prostatic cancer. Although the situation for females is a little better, there are insufficient animals available to explore that fascinating phenomenon, menopause, and the many problems associated with female reproductive senescence. I hope that the limited available information documented here will encourage others to preserve suitable animals for study and to attempt to fill some of the gaps in our knowledge.

Evidence is slowly acccumulating that Old World primates can experience menopause. Only three species have been studied to any significant extent, and these studies are incomplete. Menopause has been convincingly demonstrated in several *M. mulatta* [Hodgen et al, 1977], one *M. nemestrina* [Graham et al, 1979], and one *Pan paniscus* [Gould et al, 1981]. Careful study of aging *P. troglodytes* has recruited evidence for a perimenopausal state in this species, although menopause has not been definitively demonstrated [Graham, 1979; Gould et al, 1981].

Generally the endocrine and morphological correlates of reproductive aging in these species resemble those of the human female. The morphological differences are greatest in *M. nemestrina* and least in *P. troglodytes*, as might be expected. Common endocrine patterns emerge from all of the species studied with evidence of failing ovarian estrogen production, loss of negative feedback inhibition of gonadotropin secretion, and high circulating gonadotropin levels.

REFERENCES

Aschenbrenner, J.E. Ultrastructure of the hypophysis. Pp. 171–182 in AGING IN NONHUMAN PRIMATES. D.M. Bowden, ed. New York, Van Nostrand Reinhold, 1979.

Bigelow, B. Comparison of ovarian and endometrial morphology spanning the menopause. AMERICAN JOURNAL OF OBSTETRICS AND GYNECOLOGY 11:487–513, 1958.

Bowden, D.M; Jones, M.L. Aging research in nonhuman primates. Pp. 1–13 in AGING IN NONHUMAN PRIMATES. D.M. Bowden, ed. New York, Van Nostrand Reinhold, 1979.

Brandes, D; Garcia-Brunel, R. Aging of the male sex accessory organs. Pp. 127–157 in AGING, Vol. 4: THE AGING REPRODUCTIVE SYSTEM. E.L. Schneider, ed. New York, Raven Press, 1978.

Costoff, A.; Mahesh, V.B. Primordial follicles with normal oocytes in the ovaries of postmenopausal women. JOURNAL OF AMERICAN GERIATRICS SOCIETY 23:193–196, 1975.

Everitt, A.V.; Burgess, J.A., eds. HYPOTHALAMUS, PITUITARY AND AGING. Springfield, Il, Thomas, 1976.

Gould, K.G.; Flint, M.; Graham, C.E. Chimpanzee reproductive senescence: A possible model for evolution of the menopause. MATURITAS 3:157–166, 1981.

Graham, C.E. Reproductive function in aged female chimpanzees. AMERICAN JOURNAL OF PHYSICAL ANTHROPOLOGY 50:291–300, 1979.

Graham, C.E. Menstrual cycle of the great apes. Pp. 1–43 in REPRODUCTIVE BIOLOGY OF THE GREAT APES: COMPARATIVE AND BIOMEDICAL ASPECTS. C.E. Graham, ed. New York, Academic Press, 1981.

Graham, C.E.; Bradley, C.F. Microanatomy of the chimpanzee genital system. Pp. 77–126 in THE CHIMPANZEE, Vol. V. G.H. Bourne, ed. Basel, Karger, and Baltimore, University Park Press, 1972.

Graham, C.E.; McClure, H.M. Sertoli-Leydig cell tumor in a chimpanzee. LABORATORY ANIMAL SCIENCE 26:948–950, 1976.

Graham, C.E.; Kling, O.R.; Steiner, R.A. Reproductive senescence in female nonhuman primates. In AGING IN NONHUMAN PRIMATES. D.J. Bowden, ed. New York, Van Nostrand Reinhold, 1979.

Grodin, J.M.; Siiteri, P.K.; McDonald, P.C. Extraglandular estrogens in the menopause. Pp. 15–35 in MENOPAUSE AND AGING. K.J. Ryan; D.C. Gibson, eds. Washington, D.C., U.S. Department of Health and Welfare, Publication NIH 73-319, 1971.

Harding, J.J.; Dilley, K.J. Structural proteins of the mammalian lens: A review with emphasis on changes in development, aging and cataract. EXPERIMENTAL EYE RESEARCH 22:1–73, 1976.

Harman, S.M. Clinical aspects of aging of the male reproductive system. Pp. 29–58 in AGING, Vol. 4: THE AGING REPRODUCTIVE SYSTEM. E.L. Schneider, ed. New York, Raven, 1978.

Helfman, P.M.; Bada, J.L. Aspartic acid racemisation in dentine as a measure of aging. NATURE 262, 5563. pp. 279–281, 1976.

Hodgen, G.D.; Goodman, A.L.; O'Connor, A.; Johnson, D.K. Menopause in rhesus monkeys: Model for study of disorders in the human climacteric. AMERICAN JOURNAL OF OBSTETRICS AND GYNECOLOGY 127:581–584, 1977.

Kleinberg, D.L.; Todd, J.; Chin, P. Mammary gland responsitivity to prolactin stimulation. Pp. 203–219 in AGING IN NONHUMAN PRIMATES. D.M. Bowden, ed. New York, Van Nostrand Reinhold, 1979.

Kram, D.; Schneider, E.L. An effect of reproductive aging: Increased risk of genetically abnormal offspring. Pp. 237–270 in AGING, Vol. 4: THE AGING REPRODUCTIVE SYSTEM. E.L. Schneider, ed. New York, Raven, 1978.

Kuppe, G.; Metzger, H.; Ludwig, H. Aging and structural changes in female reproductive tract. Pp. 21–34 in AGING AND REPRODUCTIVE PHYSIOLOGY. E.Z.E. Hafez, ed. Ann Arbor, MI, Ann Arbor Science, 1976.

Lang, W.R.; Aponte, G.E. Gross and microscopic anatomy of the aged female reproductive organs. CLINICAL OBSTETRICS AND GYNECOLOGY 10:454–465, 1967.

McCormack, S.A. Plasma testosterone concentration and binding in the chimpanzee; effect of age. ENDOCRINOLOGY 89:1171–1177, 1971.

Phoenix, C.H.; Chambers, K.C. Sexual behavior in aging male rhesus monkeys: Effects of test duration on sexual performance. INTERNATIONAL JOURNAL OF PRIMATOLOGY 3:221–229, 1982.

Schneider, E.L., ed. AGING, Vol. 4: THE AGING REPRODUCTIVE SYSTEM. New York, Raven, 1978.

Sherman, B.M.; West, J.H.; Korenman, S.G. Menopausal transition: Analysis of LH, FSH, estradiol, and progesterone concentrations during menstrual cycles of older women. JOURNAL OF CLINICAL ENDOCRINOLOGY AND METABOLISM 42: 629–636, 1976.

Siebold, H.R.; Wolf, R.H. Neoplasms and proliferative lesions in 1065 nonhuman primate necropsies. LABORATORY ANIMAL SCIENCE 23:533–539, 1973.

Talbert, G.B. Effect of aging of the ovaries and female gametes on reproductive capacity. Pp. 59–83 in AGING, Vol. 4: THE AGING REPRODUCTIVE SYSTEM, E.L. Schneider, ed. New York, Raven, 1978.

van Wagenen, G. Vital statistics from a breeding colony: Reproduction and pregnancy outcome in *Macaca mulatta*. JOURNAL OF MEDICAL PRIMATOLOGY 1:3–28, 1972.

van Wagenen, G.; Simpson, M.E. EMBRYOLOGY OF THE OVARY AND TESTIS: *HOMO SAPIENS* AND *MACACA MULATTA*. New Haven, CT, Yale University Press, 1965.

Warner, M.R. Mammary pathology. Pp. 210–228 in AGING IN NONHUMAN PRIMATES. D.M. Bowden, ed. New York, Van Nostrand Reinhold, 1979.

Wolfe, L.D.; Noyes, M.J.S. Reproductive senescence among female Japanese macaques (*Macaca fuscata fuscata*). JOURNAL OF MAMMALOGY 62:698–705, 1981.

The Male Reproductive Tract and Its Fluids

Richard M. Harrison and Ronald W. Lewis

Tulane University, Delta Regional Primate Research Center, Department of Urology/Reproductive Physiology, Covington, Louisiana 70433 (R.M.H., R.W.L.), and Tulane University School of Medicine, Departments Of Urology (R.M.H., R.W.L.) and Physiology (R.M.H.), New Orleans, Louisiana 70112

INTRODUCTION

Any presentation of the male reproductive tract that attempts to be as comparative as possible over the entire primate family must first resolve a question of the validity of some of the earlier literature. In many of the early descriptive studies observations were done on only one or two specimens. Sometimes the ages of the subjects were either not known or not stated. In most cases the animals were dead; in some the animals had been injected or immersed in preservatives. Large blocks of data were sometimes accumulated from autopsy records where the animals may have died from debilitating diseases, been sacrificed for experimental studies, or died as the result of injuries. All of these studies have value to us; it is simply that we must be careful in interpreting them. The data presented in this chapter (and citing a previous reference) may differ from other sources citing the same data because of our elimination of data obtained from the following: 1) animals whose weights suggested that they were not mature adults; 2) animals whose condition before death may have influenced the weights or measurements recorded; and 3) studies in which only one or two specimens were examined. Exceptions were taken when no other studies concerning a given species could be found. Injection of preservatives was stated to cause no effect on tissue weights [Kennard and Willner, 1941a], but where sufficient data were presented for fresh noninjected tissues these were used and the injected tissues eliminated.

The authors have attempted to exclude data from nonprimate species. In the few instances when such data are given, they are believed to be justified by their significance. The data from humans are also limited where there was a choice of human and nonhuman data. Finally, the information presented below is far from inclusive. There are volumes written on the testis, spermatozoa, biochemistry of semen, and morphometric evaluations of the primate male reproductive tract [Johnson et al, 1970a,b,c; Johnson and Gomes, 1977; Rosenberg and Paulsen, 1970; Goland, 1975; Troen and Nankin, 1977; Yates and Gordon, 1977].

Overview

The male reproductive tract in primates is composed of structures that are grossly external and those that are located deep within the pelvic girdle. Although these structures differ between species, and even more between genus and families, there are common considerations among all primates, including human and nonhuman subjects. This chapter will present a brief general description of the primate male reproductive system and then describe specific anatomical and histological aspects using, primarily, the rhesus monkey as the model. Comparative notes concerning other species will be presented as warranted.

Externally, male primates have a penis and a scrotum. The penis differs greatly in size and shape among the various species. The penis in man is pendulous, it is not so completely separate from the scrotum in the nonhuman primate. In most species the distal end of the penis is composed of a glans that caps the penis and through which the urethra opens as the external urethral orifice, or meatus. The presence or absence of an os penis,

Comparative Primate Biology, Volume 3: Reproduction and Development, pages 101–148

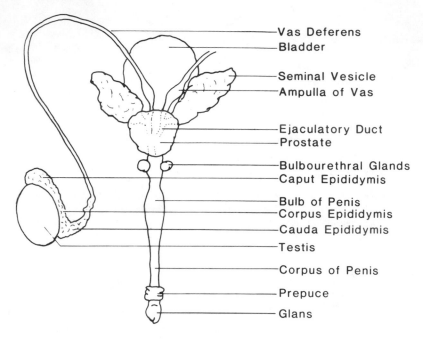

Vas Deferens
Bladder

Seminal Vesicle
Ampulla of Vas

Ejaculatory Duct
Prostate

Bulbourethral Glands
Caput Epididymis

Bulb of Penis
Corpus Epididymis

Cauda Epididymis

Testis

Corpus of Penis

Prepuce

Glans

Fig. 1. Semidiagrammatic presentation of the primate male reproductive tract.

or baculum, also differs among species and perhaps among individuals of the same species. Wislocki [1933] reported that an os penis is found in all catarrhine monkeys whereas De Bourne and Bourne [1975] noted that the penis of the rhesus monkey has a fibrous structure in the corpus fibrosum but no sign of an os penis. The majority of the tissue mass of the penis is composed of paired corpora cavernosa dorsally and a corpus spongiosum ventrally; the urethra passes through the latter tissue.

The scrotum of primates is a loose bag of skin which contains the testes. In adults it may appear as a pendulous structure, be almost nonexistent, or exist at any stage in between. The scrotal skin is usually wrinkled; it may be darker in color than the surrounding skin or may be vividly colored. The scrotal hair is relatively sparse and may differ in color from the other body hair. The appearance of a median scrotal raphe ranges from quite pronounced to nondetectable. The position of the scrotum relative to the penis is described as 1) postpenial, where the penis base is anterior to the scrotum and separate from it; 2) parapenial, where the penis appears to emerge from within the scrotal borders; or 3) prepenial, where the penis appears posterior to the scrotum.

The testes are located within the scrotum in all primates except some prosimians. They are separated from each other by a septum that is continuous with the fascia of the penis and the superficial fascia of the abdomen, perineum, and thigh. The blood vessels to and from the scrotum, as well as lymphatics, nerves, and vasa deferentia, pass from the scrotum into the peritoneal cavity within this fascial continuum. These structures are collectively referred to as the spermatic cord and pass from the scrotum into the pelvic cavity through the inguinal canal. The testes of most prosimians and monkeys are larger than those of the human relative to body size whereas those of the anthropoid apes are generally smaller. They are spherical ovoids in shape. The sperm produced within the testes pass through a system of channels, the rete testis, into the efferent ductules which then pierce the testicular capsule near its upper pole. The duct system then joins to form a single tube and becomes enlarged and tightly coiled. This convoluted tubal system makes up the epididymis which has a large, crescent-shaped head, the caput epididymis, a thinner midsection, the corpus epididymis, and a slightly enlarged terminal section, the cauda epididymis. The epididymis lies closely attached to the posteromedial surface of the testis, and in some species the separation of the two is difficult to visualize. As the ductal system moves away from the lower pole of the testis it becomes the vas deferens which passes, along with the other structures mentioned above as part of the spermatic cord, through the inguinal canal into the pelvic cavity.

Within the pelvic cavity the vasa emerge from the internal inguinal ring, curve medially and caudally, and as they approach the midline behind the bladder they enlarge, forming the ampullae. Each then joins with the duct from the ipsilateral seminal vesicle to form an ejaculatory duct. These ducts then enter the caudal prostate where they open into the urethra along the posterior wall of the urethra at or near the colliculus seminalis.

The ipsilateral seminal vesicle and vas deferens arise from the same embryonic tissue, a fact that is important in infertility evaluations. In some primate species the seminal vesicles are small outpockets of the vasa deferentia, in some they are apparently absent, and in others they are large conspicuous organs that may appear as externally lobulated sacs.

The structures mentioned above—testes, epididymides, vasa deferentia, seminal vesicles, and ejaculatory ducts—are all bilateral (Fig. 1).

The prostate in most nonhuman primates is found to have two distinct lobes. The cranial lobe appears on the external surface to be lobulated and similar in appearance to the surface of the seminal vesicles. The cranial lobe is located inferior to the seminal vesicles and posterior to the neck of the bladder, ampullae of the vasa deferentia, and the ejaculatory ducts. The caudal lobe has a smooth surface and is inferior to the cranial lobe in most species. It surrounds the urethra on all but the anterior or ventral side.

Accessory glands located distal to the prostate empty into the urethra. These include the Cowper's glands or bulbourethral glands which drain through single ducts into the penile urethra near the bulb of the penis. The penile urethra has intraepithelial and periurethral glands (Littré glands) that empty into it [Roberts and Seibold, 1971].

The fluids of the male reproductive tract are those primarily produced by the testes, epididymides, seminal vesicles, prostate, and bulbourethral glands. Some of these fluids are produced by one organ and reabsorbed or modified by another; ie, testicular fluids as such constitute a minor fraction of the semen ejaculated because of the changes in its nature that are augmented by the accessory organs. The testicular fluid is believed to be secreted by the Sertoli cells and differs in its composition from the blood and lymph that drain the testes. Waites and Einer-Jensen [1974] collected rete testis fluid from monkeys and found lower concentrations of sodium and higher concentrations of potassium when compared to plasma values.

The epididymal fluid is most important in the maturation of sperm and in their storage in the male reproductive tract. Although a great deal of data has been collected relative to the biochemical nature of the epididymal fluid from rodents, rabbits, and domestic species, the same has not been true for primates. In recent years micropuncture techniques have been used to obtain fluid for the analysis of myoinositol and inositol from the lumen of the seminiferous tubules and the epididymis of rhesus monkeys and baboons [Hinton et al, 1980; Hinton and Setchell, 1981]. Other investigators have shown changes in a number of parameters relative to the areas of the epididymis, and these will be presented later. The majority of these studies were conducted in the rhesus monkey, and very few species have had extensive study.

Most of the fluid present in the ejaculate from a primate, either human or nonhuman, is from the seminal vesicles and, to a lesser degree, from the prostate. Both glands produce secretions that are rich in enzymes as well as substances frequently referred to as marker substances. The functional state of the accessory glands can be evaluated by the analysis of these marker substances in the seminal plasma. The seminal vesicles are evaluated by the analysis of fructose, the epididymides by the analysis of glycerylphosphorylcholine (GPC), and the prostate by the analysis of citric acid and acid phosphatase [Mann and Lutwak-Mann, 1976]. The fluid from seminal vesicles is usually more alkaline, containing less water and more protein, potassium, and acid-soluble phosphatase than that from the prostate [White, 1979].

The secretions of the bulbourethral glands are minor. Data on the above fluids will be discussed later.

A general overview of the male reproductive system in nonhuman primates has been presented by Kinzey [1971].

EXTERNAL GENITALIA
Scrotum

The scrotum in primates serves many functions. It contains the main male endocrine sex organs, the testes, and the epididymides, and, in most species, plays an important role in regulating the intrascrotal temperature. It may vary in color, depending on androgen levels or maturation stage, and species. The size of the scrotum is not proportional to body size among primates.

The scrotum of the rhesus monkey (*Macaca mulatta*) is semipendulous and relatively large. The skin is usually wrinkled and darker in color than the surrounding skin. The scrotal hair is sparse and differs slightly in color from the general body hair. The perineum—the space from the anus anteriorly to include the penis and scrotum—is relatively long. The penis arises from the anterior border of the scrotum, so the scrotum is classified as postpenial. The median scrotal raphe in adult rhesus males is quite faint.

In tree shrews (*Tupaia belangeri*) the scrotum is darkly pigmented and the testes are located prepenial [Collins et al, 1982]. The epidermis in *T. glis, Galago demidovii,* and *G. senegalensis* (dwarf and lesser bush babies) is thin whereas in *Papio* (baboons) and *Gorilla* (gorillas) it is quite thick [Machida and Giacometti, 1967]. The distribution of epidermal melanotic melanocytes in the skin determines the pigmentation of the external genitali. Of 27 species studied, ranging from tree shrews to gorillas, only black-collared tamarins (*Tamarinus nigricollis*), woolly monkeys (*Lagothrix lagothricha*), howler monkeys (*Alouatta caraya*), Celebes apes (*Cynopithecus niger*), yellow baboons (*Papio cynocephalus*), and gorillas (*Gorilla gorilla gorilla*) had heavily pigmented genital epidermis whereas dwarf, lesser, and greater bush babies (*G. crassicaudatus*), angwantibo (*Arctocebus calabarensis*), slow loris (*Nycticebus coucang*), Philippine tarsier (*Tarsius syrichta*), green monkeys (*Cercopithecus aethiops*), rhesus monkeys (*Macaca mulatta*), and pig-tailed macaque (*M. nemestrina*) had little or none.

In the langurs (*Presbytis entellus entellus*), the scrotum is semipendulous, postpenial, black, wrinkled, and the hair is sparse [David and Ramaswami, 1971]. The scrotum of vervet monkeys (*Cercepithecus aethiops pygerythrus*), patas monkeys (*Erythrocebus patas*), and talapoin monkeys (*Miopithecus talapoin*) are all blue, apparently owing to dense layers of melaninlike pigment in the dermis [Dixson and Herbert, 1974]. The degree of coloration in the vervet monkeys is modulated by the degree of dermal hydration, and is related to social rank [Price et al, 1976]. The red color of

the scrotum in macaques is related to vascular changes and to androgen levels whereas the blue color in vervet monkeys, once established, is not dependent on androgens [Dixson and Herbert, 1974].

The sebaceous glands in the external genitalia of primates show differences in number and size according to species. The largest glands are found in mongoose and ring-tailed lemurs (*Lemur mongoz* and *L. catta*) and in black-collared tamarin; those of the stump-tailed macaque (*M. arctoides*) and gorilla are large; in vervet monkeys, Syke's monkeys (*Cercopithecus mitis*), white crowned mangabey (*Cerocebus atys*), rhesus monkeys, pig-tailed macaque, Celebes apes, anubis baboons (*P. anubis*), and yellow baboons, the glands are relatively smaller; the smallest sebaceous glands are found in Philippine tarsier, woolly monkeys, and the lutong (*Presbytis pyrrus*). The glands of Tupaiidea and Lorisidea are moderate in size and are bilobular [Machida and Giacometti, 1967].

Pottos (*Perodicticus potto*) and angwantibos have male scent glands located on the scrotum. In pottos they are in the central scrotal area; in angwantibos they are in a small triangular area on the posterior slope of the scrotum [Manley, 1974].

Other parameters measured in the external genitial skin of primates include alkaline phosphatase reactivity of blood capillaries, innervation, distribution and presence of melanocytes in hair follicles, presence of genital corpuscles, apocrine glands, and eccrine glands [Machida and Giacometti, 1967].

The size, shape, and position of the scrotum vary greatly in primates. The size of the testes obviously bears a significant relationship to the size of the scrotum, and testicular sizes will be presented in detail later. Some reports on scrotal size and position may present a false picture because of the cremasteric and dartos muscular responses that occur following cooling associated with death, anesthesis, or periods of stress. If the scrotum is contracted it will appear smaller, more wrinkled, and darker in color. In general the scrotum in primates is situated postpenially; that is, its anterior base is attached to the perineal side of the pendulous or free part of the penis. In the lower primates this is less frequently the case; in the tree shrew the scrotum is prepenial [Collins et al, 1982] and in marmosets it is parapenial [Hill, 1958]. The degree of obesity and age (prepubertal or adult) may influence the apparent position of the testes and scrotum. Hill and Kanagasuntheram [1959] reported that no distinct scrotal sac was found in any of the siamang (*Symphalangus syndactylus*) specimens examined, but all three were subadult cadavers. They also noted that in the concolor gibbon (*Hylobates concolor leucogenys*) there was a definite scrotal sac located postpenially in newborn and adult males. In both *Gorilla* and *Pongo* the scrotum has been reported to be small, consisting primarily in a low, transverse postpenial ridge with a wrinkled surface [Hill, 1958]. The chimpanzee (*Pan troglodytes*) has a large, well-defined scrotum [Martin and Gould, 1981].

The scrotum in primates is lined by a layer of muscular fibers (dartos muscle) within which is a fibrous layer. This fibrous layer gives rise to the scrotal septum. The scrotum usually does not have the subcutaneous adipose tissue commonly associated with other body skin. This is probably because of the unique thermoregulatory system of the scrotum.

The tissues in the scrotum are maintained at a temperature below that of the abdomen. The temperatures of the testes and associated structures are determined by the temperature of the blood entering the scrotum plus the metabolic heat generated by the tissues minus the loss of heat by the scrotum [Waites, 1970]. There are two mechanisms by which the desired temperature is achieved and maintained. One mechanism is by a countercurrent system involving the pampiniform plexus of vessels in the spermatic cord. There is a transfer of heat from arteries to veins so that the blood entering the scrotal tissues is cooler than the blood in the abdomen. This requires, however, that the scrotum be cooler. The second mechanism involves the cremasteric response. When the scrotum is cooled the cremaster muscles contract bringing the testes and epididymides closer to the body and its core heat. The dartos muscles lining the scrotum also cause the scrotum to contract, thus reducing the surface area and loss of heat. There are receptors in the scrotal skin that stimulate the responses of the tunica dartos muscles [Waites, 1970]. Conversely, when the scrotum becomes too warm, the muscles relax, allowing the scrotum to become more pendulous, for the testes and epididymides to move further from the body heat, and thereforth to reduce the scrotal temperature. These mechanisms obviously have limits, and pathologic conditions may cause elevations of scrotal temperatures beyond those limits. The cremaster muscle is striated and is not capable of prolonged contraction [Waites, 1970], so for long-term thermal regulation the dartos muscle has the dominant role. The cremasteric response may function primarily as an extremely rapid response to general stress [D'Souza, 1974]. Elevated temperatures in the testes cause a depression of spermatogenesis [Robinson and Rock, 1967] and atrophy of the testes and germinal epithelium [Venkatachalam and Ramanathan, 1962]; in the epididymides the effects may be manifested by accelerated sperm transit and by changes in the transepithelial passage of water and ions.

A more complete description of the scrotum in nearly all primate species is presented by Hill [1958] and is briefly summarized in Table 1.

Penis

The penises of primates differ greatly in size and shape, although there are some common characteristics. The penis is considered pendulous in all primates. The structure of the penis is composed of three cylindrical bodies of erectile tissue. The dorsal two bodies are the corpora cavernosa penis which are attached proximally to the subpubic arch and which fuse distally under the glans penis. The ventral body is the corpus cavernosum urethra (corpus spongiosum). The corpus spongiosum attaches to the urogenital fascial trigone where it forms the bulbus urethra. The urethra enters this structure and passes through it distally to the external urinary meatus. The distal portion of the corpus spongiosum expands to form the glans penis. The corpora cavernosa are enclosed by the tunica albuginea which proximally forms a septum between them. Distally, in most nonhuman primates, the septum disappears, the corpora fuse, and the tunica albuginea gives rise to the fibrous structure that is ossified in the adult to form an os penis or baculum. The corpus spongiosum is not surrounded by the same tissue as the corpora cavernosa.

The os penis or baculum is a highly variable structure. Its shape may vary greatly within a species [Kinzey, 1971]. It may appear as a cartilaginous strucutre or as an ossified one that is readily radiopaque [Izor et al, 1981]. Figure 2 shows the variability found in samples taken from *Callithrix*. Figure 3 shows a baculum removed from a rhesus monkey. The structure has been reported to be present in all primates studied except *Lagothrix*

TABLE 1. External Structures of the Primate Male Reproductive Tract

Genus	General penis	Glans	Prepuce	Baculum	Scrotum	Specialized epithelium	References
Tupaiidae							
Tupaia	Elongated Long	Fusiform Thin, tapering, well defined	Ample	None	Pyriform, raphe, para- or prepenial		Conaway and Sorenson, 1966; Jones, 1971; Collins et al, 1982
Anathana Dendrogale Urogale		Elongated					
Ptilocercus	Short, stout	Acorn-shaped			Very conspicuous, raphe, unpigmented		
Lemuridae							
Lemur	Large, subcylindrical	Truncated	Long, sparsely haired	Often bilobed	Pendulous, globose, hairy (exp. *L. catta*)	Horny recurved spicules on glans	Petter-Rousseaux, 1964
Lepilemur	Cylindrical, elongated	Wider than deep		Possibly bifid	Light-colored, hairy	Small pickles	Petter-Rousseaux, 1964
Hapalemur	Cylindrical, short	Well differentiated	Corporal	Well into glans	Small, hairy, sessile	Papillated, spines on penis	Petter-Rousseaux, 1964
Cheirogaleus	Median horny pad, short, broad	Not bilobed, ovate	Loose, ample	Bifid distally	Conspicuous, very hairy, bilobed	Scales on glans	Petter-Rousseaux, 1964
Microcebus	Elongated, narrow, hairy	Bilobed	No distinction from glans	Bifid	Seasonally large		Petter-Rousseaux, 1964
Phaner					Hairy	Base of glans has 4 large horny protuberances	Petter-Rousseaux, 1964
Indriidae	Cylindrical or sl. tapered, pendulous		Ample		Pendulous		
Indri	Pendulous, large	Truncated, cylindrical	Loose, hairy	Small, short, forked		Small spines on glans / Small, numerous hooks	Petter-Rousseaux, 1964
Propithecus	Pendulous	Cylindrical	Loose, hairy	Bifid	Saclike	Small lateral recurved spicules	
Avahi	Pendulous	Cylindrical	Loose	Bifid	Bilobed, sparsely haired	Two enormous hooklike spines	Petter-Rousseaux, 1964

	Penis	Apex/Glans	Prepuce	Baculum	Testes	Spines/Papillae	Reference
Daubentoniidae							
Daubentonia	Cylindrical, pendulous, septum	Abruptly truncated	Ample, loose	Large	Postpenial, hairy	Papillae and spines on glans, re-curved spicules on penis	Petter-Rousseaux, 1964
Lorisidae	Slender, cylindrical	Keratinized apex, fleshy	Ample, hairy	Sinuous	Sessile, hairy, rounded or pyriform		
Loris				Slender, straight	Sessile	Low papillae	
Nycticebus	Robust			Robust	Sessile, raphe	Low papillae	
Arctocebus		Crenated frill on rim		Slender, between corpora	Globose, firm	Papillae on glans and horny re-curved spicules	
Perodicticus	Robust	As with *Arctocebus*	Short, thick	Robust	Sessile, globular	Flat, toothlike crenations on glans, papillae	
Galago	Pendulous, long	Elongated frill, variable		Slender, may protrude	Less globular, lat-erally com-pressed, naked posterior	Horny recurved spicules, spines on glans	
Euoticus	Thick	Complicated apex		Apex enlarged		Spines on glans	
Galagoides	Longer than *Galago* or *Euoticus*	Elongated		Apex enlarged		Spinose glans	
Callithricidae	Cylindrical, small, tapered	Well defined	Ample, pigmented		Parapenial, sessile, hairless, globular	Large sebaceous glands, complex apocrine glands	
Callithrix	Short	Small, bright red	Smooth, hairy	Very small	Subglobular, ses-sile, glandular	Scrotal pustules; few, minute prickles	
Cebuella	Cylindrical, short		Ample, unpigmented		Parapenial, sparse hair		
Callimico	Tapering, long	Hemispherical, enlarged, well-defined corona	Pigmented glabrous		Sessile, globose		

(continued)

TABLE 1. External Structures of the Primate Male Reproductive Tract (Continued)

Genus	General penis	Glans	Prepuce	Baculum	Scrotum	Specialized epithelium	References
Tamarin (Saguinus)	Tapered, short	Small, truncated or hemispherical	Pigmented	Projects distally	Parapenial, hairless, globose, pigmented	Oil glands	
Tamarinus (Saguinus)		Asymmetrical, blunt, conical apex or bifid	Corporal to ample		Small, unpigmented	Small or no scrotal pustules	
Marikina (subgenus of Saguinus)							
Oedipomidas (subgenus of Saguinus)	Short	Rounded, pigmented	Pigmented		Small, raphe, parapenial naked	Few glands, pustules	
Leontocebus (Leontideus)	Elongated, pendulous	Acornlike, well defined	Corporal		Pendulous, large, bilobed sac, retropenial, bluish		
Cebidae	Cylindrical	Well defined	Varies	Usually present	Varies		
Cebus	Cylindrical, short, stout	Flattened distally, solely corona	Pigmented, lax	Sigmoid, robust, club-shaped tip	Well-developed sac, raphe, sparse hair, pigmented		
Saimiri	Cylindrical, large	Well defined, cordate		Straight, blunted distally, short	Postpenial, raphe, large peduncu-lated, bilobed	Few, small spicules	
Aotus	Short	Smooth, conical, feeble corona	Ample primary	Cartilag-inous	Unpigmented, well defined, globular, subpendulous		
Callicebus	Short	Smooth, ovate	Smooth, short		Sessile, small, globose		
Pithecia	Cylindrical, compressed laterally, small, long	Bluntly rounded	Relatively short, pigmented	Short, thick	Small, globose, raphe		

Chiropotes *Cacajao*	Cylindrical, long Short	Club-shaped, laterally compressed	Pigmented, ample		Pinkish purple Parapenial, hairless, pigmented, small		
Alouatta	Blunted	None or un-differen-tiated	Unpigmented, ample	Present	Varies from white and hairless to dark with sparse hair		
Ateles	Robust, simple	Truncated	Ample	Absent	Varies from not vis-ible to bilobed and naked		
Lagothrix	Cylindrical	Flattened, disk- or button-shaped		Absent	Globular, sessile, spicules, hairy, subcutaneous fat, raphe, parapenial		
Brachyteles	Average	Mushroomlike	Long	Absent	Grayish black, sparse hair		
Cercopithecidae	Small to moder-ate, slight	Acornlike, enlarged	Reflects consid-erable distance	Present	Large, bilobed, seminude		
Cercopithecus	Small	Rosy pink to scarlet, acorn or helmet-shaped	Light orange to scarlet		Varies from blue to greenish blue	Horny papillae	Price et al, 1976
Erythrocebus	Moderate	Acorn-shaped or pyriform		Present	Blue, sparse hair, subglobular, pendulous		Price et al, 1976
Mandrillus	Laterally com-pressed cylinder	Shorter than *Pa-pio*, thick from above downward	Corporal, bright scarlet	Present	Subpendulous to pendulous, broad, sparse hair, lilac to sky blue		
Cercocebus	Tapered, long	Elliptical, short, deep		Large, curved	Subglobular, large	Horny spicules on glans and/or penis	Fooden, 1971
Papio	Elongated, con-stricted neck	subconical, rounded, oval, well defined	Ample, often brightly colored	Strongly curved, robust	Very capacious, subpendulous to pendulous, hairy, color varies	Horny papillae	

(continued)

TABLE 1. External Structures of the Primate Male Reproductive Tract (Continued)

Genus	General penis	Glans	Prepuce	Baculum	Scrotum	Specialized epithelium	References
Theropithecus	Elongated, laterally compressed	Longer than wide	Ample	Deviates to right, long	Postpenial, small, rose color		
Macaca	Moderately long, tapered	Very diverse (aberrant in *M. arctoides*)	Ample	Present	Blue to scarlet, large, bilobed, subpendulous		
Cynopithecus	Narrows distally, elongated	Acorn-shaped, slaty tinged	Purplish-red	Very robust	Pendulous, large, pale blue with reddish raphe		
Colobus	Short	Acorn-shaped, pronounced corona	Attached proximally	Moderate	Small, bilobed, narrow neck, blue to black		
Presbytis		Acorn-shaped	Corporal	Present	Postpenial, semipendulous	Horny spicules	David and Ramaswami, 1971
Nasalis						Horny spicules	
Simias							
Rhinopithecus							
Pygathrix							
Miopithecus	Moderate	Purplish, slightly truncated	Ample	Present	Relatively large, bluish, subpendulous		
Hylobatidae	Very short, frenulum	Button-shaped, squat	Short, thick	Short, slender	Small or lacking, raphe	Large horny spicules	Hill and Kanagasuntheram, 1959
Hylobates	Small	Conical	Pigmented, corporal		Small, parapenial		
Symphalangus		Pigmented	Pigmented, well developed, corporal		Very hairy, divided	Minute spicules	Hill and Kanagasuntheram, 1959
Pongidae							
Pongo	Small	Scarcely differentiated	Slaty blue	Small	Sparse hair, purplish		
Pan	Elongated, pendulous	None in the traditional sense	Unpigmented, soft, pliable	Minute	Subpendulous, naked	Minute horny spicules	Izor et al, 1981
Gorilla	Small, short, thick	Conical, squat	Pigmented	Very short	Small		
Hominidae							
Homo	Pendulous, large	Helmet-shaped	Ample	Absent	Subpendulous, raphe, sparse hair		

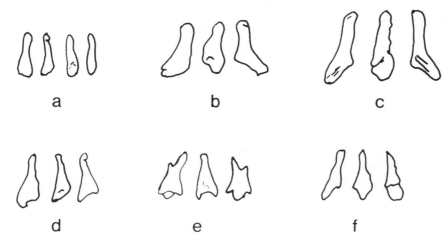

Fig. 2. Drawing of multiple views of single specimens of baculums from *Callithrix*. a) *Callithrix jacchus jacchus*; b) *C. humeralifer humeralifer*; c) *C. argentata argentata*; d, e, and f) *C. humeralifer chysoleuca*. [Adapted from Hershkovitz, 1977.]

lagotricha, Ateles paniscus, Brachyteles arachnoides, the tarsier, and man [Hershkovitz, 1977]. The baculum is almost always situated to the left in the glans, causing the left lobe of the glans to be larger and more projecting. Even when the os penis is vestigial or absent, as in *Lagothrix* and *Ateles*, asymmetry of the glans persists. It should be noted that because of the variability of the os penis the descriptions given in Table 1 are generalities and deviations from them are to be expected.

The free portion of the penis, that part that is external, is covered by a cutaneous sheath that is longer than the portion of the penis that is covered. This additional length of skin gives rise to the fold of skin that may extend beyond the glans; this tissue is the prepuce. The inner layer of prepuce may cover only the glans or may attach proximally to the corpus penis some distance from the glans. In some species and individuals the top of the glans extends beyond the prepuce. The epithelium of the glans is of a transitional type between regular epidermis and a mucous membrane. It becomes a mucous membrane within the external urinary meatus. The glans and distal corpus penis may have specialized keratinization of the epithelium that forms horny papillae, spicules, or recurved hooks [Hill, 1958].

The muscles associated with the penis are the bulbocavernosus, which arises from the bulk of the corpus spongiosum and encircles the corpus spongiosum; the ischiocavernosus which arises from the caudal ischium and inserts on the corpus cavernosum; and the levator penis, which arises from the ischium medial to the ischiocavernosus muscle and ends as a tendinous attachment along the dorsum of the penis.

The shape of the glans penis can be used to classify monkeys into various groups. To quote Fooden [1980]:

Living species of macaques are readily divisible into four clearly defined subgroups: (1) silenus-sylvanus group, (2) sinica group, (3) fascicularis group, and (4) arctoides group. Each of these species groups is characterized by a distinctive form of the glans penis. In the *silenus-sylvanus* group the glans is bluntly bilobed and broad; in the *sinica* group it is apically acute and broad (sagittate in dorsal view); in the *fascicularis* group it is bluntly bilobed and narrow; and in the *arctoides* group it is apically acute and elongated (lanceolate in dorsal view).

These differences in the shape of the glans penis are noted throughout the primate family. There is even the question of some species such as *Pan* [Graham and Bradley, 1972; Izor et al, 1981] not having any glans at all. Table 1 presents the general differences between species relative to penis and glans size and shape plus comments concerning the prepuce, specialized epithelium, and the baculum. Figure 4 shows diagramatically the shape of penises among related primates.

The intrinsic innervation of the penis has been described in both galago and tupia [Dail et al, 1971]. There is a rich cholinergic and adrenergic nerve supply to the penile arteries and intrinsic muscles of the cavernous bodies. The dorsal penile vein has only an adrenergic nerve supply.

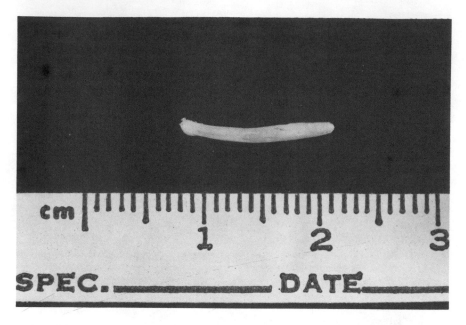

Fig. 3. Os penis (baculum) removed at autopsy from *Macaca mulatta*.

MACACA

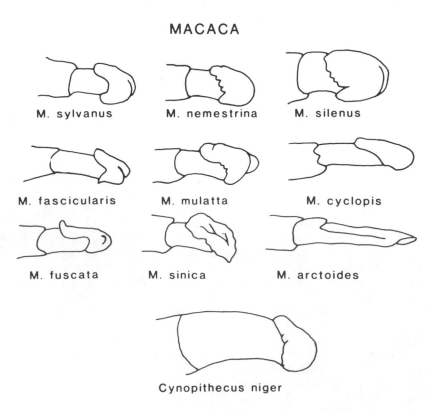

Fig. 4. Outline drawings of the penises of nine *Macaca* species and *Cynopithecus niger*.

INTERNAL GENITALIA

Testis

The testes of all primate species are similar in that they are the primary source of the male sex hormone and the only source of spermatozoa. While similar in function they are not similar in size and weight, either absolutely or relatively. As indicated in Table 2, the testes in macaques are 40 times heavier than those in gorillas, relative to total body weight.

The shape of primate testes is usually described as ovoid. Sometimes they are laterally compressed so that medial-lateral dimensions are not as great as anterior-posterior dimensions. The lower pole of the testes may be less rounded than the upper pole.

Within the scrotum the testes and epididymides are loosely enclosed by the tunica vaginalis, a serous sheath derived from the peritoneum. The tunica vaginalis has two layers, the parietal and the visceral. The parietal layer lines the scrotum, and the visceral layer forms the outer portion of the testicular parenchyma. The blood vessels, lymphatics, and conduit for sperm pass within the tunica vaginalis sheath through the inguinal canal to the pelvic cavity. As mentioned before, this group of structures is collectively termed the spermatic cord. Tightly adherent to the testis, and to a lesser degree the epididymis, is a second tissue layer termed the tunica albuginea. This tissue is a tough, elastic, fibrous structure; as mentioned above it also encloses the corpora cavernosa of the penis. In some species a third layer, the tunica vasculosa, is described internal to the tunica albuginea. This inner layer is quite thin and is composed of loose areolar connective tissue and is rich in blood vessels [Steinberger and Steinberger, 1975]. Along the posterior border of the testis the tunica albuginea thickens and extends slightly into the gland forming the mediastinum. In sagittal section the tunica albuginea is seen to extend into the testis as septa which divides the testis into lobules or compartments. In the human there are about 250 lobules in each testis and each contains three or four seminiferous tubules derived from a primitive testis cord during early fetal life [Arey, 1954]. The seminiferous tubules are basically open loops that have both ends emptying into the area of the rete testis [Steinberger and Steinberger, 1975]. The seminiferous tubules in the adult rhesus monkey are 250–300 μm in diameter [van Wagenen and Simpson, 1954]; those of lorises (*Loris*

tardigradus) average 208.4 μm in animals collected over a 1-year period [Ramakrishna and Prasad, 1967]. The seminiferous tubules are the tissues in the testes where the male gametes are produced. The walls of these tubules have two main components: an internal basal membrane that has a lamellar structure, and an external layer of collagen fibers [Vilar et al, 1970]. There are differences reported between the limiting membrane of the seminiferous tubules in man comapred to those in monkeys (*Macaca mulatta*). In monkeys the lamellar area is made up of one to three layers of flattened myoid cells, whereas in man the layers number two to six [Herno et al, 1977]. Studies on *M. fascicularis* monkeys with surgically induced varicoceles suggest that a decrease in the lamination appearance may be due to a stress situation [Fussell et al, 1981]. The cytoplasm of the contractile cells has numerous fine filaments and the rough-surfaced endoplasmic reticulum is relatively prominent. It has been suggested that the movement of the tubular contents may, in part, be an active process involving the peritubular cells [Ross and Long, 1966]. There is also some elastic tissue in the limiting membrane of the seminiferous tubule in humans [Menezes, 1977]. The collagen fiber layer between the seminiferous epithelium and the myoid cell is relatively thick. The basal membrane is attached to the germinal epithelium which is itself composed of two cell lines: the germinal cells and the Sertoli cells. The stem cells from which the spermatozoa eventually derive are termed spermatogonia and are located at the periphery of the tubules. Two types, A and B, have been identified from nuclear staining characteristics. Above the spermatogonia are large cells with conspicuous chromosomal patterns. These are the primary spermatocytes formed from division of type B spermatogonia and which divide to form secondary spermatocytes. These, in turn, divide to form the spermatids. Each of these divisions is a series of chromatin duplication and division up to the formation of the spermatids. Spermatids are haploid cells and although they undergo a complex differentiation before they become spermatozoa, there is no more division. The metamorphosis of spermatids to spermatozoa is termed spermiogenesis; the entire process from spermatogonia to the release of spermatozoa is called spermatogenesis. A detailed description of the process of spermatogenesis and the histological positions of the germinal or spermatogenic cells is provided in this volume by Baker.

TABLE 2. Testicular Weights and Dimensions in Various Primate Species

Species	Testes weight[a]	Percent body weight	Testicular dimensions[b]	References
Tupaia belangeri	0.441	0.290		Collins et al, 1982
T. ferriginea			15 × 19	Jones, 1971
Lemur fulvus			30 × 15	Petter-Rousseaux, 1964
Cheirogaleus major			20 × 10	Petter-Rousseaux, 1964
Microcebus murinus			15 × 12	Petter-Rousseaux, 1964
Loris tardigradus		0.96		Ramakrishna and Prasad, 1967
Callithrix jacchus	1.3	0.41		Harcourt et al, 1981
Saguinus oedipus geoffroyi	6.39	1.33	11.8 × 7.8 × 6.1	Dawson and Dukelow, 1976
S. geoffroyi	1.8	0.337		Hrdlicka, 1925; Schultz, 1938
Saimiri sciureus	3.2	0.41		Middleton and Rosal, 1972
Aotus trivirgatus	1.2	0.118	521.5	Schultz, 1938; Dixson et al, 1980
Alouatta villosa	25.0	0.345		Hrdlicka, 1925
Lagothrix lagothricha	11.2	0.215		Schultz, 1938
Ateles geoffroyi	13.4	0.169		Schultz, 1938
Cercopithecus aethiops	13.0	0.26		Harcourt et al, 1981
Cercocebus torquatus atys	25.1	0.20		Kennard and Willner, 1941a
Macaca fascicularis	35.2	0.80	30 × 25 × 20	Harcourt et al, 1981
M. radiata	48.2	0.56		Harcourt et al, 1981
M. mulatta	46.2	0.50		Harcourt et al, 1981
	76.0	0.730		Schultz, 1938
	16.2	0.274		Kennard and Willner, 1941b
	12.2			Fremming et al, 1955
M. nemestrina	66.7	0.668		Schultz, 1938
M. arctoides	48.2	0.46		Harcourt et al, 1981
Papio hamadryas	27.1	0.13		Harcourt et al, 1981
P. cynocephalus	52.0	0.21		Harcourt et al, 1981
P. anubis	93.5	0.35		Harcourt et al, 1981
P. ursinus	72.0	0.23		Harcourt et al, 1981
Mandrillus sphinx	88.9	0.278		Schultz, 1938
Theropithecus gelada	17.1	0.08		Harcourt et al, 1981
Presbytis rubicunda	3.6	0.059		Schultz, 1938
P. cristatus	5.5	0.08		Schultz, 1938
P. obscura	4.8	0.06		Harcourt et al, 1981
	5.8	0.079		Burton, 1981
P. entellus	11.1	0.06		Harcourt et al, 1981
		0.07	35 × 22 × 28	David and Ramaswami, 1971
Colobus polykomos	10.7	0.10		Harcourt et al, 1981
			34 × 19 × 17.2	Hill, 1952
Nasalis larvatus	11.9	0.057		Schultz, 1938
Hylobates cinereus	4.8	0.088		Schultz, 1938
H. lar	5.53	0.050	28 × 14	Kennard and Willner, 1941c; Matthews, 1946
H. concolor			13.6 × 7.8 × 9.5	Hill and Kanagasuntheram, 1959
Pan troglodytes	118.8	0.269		Schultz, 1938
Pongo pygmaeus	35.3	0.048		Schultz, 1938
Gorilla gorilla	29.6	0.02	37.5 × 10 × 6.5	Hosokawa and Kamiya, 1961; Hall-Craggs, 1962; Harcourt et al, 1981
Homo sapiens	40.5	0.06		Harcourt et al, 1981

[a]Testes weight is the total weight of both testes expressed in grams.
[b]Testicular dimensions are length × width; when three values are recorded the last two are width medial to lateral and anterior to posterior; the single value for *Aotus trivirgatus* is volume in mm^3.

The Sertoli or sustentacular cells are large, slender cells that extend from the basal (basement) membrane of the seminiferous tubules to the luminal area. Their nucleus occupies a basal position and shows extensive infolding of the nuclear envelope [Dym, 1973]. Classically the nucleus of the Sertoli cells is described as irregularly oval or pyramidal with the long axis perpendicular to the basement membrane of the tubule. Electron microscopy shows the nucleus to have elaborate lobulation in some species. The cytoplasmic organelles, inclusions, and matrix have been described in detail [Fawcett, 1975]. The Sertoli cells are believed to be the main source of androgen-binding protein (ABP) [Hansson et al, 1975]. ABPs in testicular and epididymal cytosols in monkey and man represent isomeric forms of plasma testosterone-estrogen binding globulin (TeBG) [Vigersky et al, 1976]. The relative volume of Sertoli cells in the rhesus monkey varies according to the stage of spermatogenis associated with these cells. The relative amounts of tissue volume occupied by the three main cell types were as follows: in stage I—Sertoli cells, 23.6%; pachytene spermatocytes, 15%; spermatids, 58%; in stage VII—Sertoli cells, 32%; pachytene spermatocytes 24%; spermatids, 34% [Cavicchia and Dym, 1977].

The Sertoli cells are in close association with the developing sperm cells and have been termed "nurse cells" and "support cells." One of their main functions is to provide a blood-testis barrier. In primates the peritubular cells overlap and have spaces of at least 0.3–0.4 μm, so any barrier must be an intraepithelial one. The Sertoli cells have occluding junctions between adjacent cells that effectively maintain the blood-testis barrier and serve to compartmentalize the seminiferous tubules [Dym, 1973; Chapman et al, 1978].

The Sertoli cell in *M. fascicularis* is typical of most mammalian Sertoli cells. The external surface is deeply indented where it impinged upon by the developing germ cells. A model of the Sertoli cell has been described by Russell and Karpas [1983] (see Fig. 5).

There may be a great deal of variation in the size and shape of Sertoli cells and their nuclei in the same species, depending on the reproductive state of the individual. In humans there are four or five different types of Sertoli cells under normal conditions; in various states of impaired spermatogenesis there may be a predominance of one or two normal cell types or modifications that are relatively characteristic of the impairment [Schulze et al, 1976]. In cryptorchidism the nucleus is round, in oligospermia it is deeply indented; the

Sertoli cells in Sertoli-cell-only syndrome appear to be a normal type capable of inhibiting follicle-stimulating hormone (FSH) secretion.

Antiandrogens, such as cyproterone, induce changes in the fine structure of the Sertoli cells in rhesus monkeys [Aumuller et al, 1975]. These changes include a reduction in the tight junctions that form the major part of the blood-testis barrier; a reduction in the mitochondira, microfilaments, and Golgi apparatus; and decrease in the endoplasmic reticulum. It is apparent that a proper intratubular environment is possible only with the proper androgen stimulation.

Fig. 5. Drawing of Sertoli cell from *Macaca fascicularis*, enlarged approximately 3,000×.

The space between the seminiferous tubules is termed the interstitial space. It contains connective tissue, blood vessels, lymphatics, fibroblasts, mast cells, macrophages, and specialized cells known as Leydig cells [De Bourne and Bourne, 1975]. The connective tissues of the interstitium is very loose, and much of the extracellular spaces are occupied by fluid. The collagen fibers are prominent and Leydig cells are scattered [Connell and Connell, 1977]. The Leydig cells are the main source of the male sex hormone, testosterone; they are large cells with usually a single nucleolus in the nucleus of each cell. Luteinizing hormone (LH) stimulates the Leydig cells to produce testosterone [Lipsett et al, 1966] and is probably necessary for the fetal growth of these cells. Tseng et al [1975] showed that male rhesus monkeys decapitated at approximately 80 days of gestational life had fewer Leydig cells at the normal time of delivery although the size of seminiferous tubules was normal. The testes were smaller than normal and only about 10% of normal weight.

The fine structure of the Leydig cells was studied during the nonbreeding season in squirrel monkeys (*Saimiri sciureus*)—that is, during a period when testicular regression is observed. The Leydig cells were found to be normal-appearing and were abundantly present in a layer several cells thick on the inner aspect of the tunica albuginea [Belt and Cavazos, 1971]. In African green monkeys (*Cercopithecus aethiops*) the Leydig cells were found to be basically similar to those described in other mammals. The smooth endoplasmic reticulum is more extensive and polymorphic than that found in man [Camatini et al, 1981].

The diameters of the seminiferous tubules and the relative amount of interstitial tissue will vary greatly among primate species and among individuals depending on seasonal factors. Most Tupaiidae, Lemuridae, Daubentoniidae, and Lorisidae show dramatic changes in testicular size relative to the breeding seasons. Among the macaques *M. mulatta* shows more significant changes in testicular volumes than does *M. fascicularis* when housed under identical conditions. The primates with relatively heavy testes relative to body weight, such as chimpanzees, macaques, and baboons, have proportionally more tubular tissue than interstitial tissue. The macaque may have as much as 17 times more tubular tissue per unit of body weight than does the langur [Schultz, 1938]. Among the great apes gorillas have small testes

with few, small tubules and a corresponding relative increase in interstitial tissue [Wislocki, 1942; Hall-Craggs, 1962]. In chimpanzees most of the testicular mass is composed of seminiferous tubules [Martin and Gould, 1981]. In captive gorillas there is frequently fibrosis or sclerosis and atrophy of the tubules [Steiner et al, 1955; Dixson et al, 1980; Foster and Rowley, 1982].

The seminiferous tubules converge and form straight tubules, the tubuli recti. The transitional zone at the junction of the seminiferous tubules with the tubuli recti has been studied in two species of macaque monkeys, *Macaca mulatta* and *M. nemestrina* [Dym, 1974]. The epithelium of the system as examined from the seminiferous tubules toward the tubuli recti showed gradual but significant changes. There was first a decrease in the mature germinal elements so that Sertoli cells and spermatogonia only were found and then Sertoli cells only. These cells became short and finally only the simple cuboidal cells of the tubuli recti were observed. The seminiferous tubules had a diameter of about 300 μm; in the tubuli recti, the diameter was only about 100 μm. There were ultrastructural differences noted in the transitional zone: there was less smooth endoplasmic reticulum, more fine cytoplasmic filaments, an increase in lipid droplets, and the mitochondria were more sparse. The tubuli recti converge to form the rete testis. The rete testis may extend along the axis of the testes or along the posterior surface. The rete testis in the above monkeys were axial and extended from the ducti efferentes at the upper pole to within approximately 1 cm of the lower pole. The rete testes of the bonnet monkey (*M. radiata*) is also of the axial type; ie, it is located more centrally in the testes than peripherally [Flechon et al, 1976]. The luminal surface of the epithelial cells are covered with a brush border and the epithelium varies from flat to low prismatic. Fluid and sperm pass from the testes through a number of relatively small ducts termed the efferent ducts (ductuli efferentes). These efferent ducts then converge to be continuous with the initial segment of the epididymis (ductus epididymidis).

Studies in three species of macaques (*M. mulatta*, *M. fascicularis*, and *M. arctoides*) showed no morphological differences in the efferent ducts between the species [Ramos and Dym, 1977a]. The ducts consisted of 8–16 tubules lined with ciliated and nonciliated epithelial cells. The nonciliated cells had more deeply staining cytoplasm and irregularly shaped, basally located nuclei. The ciliated cells had larger, spherical nuclei found in the mid or apical areas of the cells. At the electron-microscopy level the nuclei in the ciliated cells contained euchromatin, and those in the nonciliated cells contained many heterochromatin clumps. The ducts also contained basal cells, intraepithelial lymphocytes, and macrophages, although the last were more often found in the lumina and periductular tissue. The tissue surrounding the ducts consisted of connective tissue, smooth muscles, blood vessels, and unmyelinated nerve cells. The basal lamina beneath the epithelium was considered to be thick, 2–8 μm in thickness. Marsh and Alexander [1982] noted a thickening of the basal lamina as a consequence of vasectomy. They suggested that many types of injury may also cause such thickening. The number of ciliated cells was reported to be reduced following vasectomy. Concomitant with this observation the investigators noted a two- to four-fold increase in the diameters of the ducts and that the ducts were mainly lined with microvilli.

The nerve fibers into the testes follow the septula, and there are suggested terminations on spermatogenic cells, Sertoli cells, Leydig cells, and free endings in the stroma [Hooker, 1970]. A very comprehensive review of the nerves to the testis, epididymis, and scrotum has been presented by Hodson [1970].

Epididymis

The epididymis is a single, highly convoluted duct that receives spermatozoa from the efferent ducts and transports them to the vas deferens. The epididymis is generally divided into three regions based on external morphology, histology, biochemistry, and characteristics of the sperm contained. These regions are the head or caput epididymis, the body or corpus epididymis, and the tail or cauda epididymis. The caput and cauda are generally larger in external diameter than the corpus and differ in size depending on species and season (see Table 3). During their passage through the epididymis, the spermatozoa undergo a progressive series of morphological and physiological changes [Orgebin-Crist et al, 1975]. The end result of these changes is that the spermatozoa in the cauda epididymis are fully capable of fertilization whereas those in the caput are not. In the following presentation the histology of the epididymis and the appearance of the spermatozoa in its various regions will be described. The section on fluids will describe the biochemical differences between the testicular fluids, the epididymal fluid, semen, and serum.

Ramos and Dym [1977b] described four main cell types that compose the epithelium of the monkey epididymis: principal, apical and basal epithelial cells, and intraepithelial lymphocytes. The principal cells are tall, narrow, columnar cells characteristic of cells involved in absorption and secretion. They have stereocilia on the luminal surface and deep invaginations of the apical cytoplasm, a feature that may be unique to primates. The apical cells are mitochondrion-rich cells that extend from the base of the epithelium to the lumen. The basal cells contain few organelles.

The caput epididymis is sometimes divided into an initial segment or region that is continuous with the efferent duct, and the caput proper. The epithelial cells lining the caput epididymis in monkeys are classified as tall prismatic cells with long stereocilia in *M. radiata* [Flechon et al, 1976] and as very tall columnar or pseudo-strafied epithelium in *M. mulatta* [De Bourne and Bourne, 1975; Ramos and Dym, 1977b]. These minor differences in terms are probably more semantic than real species-related differences. The height of the epithelial cells is greatest in the initial region and slightly less in the caput proper, 108 and 81 μm, respectively, and becomes shorter distally with heights of 69 and 50 μm reported in the corpus and cauda, respectively [Ramos and Dym, 1977b]. Similar values have been reported by Alsum and Hunter [1978]. These latter investigators also reported that as the epithelial height decreased so did the stereocilia height with a concomitant increase in the luminal diameter. The nuclei of the epithelial cells in the initial region are ovoid with a distinct nucleolus [Flechon et al, 1976]. In the caput region the nuclei are located in the basal third of the cells. Ramos and Dym [1977b] reported that the nuclei of the principal cells are spindle-shaped in the initial segment but become highly infolded in the distal caput, corpus, and cauda epididymis.

At the ultrastructure level the primate epididymis has features not found in other mammals [Moore and Pryor, 1981]. The unique features include the presence of small, membrane-bound granules in the basal region of the cytoplasm of principal cells and the unusual proximity of the blood capillary network that surrounds the epididymal epithelium, to the basal lamina. The cytoplasmic granules are not observed to be fused to the plasmalemma. The epididymal tissues of man

TABLE 3. Internal Structures of the Primate Male Reproductive Tract

Genus	Epididymis	Ejaculatory duct	Seminal vesicles	Prostate	Bulbourethral glands	References
Tupaiidae						
Tupaia	Large, prominent cauda	Common, short	Elongated, white	Small, dorsolateral to urethra, pale	Relatively large Large, dark yellow, spherical	Jones, 1971; Collins et al, 1982
Anathana Dendrogale Urogale						
Ptilocerus	Relatively large		Bulky mass, 2 lobes	Large, compact, unilobular, surrounds urethra		
Lemuridae	Fossa between epididymis and testis	Common	Large, coiled, elongated	Large, conical, 3 lobes		
Lemur Lepilemur	Long cauda Cauda well developed	Common	Elongated, bent sacs Large, contains sperm	Small dorsal lobe Two laterodorsal lobes	Relatively large	Petter-Rousseaux, 1964 Petter-Rousseaux, 1964
Hapalemur Cheirogaleus	Large cauda Caput large, seasonal	Very short Very short	Elongated, bent sacs	J-shaped, paired Encircles urethra, prominent lower lobe	Large	Petter-Rousseaux, 1964 Petter-Rousseaux, 1964
Microcebus	Caput less developed	Short	Large, cross-shaped	Two lateral lobes		Petter-Rousseaux, 1964
Phaner	Poorly developed	No common duct	Small, less elaborate	Small	Just below prostate	Petter-Rousseaux, 1964
Indriidae	Swollen caput, well developed	Common	Elongated sacs bent at blind end, size varies seasonally	Large, encircles urethra, 2 lateral lobes	Large, almond-shaped	Petter-Rousseaux, 1964
Indri Propithecus Avahi			Opens into urethra Opens into urethra			
Daubentoniidae Daubentonia	Adherent at caput, not at cauda		Absent or extremely small and diffuse	Voluminous, paired, encircles urethra, prominent verumontanum	Large	Petter-Rousseaux, 1964

Lorisidae		No common duct			
Loris	Caput large, cauda long	Not common	Large	Small, verumontanum glandular	Large, 2× size of prostate
Nycticebus	Similar to *Loris*				Similar to *Loris*
Arctocebus		Not common	Conspicuous organs	Dorsal only	Very large, ovoid
Perodictus		Not common	Conspicuous organs, pyriform	Bilobed, dorsal only, no utricle	Very large
Galago *Euoticus* *Galagoides*		Common		Bilobed, no utricle	
Tarsiidae					
Tarsius	Large fossa	Common, does not enter prostate	Enormous, pear-shaped	Superficially bilobed	Conspicuous
Callithricidae					
Callithrix *Callimico*	Large Elongated, cauda exceeds caput				
Tamarin	Half size of testis, digital fossa, large cauda	Common, does not enter prostate	Relatively small		
Tamarinus (Saguinus) *Leontocebus (Leontideus)*					
Cebidae					
Cebus	Small fossa		Club-shaped	Large, 2 lobes	Large, paired
Saimiri	Small fossa	Common	Relatively large, tubular	Ensheaths urethra, broad, 2 lobes	Small
Aotus			Small, friable	Dorsal to urethra	
Callicebus			Absent	Elongated, narrow	
Pithecia	Yellowish white	Common	Absent	Dorsal and lateral to urethra	

(continued)

TABLE 3. Internal Structures of the Primate Male Reproductive Tract (*Continued*)

Genus	Epididymis	Ejaculatory duct	Seminal vesicles	Prostate	Bulbourethral glands	References
Chiropotes						
Cacajao						
Alouatta	Flattened and broad	Common	Compressed	Not large, flat platelike	Conspicuous	
Ateles	No fossa	Common	Large, lobulated	Two lobes	Paired, ovoid	
Lagothrix	Large caput, digital fossa	Common	Lobulated, narrow, fusiform	Smooth, pyramidal, none ventral	Present	
Brachyteles	Large, caput is very wide, digital fossa	Common	Large, long	Large, surrounds urethra	Large, lobulated	
Cercopithecidae			Large, dense, complex	Two lobes		
Cercopithecus	Triangular in cross section	Common	Single unbranched convoluted tube	Pyramidal	Well developed	
Erythrocebus	Similar to *Cercopithecus*	Common	Elongated, highly coiled	Two lobes	Paired, sausage-shaped	
Mandrillus	Large	Common	Massive, lobulated	Bipartite		
Cercocebus						
Papio	Caput larger than cauda	Common	Paired, massive, lobulated	Compact, not ventral	Very large, compact, bean-shape	
Theropithecus	Like *Papio*, digital fossa	Common	Smaller than *Papio*	Asymmetrical, 2 lobes	As in *Papio*	
Macaca	Enclosed by tunica vaginalis	Common	Lobulated, large, complex branching	Compact, large dorsal	Large and oval	De Bourne and Bourne, 1975
Cynopithecus						
Colobus		Common	Compact, large, fusiform	Large, pyramidal		
Presbytis	Closely attached	Common	Slender, lobulated	Compact, dorsal, 2 lobes	Small, oval	David and Ramaswami, 1971
Nasalis						
Simias						
Rhinopithecus						
Miopithecus	Large caput	Common	Fusiform mass	Pyramidal	Well developed	
Pygathrix						

Hylobatidae					
Hylobates	Laterally compressed	Common	Nodular surface, very convoluted	Glandular, base apposed to bladder neck	Small, paired, lobulated	Hill and Kanagasuntheram, 1959; Matthews, 1946
Symphalangus	Laterally compressed	Common	Smooth surface, more branched	No glandular tissue		
Pongidae						
Pongo		Common	Large			Martin and Gould, 1981
Pan			Very large		Not large Paired	Martin and Gould, 1981
Gorilla	Small	Common	Small	Moderate to small, symmetrical		Martin and Gould, 1981; Wislocki, 1942; Hall-Craggs, 1962; Oelrich, 1978

have greater ultrastructural diversity than those of monkeys.

Several investigators [Flechon et al, 1976; Ramos and Dym, 1977b] have noted that blood vessels push the basement membrane into the epithelium forming pockets, and that the capillaries appear to extend into the epithelium. Ramos and Dym [1977b], however, noted that the basal lamina of the epididymis always remains between the endothelium of the blood vessels and the epithelial cells.

In the rhesus monkey there is little cytodifferentiation of the epididymal epithelial cells until after about 130 days of fetal life [Alexander, 1972]. The epithelial cells of the efferent ducts and caput epididymis undergo surface modifications to become ciliated, or like adult nonciliated cells. Those in the corpus epididymis, and to a lesser degree those in the cauda epididymis, develop stereocilia. Castration between days 106 and 112 of gestation prevents differentiation, but administration of an androgenic drug to the mother will stimulate it. The drop in androgen levels at birth causes the epithelial cells to return to an undifferentiated state until puberty.

Cavicchia [1979] reported that the general geometric arrangement of the tight junctions in the monkey epididymis is similar to that in the rat and that the tight junctions do appear to show some permeability. According to Hinton and Howards [1981], this permeability is limited to small-molecular-weight substances, and caput epdidymis luninal levels of compounds such as inulin did not exceed 7% of the blood level in 18 hours.

In man there is a proximodistal increase in the muscle coat of the efferent ducts and epididymis. In the proximal regions circular smooth muscles predominate. An additional, incomplete layer around the corpus epididymis is formed by scanty strands of longitudinally and obliquely oriented muscles. In the distal cauda epididymis and continuous with the vas deferens there is a three-layer coat of muscle fibers [Baumgarten et al, 1971]. The arrangement of these muscle fibers will be described in the section on the vas diferens below.

As spermatozoa pass through the epididymis they undergo maturational changes and acquire the ability to fertilize ova. (The process of capacitation must still take place before the mature spermatozoa are able to penetrate the vestments around the ovum.) These changes are apparently due to the exposure of the sperm to the environment of the epididymis, at least that of the caput epididymis.

In man the operation of epididymovasostomy, where the caput epididymis is attached to the vas deferens, has reportedly resulted in fertile sperm in the ejaculate. In 1970, Young reported that only 9% of the azoospermic men operated on became fathers although 43% had sperm in the postsurgical ejaculate. Modern microsurgical techniques have undoubtedly improved those statistics. The epididymal environment is under control of the endocrine system in several species—eg, rabbits, rats, hamsters [Orgebin-Crist et al, 1975], and presumably in primates. Most of the research conducted in epididymal physiology has not been done in primates but sufficient reports are available to make it clear that the epididymis of primates does bring about certain biophysical and biochemical changes in spermatozoa during their transepididymal passage (Table 4).

Bedford [1974] noted reports of several changes in nonhuman primate epididymal spermatozoa: the thickened margin of the acrosome becomes attenuated as the sperm pass through the caput, there are changes in the nature of the sperm surface relative to charge density, and there are increases in the number of disulfide lineages within the nuclear chromatin. Hoffer et al [1981] reported that the changes in the rostral segment of the acrosome of sperm from *M. nemestrina* were more striking than those reported in other Old World monkeys. The apical segment of the acrosome in the pigtailed macaque extends beyond the rostral edge of the nucleus and folds under it. This causes an asymmetric shape to the sperm head and a small, hood-shaped apical segment. During epididymal

TABLE 4. Biochemical and Physiological Changes in Sperm During Passage Through the Epididymis

Biochemical
  Increase in water and some electrolytes
  Decrease in P-lipids
  Increase in disulfide bonds
  Decrease in nonnuclear proteins
  Increase in cAMP
  Decrease in cholesterol
  Increase in carnitine
Physiological
  Increase in cold shock susceptibility
  Increase in permeability
  Increase in negative charge
  Increase in specific gravity
  Increase in substrate utilization potential
  Change in motility pattern from circular to linear

sperm maturation, the acrosome contracts down over the nucleus, the hook shape can no longer be observed, and the sperm head becomes symmetrical as in other macaques. The cell membrane over the anterior portion of the sperm head undergoes changes during epididymal sperm maturation. In the caput region the cell membrane adheres tightly to the acrosomal cap except over the apical segment; in the cauda region the cell membrane is loosely applied, appears ruffled and highly irregular, and is separated from the acrosome by a clear space. The membrane is tightly applied to the postacrosomal region. Hoffer et al [1981] also noted that the cytoplasmic droplet appears to be a consistent finding on caput spermatozoa where it extended from the posterior ring (immediately behind the sperm head) caudally one-third to one-half the length of the midpiece. In sperm samples taken from the corpus and cauda regions the droplets had migrated to the caudal end of the midpiece.

Epididymal spermatozoa from the bonnet macaque (*M. radiata*) showed the normal changes in marginal thickness and cytoplasmic droplet migration as described above. Flechon and Hafez [1975] also reported on changes in the motility patterns of sperm in this species depending on the site from which the sperm were recovered. They found no forward motility in the sperm from the testis and efferent ducts, very few and few with forward motility in the cauda epididymis and vas deferens. Alsum and Hunter [1978] reported that in the initial segment of the epididymis of the rhesus monkey, the spermatocrit was 10%, that 92% of the sperm had a proximal cytoplasmic droplet, and that none of the sperm was motile. In the caput proper, the spermatocrit was 49%, with 86% proximal droplets and 5% motility; in the corpus the corresponding values were 60%, 2%, and 15%, and in the cauda the values were 67%, 0%, and 72%. In man 1% of the sperm in the proximal corpus were motile with a grade of 5 (on a scale of 0 [not motile] to 10 [intense progressive motility]) this improved to 20%, grade 6, in the mid corpus; 40%, grade 7, in the distal corpus; 50%, grade 8, in the proximal cauda; and 60%, grade 9, in the distal cauda [Morton et al, 1978].

Amann et al [1976] measured the epididymal transit times of spermatozoa in rhesus monkeys. They reported that in the sexually rested monkey the following transit times, in days, were recorded: caput, 1.1 ± 0.2; corpus, 3.8 ± 0.3; and cauda, 5.6 ± 0.6. In rats the epididymal passage of sperm has been shown to be accelerated when there is an increase in scrotal temperature or a decrease in androgen levels [Foldesy and Bedford, 1982]. We may assume that similar findings would be observed in primates and may be associated with entities such as varicocele. In such conditions there are frequently elevated intrascrotal temperatures and an increase in cytoplsmic droplets and decreased motility of ejaculated sperm, both of which could have resulted from accelerated epididymal passage.

Wong et al [1982] have shown that there are changes in the transepithelial transport of water and some ions in the cauda epididymis when the tissue is exposed to abdominal temperatures. They found that the reabsorption of water, sodium ions, and chloride ions was depressed, and that the secretion of potassium ions was also depressed.

Spermatophagy, phagocytosis of sperm cells, occurs in the testes and epididymides of *M. fascicularis* and *C. aethiops*. The numbers of sperm with swollen midpieces, missing mitochondrial sheaths, or decapitated head decreased from the testis in some instances and from caput to cauda in all animals [Roussel et al, 1967]. The cells that were found to apparently be responsible for the removal of dead or nonfunctional sperm included Sertoli cells, epithelial cells of the rete testis, and macrophages [Holstein, 1978].

Vas Deferens

The vas deferens (ductus deferens) is the portion of the male reproductive tract through which sperm pass from the scrotum to the urethra. Because there is a need for the movement of sperm through the vas to be very rapid during ejaculation, this part of the system is anatomically different from the parts previously discussed. The lumen is bounded by mucosa and is surrounded by a three-layered muscular layer. The innermost muscular layer is oriented longitudinally, the middle one is circumferential, and the outer one is again longitudinal [Batra, 1974; De Bourne and Bourne, 1975]. The orientation of the outer layer has also been described as "rather oblique" in bonnet macaques [Flechon et al, 1976]. The muscle layers vary in thickness along the length of the vas. The middle layer becomes thicker from the distal (epididymal) end to the proximal (urethral) end, whereas the inner layer becomes thinner and is virtually gone at the ampulla [Bastra, 1974].

The epithelium of the lumen of the vas deferens in bonnet macaques is thin and lined with polygonal cells. The epithelial cells are covered with many short microvilli; these microvilli are shorter than the stereocilia of the epididymis [Flechon et al, 1976]. In marmosets (*Callithrix jacchus*) the mucosa was of columnar, pseudo-stratified epithelial cells that contain large quantities of lipid droplets and acid phosphatase [Miraglia et al, 1970]. The muscular layers around the vasa in these animals are similar to those described above. In langurs the lumen of the vas is lined with small columnar cells with stereocilia at their free surface; the ampullar epithelial cells are secretory [David and Ramaswami, 1971]. Tree shrews have a short ampullar region in their vasa, it is lined with simple cuboidal epithelium and divided by connective tissue partitions [Collins et al, 1982]. In subadult gibbons the epithelium differs depending on species. In siamang it was described as stratified columnar with cilia; in hoolock, as nonciliated [Hill and Kanagasuntheram, 1959[.

Ramos [1979] studied the vas deferens in two species of macaque monkeys, *Macaca mulatta* and *M. arctoides*. He divided the vas into four regions: proximal, middle, distal, and ampulla. He reported that the longitudinal folds of the epithelium changed from simple in the proximal region to complex in the ampulla. The stereocilia of the epithelial cell were taller and more regular in the proximal region than in the distal region. There were no granules or cytoplasmic blebbings in the luminal epithelial cells proximally whereas the distal principal cells had large numbers of cytoplasmic granules and apical blebs. The middle region was transitional in nature with either extreme showing characteristics of the adjacent region. These variations suggest that the vas deferens may serve some functions other than just as a conduit for sperm.

Studies in man show that there was ultrastractural differences in the epithelium of the vas deferens following estrogenic treatment [Orlandini et al, 1980]. There was a decrease in the amount of mucosal folding, a decrease in the number of cell apices which present short microvilli, and a disappearance of the apical globular protrusions. It was concluded that there was an overall decrease in absorbent capacity and a fall in secretory function.

The epithelial cells of the human vas deferens have been reported to contain intranuclear inclusion bodies [Chakraborty et al, 1979]. These bodies are of four types: 1) electron-dense homogenous bodies of various shapes and sizes, 2) granular bodies, 3) lipid inclusion bodies, and 4) less electron-dense, filamentous bodies. Their numbers range greatly as do their sizes, with the smaller bodies in older men. The formation of these bodies has been postulated but their function is not known. They appear to be secretory material but have not been characterized.

The muscles of the vas deferens show an absence of any spontaneous movements under rest conditions whereas those of the epididymis show spontaneous, rhythmic contractions. These differences have been correlated to differences in muscle cell types and adrenergic innervation [Baumgarten et al, 1971]. In the upper portion of the system, ie, efferent ducts to initial cauda epididymis, the contractile cells are specialized whereas in the lower portion, ie, distal cauda and vas deferens, the cells are ordinary, large, smooth muscle cells. The amount of norepinephrine in the vas defererns was twice that found in the efferent ducts. Ventura et al [1973] postulated that the intrinsic rhythmicity of the vas was dependent on local concentrations of norepinephrine and that the powerful and coordinated contractions during ejaculation were controlled by release of norepinephrine from sympathetic nerve endings.

Seminal Vesicles

The seminal vesicles (vesiculae seminales) vary considerably among primate species in both size and shape (see Table 3). In *Loris tardigradus lydekerianus* the weights of the seminal vesicles vary during the year, with a peak prior to the breeding period [Ramakrishna and Prasad, 1967]. In rhesus monkeys the glands are relatively compact, spindle-shaped organs. They are conspicuous, densely lobulated masses and are relatively larger than in man [Eckstein, 1958]. The seminal vesicles of the tree shrew are elongated (10 mm), almost pure-white bodies. The interior is partitioned and the alveoli are lined with columnar or cuboidal epithelial cells that contain coarse basophilic secretion granules [Collins et al, 1982]. In the marmoset the seminal vesicles are contorted tubes lined with a columnar, nonciliated, pseudo-stratified epithelium [Maraglia et al, 1970]. The lamina propria beneath the epithelium contains elastic fibers; the tunica muscularis is thinner than that of the vas deferens and consists of an inner circular layer and an outer longitudinal layer. The outer adventitia is formed of loose connective tissue with elastic fibers. In langurs the epithelium of the seminal vesicles is of columnar cells that are extensively secretory [David and Ramaswami, 1971]. Hill and Kanagasuntheram [1959] describe the seminal vesicles in *Symphalangus* as 15 mm long, branches without much folding on itself, and histologically similar to the vas deferens; in *Hylobates* the glands are shorter, without much branching but with extensive folding. The seminal vesicles in the great apes vary considerably in size. In the gorilla the glands are smaller than in man, in the orang-utan they are slightly larger, and in the chimpanzee they are dramatically larger [Martin and Gould, 1981]. The glands in the apes are elongated and lobulated. In the chimpanzee the epithelium is cuboidal and secretory. The seminal vesicles are absent in *Daubentonia* [Roberts, 1972].

The seminal vesicles contribute the bulk of the ejaculatory volume. The fluid from these glands apparently provides the proteinlike substrate for the coagulation of semen, and in humans with congenital absence of seminal vesicles there is no coagulation [Amelar, 1962]. In rhesus monkeys the coagulation is brought about by the action of the secretion from the cranial lobe of the prostate on the secretion from the seminal vesicles [van Wagenen, 1936]. In humans the coagulation of semen appears to be totally due to the fluid from the seminal vesicles and contact with the other accessory gland fluids is not required [Tauber et al, 1980]. The coagulation process and liquefaction of semen are not similar to the mechanisms responsible for blood clotting and lysis. Ponig and Roberts [1978] studied seminal vesicles taken from four species of nonhuman primates (*Saimiri sciureus, Erythrocebus patas, Macaca mulatta,* and *Pan troglodytes*) and found sperm in 11 of 24 specimens examined. One of seven men who died suddenly also had sperm in the distal seminal vesicles. These authors postulated that sperm may be stored in the seminal vesicles, and noted that there was a suggestion of species variation.

The ejaculatory duct (ductus ejaculatorius) in primates is formed by the converging of the distal vas deferens and the duct of the ipsilateral seminal vesicle. The common ejaculatory duct then pierces the prostate and empties into the urethra in the area of the prostatic utricle.

Prostate

Since the prostate is so prominent as a source of disease in man, both as benign prostatis hyperplasia and as adenocarcinoma, there exists a wealth of comparative biological literature on this accessory sex gland in mammals. It is the only accessory sex gland found in all orders of mammals, including monotremes [Price, 1963]. However, homologous relationships of the human prostrate to different mammalian prostate lobes or regions are not clearly established. The prostate in the nonhuman primate usually consists of two histologically distinct divisions, the cranial and caudal lobes, which makes homologous relationships to man much less complex than in such animals as rodents. A single-lobed prostate has been reported in two species of nonhuman primates, a marmoset (*Callithrix jacchus*) and *Pongo pygmaeus* [Miralgia et al, 1970; Roberts, 1972].

Basically, comparative biological data regarding the prostate gland in the primate are available from the literature in three major areas: anatomy, biochemistry, and pathology. The majority of observations and reports deal with the macaque species, primarily the rhesus (*Macaca mulatta*), and the baboon (*Papio* sp.). Therefore, the organization of this section will be presented as observations in these three major areas with discussion of these two genera first, followed by less detailed discussion of other nonhuman primates.

Anatomy. In a comparative mammalian paper on the prostate by Price [1963], it is stressed that homologies fortunately can be traced through embryological studies, since the duct openings into the prostatic urethra remain in the same relative positions in the adult as in the fetus. A study in fetuses by Lowsley [1930] classified the prostate into five lobes: middle, two lateral, posterial, and anterior or ventral. McNeal [1968] has questioned the significance of this system of classification since the boundaries between these lobes are not apparent in the adult and these divisions are based on fetal anatomical data alone. McNeal [1968] described two separate and distinct histologic zones in the adult human prostate, a peripheral zone and a central zone. He does not deny that the posterior lobe described by Lowsley [1930] and Huggins and Webster [1984] may represent a functionally distinct area of the peripheral zone. In the later article, McNeal [1981] describes two other anatomical regions of interest in the human prostate, the preprostatic region and the anterior fibromuscular stroma. The preprostatic region contains the previously described "periurethral glands" and a "transition zone." This latter zone is the theorized site of origin of benign prostatic hyperplasia.

The prostate in the macaque and the baboon can be divided into two distinct lobes, cranial and caudal (Fig. 6A). Grossly and histologically there is a clear distinction between the lobes [van Wagenen, 1936; Price, 1963; Schoonees and DeKlerk, 1968; Roberts, 1972; Blacklock and Bouskill, 1977; Lewis et al, 1981].

The cranial lobe surface is lobulated or furrowed, resembling the seminal vesicle in appearance. This lobe lies inferior to the seminal vesicles, surrounds the terminal vasa deferential and ducts of the seminal vesicles, and lies superior to the caudal lobe from which it can be separated easily except at the anterior-medial junction of these lobes. The cranial lobe acini are larger and more irregular and folded than those in the caudal lobe. There is a prominent fibromuscular stroma dividing the lobe into a definite lobular configuration with blood vessels in the deep intralobular clefts. The epithelial cells lining the cranial acini are single-layered, tightly packed, tall columnar cells with oval or elongated, darkly staining nuclei. The nuclei are oriented with their long axis perpendicular to the prominent basement membrane. The cytoplasm of the epithelial cells is granular and strongly eosinophilic. Nerve bundles are prominent in the capsular area. Blacklock and Bouskill [1977] point out the striking similarity of the cranial lobe acini and the acini of the central zone in man as described by McNeal [1968]. We have confirmed these findings [Lewis et al, 1981]. Others had previously compared the cranial lobe to the middle lobe as described by Lowsley in 1930 [van Wagenen, 1936; Price, 1963].

Semen coagulation appears to be a main function of the cranial lobe of the prostate. Van Wagenen [1936], in an experimental study of the interaction of secretions from the various accessory sex organs in the rhesus monkey (*M. mulatta*), showed that secretions from the cranial lobe when mixed with the secretion of the seminal vesicle caused the formation of the firm white coagulum. It is of interest that secretions from the coagulating gland of the rat also produced a coagulum when mixed with the seminal vesicle fluid of the rhesus [van Wagenen, 1936]. Greer et al [1968] prevented coagulation of electroejaculated semen from two rhesus monkeys by prior surgical removal of the cranial lobe. The formation of the coagulum plug in the monkey aids in the breeding process since the male monkey will dismount the female immediately after ejaculation.

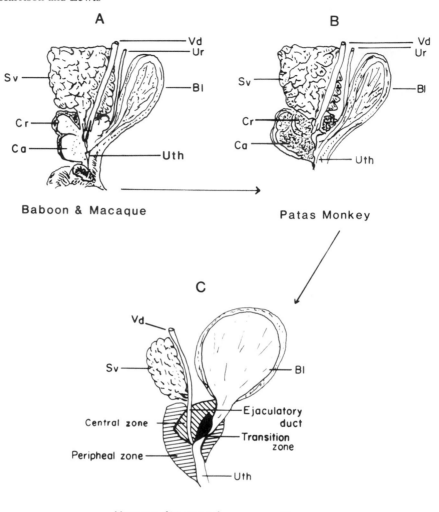

Baboon & Macaque

Patas Monkey

Human (McNeal's concept)

Fig. 6. Comparative anatomy of the nonhuman and human prostate (sagittal views). Bl = bladder; Ca = caudal lobe of prostate; Cr = cranial lobe of pros-tate; Sv = seminal vesicle; Ur = ureter; Vd = vas deferens; Uth = urethra.

In man semen is coagulated but liquefication usually occurs within 30 minutes after ejaculation, suggesting that any coagulation region in man may be functionally vestigial.

The caudal lobe surface is smooth and more closely applied to the urethra, surrounding it on its posterior and lateral surfaces. The ejaculatory ducts pass through the upper portion of this lobe to empty at the verumontanum of the urethra. The caudal lobe acini are for the most part regular, simple tubules lined by low columnar to cuboidal epithelial cells with paler staining nuclei whose elongated long axes are parallel to the basement membrane. The cytoplasm is not very granular and demon-strates pale eosinophilic staining. The fibromuscular stroma is diffuse in the caudal lobe and does not divide the acini into a lobular configuration. Blood vessels and nerve bundles are found scattered throughout the lobe. Blacklock and Bouskill [1977] compared the caudal lobe to the peripheral zone of the human prostate as described by McNeal [1968]; we are in agreement [Lewis et al, 1981]. Others had previously compared the caudal lobe to the lateral lobes as described by Lowsley [1930] in man [van Wagenen, 1936; Price, 1963].

In the gross dissection of patas monkey prostates, there was a more intimate association of the two lobes of the prostate (Fig. 6B). The cranial lobe was anterior to the upper margin of the caudal lobe [Lewis et al, 1981]. The prostate of an adult chimpanzee (*Pan troglodytes*) was recently obtained at the time of autopsy at the Delta Regional Primate Research Center in Louisiana. Gross dissection of the prostate demonstrated very firm adherence of the cranial inferior surface to the caudal lobe. A sagittal section, however, revealed clear anatomical destruction between the two lobes as described above. A suggestion of a similar relationship was seen in illustrations of the lobe of the prostate in the cape chacma baboon (*Papio ursinus*) [Schoonees and DeKlerk, 1968].

Van Camp [1969] noted that among the Anthropoidea the division of the prostate into lobes and lobules with more or less extensive branching was found and that the chimpanzee prostate had the greatest resemblance to that of man.

Chai et al [1981] described ultrastructural differences between the epithelial cells lining the cranial and caudal lobes in the baboon. The cranial secretory granules are homogenous and have a uniform density compared to the caudal lobe secretory granules which have diversified characteristics. The presence of microvilli on the surface of the caudal epithelial cells, rarely seen in the cranial lobe, could be indicative of a non-apocrine secretion as opposed to an apparent cranial lobe apocrine secretion. The mitochondrial matrices of the cranial cells were light and contained small, electron-dense particles. The contour of the nucleus was usually indented in the cranial epithelial cell, whereas in the caudal cells it was oval or nearly round. Endoplasmic reticulum was sparse in the caudal epithelial cell and widely dispersed throughout the cytoplasm of the cranial epithelial cell.

Biochemistry. Zinc is heavily concentrated in the prostate. ^{65}Zinc chloride concentrating ability in the caudal lobe exceeds that found in the cranial lobe in the baboon (*P. ursinus*); a similar concentration gradient is found in the human prostate when the lateral and posterior regions are compared to the anterior and central regions [Schoonees et al, 1969]. In this same study it was shown that castration significantly diminishes ^{65}ZnCl$_2$ in the caudal prostate but not in the cranial. Testosterone treatment significantly increased ^{65}ZnCl$_2$ uptake in both lobes [Schoonees et al, 1969]. The administration of growth hormone in intact baboons (*P. ursinus*) results in a statistically significant reduction of cranial and caudal ^{65}Zn uptake, but not in testosterone-treated animals [Schoonees et al, 1970]. In another study rhesus monkeys were

seen to concentrate ^{65}ZnCl$_2$ in the prostate at levels 15 times greater than dogs [Johnston et al, 1966].

In order to further characterize biochemical differences between the cranial and caudal lobe of the prostate and to compare these lobes to the seminal vesicles, we have recently analyzed several substances in four species of macaques (*M. mulatta*, n = 5; *M. fascicularis*, n = 7; *M. nemestrina*, n = 14; and *M. arctoides*, n = 3) and one species of baboon (*P. cynocephalus*, n = 8) (see Table 5). Tissue content of prostatic acid phosphatase was much higher in the caudal lobe of the prostate than in the cranial lobe and the seminal vesicle (see Fig. 7). This has been previously reported in baboons [Muntzing et al, 1976]. Concentrations of citric acid and total lactate dehydrogenase were alike in the cranial and caudal prostate lobes, both substances showing much lower concentrations in the seminal vesicles. Citric acid in the baboons appeared in equal concentrations in all three glands. As far as the lactate dehydrogenase (LDH) isoenzymes are concerned, the seminal vesicles showed a higher concentration of fraction 3 and less fraction 1 than in both prostate lobes. The cranial lobe had less concentration of fraction 5, similar to the seminal vesicle when compared to the caudal lobe (see Fig. 8). The LDH isoenzymes in the primate migrated in the same pattern as do those in man. Protein content and maltase activity were similar in the prostate lobes and seminal vesicles. Table 6 presents biochemical measurements from the chimpanzee prostate and seminal vesicles. From these data, the cranial lobe of the prostate showed biochemical similarities to both the caudal lobe and the seminal vesicles in a variety of primates.

Early investigators studied the effects of various hormones on the nonhuman primate prostate. Van Wagenen [1935] reported an increase in fibromuscular tissue greater in the cranial lobe than in the caudal lobe in two macaque monkeys which received injections of an estrogen daily for 32–42 days when compared to two controls. There was no change in glandular epithelium. Zuckerman [1938] injected estrogen into two castrated rhesus monkeys for a year and found "prostate" enlargement mainly due to fibromuscular growth in the utricular bed, thus substantiating the above report by van Wagenen of little effect on the glandular epithelium. In a later paper, Zuckerman and Sandys [1939] discussed the effect of steroids hormones on the prostates of juvenile rhesus monkeys. Short-term treatment (14–15 days) was with either estrogen, testosterone, both, or estrogen and progesterone. Although estrogen in the short-term study

TABLE 5. Biochemical Constituents in Nonhuman Primate Prostate and Seminal Vesicle Tissue

	PAP	Maltase	Total LDH	Citric acid	Protein	Fructose
M. mulatta						
P.-cranial	11.3 ± 1.4[1]	58.0 ± 14	139.4 ± 36	11.3 ± 1.9[1]	70.0 ± 13	0.85 ± 0.27
P.-caudal	743.3 ± 147[1]	45.4 ± 9.5	244.9 ± 101	12.0 ± 1.8[2]	64.0 ± 6	0.60 ± 0.14
S.V.	4.5 ± 1.2[1]	69.7 ± 15	51.0 ± 11	4.0 ± 2.3[1,2]	58.3 ± 9	2.36 ± 1.2
M. fascicularis						
P.-cranial	120.0 ± 97[1]	89.7 ± 8.8	144.4 ± 15	6.9 ± 1.2[1]	72.2 ± 8	0.53 ± 0.18
P.-caudal	1585.3 ± 598[1,2]	91.8 ± 10.8	213.0 ± 41[1]	9.5 ± 1.8[2]	60.5 ± 4	0.74 ± 0.11
S.V.	54.9 ± 31[2]	94.0 ± 18.0	99.5 ± 20[1]	2.3 ± 1.7[1,2]	52.7 ± 7	0.67 ± 0.15
M. nemestrina						
P.-cranial	37.1 ± 18[1]	57.7 ± 10.0	131.8 ± 16[1]	9.3 ± 1.3[1]	74.1 ± 5	0.61 ± 0.12
P.-caudal	1499.9 ± 399[1,2]	55.9 ± 8.0	174.4 ± 20[2]	10.3 ± 2.5[2]	66.7 ± 5	0.60 ± 0.10
S.V.	4.0 ± 0.9[2]	64.6 ± 8.1	68.6 ± 12[1,2]	2.5 ± 0.8[1,2]	65.2 ± 5	1.81 ± 0.30
M. arctoides						
P.-cranial	145.0 ± 87	34.5 ± 5.5	175.9 ± 36[1]	8.8 ± 2.4	69.0 ± 4	2.29 ± 0.71
P.-caudal	1872.0 ± 795	35.1 ± 5.5	313.1 ± 76[1,2]	17.3 ± 1.6	73.1 ± 6	2.53 ± 1.10
S.V.	33.9 ± 25	18.3 ± 6.0	118.3 ± 78[2]	6.8 ± 1.3	64.5 ± 5	10.57 ± 6.00
P. cynocephalus						
P.-cranial	68.9 ± 24[1]	61.7 ± 5.1	237.5 ± 83	5.7 ± 1.5	67.1 ± 8	0.21 ± 0.07
P.-caudal	1031.0 ± 505[2]	50.0 ± 4.8	275.7 ± 62[1]	7.4 ± 2.1	71.4 ± 7	0.38 ± 0.10
S.V.	4.1 ± 1[1,2]	64.3 ± 4.7	71.5 ± 8[1]	2.6 ± 1.3	66.0 ± 7	0.51 ± 0.11

Units of measurement: PAP—μg/mg protein/min; maltase—μM/g protein/hr; total LDH—B-B units/μg protein; protein—mg/g wet wt; fructose—mg/g wet wt.
Statistics: For any species-biochemical group those values with the same superscript are significantly different from each other at $P < 0.05$.

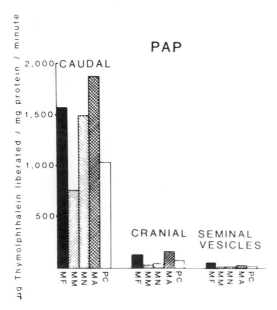

Fig. 7. Prostatic acid phosphatase levels in the caudal and cranial lobes of the prostate and in the seminal vesicles of *Macaca fascicularis* (MF), *M. mulatta* (MM), *M. nemestrina* (MN), *M. arctoides* (MA), and *Papio cynocephalus* (PC).

increased the size of the whole organ significantly, there was no change in the relative percentage of utricular, urethra, or glandular zone compared to controls. Testosterone increased the size of the whole organ by increasing greatly the size of the glandular zone and reducing the relative percentage area of the urethra and utricular regions.

In a small series of adult intact baboons (n = 4, controls, n = 4) given 5 mg of oral diethylstilbesterol (DES) daily for 3 weeks, Chai et al [1981] found variable caudal epithelial cell change. Atrophy of some acini or parts of acini with cuboidal appearance of the epithelial cells and a marked reduction in the formation of secretory granules were seen. In contrast, in the cranial lobe, there was a moderate reduction in cell size and the appearance of numerous inclusion bodies in secondary lysosomes. In addition, nuclear indentation was increased in the cranial epithelial cells, and the nuclear membrane appeared to be dilated.

Androgen receptor content may differ between the caudal and cranial prostate. This was suggested in a study of ten rhesus monkeys studied by Ghanadian et al [1977b]. There was a significantly higher uptake of ³H-testosterone, and the inhibitory effect

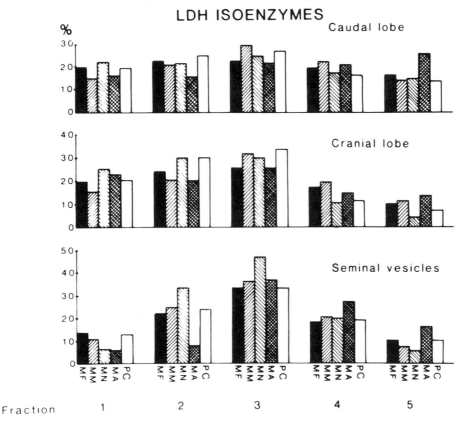

Fig. 8. LDH isoenzymes in the caudal and cranial lobes of the prostates and in the seminal vesicles of *Macaca fascicularis* (MF), *M. mulatta* (MM), *M. nemestrina* (MN), *M. arctoides* (MA), and *Papio cynocephalus* (PC).

TABLE 6. Biochemical Values From a Single Chimpanzee Prostate and Seminal Vesicles

	Cranial prostate	Caudal prostate	Seminal vesicles
Protein	111.0	77.0	122.0
PAP	355.1	7,575.8	102.5
Citric acid	93.0	135.0	80.0

Units of measurement: protein—mg/g wet wt; PAP—µg thymolphthalein released/mg protein/min; citric acid—mg/g wet wt.

of unlabeled testosterone was profoundly greater in the caudal lobe of the prostate. In this study the cranial lobe tissue was similar to seminal vesicle tissue.

In a later study Ghanadian et al [1977a] found the concentration for the total, free, and bound cytosol receptor content of the caudal lobe to be higher than in the cranial lobe in four rhesus monkeys— most significantly in the two mature animals compared to the two younger animals. Similarly cytosol androgenic receptor content was found to be higher in the caudal lobe than in the cranial lobe in an adult male baboon (*Papio anubis*) which had been castrated 24 hours before the prostate studies [Karr et al, 1979].

Ghanadian and Smith [1981] investigated testosterone metabolism in the caudal and cranial lobes of the prostate in rhesus monkeys and found dihydrotestosterone and androstanediol to represent over 80% of the metabolites. Both of these are 5α-reduced metabolites, so reductive pathways are the main route of testosterone metabolism in the prostate compared to liver tissue where androstenedione, an oxidative product, is the major metabolite; ie, the oxidative pathway is negligible in the prostate but important in the liver.

Pathology. The diseases of the prostate commonly occuring in man seem to be rare in the monkey.

Only scanty reports of carcinoma or benign prostatic hyperplasia appear in the literature [Fox, 1923; Engle and Stout, 1940; Roberts, 1972; Adams and Bond, 1979]. The rarity of reported disease may be due to the small number of primates studied, incompleteness of autopsies, and the infrequent study of aged primates.

Pathological data were collected by careful review of histological slides of cranial and caudal prostates in 100 nonhuman primates by one of the present authors (R.W.L.) and others and reported in 1981 [Lewis et al, 1981] (see Table 7). These findings revealed glandular (or cystic) benign hyperplasia in 13% of prostate examined and isolated fibromuscular hyperplasia in approximately 5% of the prostates. Cystic or glandular hyperplasia was more commonly seen in the cranial lobe, but in three species (5% of the total animals) an isolated cystic hyperplasia in the caudal lobe was seen as well. In these animals (*Pan troglodytes, Erythrocebus patas* and *Callicebus moloch*) the cystic enlargement resembled the cystic enlargement seen in the dog, being nodular and localized to one hemisphere of the caudal lobe, rarely impinging upon the urethral lumen (Fig. 9). Dilated acini appear to be located for the most part in the peripheral area of the lobe. There was no compression of normal prostatic tissue against the true prostatic capsule. The fibromuscular hyperplasia was characterized by a marked proliferation of smooth muscle fibers replacing glandular epithelium. This was found in both lobes of the prostate equally. Adams and Bond [1979] reported nodular enlargement in three of four regions of prostate in a squirrel monkey (*Saimiri sciureus*) estimated to be 11 years of age. This nodular enlargement of right and left portions of the cranial lobe and right portion of the caudal lobe (the left caudal lobe appeared normal) was characterized histologically by hypertrophic and hyperplastic glands surrounded by hyperplastic smooth muscle.

In our 1981 report, a finding consistent with a well-differentiated adenocarcinoma of the prostate was presented in an aged squirrel monkey (*Saimiri sciureus*) [Lewis et al, 1981]. This animal had been sacrificed because of inanition from senility. The animal had muscular atrophy, teeth completely worn to the gums, hepatic atrophy, and acute focal myocardial degeneration. On a transverse section of the prostate at the caudal level there was a nodule in one hemisphere that showed a marked glandular disorganization and invasion of stroma

TABLE 7. Species Represented in 100 Prostatic Tissues Examined

Species	Number of prostates examined
Macaca mulatta	25
Pan troglodytes	13
Macaca fascicularis	10
Callicebus moloch	10
Erythrocebus patas	9
Saimiri sciureus	8
Macaca arctoides	8
Papio (comatus + papio)	2
Cerocebus	2
Macaca radiata	1
Ateles geoffroyi	1
Hylobates lar	1
Unknown[a]	10
Total	100

[a]Genus not designated on stained slides.

with glandular epithelia in nests and cords. Epithelial cells were irregular with pleomorphic nuclei and hypertrophic nuclei. The abnormal architecture in this nodule was isolated and differed from the more linear distribution of the surrounding prostate in this section. There was no other region that showed the marked pleomorphism of glandular architecture. Inflammatory cells were rare in this nodule. Findings consistent with adenocarcinoma of the prostate were 1) distortion of normal architecture, 2) irregularity of glandular pattern with pleomorphism of cells lining this glands, 3) pleomorphic nuclei and hypertrophied nucleoli, and 4) invasion of single or groups of epithelial cells into stroma. Only one other carcinoma of the prostate has been reported, that being in an aged *Macaca mulatta* [Engle and Stout, 1940].

Other pathological findings reported in our series were the following: 1) acute and chronic prostatitis; 2) corpora amylacea and calcified concretions, similar to prostatic calculi seen in man; 3) squamous metaplasia; 4) thrombic and nonspecific perivasculitis; 5) nonspecific hemorrhage; and 6) steatitis [Lewis et al, 1981].

Bulbourethral and Urethral Glands

Bulbourethral Glands. The bulbourethral glands, or Cowper's glands, drain into the pelvic urethra in its bulbar region. Their exact function is not clear; in the pig they aid in the process of gelation [Mann, 1964] but in primates it is believed that

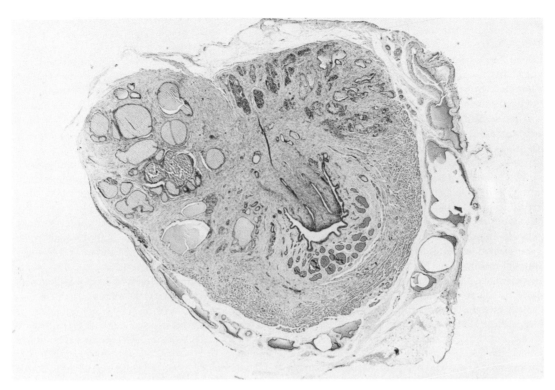

Fig. 9. Transverse section of whole mount of caudal lobe of prostate showing a cystic hyperplasic nodule in an adult callicebus (*Callicebus moloch*). ×5. [Used with permission, Lewis et al, 1981.]

they aid in the lubrication of the urethra in the first stage of ejaculation [Polakoski and Zaneveld, 1977].

In rhesus monkeys the bulbourethral glands are spindle-shaped and narrow; their width and breadth are equal, and the external surface is smooth [Sikorski, 1978]. The anterior poles insert into the urethra at the angle between the pelvic urethra and the bulb of the penis. Because of their length the glands protrude beyond the posterior border of the bulb.

In man the glands are usually wider, shorter, and, in some individuals, more irregular on the surface. There is also less distance between the glands than in the rhesus monkeys [Sikorski, 1978]. The glands in man have been described as pea-sized, yellowish-brown structures, branched tubuloalveolar glands, lined with simple low cuboidal to columnar epithlium, each gland divided by septa containing collagen, elastic and reticular fibers, skeletal and smooth muscle fibers [Hafez, 1980].

The male reproductive tract of a *Tupaia* (*T. ferraginea*) was examined by Jones [1971] who described the bulbourethral glands as glandular bodies, dark yellow in color, and 7 mm in the long axis. The ducts opened into the bulbar portion of the urethra. A more recent study in *Tupaia belangeri* [Collins et al, 1982] found the bulbourethral glands to be spherical bodies, 5 mm in diameter. Internally they were divided by connective tissue into small alveoli containing acidophil secretions. The epithelium was of simple cuboidal cells with round nuclei, a prominent nucleolus, and pronounced perinuclear basophilia.

In langurs the glands are tubuloalveolar with thick strands of elastic fibers and striated muscles in the interalveolar space. The epithelial cells are cuboidal or columnar with basal nuclei and the secretory cells are of the merocrine type [David and Ramaswami, 1971].

Hill and Kanagasuntheran [1959] described the glands in gibbons as small, lobulated bodies, 3 mm in diameter, lying on either side of the membranous urethra proximal to the bulb of the urethra. The ducts were about 10 mm in length and opened into the bulbus urethra. It should be noted that of the seven animals in the report, one was newborn, two were juveniles, one was immature, two were subadults, and only one was an adult.

In the great apes the bulbourethral glands have been described only in the chimpanzee. Graham and Bradley [1972] noted that they were not recognizable macroscopically even in the chimpanzee. The tissue consisted of scattered alveoli and ducts. The glands were lined by a mucous type of epithelium with round, basally located nuclei. The ducts were relatively large and usually lined with cuboidal or pseudo-stratified epithelial cells with round nuclei, although some tubules were lined with tall columnar cells with elongated nuclei. Histochemical studies showed the bulbourethral glands to be periodic acid Schiff (PAS)-positive in all cells and the succinic dehydrogenase reaction to be restricted mainly to the epithelium [Bourne and De Bourne, 1972].

Urethral Glands. The urethral glands, or Littré glands, are usually a simple outpocketing of the urethral mucosa but may appear as a globular secretory segment connected by a short duct to the cavernous portion of the urethra [Hafez, 1980]. In the chimpanzee they appeared as diverticula associated with the membranous urethra. They were not found in the penile urethra of the chimpanzee [Graham and Bradley, 1972]. For other reports on the urethral glands see the following section.

Table 3 summarizes the internal structures of the male primate reproductive tract as discussed above. It is apparent that the data base is far from complete.

Urethra

The primate urethra is usually thought of as part of the urinary system, but in the male it is equally important as part of the reproductive tract. It is usually described as having three regions because of its anatomical location. The urethra from the bladder to the verumontanum, or urethral crest, is the prostatic urethra; from the urethral crest through the external sphincter it is the membraneous urethra; and from there to the external urinary meatus it is the penile urethra. As a subregion, the portion of the urethra in the bulb of the penis is sometimes referred to the bulbus urethra.

The urethra from six species of nonhuman primates (rhesus monkeys, stump-tailed macaques, patas monkeys, titi monkeys [*Callicebus moloch*], squirrel monkeys and chimpanzees) were examined by Roberts and Seibold [1971]. They reported the prostatic urethra as lined with transitional epithelium that became stratified-columnar as it left the prostate. The mucosa of the membraneous urethra was stratified or pseudo-stratified columnar epithelium. The penile urethra was similarly lined with stratified or pseudo-stratified epithelium with noted intraepithelial and periurethral glands—ie Littré glands. A small amount of circular smooth muscle encircled the larger amount of longitudinal smooth muscle and cavernous tissue. The thin, loose connective tissue was external to the muscle.

The urethra of squirrel monkeys varied from the above pattern in that the mucosa in the distal prostatic, membranous, and penile urethra was uniformally pseudo-stratified columnar cells. The penile urethra of the chimpanzee was deeply folded with the basal cells appearing as stratified and the luminal cells as cuboidal.

The fossa navicularis was found to be lined with stratified squamous epithelium in the above animals.

In gibbons the penile urethra was slightly dilated in the bulb but elsewhere was collapsed, giving a stellate lumen in cross section [Hill and Kanagasuntheram, 1959]. Minute blind pockets, or urethra lacunae, were noted, as found in humans [Grant, 1962]. The submucosa of *Hylobates* contained numerous glands with ducts that penetrated the mucous membrane.

In the siamang and hoolock the prostatic urethral epithelium is of a transitional type of three to six layers. The penile urethra in hoolock has a lining of transitional epithelium that changes in the glands to stratified squamous epithelium; there are glandular outgrowths in both areas. In siamang the penile urethral epithelium is similar but without the glandular outgrowths [Hill and Kanagasuntheram, 1959].

FLUIDS OF THE MALE REPRODUCTIVE TRACT

Introduction

Most of the reports associated with the biochemical analysis of testicular and epididymal fluids from mammals have had domestic animals (rams, bulls, boars) and common laboratory rodents (hamsters, rats) as their subjects [Setchell, 1974]. Among the limited studies using nonhuman primates, the rhesus monkey has been the primary subject for many years, since this was the nonhuman primate species used most in all research. Comparative studies conducted in several species by the same investigators are rare but serve to show that there are noticeable species differences. Hinton et al [1980, 1981] used micropuncture techniques to obtain epididymal fluid from three rhesus monkeys and one baboon (*P. cynocephalus*). They reported the following values for myoinositol, expressed in mM in the rhesus and baboon, respectively: proximal caput—25.11 and 3.50; mid corpus — 18.26 and 5.90; proximal cauda — 17.02 and 1.30. These results indicate that extrapolation of data between species must be done with a realization that significant differences do exist. There are also differences depending on the method of analysis. Zinc levels in human semen, when measured by atomic absorption spectrophotometry, were found to be 15 mg%, and when measured by neutron activation analysis were 18.9 mg% [Marmar et al, 1975].

As mentioned above, the fluids vary from one region of the male reproductive tract to the next because of both absorptive and secretive mechanisms. While the base for all body fluids is the blood, significant differences between blood and reproductive-tract fluids are observed. In Table 8 some of these differences are obvious. Testicular fluid, in both man and rhesus monkey, has more lactic dehydrogenase, glucose-6-phosphatase dehydrogenase, lactic acid, and ascorbic acid then does serum while the converse is true relative to glucose and total lipids. In rats, approximately 65% of the total testicular fluid is secreted by the rete testis epithelium [Waites, 1977].

Epididymal Fluids

Changes in the composition of epididymal fluids have been studied in rhesus monkeys and langurs and are summarized in Table 9. Note that in the rhesus monkeys total protein and sialic acid appear to decrease in concentration whereas in langurs the

TABLE 8. Biochemical Parameters of Serum and Testicular Fluids From Men and Rhesus Monkeys

Parameter	Man		Rhesus monkey	
	Testicular fluid	Serum	Testicular fluid	Serum
pH	7.0	7.5	7.2–7.4	7.4–7.6
Total protein (gm/100 ml)	3.71	7.18	4.63	1.27
Lactic dehydrogenase (units/mg protein/min)	0.251	0.0007	0.154	0.0045
Glucose-6-phosphatase DH (Racker units/100 ml)	6.3	2.3	4.0	2.3
Glucose-6-phosphatase DH (units/ml)	5,250	0.0	6,533	0.0
Acid phosphatase (mg P/100 ml/hr)	112.4	0.0	91.4	1.8
Alkaline phosphatase (mg P/100 ml/hr)	19.23	4.5	29.1	44.7
Hyaluronidase (units/100 ml)	0.0	0.0	0.0	0.0
Glucose (mg/100 ml)	21.1	73.0	30.4	131.7
Glycogen (mg/100 ml)	20.2	3.0	26.3	6.5
Lactic acid (mg/100 ml)	600.0	46.8	579.0	92.0
Ascorbic acid (mg/100 ml)	30.9	0.134	9.93	0.336
Total lipids (mg/100 ml)	281.32	656.25	141.55	453.67
P-lipids (mg/100 ml)	19.93	246.55	18.37	157.53
Sodium (meq/liter)	183.12	146.33	191.29	179.57
Potassium (meq/liter)	7.76	5.12	8.18	5.63
Calcium (meq/liter)	3.78	5.71	3.13	6.85
Chloride (meq/liter)	139.65	115.37	127.62	114.32

Data adapted from Pande et al [1969].

TABLE 9. Biochemical Parameters in Epididymal Fluids From Nonhuman Primates

Parameter	Rhesus			Langur		
	Caput	Corpus	Cauda	Caput	Corpus	Cauda
pH	6.7 (1)	6.7 (1)	7.0 (1) 7.0 (2)			
Total protein (gm/100 ml)[a]	141.1 (3)	0.95 (4)	7.4 (2)	143.6 (5)	135.6 (5)	137.0 (5)
Acid phosphatase (mg P/100 ml/hr)	1.67 (1)	0.52 (1)	0.36 (1)			
Alkaline phosphatase (mg P/100 ml/hr)	5.06 (1)	8.14 (1)	10.32 (1)	5.5 (5)	6.0 (5)	7.5 (5)
Hyaluronidase (units/mg)	133 (1)	165 (1)	173 (1)			
Glycogen (mg/100 gm)	38.4 (3)	31.6 (3)	41.0 (3)			
Total lipids (mg/10^8 cells)	15.73 (4)	2.09 (4)	0.56 (4)			
P-lipids (mg/10^8 cells)[b]	25.13 (3) 3.52 (4)	14.02 (3) 0.45 (4)	16.5 (3) 0.13 (4)			
Lactic acid (mg/gm)	3.48 (3)	3.20 (3)	3.41 (3)			
Sialic acid (mg/gm)	51.06 (6)	48.6 (6)	37.1 (6)	530 (5)	490 (5)	560 (5)
GPC (mg/gm)[c]	4.1 (3)	4.45 (3)	7.32 (3) 2396 (2)			
Sodium (mg/gm)	3.09 (1)		3.42 (1) 18.2 (2)			
Potassium (mg/gm)	2.35 (1)		1.69 (1) 49.2 (2)			
Chloride (mg/gm)	2.68 (1)		3.42 (1) 10.5 (2)			
Total phosphorous (mg/100 ml)			238 (2)			
Inorganic phosphorous (mg/100 ml)			5.2 (2)			
Acid-soluble phosphorous (mg/100 ml)			230 (2)			
Lactic dehydrogenase (IU)			1845 (2)			

[a]Protein values for (4) are expressed as mg/10^8 cells.
[b]P-lipid values for (3) are expressed as mg/gm.
[c]GPC values for (2) are expressed as mg/100 ml.
References: (1) Riar et al, 1973b; (2) Jones, 1978; (3) Riar et al, 1973a; (4) Arora et al, 1975; (5) Gupta and Dixit, 1981; (6) Bose and Kar, 1968.

changes are minor or not apparent. Both species have decreases in total lipids and acid phosphatase and increases in alkaline phosphatase. These changes are reflected in sperm changes observed during epididymal transit, as indicated in Table 4.

Carnitine levels were found to be higher in the epididymis than in the testis, vas deferens, prostate, and seminal vescles [Bøhmer et al, 1978]. Maltase activity was reported to be greater in the epididymis, least in the prostate, and intermediate in the testis [Chapdelaine et al, 1978]. Inhibin levels were found to be highest in the prostate (2.060 ng/mg protein) and declining in the seminal vesicles (72.0), testis (36.2), and epididymis (28.1) [Vaze et al, 1980].

Semen

The biochemical parameters in normal human semen and in semen from men classified as oligospermic, azoospermic, and postvasectomy are presented in Table 10. In the last column data on semen from men with absent vasa deferentia, and

TABLE 10. Biochemical Parameters in Human Semen

Parameter	Normal	Oligospermic	Azoospermic	Postvasectomy	Absent vas[a]
pH	7.5–8.2 (1)				6.3–6.5 (1)
Fructose (mg%)	260 ± 9 (1) 296 ± 19 (2)	317 ± 17 (2)	323 ± 21 (2)	268 (3)	16 ± 5 (1)
Acid phosphatase[b]	1,536 ± 140 (2)	1,718 ± 136 (2)	1,858 ± 193 (2)	36.9×10^3 (3)	
Citric acid (mg%)	408 ± 12 (1) 480 ± 32 (2)	448 ± 31 (2)	523 ± 44 (2)	347.7 (3)	1,788 ± 94 (1)
Ascorbic acid (mg%)	12 ± 1 (2)	10 ± 1 (2)	10 ± 1 (2)		
GPC (mg%)	69 ± 3 (1) 23.4 (4)				9 ± 1 (1)
Carnitine (mg%)	7.0 ± 3 (5) 5.1 (4)	1.7 (5)	0.9 (5)	0.420 (5)	
Prolactin (mg/ml)	46.6 ± 2.0 (6)				
PG E (µg/ml)	63.5 ± 49.3 (7)				
PF F (µg/ml)	2.6 ± 1.9 (7)				
Zn (mg%)	11.8 ± 2.3 (8) 16.5 ± 0.4 (9)				
Mg (mg%)	13.1 ± 2.9 (9)				
Ca (mg%)	31.9 ± 0.5 (9)				
Na (mg%)	329.1 ± 4.2 (10)				
K (mg%)	113.9 ± 2.7 (10)				

[a]Reference did not state but would appear to have absent seminal vesicles.
[b]Acid phosphatase values expressed in King-Armstrong units/100 ml except for postvasectomy value which is in IU/ml.
References: (1) Calamers and Lavieri, 1974; (2) Videla et al, 1981; (3) Nikkanen, 1978; (4) Frenkel et al, 1974; (5) Wetterauer and Heite, 1978; (6) Segal et al, 1978; (7) Tusell and Gelpi, 1980; (8) Skandham, 1981; (9) Homonnai et al, 1978; (10) Skandham and Mazumdar, 1981.

presumably absent seminal vesicles, are presented. Few biochemical markers are of significant value in determining fertility status; carnitine concentration appears to be one of these, and this may be due to its bonding to sperm so that the concentration of carnitine and sperm are parallel.

In semen from azoospermic patients receiving testosterone propionate there were elevations of the following, in order: acid phosphatase, fructose, sialic acid, and alkaline phosphatase; there were no changes in cholesterol and ascorbic acid [Roy et al, 1975]. In split ejaculates from normal men there were higher concentrations of the following in the first fraction: spermatozoa, IgG, IgA, albumin, and transferrin; in the last fraction (seminal vesicle fraction) there were higher concentrations of fructose and lactoferrin. There was no IgM, $\beta_1 C/\beta_1 A$-globulin, ceruloplasmin, or fibrinogen detected [Tauber et al, 1975].

The major carbohydrate in humen semen is fructose, with lesser quantities of L-fucose, galactose, glucose, sorbitol, and inositol [Nissen et al, 1978]. Zinc-containing glycoproteins in human seminal plasma are prostatic in nature and include glycoproteins that contain N-acetyl-D-galactosamine, α-fucose, and neuraminic acid [Herrman, 1975]. The predominant amino acids in human semen are aspartic acid, serine, glycine, leucine, and lysine [Nissen et al, 1979]. These amino acids appear to have some diagnostic value, and in azoospermia the levels of basic and acidic amino acids are less than in oligospermia [Fröhlich et al, 1980]. the free fatty acids (FFAs) of major importance in human semen are palmitic, stearic, myristic, and oleic acid. There is a decrease in some of these FFAs in azoospermia [Hamfler et al, 1978]. The acid phosphatase levels in human semen show a positive correlation with citrate levels [Heite and Wetterauer, 1979].

Enzyme studies in semen have shown that a trypsin inhibitor may be associated with infertility [Herschlauser, 1974]. An antifertility factor from human semen was found to be heat-labile, to have a high molecular weight, and to affect the sperm but not the oocyte [Reddy et al, 1982]. In monkeys seminal trypsinlike activity is absent [Stambaugh and Buckley, 1970].

Three biochemical substances, lactic acid, citric acid, and fructose, were evaluated in sperm and plasma fractions from semen collected from 11 species of nonhuman primates and man [Ackerman and Roussel, 1968]. These data are presented in Table 11. Obvious species differences are found with all three substances.

TABLE 11. Biochemical Parameters in Sperm and Plasma Fractions of Semen From Nonhuman Primates

Species (n)	Lactic acid SF[a]	Lactic acid PF[b]	Citric acid SF	Citric acid PF	Fructose SF	Fructose PF
Tupaia glis (1)	215	180	20	—	0	0
Cebus apella (3)	0	4	13 ± 19	79 ± 85	0	563 ± 496
Saimiri sciureus (8)	42	151	3 ± 4	48 ± 14	0.4 ± 1	110 ± 129
Erythrocebus patas (19)	34 ± 21	194 ± 222	31 ± 52	127 ± 62	18 ± 39	315 ± 274
Cercopithecus aethiops (6)	20 ± 12	192 ± 196	5 ± 10	122 ± 25	10 ± 16	264 ± 175
Macaca mulatta (23)	32 ± 30	138 ± 115	2 ± 5	157 ± 86	14 ± 28	753 ± 900
Macaca fascicularis (7)	36 ± 17	239 ± 88	0	101 ± 65	7 ± 13	299 ± 264
Macaca arctoides (10)	28 ± 30	183 ± 186	6 ± 9	231 ± 121	0	262 ± 108
Theropithecus gelada (1)	10	130	16	168	0	160
Hylobates lar (3)	—	—	—	—	0	3 ± 5
Pan troglodytes (10)	24 ± 16	160 ± 127	15 ± 24	256 ± 191	10 ± 30	497 ± 363
Man (9)	50 ± 29	96 ± 26	83 ± 112	347 ± 129	2 ± 6	56 ± 38

[a]Sperm fraction—all parameters expressed in mg/100 ml.
[b]Plasma fraction—all parameters expressed in mg/100 ml.
Data adapted from Ackerman and Roussel [1968].

It is apparent that more biochemical studies are required before there will be a clear understanding of the composition of the fluids of the male reproductive tract. It has been shown, for example, that specific macromolecules are lost, masked, or added to the surface of spermatozoa during ejaculation [Young et al, 1982], so we know that dynamic changes are taking place throughout the system. Previous studies have not correlated seasonal reproductive cycles to changes in the fluids studied, but we would expect that such changes should occur. As microanalytical techniques, such as those described by Hinton and Howards [1982] for micropuncture and microperfusion of the testes, improve our understanding of the reproductive tract fluids, it may eventually be possible to recover testicular spermatozoa and culture them in vitro to their full fertilizing capacity. The selection of specific sites in the male reproductive tract to direct contraceptive agents will also be feasible as our skills and understanding improve [Hinton, 1980]. Recent books on the biochemistry of reproductive fluids are available for both comparative and human studies [Mann and Lutwak-Mann, 1981; Zaneveld and Chatterton, 1982].

VASCULAR ANATOMY

The vascular anatomy of the rhesus monkey was studied using a latex injection technique [Dierschke et al, 1975]. The internal spermatic (testicular) arteries arose from the abdominal aorta between the origins of the renal and inferior mesenteric arteries. From its origin to the inguinal canal the artery was relatively straight whereas from the inguinal canal to the testes the artery was highly convoluted. The testicular portion of the artery passed alongside the epididymis, across the posterior medial surface. As it passed around the distal pole to the lateral ventral side it made a series of S-shaped curves. On the lateral ventral surface it branched and the arteries then passed into the deeper portions of the testes.

The arteries to the epididymis originated from the pampiniform plexus; the testicular veins and the veins from the epididymis enter the pampiniform plexus. This pampiniform plexus is a network of vessels between the testis and inguinal canal and consists of numerous veins intertwined around the spermatic artery. Venous anastomoses around the artery result in a large area of surface contact. The veins converge so that only two or three pass through the inguinal canal. There is usually only one vessel on the left that enters the

left renal vein and one on the right that enters the vena cava.

Harrison [1949] described the arterial supply to the testes in 11 nonhuman primate species. Some differences were observed. In the Platyrrhini the vascular pattern was simple but in Catarrhini the vascular pattern was more complicated, especially in the Cercopithecidae. These all had markedly convoluted arteries on the testicular surface. In *Pan* the artery convoluted slightly and passed almost straight up to the anterior border of the testis. In *Hylobates* the artery was only slightly convoluted. The artery in the gorilla was similar to that in the chimpanzee—ie, convoluted in the spermatic cord and down the epididymal border, curved around the caudal pole of the testis, and then up the anterior border [Setchell, 1970].

In man there are lymphatic capillaries near the testis in close association with the ductus deferens. Collecting vessels are arranged around the pampiniform plexus and converge toward the inguinal canal. The proximal lymphatics have several layers of muscles and valves [Möller, 1980].

The testicular blood supply, lymphatic drainage, and fluid secretion in a wide variety of animal species were summarized by Setchell [1970].

RUDIMENTS OF FEMALE DUCT SYSTEM

Rudiments of the female duct system have been found in a number of primates [Zuckerman and Parkes, 1935, 1936a,b]. The term "uterus masculinus" is used to describe structures of Müllerian duct origin and "vagina masculina" to describe those of urogenital sinus origin. The urogenital sinus is a neutral primordium giving rise to either male or female structures; however, the Müllerian duct either regresses in the male or persists as rudimentary structures. Alcala and Conaway [1968] studied these structures in tree shrews. A distinct uterus masculinus was reported in *Lyonogale tana, L. dorsalis, Tupaia minor, T. montana,* and *T. palawanensis.* In all specimens of *T. longipes, T. glis, T. chinesis, T. gracilis,* and *Urogale everetti* examined, the uterus masculinus was absent but a vagina masculina was present. The accessory glands in all the tree shrews studied were essentially similar with the exception of the presence or absence of these rudimentary structures.

In the adult *L. tana* the uterus masculinus in cross section had a lumen with much folding and many glands. The glands were simple branched and unbranched tubular glands. The epithelium of the lumen and the ducts was simple columnar. In all specimens the uterus masculinus opened into the urethra via a vagina masculina. The epithelium gradually transformed into stratified cuboidal cells as the uterus approached the urethra. The vagina masculina had transitional epithelium with indistinct nonfunctional glands.

Minor differences were noted between the various specimens studied, but the general conclusion was that the uterus masculinus in adult male tree shrews has transformed into a functional accessory reproductive gland [Alcala and Conaway, 1968].

FINE STRUCTURE OF SPERM

Human Sperm

In the lower life forms there is a great amount of variability in the shape of sperm. In certain Crustacea the sperm are tailless, in some lungfish they have two tails; the heads may be long and slender, as in some reptiles, hooked, spade-shaped, or even twisted like a corkscrew. In primates there are significant differences between sperm from various species but there are also many similarities. The mature primate sperm has been described as having four component parts: 1) the head which contains the chromatin material in a nucleus and is partly covered by the acrosome; 2) the neck which consists of the basal plate, connecting pieces, and a centriole; 3) the midpiece which contains the mitochondria; and 4) the tail or principal piece [Fawcett, 1958] (see Fig. 10). At the scanning-electron-microscope level the structure of most primate spermatozoa is one of a relatively smooth anterior region, a rough posterior region (postnuclear sheath), and a common boundary between them [Matano et al, 1975].

The human sperm have been studied in great detail and are characterized by extreme pleomorphism [Gould, 1980]. Human spermatozoa are described as having a broad, paddle-shaped head that is relatively thin in a vertical dimension. There is an apparent differentiation of the nuclear material into anterior and posterior segments [Zamboni et al, 1971]. The mitochondrial sheath is modest and there are relatively few (10–15) gyres or turns in the mitochondrial helix. Most significant is the heterogeneity seen in ejaculates of men of normal fertility. These include variation in the shape of the nucleus, surface depressions [El-Minawi et al, 1970], vacuoles within the nuclear chromatin [Pedersen, 1974], and variation in structural quality of the nucleus as determined by its response to reagents that cleave structural bonds [Bedford et al,

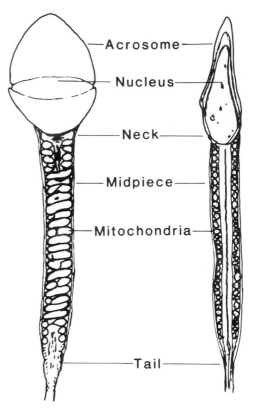

Fig. 10. Drawing of mature, "typical" primate sperm showing main anatomical components. Right drawing is of sagittal section through the sperm at a right angle to the view of the left drawing.

1973a]. Pathologic features may include abnormal formation of the acrosome [Bedford et al, 1973b], cytoplasmic droplets, distortions of the mitochondrial arrangement, and variations of the mitochondrial number [Bedford, 1974].

The neck region is arbitrarily defined as the region limited anteriorly by a plane through the implantation plate and posteriorly by a plane at the level of the anterior end of the flagellum. This includes the distal centriolar area. The dominant features of this region are the centriole (the proximal centriole), the region of the distal centriole (not found in mature spermatozoa), and the connecting piece [Pedersen, 1974]. Zamboni and Stefanini [1971] studied the fine structure of the neck region of spermatozoa from ejaculates of *M. mulatta, M. nemestrina,* and man. They reported that the striated columns that extend into the tail implant on the proximal centriole. This proximal centriole appears to be the basal body of the flagellum and the center of the sperm motility. The central tubules of the axoneme of the flagellum terminate at the lower vault of the centriole. The flagellum of the sperm consists of nine dense outer fibers surrounding the nine peripheral doublets and two singlets of the axial filament complex.

The mitochondrial sheath in the human sperm is less well organized than that of other mammalian species. The matrix is nearly homogenous, and the mitochondria are closely opposed to each other. The anterior portion of the midpiece is surrounded by cytoplasm continuous with the neck cytoplasm; the posterior portion has very little cytoplasm between the cell membrane and the surface of the mitochondria. At the posterior end of the midpiece is a ring of circumferentially oriented fibrillar material, the annulus [Pedersen, 1974]. Changes in the axial complex in the distal midpiece have been reported in *M. fascicularis* monkeys receiving gossypol [Shandilya et al, 1982].

The tail, or principal piece, of the human sperm is characterized by the presence of the fibrous sheath. This sheath consists of dense homogenous material arranged in two longitudinal columns. These columns are connected by semicircularly oriented anastomosing ribs. The axonemes, derived from the fibers of the neck region, appear as nine doublets around a central doublet or paired singlets. The fibrous columns are connected to doublets 3 and 8 by continuous laminae [Pedersen, 1974]. This arrangement appears to serve as a supportive mechanism.

The end of the human sperm tail is composed of the axoneme covered by the cell membrane only. The arms of the doublet disappear and the fibers take on a hollow appearance. The fibers gradually terminate as the end piece tapers near its tip.

Nonhuman Primate Sperm

There are species differences in the ultrastructure of primate spermatozoa. In *G. senegalensis* there is a complex system of membranes that envelop the neck and the anterior midpiece. The human sperm has no subacrosomal space or perforatorium, a structure that is quite prominent in lorisid or macaque spermatozoa. The cell membrane that overlies the acrosome cap only occasionally displays a swollen, distorted form in anthropoid sperm, but it is quite common in the spermatozoa of Prosimii. The sperm of humans have a significant proportion of their numbers with

abnormal features; this is in contrast to the sperm obtained from lorisid and macaque monkeys [Bedford, 1967].

The sperm of the orang-utan have a flat, paddle-shaped head that is relatively large. The tail is centrally attached to the posterior border of the head and the acrosome extends over the anterior three-fourths of the sperm head. The sperm are relatively uniform in the orang-utan whereas those of the gorilla are extremely pleomorphic. The gorilla sperm heads are small, much thickened posteriorly, with a thinning or hollowing anteriorly; this appearance is referred to as "clog-shaped." The midpiece is relatively short and disorganized with few mitochondria, quite similar to that of man [Gould, 1980].

The spermatozoa from chimpanzees (*Pan troglodytes* and *P. paniscus*) are more uniform. While the sperm heads are relatively small and thickened posteriorly, they do not have the clog shape seen in the gorilla sperm. The midpiece is similar to that of gorilla and man.

The sperm from various Cercopithecidae are more uniform in shape and conformation than those of the apes or man. The heads are relatively flat and paddle-shaped, the midpieces are long relative to the heads, and the mitochondria of the midpieces are relatively small and well organized.

Among the Platyrrhina the midpiece frequently inserts eccentrically into the posterior border of the head. In *Saimiri sciureus* the posterior acrosome margin appears as a serrated line; there are between 39 and 53 mitochondria gyres in this species [Bedford, 1974]. The sperm from *Cebus apella* have typically paddle-shaped heads, with a decrease in overall acrosome size. The mitochondria gyres are numerous and regular.

Hapalemur griseus and *Lemur variegatus* have common sperm characteristics. The sperm heads have an elliptical shape and the tail is commonly inserted into the posterior aspect of the head in an eccentric fashion [Gould, 1980]. The other lemurs (*L. macaco* and *L. catta*) have sperm with more rounded, paddle-shaped heads that are uniformly flattened dorsoventrally.

The head of sperm from *Tupaia* have been described as "like a Japanese round fan with a slightly concave ventral surface and a slightly convex dorsal face" [Gould, 1980]. In *Nycticebus coucang* there are frequently cavities in the nuclear material of the sperm head. The head structure of the *Galago* sperm is quite complex and is similar to that seen in more primitive species. The possible significance of these variations in sperm heads and references to sperm morphology in 34 nonhuman primate species has been presented by Gould [1980].

The preparation of gametes and reproductive tract structures for scanning electron microscopy (SEM) has been described by Gould [1973]. Similar techniques were used by Hafez and Kanagawa [1973] to describe human, rabbit, and monkey spermatozoa as observed using SEM.

CONCLUSIONS

It is apparent from the above material that there are a number of holes in our knowledge of the male reproductive tract in primates. A review of Tables 1–3 indicates that for some species there are no data listed. The days are past that an investigator could justify the sacrifice of nonhuman primates simply for descriptive studies, and many of these species are now so rare that reliable data from noninvasive studies may never be obtained. It is clear that a maximum effort should be made to get all the data possible when the material is available, from whatever source.

The general conclusion concerning the comparative nature of the male reproductive tract as described in this report is that there are as many dissimilarities as there are similarities among the primate family. The similarities are generally along the evolutionary or taxonomic scale, and those species usually considered to be more closely related to man—ie, the anthropoid apes—are, in fact, more similar to him than the smaller prosimians and monkeys.

Studies on the reproductive tract fluids in nonhuman primates will not contribute as much to the understanding of the fluids in humans as many investigators formerly believed. The seasonal changes and the inability to control, without stress, the ejaculatory frequency are but two problems that led us to that conclusion. Prostatic pathology, on the other hand, does appear to be an area suitable for continued comparative studies.

ACKNOWLEDGMENTS

The authors wish to express their thanks to their co-workers who have contributed to this chapter, either by sharing the work load or by their suggestions and comments. We wish to especially thank the following for their contributions: Drs. Nancy J. Alexander, J.M. Bedford, L.D. Russell, and L.J.D. Zaneveld. We wish to thank Drs. James A. Roberts and Bernice Kaack for their editorial assistance, and Janell LeBlanc, Jan Hardy, and Mary Soike for their typing assistance.

Special thanks are extended to James Paysee, who is in charge of the Science Information Service at the Delta Regional Primate Center.

Support during the preparation of this chapter was provided by the base grant to the Delta Regional Primate Research Center, Tulane University (NIH RR00164).

REFERENCES

Ackerman, D.R.; Roussel, J.D. Fructose, lactic acid and citric acid content of the semen of eleven subhuman primate species and of man. JOURNAL OF REPRODUCTION AND FERTILITY 17:563–566, 1968.

Adams, M.R.; Bond, M.G. Benign prostatic hyperplasia in a squirrel monkey (Saimiri sciureus). LABORATORY ANIMAL SCIENCE 29:674–676, 1979.

Alcala, J.R.; Conaway, C.H. The gross and microscopic anatomy of the uterus masculinus of tree shrews. FOLIA PRIMATOLOGICA 9:216–245, 1968.

Alexander, N.J. Prenatal development of the ductus epididymidis in the rhesus monkey. The effect of fetal castration. AMERICAN JOURNAL OF ANATOMY 135:119–134, 1972.

Alsum, D.J.; Hunter, A.G. Regional histology and histochemistry of the ductus epididymis in the rhesus monkey (Macaca mulatta). BIOLOGY OF REPRODUCTION 19:1063–1069, 1978.

Amann, R.P.; Johnson, L.; Thompson, D.L. Jr.; Pickett, B.W. Daily spermatozoal production, epididymal spermatozoal reserves and transit time of spermatozoa through the epididymis of the rhesus monkey. BIOLOGY OF REPRODUCTION 15:586–592, 1976.

Amelar, R.D. Coagulation, liquefaction and viscosity of human semen. JOURNAL OF UROLOGY 87:187–190, 1962.

Arey, L.B. The genital system. Pp. 312–339 in DEVELOPMENTAL ANATOMY. A TEXTBOOK AND LABORATORY MANUAL OF EMBRYOLOGY. L.B. Arey, ed. Philadelphia, W.B. Saunders, 1954.

Arora, R.; Dinakar, N.; Prasad, M.R.N. Biochemical changes in the spermatozoa and luminal contents of different regions of the epididymis of the rhesus monkey, Macaca mulatta. CONTRACEPTION 11:689–700, 1975.

Aumuller, G.; Schenck, B.; Neumann, F. Fine structure of monkey (Macaca mulatta) Sertoli cells after treatment with cyproterone. ANDROLOGIA 7:317–328, 1975.

Batra, S.K. Sperm transport through vas deferens: Review of hypotheses and suggestions for a quantitative model. FERTILITY AND STERILITY 25:186–202, 1974.

Baumgarten, H.G.; Holstein, A.F.; Rosengren, E. Arrangement, ultrastructure, and adrenergic innervation of smooth musculature of the ductuli efferentes, ductus epididymidis and ductus deferens of man. ZEITSCHRIFT FÜR ZELLFORSCHUNG UND MIKROSKOPISCHE ANATOMIE 120:37–79, 1971.

Bedford, J.M. Observations on the fine structure of spermatozoa of the bush baby (Galago senegalensis), the African green monkey (Cercopithecus aethiops) and man. AMERICAN JOURNAL OF ANATOMY 121:443–460, 1967.

Bedford, J.M. Biology of primate spermatozoa. CONTRIBUTIONS TO PRIMATOLOGY 3:97–193, 1974.

Bedford, J.M.; Bent, M.J.; Calvin, H.C. Variations in the structural character and stability of nuclear chromatin in morphologically normal human spermatozoa. JOURNAL OF REPRODUCTION AND FERTILITY 33:19–30, 1973a.

Bedford, J.M.; Calvin, H.; Cooper, G.W. The maturation of spermatozoa in the human epididymis. JOURNAL OF REPRODUCTION AND FERTILITY, SUPPLEMENT 18:199–213, 1973b.

Belt, W.D.; Cavazos, L.F. Fine structure of the interstitial cells of Leydig in the squirrel monkey during seasonal regression. ANATOMICAL RECORD 169:115–127, 1971.

Blacklock, N.J.; Bouskill, V. The zonal anatomy of the prostate in man and in the rhesus monkey (Macaca mulatta). UROLOGICAL RESEARCH 5:163–167, 1977.

Bøhmer, T.; Hoel, P.; Purvis, K.; Hansson, V. Carnitine levels in human accessory sex organs. ARCHIVES OF ANDROLOGY 1:53–59, 1978.

Bose, A.R.; Kar, A.B. Distribution of sialic acid in the genital organs of male rhesus monkeys: Effects of castration and replacement therapy. CURRENT SCIENCE 37:168–169, 1968.

Bourne, G.H.; De Bourne, M.N.G. The histology and histochemistry of the chimpanzee tissues and organs. Pp. 1–76 in THE CHIMPANZEE, Vol. 5, HISTOLOGY, REPRODUCTION AND RESTRAINT. G.H. Bourne, ed. Baltimore, University Press, 1972.

Braz, I.; Shandilya, L.N.; Ramaswami, L.S. Effect of α-chlorohydrin on the male reproductive organs of the Indian langur (Presbytis entellus entellus Dufresne. ANDROLOGIA 8:290–296, 1976

Burton, G.J. The relationship between body and gonadal weights of the dusky leaf monkey (Presbytis obscura). INTERNATIONAL JOURNAL OF PRIMATOLOGY 2:351–368, 1981.

Bustos-Obregon, E. Ultrastructure and function of the lamina propria of mammalian seminiferous tubules. ANDROLOGIA 8:179–185, 1976.

Calamera, J.C.; Lavieri, J.C. Glycerylphosphorylcholine in human seminal plasma of normal subjects and sterile patients. ANDROLOGIA 6:67–70, 1974.

Camatini, M.; Franchi, E.; De Curtis, I. Ultrastructure of Leydig cells in the African green monkey. JOURNAL OF ULTRASTRUCTURE RESEARCH 76:224–234, 1981.

Cavicchia, J.C. Fine structure of the monkey epididymis: A correlated thin-section and freeze-cleave study. CELL AND TISSUE RESEARCH 201:451–458, 1979.

Cavicchia, J.C.; Dym, M. Relative volume of Sertoli cells in monkey seminiferous epithelium: Stereological analysis. AMERICAN JOURNAL OF ANATOMY 150:501–507, 1977.

Chai, L.S.; Karr, J.P.; Murphy, G.P.; Sandberg, A.A. Effect of DES on the morphology of the lobes of the baboon prostate. INVESTIGATIVE UROLOGY 19:202–208, 1981.

Chakraborty, J.; Nelson, L.; Jhunjhunwala, J.; Young, M.; Kropp, K. Intranuclear inclusion bodies in epithelia cells of human vas deferens. ARCHIVES OF ANDROLOGY 2:1–12, 1979.

Chapdelaine, P.; Trembley, R.R.; Dube, J.Y.; St.-Yves, C.; Mailhot, J. Origin of maltase and variations in infertile men. ARCHIVES OF ANDROLOGY 1:61–68, 1978.

Chapman, E.S.; Heidger, P.M. Jr.; Harrison, R.M.; Roberts, J.A.; Domingue, G.J.; Schlegel, J.U. Vasectomy in rhesus monkeys. IV. Electron microscopic studies of the seminiferous epithelium. ANATOMICAL RECORD 192:41–54, 1978.

Collins, P.M.; Tsang, W.N.; Lofts, B. Anatomy and function of the reproductive tract in the captive male tree shrew (Tupaia belangeri). BIOLOGY OF REPRODUCTION 26:169–182, 1982.

Conaway, C.H.; Sorenson, M.W. Reproduction in tree shrews. Pp. 471–492 in COMPARATIVE BIOLOGY OF REPRODUCTION IN MAMMALS. I.W. Rowlands, ed. New York, Academic Press, 1966.

Connell, C.J.; Connell, G.M. The interstitial tissue of the testis. Pp. 333–369 in THE TESTIS, Vol. IV, ADVANCES IN PHYSIOLOGY, BIOCHEMISTRY, AND FUNCTION. A.D. Johnson; W.R. Gomes, eds. New York, Academic Press, 1977.

Dail, W.G.; Norvell, J.E.; Haines, D.E. The intrinsic adrenergic and cholinergic innervation of the genitalia of galago and tupia. The penis. FOLIA PRIMATOLOGICA 16:221–230, 1971.

David, G.F.X.; Ramaswami, L.S. Reproductive systems of the North Indian langur (Presbytis entellus entellus Dufresne). JOURNAL OF MORPHOLOGY 135:99–129, 1971.

Davis, D.D. The baculum of the gorilla. FIELDIANA ZOOLOGY 31:645–647, 1951.

Dawson, G.A.; Dukelow, W.R. Reproductive characteristics of free-ranging Panamanian tamarins (Saguinus oedipus geoffroyi). JOURNAL OF MEDICAL PRIMATOLOGY 5:266–275, 1966.

De Bourne, M.N.G.; Bourne, G.H. Histology and histochemistry of the rhesus monkey. XXXI. Male reproductive system. Pp. 260–276 in THE RHESUS MONKEY. Vol. I. ANATOMY AND PHYSIOLOGY. G.H. Bourne, ed. New York, Academic Press, 1975.

Dierschke, D.J.; Walsh, S.W.; Mapletoft, R.J.; Robinson, J.A.; Ginther, O.J. Functional anatomy of testicular vascular pedicle in rhesus monkey: Evidence for a local testosterone concentrating mechanism. PROCEEDINGS OF THE SOCIETY FOR EXPERIMENTAL BIOLOGY AND MEDICINE 148:236–242, 1975.

Dixson, A.F.; Gardner, J.S.; Bonney, R.C. Puberty in the male owl monkey (Aotus trivirgatus griseimembra): A study of physical and hormonal development. INTERNATIONAL JOURNAL OF PRIMATOLOGY 1:129–139, 1980.

Dixson, A.F.; Herbert, J. The effects of testosterone on the sexual skin and genitalia of the male talapoin monkey. JOURNAL OF REPRODUCTION AND FERTILITY 38:217–219, 1974.

Dixson, A.F.; Moore, H.D.M.; Holt, W.V. Testicular atrophy in captive gorillas (Gorilla gorilla gorilla). JOURNAL OF ZOOLOGY (LONDON) 191:315–322, 1980.

Dixson, A.F.; Van Horn, R.N. Comparative studies of morphology and reproduction in two sub-species of the greater bush baby, Galago crassicaudatus crassicaudatus and Galago c. argentatus. JOURNAL OF ZOOLOGY 183:517–526, 1977.

D'Souza, F. A preliminary field report on the lesser tree shrew, Tupaia minor. Pp. 167–182 in PROSIMIAN BIOLOGY. R.D. Martin; G.A. Doyle; A.C. Walker, eds. London, Duckworth, 1974.

Dym, M. The fine structure of the monkey (Macaca) Sertoli cell and its role in maintaining the blood-testis barrier. ANATOMICAL RECORD 175:639–656, 1973.

Dym, M. The fine structure of monkey Sertoli cells in the transitional zone at the junction of the seminiferous tubules with the tubuli recti. AMERICAN JOURNAL OF ANATOMY 140:1–26, 1974.

Eckstein, P. II. Reproductive organs. A. Internal reproductive organs. Pp. 542–629 in PRIMATOLOGIA, HANDBOOK OF PRIMATOLOGY, III, VERDAUUGSTRAKT, UROGENITALORGANE, ENDOKRINE ORGANE. H. Hofer; A.H. Schultz; D. Starck, eds. New York, Karger, 1958.

El-Minawi, M.F.; Moskal, P.A.; Van Pelt, L. Normarski interference contrast microscopy of human, monkey, and rabbit spermatozoa. FERTILITY AND STERILITY 21:383–389, 1970.

Engle, E.T.; Stout, A.P. Spontaneous primary carcinoma of the prostate in a monkey (Macaca mulatta). AMERICAN JOURNAL OF CANCER 39:334–337, 1940.

Fawcett, D.W. The structure of the mammalian sper-

matozoon. INTERNATIONAL REVIEW OF CYTOLOGY 7:195–234, 1958.

Fawcett, D.W. Ultrastructure and function of the Sertoli cell. Pp. 21–55 in HANDBOOK OF PHYSIOLOGY, Section 7: ENDOCRINOLOGY, Vol. V. MALE REPRODUCTION SYSTEM. D.W. Hamilton; R.O. Greep, eds. Washington, D.C., American Physiological Society, 1975.

Flechon, J.E.; Hafez, E.S.E. Spermination and epididymal maturation of spermatozoa in the bonnet macaque (Macaca radiata) as viewed by scanning electron microscopy. FERTILITY AND STERILITY 26:1219–1227, 1975.

Flechon, J.E.; Bustos-Obregon, E.; Steger, R.W.; Hafez, E.S.E. Ultrastructure of testes and excurrent ducts in the bonnet monkey (Macaca radiata). JOURNAL OF MEDICAL PRIMATOLOGY 5:321–335, 1976.

Foldesy, R.G.; Bedford, J.M. Biology of the scrotum. 1. Temperature and androgen as determinants of the sperm storage capacity of the rat cauda epididymidis. BIOLOGY OF REPRODUCTION 26:673–682, 1982.

Fooden, J. Male external genitalia and systematic relationships of the Japanese macaque (Macaca fuscata Blyth, 1875). PRIMATES 12:305–311, 1971.

Fooden, J. Classification and distribution of living macaques (Macaque Lacépède, 1799). Pp. 1–9 in THE MACAQUES: STUDIES IN ECOLOGY, BEHAVIOR AND EVOLUTION. D.G. Lindburg, ed. New York, Van Nostrand Reinhold, 1980.

Foster, J.W.; Rowley, M.J. Testicular biopsy in the study of gorilla infertility. AMERICAN JOURNAL OF PRIMATOLOGY, SUPPLEMENT 1:121–125, 1982.

Fox, H. The male genitalia. Pp. 313–315 in DISEASES OF CAPTIVE WILD MAMMALS AND BIRDS. H. Fox, ed. Philadelphia, J.B. Lippincott, 1923.

Fremming, B.D.; Benson, R.E.; Young, R.J. Weights of organs in sixty-six male Macaca mulatta monkeys. JOURNAL OF APPLIED PHYSIOLOGY 8:155–158, 1955.

Frenkel, G.; Peterson, R.N.; Davis, J.E.; Freund, M. Glycerylphosphorylcholine and carnitine in normal human semen and in postvasectomy semen: Differences in concentration. FERTILITY AND STERILITY 25:84–87, 1974.

Fröhlich, J.U.; Nissen, H.P.; Heinze, I.; Shirren, C.; Kreysel, H.W. Free amino acid composition of human seminal plasma in different andrological diagnoses. ANDROLOGIA 12:162–166, 1980.

Fussell, E.N.; Lewis, R.W.; Roberts, J.A.; Harrison, R.M. Early ultrastructural findings in experimentally produced varicocele in the monkey testis. JOURNAL OF ANDROLOGY 2:111–119, 1981.

Ghanadian, R.; Auf, G.; Smith, C.B.; Chisholm, G.D.; Blacklock, N.J. Androgen receptors in the prostate of the rhesus monkey. UROLOGICAL RESEARCH 5:169–173, 1977a.

Ghanadian, R.; Smith, C.B.; Chisholm, G.S.; Blacklock, N.J. Differential androgen uptake by the lobes of the rhesus monkey prostate. BRITISH JOURNAL OF UROLOGY 49:701–704, 1977b.

Ghanadian, R.; Smith, C.B. Androgen metabolism within the lobes of rhesus monkey prostate. EUROPEAN UROLOGY 7:89–91, 1981.

Goland, M. NORMAL AND ABNORMAL GROWTH OF THE PROSTATE. Springfield, IL, Thomas, 1975.

Goss, J.J. The external genitalia of the gorilla, *Gorilla gorilla gorilla* (Savage and Wyman). ZOOLOGICA 32:97–99, 1947.

Gould, K.G. Preparation of mammalian gametes and reproductive tract for scanning electron microscopy. FERTILITY AND STERILITY 24:448–456, 1973.

Gould, K.G. Scanning electron microscopy of the primate sperm. INTERNATIONAL REVIEW OF CYTOLOGY 63:323–355, 1980.

Graham, C.E.; Bradley, C.F. Microanatomy of the chimpanzee genital system. Pp. 77–126 in THE CHIMPANZEE, Vol. 5. HISTOLOGY, REPRODUCTION AND RESTRAINT. G.H. Bourne, ed. Baltimore, University Press, 1972.

Grant, J.C.B. AN ATLAS OF ANATOMY. Baltimore, Williams and Wilkins, 1962.

Greer, W.E.; Roussel, J.D.; Austin, C.R. Prevention of coagulations in monkey semen by surgery. JOURNAL OF REPRODUCTION AND FERTILITY 15:153–155, 1968.

Gupta, C.L.; Dixit, V.P. Effects of danazol on the epididymal function in male langurs (*Presbytis entellus entellus* Dufresne). ANDROLOGIA 13:314–321, 1981.

Hafez, E.S.E. Embryology and functional anatomy of male reproductive organs. Pp. 5–28 in SURGERY OF THE MALE REPRODUCTIVE TRACT, CLINICS IN ANDROLOGY, Vol. 2. L.I. Lipshultz; J.N. Corriere Jr.; E.S.E. Hafez, eds. Boston, Maritunus Nijhoff, 1980.

Hafez, E.S.E.; Kanagawa, H. Scanning electron microscopy of human, monkey and rabbit spermatozoa. FERTILITY AND STERILITY 24:776–787, 1973.

Hall-Craggs, E.C.B. The testis of *Gorilla gorilla beringei*. PROCEEDINGS OF THE ZOOLOGICAL SOCIETY OF LONDON 139:511–514, 1962.

Hamfler, H.W.; Nissen, H.P.; Heinze, I.; Kreysel, H.W.; Schirren, C. Free fatty acid composition of human semen from different clinical diagnosis. ANDROLOGIA 10:498–501, 1978.

Hamilton, D.W. The epididymis. Pp. 411–426 in FRONTIERS IN REPRODUCTION AND FERTILITY CONTROL. R.O. Greep; M.A. Koblinsky, eds. Cambridge, MA, MIT Press, 1977.

Hansson, V.; Ritzén, E.M.; French, F.S.; Nayfeh, S.N. Androgen transport and receptor mechanisms in testis and epididymis. Pp. 173–201 in HANDBOOK OF PHYSIOLOGY, Section 7; ENDOCRINOLOGY, Vol. V, MALE REPRODUCTIVE SYSTEM. D.W. Hamilton; R.O. Greep, eds. Washington, D.C., American Physiological Society, 1975.

Harcourt, A.H.; Harvey, P.H.; Larson, S.G.; Short, R.V. Testis weight, body weight and breeding system in primates. NATURE 293:55–57, 1981.

Harrison, R.G. The comparative anatomy of the blood supply of the mammalian testis. PROCEEDINGS OF THE ZOOLOGICAL SOCIETY OF LONDON 119:325–344, 1949.

Heite, H.-J.; Wetterauer, W. Zur kenntnis der sauren phosphatase in seminalplasma—bestimmungsmethode und diagnostische bedeutung. ANDROLOGIA 11:113–122, 1979.

Hermo, L.; Lalli, M.; Clermont, Y. Arrangement of connective tissue components in the walls of seminiferous tubules of man and monkey. AMERICAN JOURNAL OF ANATOMY 148:433–445, 1977.

Herrman, W.P. Demonstrations of glycoproteins containing zinc in human seminal plasma. ANDROLOGIA 7:329–339, 1975.

Hershkovitz, P. External genitalia and accessory structures. Pp. 112–119 in LIVING NEW WORLD MONKEYS (PLATYRRHINI). WITH AN INTRODUCTION TO PRIMATES. P. Hershkovitz, ed. Chicago, University of Chicago Press, 1977.

Hill, W.C.O. Note on the male external genitalia of the chimpanzee. PROCEEDINGS OF THE ZOOLOGICAL SOCIETY OF LONDON 116:129–132, 1946.

Hill, W.C.O. The external and visceral anatomy of the olive colobus monkey (*Procolobus verus*). PROCEEDINGS OF THE ZOOLOGICAL SOCIETY OF LONDON 122:127–186, 1952.

Hill, W.C.O. Observations on the genitalia of the woolly monkey (*Lagothrix*). PROCEEDINGS OF THE ZOOLOGICAL SOCIETY OF LONDON 122:973–984, 1953a.

Hill, W.C.O. PRIMATES. COMPARATIVE ANATOMY AND TAXONOMY. I. STREPSIRHINI. Edinburgh, Edinburgh University Press, 1953b.

Hill, W.C.O. PRIMATES. COMPARATIVE ANATOMY AND TAXONOMY. II. HAPLORHINI: TARSIOIDEA. Edinburgh, Edinburgh University Press, 1955.

Hill, W.C.O. PRIMATES. COMPARATIVE ANATOMY AND TAXONOMY. III. PITHECOIDEA. PLATYRRHINI. Edinburgh, Edinburgh University Press, 1957.

Hill, W.C.O. II. Reproductive organs, B. External genitalia. Pp. 630–704 in PRIMATOLOGIA, HANDBOOK OF PRIMATOLOGY, III, VERDAUUGSTRAKT, UROGENITALORGANE, ENDOKRINE ORGANE. H. Hofer, A.H. Schultz; D.

Starck, eds. New York, Karger, 1958.

Hill, W.C.O. PRIMATES. COMPARATIVE ANATOMY AND TAXONOMY. IV. CEBIDAE, PART A. Edinburgh, Edinburgh University Press, 1960.

Hill, W.C.O. PRIMATES. COMPARATIVE ANATOMY AND TAXONOMY. V. CEBIDAE, PART B. New York, Interscience, 1962.

Hill, W.C.O. PRIMATES. COMPARATIVE ANATOMY AND TAXONOMY. VI. CATARRHINI. CERCOPITHECOIDEA. New York, Interscience, 1966.

Hill, W.C.O. PRIMATES. COMPARATIVE ANATOMY AND TAXONOMY. VIII. CYNOPITHECINAE. PAPIO, MANDRILLUS, THEROPITHECUS. New York, Wiley, 1970.

Hill, W.C.O. PRIMATES. COMPARATIVE ANATOMY AND TAXONOMY. VII. CYNOPITHECINAE. CERCOCEBUS, MACACA, CYNOPITHECUS. New York, Wiley, 1974.

Hill, W.C.O.; Kanagasuntheram, R. The male reproductive organs in certain gibbons (Hylobatidae). AMERICAN JOURNAL OF PHYSICAL ANTHROPOLOGY 17:227–241, 1959.

Hinton, B.T. The epididymal microenvironment. A site of attack for a male contraceptive? INVESTIGATIVE UROLOGY 18:1–10, 1980.

Hinton, B.T.; Howards, S.S. Permeability characteristics of the epithelium in the rat caput epididymis. JOURNAL OF REPRODUCTION AND FERTILITY 63:95–99, 1981.

Hinton, B.T.; Howards, S.S. Micropuncture and microperfusion techniques for the study of testicular physiology. ANNALS OF THE NEW YORK ACADEMY OF SCIENCE 383:29–43, 1982.

Hinton, B.T.; Setchell, B.P. Micropuncture and microanalytical studies of rhesus monkey and baboon epididymis and the human ductus deferens. AMERICAN JOURNAL OF PRIMATOLOGY 1:251–256, 1981.

Hinton, B.T.; White, R.W.; Setchell, B.P. Concentrations of myo-inositol in the luminal fluid of the mammalian testis and epididymis. JOURNAL OF REPRODUCTION AND FERTILITY 58:395–399, 1980.

Hirschhauser, C. Abnormal human seminal plasma inhibitor content in one infertile man. ANDROLOGIA 6:95–97, 1974.

Hodson, N. The nerves of the testis, epididymis, and scrotum. Pp. 47–99 in THE TESTIS. I. DEVELOPMENT, ANATOMY, AND PHYSIOLOGY. A.D. Johnson; W.R. Gomes; N.L. Vandermark, eds. New York, Academic Press, 1970.

Hoffer, A.P.; Shalev, M.; Frisch, D.H. Ultrastructure and maturational changes in spermatozoa in the epididymis of the pigtail monkey, Macaca nemestrina. JOURNAL OF ANDROLOGY 2:140–146, 1981.

Holstein, A.F. Spermatophagy in the seminiferous tubules and excurrent ducts of the testis in rhesus monkey and man. ANDROLOGIA 10:331–352, 1978.

Homonnai, Z.T.; Matzkin, H.; Fainman, N.; Paz, G.; Kraicer, P.F. The cation composition of the seminal plasma and prostatic fluid and its correlation to sperm quality. FERTILITY AND STERILITY 29:539–542, 1978.

Hooker, C.W. The intertubular tissue of the testis. Pp. 483–550 in THE TESTIS. I. DEVELOPMENT, ANATOMY, AND PHYSIOLOGY. A.D. Johnson; W.R. Gomes; N.L. Vandermark, eds. New York, Academic Press, 1970.

Hosokawa, H.; Kamiya, T. Anatomical sketches of visceral organs of the mountain gorilla (Gorilla gorilla beringei). PRIMATES 3:1–28, 1962.

Hrdlicka, A. Weight of the brain and of the internal organs in American monkeys with data on brain weight in other apes. AMERICAN JOURNAL OF PHYSICAL ANTHROPOLOGY 8:201–211, 1925.

Huggins, C.; Webster, W.O. Duality of human prostate in response to estrogen. JOURNAL OF UROLOGY 59:258–266, 1948.

Izor, R.J.; Walchuk, S.L.; Wilkins, L. Anatomy and systematic significance of the penis of the pygmy chimpanzee, Pan paniscus. FOLIA PRIMATOLOGICA 35:218–224, 1981.

Johnson, A.D.; Gomes, W.R. THE TESTIS. IV. ADVANCES IN PHYSIOLOGY, BIOCHEMISTRY, AND FUNCTION. New York, Academic Press, 1977.

Johnson, A.D.; Gomes, W.R.; Vandemark, N.L. THE TESTIS. I. DEVELOPMENT, ANATOMY, AND PHYSIOLOGY. New York, Academic Press, 1970a.

Johnson, A.D.; Gomes, W.R.; Vandemark, N.L. THE TESTIS. II. BIOCHEMISTRY. New York, Academic Press, 1970b.

Johnson, A.D.; Gomes, W.R.; Vandemark, N.L. THE TESTIS. III. INFLUENCING FACTORS. New York, Academic Press, 1970c.

Johnston, G.S.; Gibbons, R.P.; Schmidt, J.D.; Murphy, G.P.; Scott, W.W. Fluid and tissue kinetics of ^{65}zinc in the dog and monkey. INVESTIGATIVE UROLOGY 3:419–426, 1966.

Jones, F.W. The genitalia of tupaia. JOURNAL OF ANATOMY 51:118–126, 1971.

Jones, R. Comparative biochemistry of mammalian epididymal plasma. COMPARATIVE BIOCHEMISTRY AND PHYSIOLOGY B61:365–370, 1978.

Kanagawa, H.; Hafez, E.S.E.; Nawar, M.M.; Jaszczak, S. Patterns of sexual behavior and anatomy of copulatory organs in macaques. ZEITSCHRIFT FÜR TIERPSYCHOLOGIE 31:449–460, 1972.

Karr, J.P.; Kirdani, R.; Murphy, G.P.; Sandberg, A.A. Androgen binding in the baboon prostate. ARCHIVES OF ANDROLOGY 2:123–128, 1979.

Kennard, M.A.; Willner, M.D. Findings in 216 routine autopsies of Macaca mulatta. ENDOCRINOLOGY 28:955–966, 1941a.

Kennard, M.M.; Willner, M.D. Weights of brains and organs of 132 New and Old World monkeys. ENDOCRINOLOGY 28:977–984, 1941b.

Kennard, M.A.; Willner, M.D. Findings at autopsies of seventy anthropoid apes. ENDOCRINOLOGY 28:967–976, 1941c.

Kinzey, W.G. Male reproductive system and spermatogenesis. Pp. 85–114 in COMPARATIVE REPRODUCTION OF NONHUMAN PRIMATES. E.S.E. Hafez, ed. Springfield, IL, Thomas, 1971.

Lewis, R.W.; Kim, J.C.S.; Irani, D.; Roberts, J.A. The prostate of the nonhuman primate: Normal anatomy and pathology. THE PROSTATE 2:51–70, 1981.

Lowsley, O.S. Embryology, anatomy and surgery of the prostate gland. AMERICAN JOURNAL OF SURGERY 8:526–541, 1930.

Machida, H.; Giacometti, L. The anatomical and histochemical properties on the skin of the external genitalia of the primates. FOLIA PRIMATOLOGICA 6:48–69, 1967.

Manley, G.H. Functions of the external genital glands of *Perodicticus* and *Arctocebus*. Pp. 313–329 in PROSIMIAN BIOLOGY. R.D. Martin; G.A. Doyle; A.C. Walker, eds. London, Duckworth, 1974.

Mann, T. Male accessory organs of reproduction and their secretory product: The seminal plasma. Pp. 37–78 in THE BIOCHEMISTRY OF SEMEN AND OF THE MALE REPRODUCTIVE TRACT. T. Mann, ed. New York, Wiley, 1964.

Mann, T.; Lutwak-Mann, C. Evaluation of the functional state of male accessory glands by the analysis of seminal plasma. ANDROLOGIA 8:237–242, 1976.

Mann, T.; Lutwak-Mann, C. MALE REPRODUCTIVE FUNCTION AND SEMEN. New York, Springer-Verlag, 1981.

Marmar, J.L.; Katz, S.; Praiss, D.E.; DeBenedictis, T.J. Semen zinc levels in infertile and postvasectomy patients and patients with prostatitis. FERTILITY AND STERILITY. 26:1057–1063, 1975.

Marsh, L.D.; Alexander, N.J. Vasectomy: Effects on the efferents ducts in *Macaca mulatta*. AMERICAN JOURNAL OF PATHOLOGY 107:310–315, 1982.

Martin, D.E.; Gould, K.G. The male ape genital tract and its secretions. Pp. 127–162 in REPRODUCTIVE BIOLOGY OF THE GREAT APES. C.E. Graham, ed. New York, Academic Press, 1981.

Martin, R.D. Tree shrews: Unique reproductive mechanisms of systematic importance. SCIENCE 152:1402–1404, 1966.

Matano, Y.; Matsubayashi, K.; Omichi, A. Scanning electron microscopy of primate spermatozoa. Pp. 121–124 in CONTEMPORARY PRIMATOLOGY. S. Kondo; M. Kawai; A. Ehara, eds. Basel, Karger, 1975.

Matthews, L.H. Notes on the genital anatomy and physiology of the gibbon (*Hylobates*). PROCEEDINGS OF THE ZOOLOGICAL SOCIETY OF LONDON 116:339–364, 1946.

McNeal, J.E. Regional morphology and pathology of the prostate. AMERICAN JOURNAL OF CLINI-

CAL PATHOLOGY 49:347–357, 1968.

McNeal, J.E. The zonal anatomy of the prostate. THE PROSTATE 2:35–49, 1981.

Menezes, A.P. Elastic tissue in the limiting membrane of the human seminiferous tubule. AMERICAN JOURNAL OF ANATOMY 150:349–374, 1977.

Middleton, C.C.; Rosal, J. Weights and measurements of normal squirrel monkeys (*Saimiri sciureus*). LABORATORY ANIMAL SCIENCE 22:583–586, 1972.

Miraglia, T.; Filho, M.T.; Branco, A.L.C. The male reproductive system of the common marmoset (*Callithrix jacchus*). ACTA ANATOMICA 76:594–611, 1970.

Möller, R. Arrangement and fine structure of lymphatic vessels in the human spermatic cord. ANDROLOGIA 12:564–576, 1980.

Moore, H.D.M.; Pryor, J.P. The comparative ultrastructure of the epididymis in monkeys and man: A search for a suitable animal model for studying epididymal physiology in primates. AMERICAN JOURNAL OF PRIMATOLOGY 1: 241–250, 1981.

Morton, B.E.; Sagadraca, R.; Fraser, C. Sperm motility within the mammalian epididymis: Species variation and correlation with free calcium levels in epididymal plasma. FERTILITY AND STERILITY 29:695–698, 1978.

Muntzing, J.; Myhrberg, H.; Saroff, T.; Sandberg, A.A.; Murphy, G.P. Histochemical and ultrastructural study of prostatic tissue from baboons treated with antiprostatic drug. INVESTIGATIVE UROLOGY 14:162–167, 1976.

Nikkanen, V. Seminal fructose, citric acid and acid phosphatase before and after vasectomy in men. ANDROLOGIA 10:464–466, 1978.

Nissen, H.P.; Schirren, C.; Heinze, I.; Kreysel, H.W. L-fucose content in human semen. ANDROLOGIA 10:211–214, 1978.

Nissen, H.P.; Schirren, C.; Kreysel, H.W.; Heinze, I. Verteilung der aminosäuren in humansperma unter diagnostischen geuchtspunkten. ANDROLOGIA 11:109–112, 1979.

Oelrich, T.M. Pelvic and perineal anatomy of the male gorilla: Selected observations. ANATOMICAL RECORD 191:433–445, 1978.

Orgebin-Crist, M.-C.; Danzo, B.J.; Davies, J. Endocrine control of the development and maintenance of sperm fertilizing ability in the epididymis. Pp. 319–338 in HANDBOOK OF PHYSIOLOGY, Section 7: ENDOCRINOLOGY, Vol. V. MALE REPRODUCTIVE SYSTEM. D.W. Hamilton; R.O. Greep, eds. Washington, D.C., American Physiological Society, 1975.

Orlandini, G.E.; Gulisano, M.; Pacini, P. Scanning electron microscopy of the human vas deferens epithelium following oestrogenic treatment. ANDROLOGIA 12:186–190, 1980.

Pande, J.K.; Dasgupta, P.R.; Kar, A.B. Chemical composition of fluid collected from the testis of the rhesus monkey and goat. INDIAN JOURNAL OF EXPERIMENTAL BIOLOGY 5:65–67, 1967.

Pande, J.K.; Dasgupta, P.R.; Kar, A.B. Comparative biochemistry of testicular fluid in some mammals. GENERAL AND COMPARATIVE ENDOCRINOLOGY, supplement 2:156–161, 1969.

Pedersen, H. The human spermatozoa. An electron microscopical study including comparative details of *Macaca arctoides* spermatozoa. DANISH MEDICAL BULLETIN 21 (SUPPLEMENT 1):3–35, 1974.

Petter-Rousseaux, A. Reproductive physiology and behavior of the Lemuroidea. Pp. 91–132 in EVOLUTIONARY AND GENETIC BIOLOGY OF PRIMATES, Vol. II. J. Buettner-Janusch, ed. New York, Academic Press, 1964.

Polakoski, K.L.; Zaneveld, L.J.D. Biochemical examination of the human ejaculate. Pp. 265–286 in TECHNIQUES OF HUMAN ANDROLOGY. E.S.E. Hafez, ed. New York, North Holland, 1977.

Ponig, B.F.; Roberts, J.A. Seminal vesicles as organs of sperm storage. UROLOGY 11:384–385, 1978.

Price, D. Comparative aspects of development and structure in the prostate. NATIONAL CANCER INSTITUTE MONOGRAPHS 12:1–25, 1963.

Price, J.S.; Burton, J.L.; Shuster, S.; Wolff, K. Control of scrotal colour in the vervet monkey. JOURNAL OF MEDICAL PRIMATOLOGY 5:296–304, 1976.

Ramakrishna, P.A.; Prasad, M.R.N. Changes in the male reproductive organs of *Loris tardigradus lydekkerianus* (Cabrera). FOLIA PRIMATOLOGIA 5:176–189, 1967.

Ramos, A.S. Jr. Morphologic variations along the length of the monkey vas deferens. ARCHIVES OF ANDROLOGY 3:187–196, 1979.

Ramos, A.S. Jr.; Dym, M. Ultrastructure of the ductuli efferents in monkeys. BIOLOGY OF REPRODUCTION 17:339–349, 1977a.

Ramos, A.S. Jr.; Dym, M. Fine structure of the monkey epididymis. AMERICAN JOURNAL OF ANATOMY 149:501–531, 1977b.

Reddy, J.M.; Audhya, T.K.; Goodpasture, J.C.; Zaneveld, L.J.D. Properties of a highly purified antifertility factor from human seminal plasma. BIOLOGY OF REPRODUCTION 27:10776–1083, 1982.

Riar, S.S.; Setty, B.S.; Kar, A.B. Studies on the physiology and biochemistry of mammalian epididymis: Biochemical composition of epididymis. A comparative study. FERTILITY AND STERILITY 24:355–363, 1973a.

Riar, S.S.; Setty, B.S.; Kar, A.B. Studies on physiology and biochemistry of mammalian epididymis: Histology, enzyme and electrolyte composition of epididymis. A comparative study. INDIAN JOURNAL OF EXPERIMENTAL BIOLOGY 11:365–372, 1973b.

Roberts, J.A. The male reproductive system. Pp. 878–888 in PATHOLOGY OF SIMIAN PRIMATES,

PART I. R.N.T.-W. Fiennes, ed. Basel, Karger, 1972.

Roberts, J.A.; Seibold, H.R. The histology of the primate urethra. FOLI PRIMATOLOGICA 14:59–69, 1971.

Robinson, D.; Rock, J. Intrascrotal hyperthermia induced by scrotal insulation: Effect on spermatogenesis. OBSTETRICS AND GYNECOLOGY 29:217–223, 1967.

Rosemberg, E.; Paulsen, C.A. THE HUMAN TESTIS. New York, Plenum, 1970.

Ross, M.H.; Long, I.R. Contractile cell in human seminiferous tubules. SCIENCE 153:1271–1273, 1966.

Roussel, J.D.; Stallcup, O.T.; Austin, C.R. Selective phagocytosis of spermatozoa in the epididymis of bulls, rabbits, and monkeys, FERTILITY AND STERILITY 18:509–516, 1967.

Roy, S.; Das, P.P.; Taneja, S.L. Effect of androgen on different biochemical constituents of human semen. ANDROLOGIA 7:195–198, 1975.

Russell, L.D.; Karpas, S. Reconstruction of a stage V monkey Sertoli cell: Size, dimensions and general shape. ANATOMICAL RECORD 205:171A, 1983.

Schoonees, R.; DeKlerk, J.N. Anatomy, radioisotopic blood flow and glandular secretory activity of the baboon prostate. SOUTH AFRICAN MEDICAL JOURNAL (SUPPLEMENT) 42:87–94, 1968.

Schoonees, R.; DeKlerk, J.N.; Mirand, E.A.; Murphy, G.P. The effect of bovine growth hormone on zinc-65 metabolism and prostatic blood flow of intact, testosterone treated, and castrated adult male chacma baboons. INVESTIGATIVE UROLOGY 8:103–115, 1970.

Schoonees, R.; DeKlerk, J.N.; Murphy, G.P. Correlation of prostatic blood flow with ^{65}zinc activity in intact, castrated and testosterone-treated baboons. INVESTIGATIVE UROLOGY 6:476–484, 1969.

Schultz, A.H. The relative weight of the testes in primates. ANATOMICAL RECORD 72:387–394, 1938.

Schulze, C.; Holstein, A.F.; Schirren, C.; Korner, F. On the morphology of the human Sertoli cell under normal conditions and in patients with impaired fertility. ANDROLOGIA 8:167–178, 1976.

Segal, S.; Ron, M.; Laufer, N.; Ben-David, M. Prolactin in seminal plasma of infertile men. ARCHIVES OF ANDROLOGY 1:49–52, 1978.

Setchell, B.P. Testicular blood supply, lymphatic drainage, and secretion of fluid. Pp. 101–239 in THE TESTIS. I. DEVELOPMENT, ANATOMY AND PHYSIOLOGY. A.D. Johnson; W.R. Gomes; N.L. Vandemark, eds. New York, Academic Press, 1970.

Setchell, B.P. Secretions of the testis and epididymis. JOURNAL OF REPRODUCTION AND FERTILITY 37:165–177, 1974.

Shandilya, L.; Clarkson, T.B.; Adams, M.R.; Lewis, J.C. Effects of gossypol on reproductive and endocrine functions of male cynomolgus monkeys (*Ma-*

caca fascicularis). BIOLOGY OF REPRODUCTION 27:241–252, 1982.

Sikorski, A. Comparative anatomy of the bulbourethral glands (preliminary report). FOLIA MORPHOLOGIA (WARSZAWA) 37:151–156, 1978.

Skandhan, K.P. Zinc in normal human seminal plasma. ANDROLOGIA 13:346–351, 1981.

Skandhan, K.P.; Mazumdar, B.N. Correlation of sodium and potassium in human seminal plasma with fertilizing capacity of normal and infertile subjects. ANDROLOGIA 13:147–154, 1981.

Stambaugh, R.; Buckley, J. Comparative studies of the acrosomal enzymes of rabbit, rhesus monkey, and human spermatozoa. BIOLOGY OF REPRODUCTION 3:275–282, 1970.

Steinberger, E.; Steinberger, A. Spermatogenic function of the testis. Pp. 1–19 in HANDBOOK OF PHYSIOLOGY, Section 7: ENDOCRINOLOGY, Vol. V. MALE REPRODUCTIVE SYSTEM. D.W. Hamilton; R.O. Greep, eds. Washington, D.C., American Physiological Society, 1975.

Steiner, P.E. Anatomical observations in a *Gorilla gorilla*. AMERICAN JOURNAL OF PHYSICAL ANTHROPOLOGY 12:145–179, 1954.

Tauber, P.F.; Propping, D.; Schumacher, G.F.B.; Zaneveld, L.J.D. Biochemical aspects of the coagulation and liquefaction of human semen. JOURNAL OF ANDROLOGY 1:280–288, 1980.

Tauber, P.F.; Zaneveld, L.J.D.; Propping, D.; Schumacher, G.F.B. Components of human split ejaculates. 1. Spermatozoa, fructose, immunoglobulins, albumin, lactoferrin, transferrin and other plasma proteins. JOURNAL OF REPRODUCTION AND FERTILITY 43:249–267, 1975.

Troen, P.; Nankin, H.R. THE TESTIS IN NORMAL AND INFERTILE MEN. New York, Raven, 1977.

Tseng, M.T.; Alexander, N.J.; Kittinger, G.W. Effects of fetal decapitation on the structure and function of Leydig cells in rhesus monkeys (*Macaca mulatta*). AMERICAN JOURNAL OF ANATOMY 143:349–362, 1975.

Tusell, J.M.; Gelpi, E. Prostaglandins E and F, and 19-hydroxylated E and F (series I and II) in semen of fertile men. Gas and liquid chromatographic separation with selected ion detection. JOURNAL OF CHROMATOGRAPHY 181:295–310, 1980.

Van Camp, K. Histological and biochemical studies on prostatic tissue of mammalians. ACTA ZOOLOGICA ET PATHOLOGIA ANLVERPIENSIA 48:123–136, 1969.

van Wagenen, G. The effects of oestrin on the urogenital tract of the male monkey. ANATOMICAL RECORD 63:387–403, 1935.

van Wagenen, G. The coagulating function of the cranial lobe of the prostate gland in the monkey. ANATOMICAL RECORD 66:411–421, 1936.

van Wagenen, G.; Simpson, M.E. Testicular development in the rhesus monkey. ANATOMICAL RECORD 118:231–251, 1954.

Vaze, A.Y.; Thakur, A.N.; Seth, A.R. Levels of inhibin in human semen and accessory reproductive organs. ANDROLOGIA 12:66–71, 1980.

Venkatachalam, P.S.; Ramanathan, K.S. Effects of moderate heat on the testes of rats and monkeys. JOURNAL OF REPRODUCTION AND FERTILITY 4:51–56, 1962.

Ventura, W.P.; Freund, M.; Davis, J.; Pannuti, C. Influence of norepinephrine on the motility of the human vas deferens: A new hypothesis of sperm transport by the vas deferens. FERTILITY AND STERILITY 24:68–77, 1973.

Videla, E.; Blanco, A.M.; Galli, M.E.; Fernandez-Callazo, E. Human seminal biochemistry: Fructose, ascorbic acid, citric acid, acid phosphatase and their relationship with sperm count. ANDROLOGIA 13:212–214, 1981.

Vigersky, R.A.; Loriaux, D.L.; Howards, S.S.; Hodgen, G.B.; Libsett, M.B.; Chrambach, A. Androgen binding proteins of testis, epididymis, and plasma in man and monkey. JOURNAL OF CLINICAL INVESTIGATION 58:1061–1068, 1976.

Vilar, O.; Paulsen, C.A.; Moore, D.J. Electron microscopy of the human seminiferous tubules. Pp. 63–74 in THE HUMAN TESTIS. E. Rosemberg; C.A. Paulsen, eds. New York, Plenum, 1970.

Waites, G.M.H. Temperature regulation and the testis. Pp. 241–279 in THE TESTIS. I. DEVELOPMENT, ANATOMY, AND PHYSIOLOGY, A.D. Johnson; W.R. Gomes; N.L. Vandemark, eds. New York, Academic Press, 1970.

Waites, G.M.H. Fluid secretion. Pp. 91–123 in THE TESTIS. IV. ADVANCES IN PHYSIOLOGY, BIOCHEMISTRY, AND FUNCTION. A.D. Johnson; W.R. Gomes, eds. New York, Academic Press, 1977.

Waites, G.M.H.; Einer-Jensen, N. Collection and analysis of rete testis fluid from macaque monkeys. JOURNAL OF REPRODUCTION AND FERTILITY 41:505–508, 1974.

Wetterauer, U.; Heite, H.-J. Carnitine in seminal fluid as parameter for epididymal function. ANDROLOGIA 10:203–210, 1978.

White, I.G. Accessory sex organs and fluids of the male reproductive tract. Pp. 105–123 in ANIMAL MODELS FOR RESEARCH ON CONTRACEPTION AND FERTILITY. N.J. Alexander, ed. London, Harper and Row, 1979.

Wislocki, G.B. The reproductive systems. Pp. 231–247 in THE ANATOMY OF THE RHESUS MONKEY. C.G. Hartman; W.L. Straus, Jr., eds. New York, Hafner Publishing Co., 1933.

Wislocki, G.B. Size, weight and histology of the testes in the gorilla. JOURNAL OF MAMMALOGY 23:281–287, 1942.

Wong, P.Y.D.; Au, C.L.; Bedford, J.M. Biology of the scrotum. II. Suppression by abdominal temperature of transepithelial ion and water transport in the cauda epididymidis. BIOLOGY OF REPRODUCTION 26:683–689, 1982.

Yates, R.D.; Gordon, M. MALE REPRODUCTIVE SYSTEM. New York, Masson, 1977.

Young, D.H. Surgical treatment of male infertility. JOURNAL OF REPRODUCTION AND FERTILITY 23:541–542, 1970.

Young, L.G.; Gould, K.G.; Hinton, B.T. Changes in surface components of chimpanzee spermatozoa at ejaculation. JOURNAL OF ANDROLOGY 3:30, 1982.

Zamboni, L.; Stefanini, M. The fine structure of the neck of mammalian spermatozoa. ANATOMICAL RECORD 169:155–172, 1971.

Zamboni, L.; Zemjanis, R.; Stefanini, M. The fine structure of monkey and human spermatozoa. ANATOMICAL RECORD 169:129–154, 1971.

Zaneveld, L.J.D.; Chatterton, R.T. BIOCHEMISTRY OF MAMMALIAN REPRODUCTION. I. GAMETES AND GENITAL TRACT FLUIDS, II. RE-PRODUCTIVE ENDOCRINOLOGY. New York, Wiley, 1982.

Zuckerman, S. The effects of prolonged oestrogenic stimulation on the prostate of the rhesus monkey. JOURNAL OF ANATOMY (LONDON) 72:264–276, 1938.

Zuckerman, S.; Parkes, A.S. Observations on the structure of the uterus masculinus in various primates. JOURNAL OF ANATOMY (LONDON) 69:484–496, 1935.

Zuckerman, S.; Parkes, A.S. Effects of sex hormones on the prostate of monkeys. LANCET 230:242–247, 1936a.

Zuckerman, S.; Parkes, A.S. The effects of oestrogens on the prostate and uterus masculinus of various species of primate. JOURNAL OF ANATOMY (LONDON) 70:323–330, 1936b.

Zuckerman, S.; Sandys, O.C. Further observations on the effects of sex hormones on the prostate and seminal vesicles of monkeys. JOURNAL OF ANATOMY (LONDON) 73:597–616, 1939.

Endocrine Regulation of Male Reproduction

E.J. Wickings, G.R. Marshall, and E. Nieschlag

Department of Experimental Endocrinology and Max Planck Clinical Research Unit for Reproductive Medicine, University Women's Hospital, D-4400 Münster, Federal Republic of Germany

INTRODUCTION

The aim of this chapter is to bring together those principles of endocrinology and male genital tract anatomy described in the preceding chapters in describing the dynamic systems which maintain reproduction in the mature male primate.

Most data are available for rhesus monkeys, and indeed this is where our own expertise lies. Furthermore, results from rhesus monkeys are representative for many species of nonhuman primates and also in certain aspects for humans so that their popularity is warranted. Attention will be drawn to differences demonstrated between species, where data are available. Where relevant, observations made in feral monkeys will be described, and this will allow a discussion of the effects of housing conditions and handling procedures on male reproductive function.

HYPOTHALAMIC-PITUITARY-TESTICULAR AXIS

Introduction

It is not physiologically possible to separate the endocrine and exocrine testicular functions, as chemical products of the seminiferous tubules and interstitial tissue are exchanged and influence the other compartment. Nor can one separate the three components of the hypothalamic-pituitary-testicular axis without ignoring the very complex regulatory interactions, especially between the hypothalamus and pituitary. However, for clarity of presentation, the principal mechanisms controlling stimulation of successive components of this endocrine axis will be described individually be-fore discussing their role in regulating spermatogenesis.

The relative paucity of data on male reproductive function is not least caused by the difficulty of developing sensitive assay systems for primate gonadotropins, in particular for follicle-stimulating hormone (FSH). The recent availability of the in vitro bioassay for luteinizing hormone (LH) using Leydig cell testosterone production has solved this problem for LH [Neill et al, 1977; Wickings et al, 1979].

Regulation of Leydig Cell Function

Pituitary Function and Regulation. Following the isolation and characterization of luteinizing hormone–releasing hormone (LHRH) [Schally et al, 1973], the stimulatory effect of this decapeptide on gonadotropin secretion could be demonstrated in humans and female rhesus monkeys [Krey et al, 1973; Spies et al, 1972]. Early reports of the failure to identify increases in LH following LHRH administration in male rhesus monkeys therefore raised considerable controversy and led to the opinion that male rhesus monkeys were resistant to LHRH [Arimura et al, 1973; Ehara et al, 1972; Krey et al, 1973]. In these studies LH was measured using the heterologous radioimmunoassay of Niswender et al [1971], an assay not sensitive enough for quantitating basal LH levels in intact male monkeys. Nor is this assay specific for LH, as LH-like factors interfering in the assay have been identified in the serum of hypophysectomized female monkeys [Peckham et al, 1977]. The use of a different radioimmunoassay [Robinson et al, 1975] and of in vitro bioassay systems [Steiner et al, 1980; Wickings et al, 1979], however, conclu-

Comparative Primate Biology, Volume 3: Reproduction and Development, pages 149–170

sively demonstrated that LHRH can stimulate LH release in male rhesus monkeys [Ferin et al, 1974; Toivola et al, 1978; Wickings et al, 1980a]. In addition, crab-eating monkeys, *M. fascicularis* [Mori and Hafez, 1973], and baboons [Koyama, 1976] responded to LHRH with an increase in LH. These methodological problems are not shared by workers using apes, since chimpanzee and gorilla gonadotropins are sufficiently similar to the human hormones to be measurable in corresponding human radioimmunoassay systems [Howland et al, 1971; Nadler et al, 1979].

Prior to the proof of the stimulatory effects of LHRH on LH secretion, neural structures containing LHRH had been characterized in the hypothalamus of the adult male rhesus [Silverman et al, 1977]. The main feature was the lack of any organization in the distribution of the LHRH-containing cell bodies and fibers, with LHRH neurons identifiable from the mammillary body to the preoptic area. High concentrations of LHRH neurons were found in the stria terminalis, medial preoptic nucleus, and infundibular nucleus. The function of LHRH neurons identified outside the medial basal hypothalamus is not clear but may be related to the role of LHRH in the total reproductive capacity or could indicate a neurotransmitter role for LHRH. LHRH neurons, not connected with the regulation of the anterior pituitary, have also been identified in the baboon and form a large proportion of all LHRH-containing neurons in this species [Marshall and Goldsmith, 1980]. In addition LHRH axons pass down the infundibular stalk and impinge on the posterior pituitary. The role of these axons is unclear since cells secreting LH have only been identified in the pars distalis and pars tuberalis of the adult male monkey [Herbert, 1978].

Abolition of the LHRH stimulus to the pituitary, either by transecting the hypothalamo-hypophyseal stalk [Marshall et al, 1983] or by active immunization against LHRH (marmoset [Hodges and Hearn, 1977], rhesus [Chappel et al, 1980]) leads to decreases in circulating levels of LH and testosterone accompanied by testicular atrophy.

LH is secreted in a pulsatile manner in mature male monkeys [Plant, 1980; Steiner et al, 1980; Wickings and Nieschlag, 1981], and in turn, each secretory pulse of testosterone is preceded by an LH pulse. Collecting portal blood from female rhesus monkeys, Carmel et al [1976] showed that LHRH was also secreted in an episodic fashion, and the supposition that pulsatile LHRH secretion produced LH pulses became widely accepted. Direct evidence of this has recently been presented

for sheep that this is indeed the case [Clarke and Cummins, 1982]. Imposing physiological LHRH pulses on a quiescent pituitary-testicular axis led to recrudescence of full testicular function in rhesus monkeys [Wickings et al, 1981c].

The response of FSH to LHRH is more difficult to quantitate. Monkey FSH radioimmunoassays applicable to the female are too insensitive to detect basal FSH levels in the intact male. Indeed FSH levels following LHRH stimulation are also very low. Even over a 25-fold dose range of LHRH up to 25 μg per animal Toivola et al [1978] failed to see any stimulation of FSH. A dose of 100 μg was, however, able to elicit a small but significant response [Chrousos et al, 1981]. In chimpanzees LHRH "stimulated" FSH from undetectable levels ($<$ 10 μg FSH (LER 907)/100 ml) by 20%, hardly a spectacular increase [Hobson and Fuller, 1977]. The inability to quantitate basal levels of FSH in male monkeys is a serious drawback to the elucidation of pituitary-testicular function.

Leydig Cell Function. The LH receptor on the membrane of the Leydig cell forms the link between the pituitary LH stimulus and testicular steroidogenic activity. Such receptors have been demonstrated on rhesus and green monkey Leydig cells and also on human cells [Davies et al, 1979; Zaidi et al, 1982a]. These receptors bind human LH and human chorionic gonadotropin (hCG) with high affinity and low capacity and high specificity. Binding kinetics indicate that only partial occupation of the total receptor population is necessary for stimulation of testosterone production. In contrast to the rat, where Leydig LH receptors bind LH from many different species, primate LH receptors are specific for primate hormones.

Adult male rhesus monkeys respond to in vivo hCG stimulation (5,000 IU/day for 3 days) with a tenfold increase in serum testosterone levels [Wickings and Nieschlag, 1978], compared to the two- to 2.5-fold testosterone increase seen in men [Nieschlag et al, 1973]. hCG is, however, antigenic in nonhuman primates, and repeated subcutaneous injections are sufficient to stimulate antibody production [Catchpole and van Wagenen, 1975; Nieschlag and Wickings, 1980a]. The rhesus monkey testis responds rapidly to the LH released following IV LHRH stimulation; significant elevations in serum testosterone levels were already evident 30 minutes after injection, and maximum concentrations were reached at 60 minutes [Toivola et al, 1978; Wickings et al, 1981c]. The nonhuman primate testis is far more responsive than the human testis to such

TABLE 1. Circadian Variations in Circulating Testosterone Levels (ng/ml) in Various Primate Species

Species	Nadir		Maxima		Reference
	Time of day	Testosterone	Time of day	Testosterone	
Macaca mulatta	1100–1400	2–3	2000–2400	8–9	Plant, 1980
Macaca mulatta	0900	5.0 ± 0.8[a]	2100	17.0 ± 1.5[a]	Goodman et al, 1974
Macaca mulatta	1200–1500	2–3	2100–0400	11–14	Perachio et al, 1977
Macaca mulatta	1600	7.8 ± 5.3[b]	2200	17.8 ± 8.1[b]	Michael et al, 1974
Macaca radiata	1000	2.8 ± 0.9[b]	2200	21.3 ± 4.1[b]	Mukku and Vandenbergh, 1981
Macaca fascicularis	0700–1100	9.1 ± 0.8[b]	1900–2300	12.2 ± 0.8[b]	Steiner et al, 1980
Macaca fuscata	0900	2–3	2100–0500	7–13	Enomoto, 1980
Papio ursinus	0800	9.6 ± 1.5[a]	2000	18.3 ± 3.2[a]	Bielert et al, 1981
Cercopithecus aethiops	0900–1500	3–6	2100–0600	8–20	Beattie and Bullock, 1978
Homo sapiens	1600–2400	4–6	0400–1200	6–8	Nieschlag, 1974

[a]Mean ± SE.
[b]Mean ± SD.

external stimuli, since prolonged LHRH infusions are required in men to produce an increase in circulating testosterone levels [Kley et al, 1975].

Leydig cell function in intact monkeys is affected by a variety of external and endogenous factors—for example, the diurnal variations evident in serum testosterone levels. The extent and synchronization of these diurnal fluctuations vary among species (Table 1). In rhesus monkeys testosterone levels changed by as much as 100%, with highest values measured at night [Goodman et al, 1974; Michael et al, 1974; Perachio et al, 1977; Plant, 1980]. Similar patterns have also been described for other macaques—*M. radiata* [Mukku et al, 1981], *M. fascicularis* [Steiner et al, 1980], chacma baboons [Bielert and Vandenbergh, 1981], and green monkeys [Beattie and Bullock, 1978]. The nocturnal increase in testosterone has in turn been attributed to an increase in both frequency and amplitude of LH pulses [Plant, 1980; Steiner et al, 1980].

Exogenous factors affecting the endocrine hypothalamic-pituitary-testicular axis include social environment and access to receptive females. Dominance rank of male rhesus monkeys correlates positively with serum testosterone levels, as does the frequency of aggressive behavior [Rose et al, 1971]. Both rhesus and pig-tailed macaques showed an increase in testosterone levels when introduced to females [Bernstein et al, 1977, 1978]. The effect of copulatory behavior on serum testosterone and LH levels is more difficult to assess. Increases in serum LH have been reported in *M. fascicularis* following mating [Mori and Hafez, 1973] but testosterone levels were not affected by either mating or electroejaculation [Goldfoot et al, 1975; Phoenix et al, 1977].

Handling procedures and anesthesia also affect pituitary and Leydig cell function. Immobilizing baboons (*Papio hamadryas*) for 2 hours caused a suppression of testosterone levels lasting 48 hours [Goncharov et al, 1979]. Ketamine anesthesia, commonly used when handling male primates, did not affect serum testosterone for at least 3 hours although basal and LHRH-stimulated serum LH levels tended to decrease during this period (*M. fascicularis* [Mori and Hafez, 1973], *M. mulatta* [Wickings and Nieschlag 1980b]). Barbiturate anesthesia stimulated both LH and testosterone levels for 60 and 150 minutes respectively in male rhesus monkeys [Zaidi et al, 1982b].

Regulatory Mechanisms. Releasing the hypothalamic-hypophyseal unit from the negative feedback of testosterone by castration allowed LH production to increase sharply over the following 20–40 days (10-fold over precastration levels) [Atkinson et al, 1970]. The supplementation of testosterone in the upper physiological range or testosterone together with estradiol at the time of castration prevented this postcastration rise in gonadotropin levels and pulse frequency [Plant et al, 1978; Plant, 1982; Resko et al, 1977]. If combined testosterone and estradiol administration was initiated up to 50 days postcastration, gonadotropins could be suppressed, but this was no longer the case in long-term, castrated monkeys (longer than 70 days) which were then resistant to the application of steroids. The mechanisms controlling gonadotropin secretion in this situation remain unclear, but nonsteroidal testicular factors—eg, inhibin—do not seem to be involved.

At the time when estradiol replacement was effective, steroid administration significantly suppressed FSH, and also exerted a positive feedback by eliciting an LH surge acutely after administration in castrate monkeys. Intact male monkeys did not respond to this positive feedback of estradiol [Yamaji et al, 1971], although the basal LH levels did show a slight decrease and testosterone dropped precipitously [Steiner et al, 1978]. Intact male marmosets, in contrast, did respond to the positive feedback of estradiol with an LH surge [Hodges and Hearn, 1978].

Hormonal Control of Spermatogenesis

Hormonal control of primate spermatogenesis, aside from several clinical studies in man, has been investigated primarily in macaques. The general concept of hormonal regulation is that LH and FSH are both necessary for quantitatively normal spermatogenesis [Steinberger, 1971]. The effects of LH, furthermore, are exerted through testosterone, regulated by LH.

Spermatogenesis is composed of three general processes: 1) mitosis, by which spermatogonia divide either to renew and proliferate their number or finally to produce spermatocytes; 2) meiosis, by which the diploid primary spermatocytes divide and produce haploid spermatids; and 3) spermiogenesis, by which the spermatids are transformed into the highly differentiated testicular spermatozoa [Clermont, 1972]. The cells that undergo each of these processes are segregated into specific concentric layers around the lumen of a seminiferous tubule and together with the Sertoli cells constitute the seminiferous epithelium.

Because of the synchrony of the processes of spermatogenesis and the precise location of each cell type, several characteristic cellular associations can be identified when cross sections of the testis are examined. These associations are temporally related in the cycle of the seminiferous epithelium. With the exception of man, the cellular associations are numerically arrayed along the length of the tubule to form a wave of the cycle of the seminiferous epithelium.

Spermatogenesis of only a few primate species has been investigated in detail. They are man [Heller, 1964], *M. mulatta* [Arsenieva et al, 1961; Barr, 1973; Clermont and LeBlond, 1959], *M. fascicularis* [Dang, 1970], *M. arctoides* [Clermont and Antar, 1973], *Cercopithecus aethiops* [Clermont, 1969], *C. sabaeus* [Barr, 1973], *Papio cynocephalus* [Barr, 1973], *P. anubis* [Chowdhury and Marshall, 1980; Chowdhury and Steinberger, 1976], and the New World monkey *Saimiri sciureus* [Barr, 1973]. Twelve cellular associations of the cycle have been identified for all eight species of nonhuman primates. The cycle duration is between 9 and 12 days and the duration of spermatogenesis is between 36 and 48 days, depending on the species. There are six cellular associations in man which are haphazardly arranged along the tubule so that no wave of the cycle has been described [Heller, 1964], although this has recently been disputed [Schulze, 1981]. The chaotic arrangement of the associations has complicated kinetic studies in man, but the duration of the cycle has been determined to be 16 days and that of spermatogenesis is about 74 days. The olive baboon, *P. anubis*, has the interesting feature that some of its seminiferous tubules have a somewhat haphazard arrangement of stages similar to that of man, whereas other tubules have the more conventional wave arrangement. It seems, then, that *P. anubis* spermatogenesis is intermediate between man and other primates, at least in this respect.

The overall similarity of cell types, cellular associations, and kinetics of spermatogenesis may be suggestive of a similar hormonal regulation in these several primates. Smith [1944–45] reported that the seminiferous epithelium of long-term hypophysectomized rhesus monkeys comprised only spermatogonia and Sertoli cells whereas that of long-term hypophysectomized rats contained the more advanced primary spermatocytes as well. This is suggestive of a difference in hormonal regulation between the two species, which is fundamentally important because the overwhelming majority of studies of hormonal control of spermatogenesis have been done in rats [Steinberger, 1971]. Although clinical reports of the effect of hypophysectomy on human spermatogenesis are contradictory (and difficult to interpret because of the problem of ascertaining completeness of hypophysectomy), at least one report [MacLeod et al, 1966] states that the seminiferous epithelium consisted of spermatogonia and Sertoli cells only.

Unfortunately, it is not possible to perform direct gonadotropin replacement studies in nonhuman primates because of the lack of sufficient quantities of purified homologous primate gonadotropins. It is, furthermore, not feasible to use heterologous preparations because of their antigenic nature. Thus studies of hormonal regulation of spermatogenesis in nonhuman primates must rely on indirect methods.

FSH and Spermatogenesis. There have been several studies investigating the role of FSH in three macaque species using immunization with heterologous FSH preparations. Wickings and Nieschlag [1980c] actively immunized four rhesus monkeys with ovine FSH and followed these animals for over 2 years. The sperm counts of all four animals declined after immunization, but on only one occasion was azoospermia found. The testes were biopsied after 1 year and the seminiferous tubules were decreased in size and some tubules contained Sertoli cells only. Wickings et al [1980b] also passively immunized rhesus monkeys against FSH, using a homologous rhesus anti-ovine FSH serum, and histological examination of testicular biopsies revealed that there was a reduction of germ cell numbers and that some tubules contained Sertoli cells only. Serum testosterone levels were not different from the control animals in these two studies, but the evidence from bioassays and in vitro binding studies was that FSH was bound to the antibodies generated and thus neutralized.

Rani et al [1978] passively immunized adult bonnet monkeys against ovine FSH. In these monkeys there was a reduction in the testicular hyaluronidase activity and in vitro thymidine incorporation of the testes after 130 days of immunization. These two biochemical parameters in the testis are usually associated with spermatogenesis and can serve as crude measures of the status of spermatogenesis. Murty et al [1979] investigated spermatogenesis directly in similarly immunized bonnet monkeys. A reduction in total sperm count was found between 130 and 200 days of antiserum treatment, yet testicular biopsies taken at 120 days revealed no significant differences between control and treated monkeys. Cessation of antiserum treatment caused a return to control levels of the parameters measured. Neither testosterone nor LH, however, was measured in these two studies.

Moudgal [1981] also investigated fertility in bonnet monkeys passively immunized against FSH. After 240 days of treatment the sperm counts were reduced but testosterone levels were unchanged. The biochemical parameters of testicular hyaluronidase and in vitro thymidine uptake were also reduced. All parameters returned to normal following cessation of treatment.

Finally Madhwa Raj et al [1982] actively immunized monkeys of the species *M. fascicularis* with either ovine FSH or its β subunit. The sperm counts of two monkeys decreased after about 5 months of immunization and one had consistently low sperm counts of less than 10,000 sperm per ejaculate. Plasma testosterone was not reduced in either monkey.

Bremner et al [1981] recently studied the role of FSH in man. Five normal men had their LH and FSH levels suppressed with testosterone enanthate injections. Once sperm counts had decreased to azoospermia or less than 3 million sperm/ml, hCG was adminstered to them. The hCG stimulated testosterone production, which restored spermatogenesis but not in a quantitative manner. It was concluded that FSH was necessary for normal spermatogenesis. Matsumoto et al [1982] have reported that FSH administered to men who have had their pituitary and testicular function suppressed with testosterone enanthate was capable of partially restoring sperm production.

Testosterone and Spermatogenesis. Smith [1944–45] was able to partially reestablish spermatogenesis in hypophysectomized rhesus monkeys with daily injections of testosterone propionate. Only some of the seminiferous tubules contained spermatogenesis. To ensure that the local levels of testosterone in the testes were sufficiently high, Smith implanted testosterone pellets directly into one testis of one monkey. Even in this case, spermatogenesis was observed in only some tubules adjacent to the implant.

We recently confirmed this result in rhesus monkeys which had the pituitary stalk irreversibly transected [Marshall et al, 1983]. Testicular volumes, testosterone, and LH levels in serum all declined following surgery. Testosterone enanthate was administered weekly, which resulted in peak serum levels that were 25 times greater than presurgical levels. Testicular volumes increased but after 13 weeks of treatment had not returned to presurgical values. Sperm production was stimulated, but not quantitatively, as indicated by sperm numbers per ejaculate and testicular volume.

It can be concluded that testosterone is capable of stimulating spermatogenesis in at least four primates: man, and rhesus, crab-eating, and bonnet monkeys. The androgen, however, could not stimulate a fully quantitatively normal spermatogenesis, and some other factor, almost certainly FSH, is necessary. The immunization studies bear this out. It therefore seems reasonable to conclude that FSH and LH (or testosterone) are needed for fully normal spermatogenesis.

Inhibin and Spermatogenesis. Inhibin, a factor which suppresses FSH in rodents [De Jong, 1979], has not been clearly demonstrated in nonhuman primates, but has been described in man [De Jong, 1979; De Kretser et al, 1974]. The issue of inhibin is controversial and remains to be resolved. In nonhuman primates, or at least in the rhesus monkey, the evidence does not support the need for any additional factor, such as inhibin in regulatory feedback mechanisms. Plant et al [1978] found that all negative feedback effects on FSH could be accounted for by testosterone. Resko et al [1980] found that neither FSH nor LH was affected by cryptorchidism. In this latter study, the seminiferous epithelium was reduced in size and in some animals comprised only Sertoli cells and spermatogonia. Hence, they concluded that either the seminiferous epithelium plays no role in the feedback on gonadotropin secretion or that cryptorchidism does not affect the tubule element (ie, inhibin) of the feedback control.

Androgenic Dependency of Accessory Sexual Functions and Characteristics

Hormonal Regulation of Epididymal Function. The epididymis is the site of spermatozoal maturation and storage [Orgebin-Christ et al, 1981] and consists of a long tortuous tubule having a tall columnar epithelium with stereocilia which vary in height and length along the tubule. Several investigators [Dinaker et al, 1974; Mangat, 1981; Setty et al, 1977] have shown that this epithelium in the rhesus monkey is maintained by relatively high levels of testosterone. They have variously shown that the organ weight, amounts of RNA and DNA, and certain enzyme activities decrease after castration, and testosterone only partially restores these. These results suggest that the increase in size of the organ is due not only to an increase in cell number but to increased cell size—ie, both hyperplasia and hypertrophy.

Unfortunately, the epididymal concentration of testosterone was not measured in any of these studies, and it is therefore not known if the doses of steroid used reestablished these levels. Thus it is difficult to assess if the partial restoration of the epididymal function is due to too little androgen or to a lack of other factors.

The androgen dependency of this organ has been shown biochemically in that an androgen receptor has been identified in the cytosol and also in the nucleus of epididymal cells [Blaquier, 1974]. The receptor's characteristics are similar to those previously reported for androgen receptors in other rodents, and it typically has a greater affinity for dihydrotestosterone than testosterone.

Hormonal Regulation of Accessory Sex Organs. The same authors who have investigated epididymal function in rhesus monkeys have also investigated the sex accessory organs, namely, the bulbourethral glands, prostate, and seminal vesicles [Dinaker et al, 1974; Mangat, 1979]. The functions of all of these organs are androgen-dependent. It was found that the lowest doses of testosterone used in these two studies restored the weight and function of the prostate and bulbourethral glands [Dinaker et al, 1974], and only slight increases in androgen levels were necessary to fully restore the seminal vesicles. Interestingly, the androgen levels which restored these accessory sex organs were unable to restore epididymal function as stated above.

Sex Skin. A secondary sex characteristic found among the males of some nonhuman primates is the sex skin. This highly colored and usually edematous perineal skin is found in both sexes, but the function in the male is unknown. It has been suggested to serve as a behavioral signal during sexual and aggressive interactions [Wickler, 1967; Crook, 1972]. It has been known since 1938 [Zuckerman and Parkes, 1938] that testosterone restores the red color of the sex skin in rhesus monkeys, and Vandenbergh [1965] has more recently studied the hormonal regulation of the sex skin. He found that although the red color faded after castration, it did not reach normal body skin color and hence speculated that this could be the result of adrenal steroids. It should be noted, however, that the red color may be due to changes in the vascularization of the skin, but the edema is believed due to the hyaluronic acid content, at least in females [Carlisle et al, 1981]. Estradiol supplementation through implants could not fully restore the sex skin color and edema. Vandenbergh [1965] reported that "low doses" of testosterone (ie, one 75-mg testosterone implant) increased the sex skin color and amount of edema but did not return the intensity of color or the extent of edema to normal in-season adult male levels, whereas three 75-mg implants could do so. Unfortunately the circulating levels of testosterone resulting from the implants were not monitored, and it is thus not known to what degree testosterone levels resembled normal in-season values.

The sex skin of some cercopithecine monkeys such as the talapoin (*Miopithecus talapoin*) is blue [Dixson and Herbert, 1974]. Castration of six adult male talapoin monkeys did not result in any change in the color of the sex skin over a period of 6–14 months, even though testosterone levels had declined to less than 1 ng/ml. The blue color was presumed by these authors to be due to a melanin-like pigment in the dermis which seemed to be unaffected by the testosterone levels of the monkeys. These authors did not administer testosterone or estradiol to the castrated adult monkeys, but did so to intact juveniles. The sex skin color was unaffected, but the size of the penis and body habitus was increased by testosterone.

It can be speculated from these data that the sex skin of a seasonally breeding monkey is hormonally regulated, whereas that of a nonseasonal breeder is not hormonally dependent.

SEASONAL DEPENDENCY OF REPRODUCTIVE FUNCTIONS

Introduction

Some of the factors affecting Leydig cell function were described on page 150, but no mention was made of seasonality as this topic merits a detailed discussion of its own. Table 2 is a comprehensive list of seasonally reproducing primates, and includes those species most commonly used in biomedical research. The great apes, gorillas and chimpanzees, do not appear to have a breeding season, but such observations are hampered by the low reproductive capacity of these species, both in their natural habitat [Tutin, 1980; Harcourt et al, 1980] and in captivity [Dahl, 1982].

Reports in the literature of seasonality are often at variance, and housing conditions must be carefully compared in order to reconcile such discrepancies. For example, male squirrel monkeys maintained in breeding colonies show seasonal variations in sexual and social behavior [Coe and Rosenblum, 1978; Mendoza et al, 1978]. Squirrel monkeys housed individually and allowed only restricted access to females did not show any circannual variation in plasma androgen levels, although large fluctuations were evident and "fatting" and sexual behavior exhibited an annual cyclicity [Wilson et al, 1978]. Hence, although the reproductive status of the female may be an organizing factor for male seasonality, changes in gonadal activity and androgen status also occur and may serve as mediators.

The phenomenon of "fatting" (the increase in body weight occurring at the beginning of the breeding season in several species of New World monkeys) was thought initially to be androgen-dependent. Although positive correlations exist between testicular size, plasma androgens, and body weight [Nadler and Rosenblum, 1972], gonadal androgens would not seem to be the only factor controlling this dramatic increase in body weight.

The distribution of macaque species between seasonal and nonseasonal breeders is interesting. There is a wealth of data in the literature concerning seasonality in *M. mulatta*, for both feral and laboratory-maintained colonies. Bonnet and crab-eating monkeys are being increasingly recommended as nonhuman primate models to replace the now difficult to obtain and expensive rhesus monkey. Neither of these two species is a seasonal breeder, which can only be of advantage in long-term studies of reproductive functions.

The report of *M. arctoides* as nonseasonal is not well documented, as circannual fluctuations in serum testosterone are evident with a nadir in September (6.67 ng/ml) and a peak in June (14.77 ng/ml) [Slob et al, 1979]. Births occurred through-

TABLE 2. Observations on Seasonality in Reproduction in Nonhuman Primates

Species	Seasonal		Nonseasonal	
		Reference	Species	Reference
Saimiri sciureus		Coe and Rosenblum, 1978	*Saimiri sciureus*	Wilson et al, 1978
		Mendoza et al, 1978	*Aotus trivirgatus*	Dixson et al, 1980
Cercopithecus mitis kolbi		Omar and De Vos, 1971	*Ateles belzebuth,*	Klein, 1971
Neuman			*Ateles geoffroyi*	
Macaca mulatta			*Macaca fascicularis*	Mahone and Dukelow, 1979
Free-ranging		Drickamer, 1974	*Macaca radiata*	Murty et al, 1980
		Conaway and Sade, 1965	*Macaca arctoides*	Slob et al, 1979
		Zamboni et al, 1974	*Macaca nigra*	Dixson, 1977
		Vandenbergh and Vessey,	*Macaca nemestrina*	Bernstein et al, 1978
		1968	*Pan troglodytes*	Graham and Hodgen, 1979
Laboratory		Wickings and Nieschlag,		
		1980a		
		Gordon et al, 1976		
		Michael and Keverne, 1971		
		Robinson et al, 1975		
Macaca fuscata		Kawai et al, 1967		
		Matsubayashi, 1974		
Macaca sylvana		Roberts, 1978		

out the year at an almost constant rate, except for a peak in August. Breeding conditions, however, were not rigidly controlled in this study, so that this report remains inconclusive. Observations of birth frequencies are, in addition, hampered by the poor reproductive capacity of stump-tailed monkeys in captivity [MacDonald, 1971].

It is not clear what causes the seasonality in reproductive functions in rhesus monkeys, although climatic factors are certainly involved in their synchrony. As this annual cycle of testicular recrudescence, maturity, regression, and quiescence offers distinct advantages for those workers investigating stimulation and suppression of testicular functions, these events and their possible causes will be further discussed.

Seasonal Dependency of Male Reproductive Functions in Feral Rhesus Monkeys

Observations made on free-ranging rhesus monkeys in their natural habitat in India gave an early indication that reproduction was seasonally dependent, with conceptions occurring in the months September to December and births being observed some 6 months later (March to June), at the onset of the rainy season and increasing food supply [Lindburg, 1971; Southwick et al, 1961]. The role of latitude in synchronizing this seasonality has been discussed for colonies in both the northern [Van Horn, 1980] and southern hemispheres [Bielert and Vandenbergh, 1981]. Rhesus monkeys in the southern hemisphere have a season 6 months out of phase with their northern counterparts. Climactic variations between the neighboring rhesus colonies of La Parguera (55 cm rainfall/year) and Cayo Santiago (150 cm rainfall/year) in Puerto Rico induce a shift in birth seasons of approximately 90 days [Varley and Vessey, 1977]. Photoperiod itself does not seem to have a direct influence on reproductive status [Lancaster and Lee, 1965; Vandenbergh and Vessey, 1968], although the natural breeding season does seem to be triggered by decreasing temperatures and precipitation, declining day length, and a reduction in food supply [Lindburg, 1971].

The physiological events in male rhesus monkeys underlying the breeding season involve growth of the testes and regeneration of the seminiferous epithelium from a regressed state such that out-of-season tubules may be populated by Sertoli cells only, with some spermatogonia and occasional spermatocyctes [Conaway and Sade,

1965]. Sperm production and the numbers of ejaculated spermatozoa also increased at this time [Zamboni et al, 1974]. Regression of spermatogenesis occurred rapidly at the end of the breeding season, and by February the seminiferous tubules were largely depleted of spermatocytes and spermatids.

Seasonal Dependency of Male Reproductive Functions in Laboratory-Maintained Rhesus Monkeys

Sexual Behavior. Sexual behavior remains seasonal in monkeys maintained under constant or controlled environmental conditions within the laboratory. Ejaculatory behavior of males on a 14-hour light: 10-hour dark period was maximal during December and declined in February, although the female rhesus monkeys used in the mating tests were still sexually receptive [Michael and Keverne, 1971]. Mating behavior of intact males with ovarectomized, estrogen-primed females—ie, continuously receptive females—also showed similar patterns, although the seasonal fluctuations were less well defined. Indeed, seasonal variations in sexual activity were also observed in castrated male monkeys receiving continual replacement of testosterone [Michael and Zumpe, 1976]. Hence the increases in testosterone accompanying testicular recrudescence are not necessary for triggering mating behavior.

Spermatogenesis. Changes in testicular appearance and histology similar to those seen in feral monkeys have been observed in rhesus monkeys maintained under controlled conditions. Richter et al [1978] described the annual cycle of morphological events, including regression and degeneration of the germinal epithelium, reduction in tubule diameter during January and February, total depopulation of the tubules from March to May so that only Sertoli cells and spermatogonia were present, recrudescence starting in July, and complete spermatogenesis in all tubules by September.

The simplest method of determining the stage of the circannual cycle is to measure testicular volume. Total volumes fluctuated from approximately 30 ml in season to only half that value out of season [Wickings and Nieschlag, 1980a]. Sperm counts also varied with time; indeed, using penile electrostimulation [Mastroianni and Manson, 1963] in conscious monkeys, no ejaculates could be ob-

TABLE 3. Seasonal Differences in Pituitary and Testicular Function and Capacity in Four Adult Rhesus Monkeys (mean ± se; Δ indicates the increment of stimulated hormone values over basal levels after 50 μg LHRH IV)

	Quiescence (March–May)	Recrudescence (August–September)	In season (October)
LH (miU/ml)			
Basal levels	4.5 ± 1.4	18.0 ± 4.2	10.0 ± 7.0
Δ 30 min after LHRH	12.1 ± 3.0	244 ± 44	49.2 ± 19.6
No. of pulses per 24 hr	0–3	8–10	4–6
Testosterone (nmole/liter)			
Basal levels	5.5 ± 0.5	8.9 ± 2.0	23.5 ± 5.8
Δ 60 min after LHRH	25.5 ± 3.2	17.3 ± 8.9	31.0 ± 14.5
Production rate (mg/day)	1.2 ± 0.3	1.2 ± 0.2	3.1 ± 0.6
No. of pulses per 24 hr	0	5–6	5–7

tained out of season. Sperm counts from August to January varied between 11 and 1,126 million per ejaculate [Wickings and Nieschlag, 1980a]. Using rectal stimulation which does not require the androgen-dependent penile erection, ejaculates could be obtained on all occasions throughout the year, and sperm counts were in the same range as for penile stimulation [Van Pelt and Keyser, 1970]. No overt seasonal variations in sperm counts were evident, but lowest counts were obtained between March and June in a population of male rhesus monkeys studied over 4 years in a constant environment, completely isolated from female monkeys [Ewing, 1982].

Endocrine Parameters

Hypothalamic–pituitary interaction. The requirement of the pulsatile mode of LH secretion for fully developed functions has already been discussed. In the sexually quiescent monkey between March and May, very few LH pulses of low amplitude could be detected and very little diurnal rhythm was seen in either LH or testosterone levels. During recrudescence, the highest pulse frequency of 8–10 pulses per day occurring at 2- to 4-hour intervals was seen. Basal LH concentrations also increased during recrudescence to reach maximum levels prior to the in-season period. The number of LH pulses per 24 hours decreased to 4–6 per day in season, with pulses occurring more frequently during the dark phase of the 24-hour period [Plant,

1980; Wickings and Nieschlag, 1981]. The pituitary retained its capacity to respond to exogenous LHRH, although the reponse was much diminished out of season (Table 3). This indicated that hypothalamic activity was decreased during quiescence, and the lower LH response was probably due to the lack of the self-priming of the pituitary.

Testicular function. Serum testosterone levels parallel LH levels throughout the year; maximum values were seen only during the in-season period [Wickings and Nieschlag, 1980a]. This circannuality in testosterone has been reported for laboratory monkeys maintained under either natural daylight conditions or in constant light-dark periods, and was unaffected by the presence or absence of female partners [Beck and Wuttke, 1979; Gordon et al, 1976; Michael and Bonsall, 1977; Plant et al, 1974; Robinson et al, 1975].

Although not every LH pulse elicits a secretory episode of testosterone, it is generally possible to relate each testosterone pulse to a preceding LH pulse, the time difference in the maxima being approximately 40 minutes for blood samples collected at 20-minute intervals. The number of identifiable testosterone pulses does not change between the recrudescent phase and the in-season period, but an increase in the amplitude of the pulses is evident.

The Leydig cells also retain their capacity to respond to trophic stimuli the whole year round, but only reach their full secretory capacity in season. This is seen not only in terms of the response to LH stimulation following LHRH, where the response is the same as that during quiescence (Table 3) but also in the response to hCG stimulation tests [Nieschlag and Wickings, 1980b]. In season the Leydig cell requires smaller amounts of LH to produce a larger increment in testosterone. Testosterone production rates are also lowest during quiescence and recrudescence, and only increase in season (Table 3) [Wickings and Nieschlag, 1977].

This sequence of maturation occurring during recrudescence suggests that events triggering the hypothalamus initiate first pituitary and then testicular development. Additional proof for the mediatory, but not initiatory role of the hypothalamus is given in experiments mimicking hypothalamic activity by pulsatile administration of low doses of LHRH during the period of sexual quiescence. This treatment accelerates pituitary and testicular development so that within 7 weeks of initiating treatment testicular function is fully developed in terms of both steroidogenesis and sperm production [Wickings et al, 1981c]. Treatment begun in March reproduced the in-season status by May, but withdrawal of pulsatile LHRH administration resulted in degeneration of the testis to its quiescent state, before then entering recrudescence at the appropriate time.

Seasonal Fluctuations of Reproductive Function in Men. Up until the widespread use of oral contraceptives in the mid-1960s, distinct seasonal fluctuations in human conceptions and births existed. Considerable variation was evident among the various ethnic groups studied [Cowgill, 1966], and it is clear that social, cultural, and economic factors, rather than climatic parameters such as latitude or photoperiod, are important. One physical factor that does seem to influence the timing of conception is temperature, and the correlation, at least for the Hong Kong population, was a negative one [Chang et al, 1963].

Seasonal fluctuations were found in sperm counts from 4,435 subjects collected for more than 5 years [Tjoa et al, 1982]. Nearly all subjects (95.7%) were fertile, and all were undergoing elective vasectomy. Highest counts were found between February and March and lowest counts were seen in September. Considerable temporal fluctuations were evident both within and between calendar years.

Circannual variations in plasma testosterone have been found in young healthy men leading a rela-

tively constant life-style. Maximum values occurred in October (July to December), and there was a shift in the acrophase of the diurnal variation over the year [Reinberg et al, 1975]. The same workers also identified significant circannual fluctuations in LH and FSH in young men, with the acrophases being located in April to May for LH and February for FSH [Reinberg et al, 1978]. Sexual activity showed a peak in September, although this parameter was scored subjectively. The mode of blood sampling (one sample every 4 hours) did not take into account the pulsatile mode of release of LH, so that the circannual variations seen in this parameter could be caused by sampling at different points of a secretory pulse. It is difficult to reconcile the phase shift of approximately 6 months between maximal pituitary activity in winter/spring and that of testicular activity in autumn. The shift in circadian acrophase of plasma testosterone may be related to the LH circannual variation. However, the fluctuations in all three parameters fall within 20% of the annual means, and even the nadir levels are within the normal physiological range for the three hormones. This situation cannot be compared with the very marked changes seen in the rhesus monkeys, which in the quiescent state can be described as being hypogonadotropically hypogonadal [Wickings and Nieschlag, 1980a].

Mechanisms Controlling Seasonality

The first issue that remains to be resolved is what are the environmental cues that signal seasonal changes. On the one hand, several observations of seasonality in laboratory colonies have been carried out on monkeys maintained in controlled conditions. The usual cues of photoperiod and temperature variation have been eliminated. On the other hand, feral and free-ranging populations may show seasonality, but the peak of fertility in the northern hemisphere is 6 months out of phase with that of southern hemisphere colonies. Furthermore, the intriguing observation of a shift of 90 days in the two Puerto Rican colonies would suggest that climatic variations may influence seasonality. In seasonal rodent and ovine species, the pineal gland is intimately involved in the regulation of seasonality, usually through photoperiodic stimulation. Evidence, although limited, would suggest that photoperiod and hence the pineal gland are not involved in the regulation of seasonality in rhesus monkeys.

A recent report of the lack of effect of melatonin on basal and LHRH-stimulated LH and FSH levels in male rhesus monkeys would further support this concept [Chrousos et al, 1982]. There are two notes of caution which must be considered when evaluating this study. Chrousos et al [1982] used an LH assay which has been found to be inappropriate for determining small changes in LH in male rhesus monkeys [Peckham and Knobil, 1976]. Secondly, the melatonin was administered only in the morning, and this substance has been found to be most effective in hamsters when administered in the evening [Tamarkin et al, 1976]. Pinealectomy or superior cervical ganglionectomy as done in rams [Lincoln, 1979] would directly provide the answer whether the pineal gland is involved in the regulation of seasonality in nonhuman primates.

The evidence of Wickings et al [1981c] suggests that seasonality is mediated through the hypothalamus. These workers were able to stimulate the testes and ejaculatory behavior of out-of-season monkeys with pulsatile administration of LHRH. One interesting clue to the mystery may be found in prolactin, which is high out of season and low in season. It is well established in female rats [Beck and Wuttke, 1977] and in women [Bohnet et al, 1976] that prolactin affects gonadotropin secretion. If prolactin is a mediator of seasonality, then it would seem likely that it should affect the frequency of LH and hence LHRH pulses. Parenthetically, the stimulation of spermatogenesis by testosterone alone in stalk-sectioned monkeys—ie, animals with high circulating prolactin levels caused by the removal of the hypothalamic inhibitory influence—would suggest that prolactin has little or no peripheral effect.

We have performed some preliminary experiments in which out-of-season prolactin levels were decreased with bromocryptine, a dopamine agonist, and in-season levels were increased with sulpiride, a dopamine antagonist. The pulsatile LH levels were monitored over 24 hours both before and at the end of treatment. The decrease in prolactin levels had little effect on the low pulsatile frequency of LH whereas the pharmacological increase in prolactin had an inconsistent influence in that the frequency of LH pulses decreased in two monkeys but was unaffected in the other two treated animals. The results, at best suggestive, may hint at the role of prolactin in the regulation of seasonality. Perhaps prolactin is, then, an inhibitor, but the bromocryptine studies suggest the need for a stimulator of pulsatile LHRH release.

As previously stated, regulation of seasonality in male primates remains to be investigated. It has been demonstrated that primates are seasonal but the environmental influences remain to be determined. Until such time as that is done, it is premature to consider mechanisms.

REGULATION OF FERTILITY

Introduction

The regulation of fertility can operate in either of two directions, for the suppression of testicular function or for the improvement of fertility. The first of these was our initial aim, looking for a possible method for male fertility control, but the diagnosis and treatment of male infertility is of no less pressing concern for the andrologist in clinical practice. Characterization of the pituitary and testicular functions of the mature rhesus monkey showed that this nonhuman primate provides a good model for the human situation [Nieschlag and Wickings, 1980a,b], and this section contains much of our own data on studies concerning the use of LHRH agonists for the suppression of spermatogenesis and in one instance for the stimulation of testicular function, and also other methods of enhancing testicular activity.

Infertility in Male Gorillas

There is a need for improving therapeutic measures not only in andrology, but also in primate husbandry, as exemplified by the plight of the gorilla. The reproductive capacity of gorillas both in their natural habitat and in captivity is very low, and thus is one of the major factors involved in the demise of this species. This low reproductive capacity is related on the one hand to the very low frequency of copulation and on the other to the very high frequency of infertility seen among male and possibly female gorillas [Beck, 1982]. Of all the mature male gorillas in North American zoos, only 21% sired offspring in the period 1978–79.

Seminal parameters in eight fertile animals showed that sperm numbers were low (41 million per ejaculate), sperm motility was poor (32% motile sperm), and a high percentage (51%) of sperm were abnormally formed [Gould and Kling, 1982]. This situation is more similar to that in humans than to that in other nonhuman primates, where very few abnormally formed sperm are usually present [Afzelius, 1981]. Seminal parameters in infertile gorillas indicated severe degrees of oligoasthenoteratozoospermia, and in several instances azoospermia or aspermia. Serum gonadotropins in these infertile gorillas were elevated and concentrations of androgens tended to be lower, but were not significantly reduced [Gould and Kling, 1982].

Results of occasional testicular biopsies revealed that interstitial tissue is very prominent, and may be due either to a relative hypoplasia or atrophy of the seminiferous tubules or to hyperplasia of the interstitial compartment. Degeneration or sloughing of the germinal epithelium was evident, and one remarkable observation was that spermatogenesis was interrupted at the spermatid stage [Foster and Rowley, 1982]. The male gorilla is apparently susceptible to infections of the genital tract [Kraemer and Vera Cruz, 1971], and both bacterially and virally mediated orchitis may result in this very poor reproductive status.

Stimulation of Testicular Functions

Pulsatile Administration of LHRH During Sexual Quiescence in Rhesus Monkeys. The results of pulsatile administration of the decapeptide LHRH (100 ng every 96 min subcutaneously for 7 weeks, using the Auto-Syringe portable pump) alternating weekly with low-dose LHRH-agonist treatment to rhesus monkeys have already been mentioned. Prior to treatment, basal LH and testosterone levels in the two monkeys treated were low and no spontaneous LH pulses occurred over a 24-hour period. In week 7 of treatment 15 LH pulses per 24 hours could be identified, and basal LH and testosterone were in the range of a normal in-season monkey. Nine testosterone pulses were found, but in some instances levels were still increasing when the next LH pulse occurred so that responses to individual LH pulses became blurred.

Ejaculates could be obtained using penile electroejaculation after 5 weeks of treatment, when we were unable to obtain a response from control monkeys. By week 7 sperm counts were between 120 and 250 million per ejaculate (normal range for our colony is 110–1,110 million/ejaculate), and the percentage of motile sperm was 70–80%. Testicular volumes had increased to above 20 ml and the frequency of spontaneous ejaculations increased from 0–1 per week to 4–6 per week, as measured by counting the ejaculatory plugs under the cages each morning [Wickings et al, 1981c].

Although mimicking hypothalamic activity was successful in stimulating pituitary and testicular development, the method was very impractical for routine use, requiring constant monitoring of pump function and correct placement of the catheter subcutaneously. The use of long-acting LHRH agonists has been applied to the treatment of male infertility [Aparicio et al, 1976; Nieschlag and Von der Ohe, 1981] and hypogonadotropic hypogonadism [Mortimer et al, 1974; Smith et al, 1979], but with varying degrees of success. Some of the failures can be attributed to overdosage of the agonist, resulting in suppression and not stimulation of the pituitary-testicular axis. We were concerned with finding the correct dosage regimen, avoiding the desensitizing effects, and compared the feasibility of this approach with that of using pulsatile LHRH adminstration.

Low-dose LHRH-Agonist Treatment During Sexual Quiescence in Rhesus Monkeys. Because of the danger of down-regulating pituitary and testicular receptors with too much of LHRH agonist, low-dose intermittent treatment with D-Ser(TBu)^6-LHRH ethylamide (Buserelin, Hoechst) was chosen [Wickings et al, 1981c]. Rhesus monkeys were given the agonist daily at a dose of 1 μg/day for two periods of 5 weeks separated by a 1-week pause.

No stimulation of LH was achieved although an increase in testosterone levels was evident at the end of the treatment period. There was no desensitization of the pituitary with the dose of agonist used, as the treatment dose of agonist during the 11-week test period elicited increases in both LH and testosterone on all occasions tested. The response at the end of treatment was in fact even greater than that beforehand. Testicular volumes increased slightly above those of untreated controls. Two of the four treated monkeys produced ejaculates at the end of treatment, but sperm counts were below the normal range although sperm motility and morphology were normal.

Hence some stimulation of pituitary and testicular functions could be achieved using low-dose LHRH-agonist treatment, but the extent of this was not comparable with that seen under pulsatile LHRH administration or during naturally occurring recrudescence.

Administration of hCG During Sexual Quiescence in Rhesus Monkeys. Acute stimulation of adult rhesus monkeys with hCG results in an increase in serum testosterone at all times of the year [Wickings and Nieschlag, 1980a]. Treatment with very low doses of hCG (3 × 100 IU per week) for 11 weeks produced an initial stimulation of testosterone levels in serum to approximately 60 nmol/liter, more than 10-fold higher than values in quiescence. Levels then fell after 2 weeks in two monkeys and after 8 weeks in the remaining two monkeys, and fluctuated between 2 and 20 nmol/liter thereafter. No effects were seen on testicular volumes, and none of the monkeys responded to electrostimulation under treatment, despite the high circulating levels of testosterone.

This failure of hCG to produce a long-term stimulation of testosterone levels is not related to any down-regulation of the testicular LH/hCG receptors, but rather to production of antibodies against hCG. The two monkeys that showed only a transient rise in testosterone under hCG had previously received a total of 90,000 IU hCG subcutaneously, given irregularly over a period of 2–3 years. Antibody titers were not detectable at the onset of low-dose hCG treatment, but were evident at 2 weeks and thereafter, at approximately the same titer. The remaining two monkeys had never received hCG before this study and significant binding of hCG in serum was found after 8 weeks of treatment (ie, after 2,400 IU hCG given in 24 separate subcutaneous injections). Although binding was not as high in these two monkeys, significant neutralization of hCG occurred, as seen in the fall in serum testosterone levels concomitant with antibody detection. None of the SC injections had been given with any vehicle other than saline. This study demonstrates the dangers of using human hormones in monkeys, even at low doses and without adjuvants.

High-dose Testosterone Treatment in Stalk-sectioned Rhesus Monkeys. Regression of testicular function in adult monkeys following transection of the pituitary stalk is more pronounced than during quiescence in intact monkeys. The testes became very small (< 10 ml). The effect of replacing testosterone in very high doses, maintaining circulating levels at approximately 200–300 nmol/liter (10× times higher than normal physiological levels) was to increase testicular volumes and to induce spermatogenesis to a certain degree. Of the four treated monkeys sperm production was induced in all animals and sperm counts of 16–130 million per ejaculate were seen in three monkeys [Marshall et al, 1983]. These results would substantiate the theory that both FSH and LH or testosterone are required for the restoration and maintenance of complete spermatogenesis in rhesus monkeys.

Suppression of Testicular Functions

Treatment of Rhesus Monkeys With High Doses of LHRH Agonists. Whereas low doses of LHRH ag-

onists can induce some measure of testicular recrudescence, high doses of the same compounds produce pituitary desensitization and paradoxical antifertility effects [Belchetz et al, 1978; Sandow et al, 1978].

Compared to smaller animal species the rhesus monkey is resistant to the down-regulatory effects of LHRH agonists. Treatment with 4 and 20 μg Buserelin per day for 12 weeks failed to suppress pituitary and testicular functions significantly [Wickings et al, 1981b]. Similarly 25 μg of the same agonist per day failed to affect sperm counts and motility over a 7-week treatment period, although serum testosterone levels were suppressed [Resko et al, 1982]. Treatment with these doses of LHRH agonists failed to keep LH levels elevated over the entire interval between successive injections so that the pituitary could recover from the suppressive effects, resulting in inadequate testicular suppression. Increasing the treatment dose to 100 μg/day and dividing this into two injections spaced approximately 12 hours apart resulted in a significant decrease in basal serum LH and testosterone concentrations, but these were still not below levels seen in sexually quiescent monkeys [Bint Akhtar et al, 1982]. Testicular volumes also decreased to out-of-season values, and although ejaculate weights and sperm counts were reduced under treatment, values were still within the normal range for this colony.

Giving the more potent agonist (D-Trp[6])-LHRH to rhesus monkeys for 19 weeks at a dose of 500 μg twice weekly caused desensitization of the pituitary, but no inhibition of testicular function occurred [Sundaram et al, 1982]. Increasing the frequency of injections to 500 μg/day for 3 months caused the abolition of testosterone release following injection of the agonist in two of the four treated monkeys, but the other two animals remained unaffected. The first two monkeys also stopped ejaculating, and ejaculates collected after cessation of treatment were azoospermic for 4–8 weeks.

The mode of application of LHRH agonists can greatly influence their effectiveness in suppressing pituitary and testicular functions. Daily injections exert their effects primarily through pituitary desensitization of the testis, whereas constant infusion of the agonist causes down-regulation of the pituitary LHRH receptors, resulting in desensitization of the pituitary, and the testis remains dormant under the lack of LH stimulation [Belchetz et al, 1978]. Applying this mode of administration to rhesus monkeys, using osmotic minipumps to achieve a constant subcutaneous infusion at a rate of 48 μg Buserelin/day, showed that this dose, lower than that ineffective as twice-daily injections, produced complete suppression of the pituitary in the four treated animals [Bint Akhtar et al, 1983]. Basal serum LH levels became undetectable, and no response to acute LHRH stimulation was evident after 4 weeks of treatment. After 13 weeks of treatment all monkeys ceased to respond to electrostimulation and testosterone-containing Silastic capsules were implanted to sustain physiological levels of testosterone. This restored ejaculatory behavior, and three of the four monkeys were found to be azoospermic. The fourth monkey had very low sperm counts but was also azoospermic at the end of the treatment. Recovery of all functions occurred rapidly after removing the minipumps, and serum LH and testosterone levels showed an initial rebound effect before returning to pretreatment levels.

The use of such minipumps in monkeys has shown that an LHRH agonist-based method of male fertility control is feasible, and that the mode of application is critical. Furthermore all suppressive effects were completely reversible.

High-dose LHRH-Agonist Treatment in Baboons. As the osmotic minipumps used in rhesus monkeys cannot be used in humans, other means of producing constant release of agonists are required. Studies in baboons have used pellets based on a cholesterol matrix containing either D-Trp^6-Pro-NHEA-LHRH (LHRH-T) or D-Ala^6-ProNHEA^9-LHRH (LHRH-A) at a dose of 5 mg agonist per animal [Vickery and McRae, 1980]. Pellets were removed 44 days after implantation. Serum testosterone levels were suppressed to very low values after 26 days until removal of the pellets containing LHRH-T, although LH levels were only decreased in one of the two baboons treated. Similarly, treatment with LHRH-A caused a reduction in testosterone levels in all three baboons, following an initial rise. Measurement of circulating LHRH-T levels indicated a considerable variation in the release of the agonist from the pellets.

Although the use of cholesterol pellets impregnated with LHRH agonists provides an alternative to the osmotic minipump, the irregular rates of release and the necessity for surgical implantation and removal are serious drawbacks to this approach.

High-dose LHRH-Agonist Treatment in Men. Pituitary and testicular desensitization occurred in men treated with Buserelin (5 μg/day for 17 weeks), but no effects on seminal parameters were reported [Bergquist et al, 1979].

Treatment with D-Trp^6-LHRH (50 μg/day for 6–10 weeks) in eight men caused five to withdraw from the study because of unacceptable side effects—eg, loss of libido and potency and the occurrence of hot flashes. The remaining three subjects had very low circulating levels of testosterone and sperm counts below 5 million/ml [Linde et al, 1981]. No testosterone substitution was attempted in this study, a prerequisite if such side effects are to be avoided.

CONCLUDING REMARKS

It is evident from the data presented that comparison of reproductive function among primate species is possible only on a limited basis. Studies on the endocrine regulation of testicular function in great apes is severely hindered by their scarcity and the difficulties of maintenance under laboratory conditions. Macaque species have been studied most thoroughly in this respect, and at the other end of the scale few New World monkey species have been characterized. Another major problem is the lack of sufficient quantities of homologous protein hormones for direct investigation of the effects of these hormones on reproductive function. Neurological and neuroendocrine regulatory mechanisms of male reproductive function remain to be elucidated—for example, the factors controlling hypothalamic LHRH secretion. Cellular and molecular events at the testicular level also remain largely unexplored.

ACKNOWLEDGMENTS

Our studies were supported by the Deutsche Forschungsgemeinschaft and the World Health Organization, Special Programme of Research for Human Reproduction. We are grateful to Ms. C. Seiler for her help in the preparation of the manuscript.

REFERENCES

Afzelius, B.A. Abnormal human spermatozoa including comparative data from apes. AMERICAN JOURNAL OF PRIMATOLOGY 1:175–182, 1981.

Aparicio, N.J.; Schwarzstein, L.; Turner, E.A.; Turner, D.; Mancini, R.; Schally, A.V. Treatment of idiopathic normogonadotropic oligoasthenospermia with synthetic luteinizing hormone–releasing hormone.

FERTILITY AND STERILITY 27:549–555, 1976.

Arimura, A.; Spies, H.G.; Schally, A.V. Relative insensitivity of rhesus monkeys to the LH-releasing hormone (LH-RH). JOURNAL OF CLINICAL ENDOCRINOLOGY AND METABOLISM 36:372–374, 1973.

Arsenieva, M.; Dubinin, N.P.; Orlova, N.N.; Bakulina, E.D. Radiation analysis duration of meiotic phases in spermatogenesis of monkey (*Macaca mulatta*). DOKLADY BIOLOGICAL SCIENCES 141:984–986, 1961.

Atkinson, L.E.; Bhattacharya, A.N.; Monroe, S.E.; Dierschke, D.J.; Knobil, E. Effects of gonadectomy on plasma LH concentration in the rhesus monkey. ENDOCRINOLOGY 87:847–849, 1970.

Barr, A.B. Timing of spermatogenesis in four nonhuman primate species. FERTILITY AND STERILITY 24:381–389, 1973.

Beattie, C.W.; Bullock, B.C. Diurnal variation of serum androgen and estradiol-17β in the adult male green monkey (*Cercopithecus* sp.). BIOLOGY OF REPRODUCTION 19:36–39, 1978.

Beck, B.B. Fertility in North American male lowland gorillas. AMERICAN JOURNAL OF PRIMATOLOGY SUPPLEMENT 1:7–11, 1982.

Beck, W.; Wuttke, W. Desensitization of the dopaminergic inhibition of pituitary luteinizing hormone release by prolactin in ovariectomized rats. JOURNAL OF ENDOCRINOLOGY 74:67–74, 1977.

Beck, W.; Wuttke, W. Annual rhythm of luteinizing hormone, follicle stimulating hormone, prolactin and testosterone in the serum of male rhesus monkeys. JOURNAL OF ENDOCRINOLOGY 83:131–139, 1979.

Belchetz, P.E.; Plant, T.M.; Keogh, E.J.; Knobil, E. Hypophysial responses to continuous and intermittent delivery of hypothalamic gonadotropin-releasing hormone. SCIENCE 202:631–632, 1978.

Bergquist, C.; Nillius, S.J.; Bergh, T.; Skarin, G.; Wide, L. Inhibitory effects on gonadotropin secretion and gonadal function in men during chronic treatment with a potent stimulatory luteinizing hormone–releasing hormone analogue. ACTA ENDOCRINOLOGICA 91:601–608, 1979.

Bernstein, I.S.; Rose, R.M.; Gordon, T.P. Behavioral and hormonal reponses of male rhesus monkeys introduced to females in the breeding and non-breeding season. ANIMAL BEHAVIOR 25:609–614, 1977.

Bernstein, I.S.; Gordon, T.P.; Rose, R.M.; Peterson, M.S. Influences of sexual and social stimuli upon circulating levels of testosterone in male pigtail macaques. BEHAVIORAL BIOLOGY 24:400–404, 1978.

Bielert, C.; Vandenbergh, J.G. Seasonal influences on births and male sex skin coloration in rhesus monkeys (*Macaca mulatta*) in the southern hemisphere.

JOURNAL OF REPRODUCTION AND FERTILITY 62:229–233, 1981.

Bint Akhtar, F.; Wickings, E.J.; Zaidi, P.; Nieschlag, E. Pituitary and testicular functions in sexually mature rhesus monkeys under high-dose LRH-agonist treatment. ACTA ENDOCRINOLOGICA 101:113–118, 1982.

Bint Akhtar, F.; Marshall, G.R.; Wickings, E.J.; Nieschlag, E. Reversible induction of azoospermia in rhesus monkeys by constant infusion of a GnRH agonist using osmotic mini-pumps. JOURNAL OF CLINICAL ENDOCRINOLOGY AND METABOLISM 56:534–540, 1983.

Blaquier, J. Androgen receptors from the epididymis of the rhesus monkey. ENDOCRINE RESEARCH COMMUNICATIONS 1:155–167, 1974.

Bohnet, H.G.; Dahlen, H.G.; Wuttke, W.; Schneider, H.P.G. Hyperprolactinemic anovulatory syndrome. JOURNAL OF CLINICAL ENDOCRINOLOGY AND METABOLISM 42:132–143, 1976.

Bremner, W.J.; Matsumoto, A.M.; Sussman, A.M.; Paulsen, C.A. Follicle-stimulating hormone and human spermatogenesis. JOURNAL OF CLINICAL INVESTIGATION 68:1044–1052, 1981.

Carlisle, K.S.; Brenner, R.M.; Montagna, W. Hormonal regulation of sex skin in *Macaca nemestrina*. BIOLOGY OF REPRODUCTION 25:1053–1063, 1981.

Carmel, P.W.; Araki, S.; Ferin, M. Pituitary stalk portal blood collection in rhesus monkeys: Evidence for pulsatile release of GnRH. ENDOCRINOLOGY 99:243–248, 1976.

Catchpole, H.R.; van Wagenen, G. Reproduction in the rhesus monkey, *Macaca mulatta*. Pp. 118–140 in THE RHESUS MONKEY, Vol. II. G.H. Bourne, ed. New York, Academic Press, 1975.

Chang, K.S.F.; Chan, S.T.; Low, W.D.; Ng, C.K. Climate and conception rates in Hong Kong. HUMAN BIOLOGY 35:367–375, 1963.

Chappel, S.C.; Ellinwood, W.E.; Huckins, C.; Herbert, D.C.; Spies, H.G. Active immunization of male rhesus monkeys against luteinizing hormone releasing hormone. BIOLOGY OF REPRODUCTION 22:333–342, 1980.

Chowdhury, A.K.; Marshall, G.R. Irregular pattern of spermatogenesis in the baboon (*Papio anubis*) and its possible mechanism. Pp. 129–137 in TESTICULAR DEVELOPMENT, STRUCTURE AND FUNCTION. A. Steinberger; E. Steinberger, eds. New York, Raven, 1980.

Chowdhury, A.K.; Steinberger, E. A study of germ cell morphology and duration of spermatogenic cycle in the baboon, *Papio anubis*. ANATOMICAL RECORD 185:155–169, 1976.

Chrousos, G.P.; Poplack, D.; Kostolich, M.; Wiede, C.; Olitt, A.; Brown, T.; Bercu, B.B. Hypothalamic-adenohypophyseal function in male rhesus monkeys: A primate model. JOURNAL OF MEDICAL PRIMATOLOGY 10:61–71, 1981.

Chrousos, G.P.; Brown, T.; Bercu, B.B. Pharmacological effects of melatonin on hypothalamic-adenohypophyseal function in the nonhuman primate. NEUROENDOCRINOLOGY 34:343–346, 1982.

Clarke, I.J.; Cummins, J.T. The temporal relationship between gonadotropin-releasing hormone (GnRH) and luteinizing hormone (LH) secretion in ovariectomized ewes. ENDOCRINOLOGY 111:1737–1739, 1982.

Clermont, Y. Two classes of spermatogonial stem cells in the monkey, Cercopithecus aethiops. AMERICAN JOURNAL OF ANATOMY 126:57–72, 1969.

Clermont, Y. Kinetics of spermatogenesis in mammals: Seminiferous epithelium cycle and spermatogonial renewal. PHYSIOLOGICAL REVIEWS 52:198–235, 1972.

Clermont, Y.; Antar, M. Duration of the cycle of the seminiferous epithelium and the spermatogonial renewal in the monkey (Macaca arctoides). AMERICAN JOURNAL OF ANATOMY 136: 153–166, 1973.

Clermont, Y.; LeBlond, G.P. Differentiation and renewal of spermatogonia in the monkey, Macacus rhesus. AMERICAN JOURNAL OF ANATOMY 104:237–273, 1959.

Coe, C.L.; Rosenblum, L.A. Annual reproductive strategy of the squirrel monkey (Saimiri sciureus). FOLIA PRIMATOLOGICA 29:19–42, 1978.

Conaway, C.H.; Sade, D.S. The seasonal spermatogenic cycle in free ranging rhesus monkeys. FOLIA PRIMATOLOGICA 3:1–12, 1965.

Cowgill, U.M. Season of birth in man. Contemporary situation with special reference to Europe and the southern hemisphere. ECOLOGY 47:614–623, 1966.

Crook, J.H. Sexual selection, dimorphism, and social organization in the primate. Pp. 231–281 in SEXUAL SELECTION AND THE DESCENT OF MAN. B. Campbell, ed. Chicago, Aldine, 1972.

Dahl, J.F. The feasibility of improving the captive environments of the Pongidae. AMERICAN JOURNAL OF PRIMATOLOGY SUPPLEMENT 1:77–85, 1982.

Dang, D. Le cycle de l'épithelium séminifère du singe crabier (Macaca fascicularis). Ph.D. Dissertation, Faculté des Sciences, Paris, 1970.

Davies, T.F.; Walsh, P.C.; Hodgen, G.D.; Dufau, M.L.; Catt, K.J. Characterization of the primate luteinizing hormone receptor in testis homogenates and Leydig cells. JOURNAL OF CLINICAL ENDOCRINOLOGY AND METABOLISM 48:680–685, 1979.

De Jong, F.H. Inhibin—fact or artefact. MOLECULAR AND CELLULAR ENDOCRINOLOGY 13:1–10, 1979.

De Kretser, D.M.; Burger, H.G.; Hudson, B. The relationship between germinal cells and serum FSH levels in males with infertility. JOURNAL OF CLINICAL ENDOCRINOLOGY AND METABOLISM 38:787–793, 1974.

Dinaker, N.; Arora, R.; Prasad, M.R.N. Effects of microquantities of testosterone on the epididymis and accessory glands of the castrated rhesus monkey, Macaca mulatta. JOURNAL OF ENDOCRINOLOGY 60:399–408, 1974.

Dixson, A.F. Observations on the diplays, menstrual cycles and sexual behavior of the "black ape" of Celebes (Macaca nigra). JOURNAL OF ZOOLOGY 182:63–84, 1977.

Dixson, A.F.; Herbert, J. The effects of testosterone on the sexual skin and genitalia of the male talapoin monkey. JOURNAL OF REPRODUCTION AND FERTILITY 38:217–219, 1974.

Dixson, A.F.; Martin, R.D.; Bonney, R.C.; Fleming, D. Reproductive biology of the owl monkey, Aotus trivirgatus griseimembra. Pp. 61–68 in NON-HUMAN PRIMATE MODELS FOR STUDY OF HUMAN REPRODUCTION. T.C. Anand Kumar, ed. Basel, Karger Verlag, 1980.

Drickamer, L.C. A ten-year summary of reproductive data for free-ranging Macaca mulatta. FOLIA PRIMATOLOGICA 21:61–80, 1974.

Ehara, Y.; Ryan, K.J.; Yen, S.S.C. Insensitivity of synthetic LRF in LH-release of rhesus monkeys. CONTRACEPTION 6:465–472, 1972.

Enomoto, T. Diurnal variations in plasma testosterone and cortisol in the male Japanese monkey. JOURNAL OF THE ANTHROPOLOGICAL SOCIETY OF NIPPON 88:285–287, 1980.

Ewing, L.L. Seasonal variation in primate fertility with an emphasis on the male. AMERICAN JOURNAL OF PRIMATOLOGY SUPPLEMENT 1:145–160, 1982

Ferin, M.; Warren, M.; Dyrenfurth, I.; Vande Wiele, R.L.; White, W.F. Response of rhesus monkeys to LH-RH throughout the ovarian cycle. JOURNAL OF CLINICAL ENDOCRINOLOGY AND METABOLISM 38:231–237, 1974.

Foster, J.W.; Rowley, M.J. Testicular biopsy in the study of gorilla infertility. AMERICAN JOURNAL OF PRIMATOLOGY SUPPLEMENT 1:121–125, 1982.

Goldfoot, D.A.; Slob, A.K.; Scheffler, G.; Robinson, J.A.; Wiegand, S.J.; Cords, J. Multiple ejaculations during prolonged sexual tests and lack of resultant serum testosterone increases in male stumptailed macaques (Macaca arctoides). ARCHIVES OF SEXUAL BEHAVIOR 4:547–560, 1975.

Goncharov, N.P.; Taranov, A.G.; Antonichev, A.V.; Gorlushkin, V.M.; Aso, T.; Cekan, S.Z.; Diczfalusy, E. Effect of stress on the profile of plasma steroids in baboons (Papio hamadryas). ACTA EN-

DOCRINOLOGICA 90:372–384, 1979.

Goodman, R.L.; Hotchkiss, J.; Karsch, F.J.; Knobil, E. Diurnal variation in the serum testosterone concentration in the adult male rhesus monkey. BIOLOGY OF REPRODUCTION 11:624–630, 1974.

Gordon, T.P.; Rose, R.M.; Bernstein, I.S. Seasonal rhythm in plasma testosterone levels in the rhesus monkey (Macaca mulatta). HORMONES AND BEHAVIOR 7:229–243, 1976.

Gould, K.G.; Kling, O.R. Fertility in the male gorilla (Gorilla gorilla): Relationship to semen parameters and serum hormones. AMERICAN JOURNAL OF PRIMATOLOGY 2:311–316, 1982.

Graham, C.E.; Hodgen, G.D. The use of chimpanzees in reproductive biology. JOURNAL OF MEDICAL PRIMATOLOGY 8:265–272, 1979.

Harcourt, A.H.; Fossey, D.; Stewart, K.J.; Watts, D.P. Reproduction in wild gorillas and some comparisons with chimpanzees. JOURNAL OF REPRODUCTION AND FERTILITY SUPPLEMENT 28:59–70, 1980.

Heller, C.G. Kinetics of the germinal epithelium in man. RECENT PROGRESS IN HORMONE RESEARCH 20:545–575, 1964.

Herbert, D.C. Identification of the LH and TSH-secreting cells in the pituitary gland of the rhesus monkey. CELL AND TISSUE RESEARCH 190:151–161, 1978.

Hobson, W.; Fuller, G.B. LH-RH-induced gonadotropin release in chimpanzees. BIOLOGY OF REPRODUCTION 17:294–297, 1977.

Hodges, J.K.; Hearn, J.P. Effects of immunization against luteinizing hormone–releasing hormone on reproduction of the marmoset monkey Callithrix jacchus. NATURE 265:746–748, 1977.

Hodges, J.K.; Hearn, J.P. A positive feedback effect of estradiol on LH release in the male marmoset monkey. Callithrix jacchus. JOURNAL OF REPRODUCTION AND FERTILITY 52:83–86, 1978.

Howland, B.E.; Faiman, C.; Butler, T.M. Serum levels of FSH and LH during the menstrual cycle of the chimpanzee. BIOLOGY OF REPRODUCTION 4:101–105, 1971.

Kawai, M.; Azuma, S.; Yoshiba, K. Ecological studies of reproduction in Japanese monkeys (Macaca fuscata). I. Problems of the birth season. PRIMATES 8:35–74, 1967.

Klein, L.L. Observations on copulation and seasonal reproduction in two species of spider monkeys, Ateles belzebuth and A. geoffroyi. FOLIA PRIMATOLOGICA 15:233–248, 1971.

Kley, H.K.; Nieschlag, E.; Wiegelmann, W.; Krüskemper, H.L. Estrone, estradiol, and testosterone in normal and hypogonadal men following LH-RH or hCG stimulations. ACTA ENDOCRINOLOGICA 81:616–621, 1975.

Koyama, T. Mechanism of LH release with synthetic LH-RH. FOLIA ENDOCRINOLOGICA JAPONICA 52:881–897, 1976.

Kraemer, D.C.; Vera Cruz, N.C. Infectious diseases influencing reproduction. Pp. 426–452 in COMPARATIVE REPRODUCTION OF NONHUMAN PRIMATES. E.S.E. Hafez, ed. Springfield, IL, Thomas, 1971.

Krey, L.C.; Butler, W.R.; Weiss, G.; Weick, R.F.; Dierschke, D.J.; Knobil, E. Influences of endogenous and exogenous gonadal steroids on the action of synthetic LRF in the rhesus monkey. Pp. 39–47 in HYPOTHALAMIC-HYPOPHYSIOTROPIC HORMONES, Vol. 263. C. Gual; E. Rosemberg, eds. Amsterdam, Excerpta Medica, 1973.

Lancaster, J.B.; Lee, R.B. The annual reproductive cycle in monkeys and apes. PRIMATE BEHAVIOR 1:486–513, 1965.

Lincoln, G.A. Differentiated control of luteinizing hormone and follicle-stimulating hormone by luteinizing hormone–releasing hormone in the ram. JOURNAL OF ENDOCRINOLOGY 80:133–140, 1979.

Lindburg, D.G. The rhesus monkey in North India: An ecological and behavioural study. PRIMATE BEHAVIOR 2:1–106, 1971.

Linde, R.; Doelle, G.C.; Alexander, N.; Kirchner, F.; Vale, W.; Rivier, J.; Rabin, D. Reversible inhibition of testicular steroidogenesis and spermatogenesis by a potent gonadotropin-releasing hormone agonist in men. NEW ENGLAND JOURNAL OF MEDICINE 305:663–667, 1981.

MacDonald, G.J. Reproductive patterns of three species of macaques. FERTILITY AND STERILITY 22:373–377, 1971.

MacLeod, J.; Pazainos, A.; Ray, B. The restoration of human spermatogenesis and of the reproductive tract with urinary gonadotropins following hypophysectomy. FERTILITY AND STERILITY 17:7–23, 1966.

Madhwa Raj, H.G.; Murty, G.S.R.C.; Sairam, M.R.; Talbert, L.M. Control of spermatogenesis in primates: Effects of active immunization against FSH in the monkey. INTERNATIONAL JOURNAL OF ANDROLOGY SUPPLEMENT 5:27–33, 1982.

Mahone, J.P.; Dukelow, W.R. Seasonal variation of reproductive parameters in the laboratory-housed male cynomolgus macaque (Macaca fascicularis). JOURNAL OF MEDICAL PRIMATOLOGY 8:179–183, 1979.

Mangat, H.K. Evaluation of various doses of testosterone on accessory reproductive organs and plasma testosterone in intact and gonadectomized rhesus monkeys (Macaca mulatta). ANDROLOGIA 11:449–452, 1979.

Marshall, G.R.; Wickings, E.J.; Lüdecke, D.K.; Nieschlag, E. Stimulation of spermatogenesis in stalk-sectioned rhesus monkeys by testosterone alone. JOURNAL OF CLINICAL ENDOCRINOL-OGY AND METABOLISM 57:152–159, 1983.

Marshall, P.E.; Goldsmith, P.C. Neuroregulatory and neuroendocrine GnRH pathways in the hypothalamus and forebrain of the baboon. BRAIN RESEARCH 193:353–372, 1980.

Mastroianni, L.; Manson, W.A. Collection of monkey semen by ejaculation. PROCEEDINGS OF THE SOCIETY 'FOR EXPERIMENTAL BIOLOGY AND MEDICINE 112:1025–1027, 1963.

Matsubayashi, K. Seasonal variation in urinary 17-oxosteroids and seminal fructose in male Japanese macaque monkeys (*Macaca fuscata fuscata*). LABORATORY ANIMALS 8:253–255, 1974.

Matsumoto, A.M.; Paulsen, C.A.; Bremner, W.J. Follicle stimulating hormone reinitiates sperm production in gonadotropin-suppressed normal men. Sixty-fourth Annual Meeting of the Endocrine Society, San Francisco, Abstract 472, 1982.

Mendoza, S.P.; Lowe, E.L.; Resko, J.A.; Levine, S. Seasonal variations in gonadal hormones and social behavior in squirrel monkeys. PHYSIOLOGY AND BEHAVIOR 20:515–522, 1978.

Michael, R.P.; Bonsall, R.W. A three-year study of an annual rhythm in plasma androgen levels in male rhesus monkeys (*Macaca mulatta*) in a constant laboratory environment. JOURNAL OF REPRODUCTION AND FERTILITY 49:129–131, 1977.

Michael, R.P.; Keverne, E.B. An annual rhythm in the sexual activity of the male rhesus monkey, *Macaca mulatta*, in the laboratory. JOURNAL OF REPRODUCTION AND FERTILITY 25:95–98, 1971.

Michael, R.P.; Zumpe, D. Environmental and endocrine factors influencing annual changes in sexual potency in primates. PSYCHONEUROENDOCRINOLOGY 1:303–313, 1976.

Michael, R.P.; Setchell, K.D.; Plant, T.M. Diurnal changes in plasma testosterone and studies in plasma corticosteroids in non-anesthetized male rhesus monkeys (*Macaca mulatta*). JOURNAL OF ENDOCRINOLOGY 63:325–335, 1974.

Mori, J.; Hafez, E.S.E. Release of LH by synthetic LH-RH in the monkey *Macaca fascicularis*. JOURNAL OF REPRODUCTION AND FERTILITY 34:155–157, 1973.

Mortimer, C.H.; McNeilly, A.S.; Fisher, R.A.; Murray, M.A.F.; Besser, G.M. Gonadotropin-releasing hormone therapy in hypogonadal males with hypothalamic or pituitary dysfunction. BRITISH MEDICAL JOURNAL 4:617–621, 1974.

Moudgal, N.R. A need for FSH in maintaining fertility in adult male subhuman primates. ARCHIVES OF ANDROLOGY 7:117–125, 1981.

Mukku, V.R.; Murty, G.S.R.C.; Srinath, B.R.; Ramasharma, K.; Kotagi, S.G.; Moudgal, N.R. Regulation of testosterone rhythmicity by gonadotropins in bonnet monkeys (*Macaca radiata*). BIOLOGY OF REPRODUCTION 24:814–819, 1981.

Murty, G.S.R.C.; Ramasharma, K.; Mukku, V.R.; Srinath, B.R.; Moudgal, N.R. Reproductive endocrinology of bonnet monkeys. Pp. 50–54 in NONHUMAN PRIMATE MODELS FOR STUDY OF HUMAN REPRODUCTION. T.C. Anand Kumar, ed. Basel, Karger Verlag, 1980.

Murty, G.S.R.C.; Rani, C.S.S.; Moudgal, N.R.; Prasad, M.R.N. Effect of passive immunization with specific antiserum to FSH on the spermatogenic process and fertility of adult male bonnet monkeys (*Macaca radiata*). JOURNAL OF REPRODUCTION AND FERTILITY SUPPLEMENT 26:147–163, 1979.

Nadler, R.D.; Rosenblum, L.A. Hormonal regulation of the "fatted" phenomenon in squirrel monkeys. ANATOMICAL RECORD 173:181–187, 1972.

Nadler, R.C.; Graham, C.E.; Collins, D.C.; Gould, K.G. Plasma gonadotropins, prolactin, gonadal steroids, and genital swelling during the menstrual cycle of lowland gorillas. ENDOCRINOLOGY 105:290–296, 1979.

Neill, J.D.; Dailey, R.A.; Tsou, R.C.; Reichert, L.E. Immunoreactive LH-like substances in serum of hypophysectomized and prepubertal monkeys: Inactive in an in vitro LH bioassay. ENDOCRINOLOGY 100:856–861, 1977.

Nieschlag, E. Circadian rhythm of plasma testosterone. Pp. 117–128 in CHRONOBIOLOGICAL ASPECTS OF ENDOCRINOLOGY. J. Aschoff; F. Ceresa; F. Halberg, eds. Stuttgart, F.K. Schattauer Verlag, 1974.

Nieschlag, E.; Von der Ohe, M. Trial of an LH-RH agonist for the treatment of male infertility. Pp. 295–299 in ADVANCES IN DIAGNOSIS AND TREATMENT OF INFERTILITY. V. Insler; G. Bettendorf, eds. New York, Elsevier/North Holland, 1981.

Nieschlag, E.; Wickings, E.J. Does the rhesus monkey provide a suitable model for human testicular functions? Pp. 103–119 in ANIMAL MODELS IN HUMAN REPRODUCTION. M. Serio; L. Martini, eds. New York, Raven, 1980a.

Nieschlag, E.; Wickings, E.J. Testicular and adrenal steroids in the adult rhesus monkey and in man. Pp. 136–147 in NON-HUMAN PRIMATE MODELS FOR STUDY OF HUMAN REPRODUCTION. T.C. Anand Kumar, ed. Basel, Karger Verlag, 1980b.

Nieschlag, E.; Kley H.K.; Wiegelmann, W.; Solbach, H.G.; Krüskemper, H.L. Lebensalter und endokrine Funktion der Testes des erwachsenen Mannes. DEUTSCHE MEDIZINISCHE WOCHENSCHRIFT 98:1281–1284, 1973.

Niswender, G.D.; Monroe, S.E.; Peckham, W.D.; Midgley, A.R.; Knobil, E.; Reichert, L.E. Radioimmunoassay for rhesus monkey luteinizing hormone (LH) with anti-ovine LH serum and ovine LH-[131] I. ENDOCRINOLOGY 88:1327–1331, 1971.

Omar, A.; De Vos, A. The annual reproductive cycle of an African monkey (Cercopithecus mitis kolbi Neuman). FOLIA PRIMATOLOGICA 16:206–215, 1971.

Orgebin-Christ, M.-C.; Olson, G.E.; Danzo, B.J. Factors influencing maturation of spermatozoa in the epididymis. Pp. 393–417 in INTRAGONADAL REGULATION OF REPRODUCTION. P. Franchimont; C.P. Channing, eds. New York, Academic Press, 1981.

Peckham, W.D.; Knobil. E. Quantitative changes in the pituitary gonadotropins of the male rhesus monkey following castration. ENDOCRINOLOGY 98:1061–1064, 1976.

Peckham, W.D.; Foster, D.L.; Knobil. E. A new substance resembling luteinizing hormone in the blood of rhesus monkeys. ENDOCRINOLOGY 100:826–834, 1977.

Perachio, A.A.; Alexander, M.; Marr, L.D.; Collins, D.C. Diurnal variations of serum testosterone levels in intact and gonadectomized male and female rhesus monkeys. STEROIDS 29:21–33, 1977.

Phoenix, C.H.; Dixson, A.F.; Resko, R.A. Effects of ejaculation on levels of testosterone, cortisol and luteinizing hormone in peripheral plasma of rhesus monkeys. JOURNAL OF COMPARATIVE AND PHYSIOLOGICAL PSYCHOLOGY 91:120–127, 1977.

Plant, T.M. The neuroendocrine basis of the diurnal variation of testicular testosterone secretion in the adult rhesus monkey (Macaca mulatta). Pp. 419–423 in TESTICULAR DEVELOPMENT, STRUCTURE AND FUNCTION. A. Steinberger; E. Steinberger, eds. New York, Academic Press, 1980.

Plant, T.M. Effect of orchidectomy and testosterone replacement treatment on pulsatile luteinizing hormone secretion in the adult rhesus monkey (Macaca mulatta). ENDOCRINOLOGY 110:1905–1913, 1982.

Plant, T.M.; Hess, D.L.; Hotchkiss, J.; Knobil, E. Testosterone and the control of gonadotropin secretion in the male rhesus monkey (Macaca mulatta). ENDOCRINOLOGY 103:535–541, 1978.

Plant, T.M.; Zumpe, D.; Sauls, M.; Michael, R.P. An annual rhythm in the plasma testosterone of adult male rhesus monkeys maintained in the laboratory. JOURNAL OF ENDOCRINOLOGY 62:403–404, 1974.

Rani, C.S.S.; Murty, G.S.R.C.; Moudgal, N.R. Effect of chronic neutralization of endogenous FSH on testicular function in the adult bonnet monkey—assessment using biochemical parameters. INTERNATIONAL JOURNAL OF ANDROLOGY 1:489–500, 1978.

Reinberg, A.; Lagoguey, M.; Cesselin, F.; Touitou, Y.;

Legrand, J.-C.; Delasalle, A.; Antreassian, J.; Lagoguey, A. Circadian and circannual rhythms in plasma hormones and other variables of five healthy young human males. ACTA ENDOCRINOLOGICA 88:417–427, 1978.

Reinberg, A.; Lagoguey, M.; Chauffournier, J.-M.; Cesselin, F. Circannual and circadian rhythms in plasma testosterone in five healthy young Parisian males. ACTA ENDOCRINOLOGICA 80:732–743, 1975.

Resko, J.A.; Belanger, A.; Labrie, F. Effects of chronic treatment with a potent luteinizing hormone–releasing hormone agonist on serum luteinizing hormone and steroid levels in male rhesus monkeys. BIOLOGY OF REPRODUCTION 26:378–384, 1982.

Resko, J.A.; Jackson, G.L.; Huckins, C.; Stadelman, H.; Spies, H.G. Cryptorchid rhesus macaques: Long term studies on changes in gonadotropins and gonadal steroids. ENDOCRINOLOGY 107:1127–1136, 1980.

Resko, J.A.; Quadri, S.K.; Spies, H.G. Negative feedback control of gonadotropins in male rhesus monkeys: Effects of time after castration and interactions of testosterone and estradiol-17β. ENDOCRINOLOGY 101: 215–224, 1977.

Richter, K.D.; Korte, R.; Senge, T. Morpho-funktionelle Studien an Hoden gesunder Rhesusaffen. Pp. 41–46 in PHYSIOLOGIE UND PATHOPHYSIOLOGIE DES HODENS. T. Senge; F. Neumann; U.W. Tunn, eds. Stuttgart, Thieme-Verlag, 1978.

Roberts, M.S. The annual reproductive cycle of captive Macaca sylvana. FOLIA PRIMATOLOGICA 29:229–235, 1978.

Robinson, J.A.; Scheffler, G.; Eisele, S.G.; Goy, R.W. Effects of age and season on sexual behavior and plasma testosterone and dihydrotestosterone concentrations of laboratory-maintained male rhesus monkeys (Macaca mulatta). BIOLOGY OF REPRODUCTION 13:203–210, 1975.

Rose, R.M.; Holaday, J.W.; Bernstein, I.S. Plasma testosterone, dominance rank and aggressive behavior in male rhesus monkeys. NATURE 231:366–368, 1971.

Sandow, J.; Von Rechenberg, W.; Jerzabek, G.; Stoll, W. Pituitary inhibition by a highly active analog of luteinizing hormone–releasing hormone. FERTILITY AND STERILITY 30:205–209, 1978.

Schally, A.V.; Arimura, A.; Kastin, A.J. Hypothalamic regulatory hormones. SCIENCE 179:341–350, 1973.

Schulze, W. Quantitative aspects of the spermatogonial populations and the stages of the spermatogenic cycle in aged human testes. ACTA ANATOMICA 111: 139, 1981 (abstract).

Setty, B.S.; Riar, S.S.; Kar, A.B. Androgenic control of epididymal function in rhesus monkey and rabbits. FERTILITY AND STERILITY 28:674–681, 1977.

Silverman, A.J.; Antunes, J.L.; Ferin, M.; Zimmerman, E.A. The distribution of luteinizing hormone-releasing hormone (LHRH) in the hypothalamus of the rhesus monkey. Light microscopic studies using immunoperoxidase technique. ENDOCRINOLOGY 101:134–142, 1977.

Slob, A.K.; Ooms, M.P.; Vreeburg, J.T.M. Annual changes in serum testosterone in laboratory housed male stumptailed macaques (Macaca arctoides). BIOLOGY OF REPRODUCTION 20:981–984, 1979.

Smith, P.E. Maintenance and restoration of spermatogenesis in hypophysectomized rhesus monkeys by androgen administration. YALE JOURNAL OF BIOLOGY AND MEDICINE 17:281–287, 1944–45.

Smith, R.; Donald, R.A.; Espiner, E.A.; Stronach, S. The effects of prolonged administration of D-Ser(TBu)[6]-LH-RH-EA[10] (HOE 766) in subjects with hypogonadotropic hypogonadism. CLINICAL ENDOCRINOLOGY 11:553–559, 1979.

Southwick, C.H.; Beg, M.A.; Siddiqi, M.R. A population survey of rhesus monkeys in northern India. II. Transportation routes and forest areas. ECOLOGY 42:699–710, 1961.

Spies, H.G.; Frantz, R.C.; Niswender, G.D. Patterns of luteinizing hormone in serum following administration of stalk-median eminence extracts to rhesus monkeys. PROCEEDINGS OF THE SOCIETY FOR EXPERIMENTAL BIOLOGY AND MEDICINE 140:161–166, 1972.

Steinberger, E. Hormonal control of mammalian spermatogenesis. PHYSIOLOGICAL REVIEWS 51:1–22, 1971.

Steiner, R.A.; Peterson, A.P.; Yu, J.Y.L.; Conner, H.; Gilbert, M.; terPenning, B.; Bremner, W.J. Ultradian luteinizing hormone and testosterone rhythms in the adult male monkey, Macaca fascicularis. ENDOCRINOLOGY 107:1489–1493, 1980.

Steiner, R.A.; Schiller, H.S.; Barber, J.; Gale, C.C. Luteinizing hormone regulation in the monkey (Macaca nemestrina): Failure of testosterone and dihydrotestosterone to block the estrogen-induced gonadotropin surge. BIOLOGY OF REPRODUCTION 19:51–56, 1978.

Sundaram, K.; Connell, K.G.; Bardin, C.W.; Samojlik, E.; Schally, A.V. Inhibition of pituitary-testicular function with (D-Trp)[6] luteinizing hormone releasing hormone in rhesus monkeys. ENDOCRINOLOGY 110:1308–1314, 1982.

Tamarkin, L.; Westrom, W.K.; Hamill, A.I.; Goldman, B.D. Effect of melatonin on the reproduction systems of male and female Syrian hamsters: A diurnal rhythm in sensitivity to melatonin. ENDOCRINOLOGY 99:1534–1541, 1976.

Tjoa, W.S.; Smolensky, M.H.; Hsi, B.P.; Steinberger, E.; Smith, K.D. Circannual rhythm in human sperm count revealed by serially independent sampling. FERTILITY AND STERILITY 38:454–459, 1982.

Toivola, P.T.K.; Bridson, W.E.; Robinson, J.A. Effects of LH-RH on the secretion of LH, FSH and testosterone in adult male rhesus monkeys. ENDOCRINOLOGY 102:1815–1821, 1978.

Tutin, C.E.G. Reproductive behavior of wild chimpanzees in the Gombe National Park, Tanzania. JOURNAL OF REPRODUCTION AND FERTILITY SUPPLEMENT 28:43–57, 1980.

Vandenbergh, J.G. Hormonal basis of sex skin in male rhesus monkeys. GENERAL AND COMPARATIVE ENDOCRINOLOGY 5:31–34, 1965.

Vandenbergh, J.G.; Vessey, S.H. Seasonal breeding of free-ranging rhesus monkeys and related ecological factors. JOURNAL OF REPRODUCTION AND FERTILITY 15:71–79, 1968.

Van Horn, R.N. Seasonal reproductive patterns in primates. PROGRESS IN REPRODUCTIVE BIOLOGY 5:181–221, 1980.

Van Pelt, L.F.; Keyser, P.E. Observations on semen collection and quality in macaques. LABORATORY ANIMALS 20:726–733, 1970.

Varley, M.A.; Vessey, S.H. Effects of geographical transfer on the timing of seasonal breeding of rhesus monkeys. FOLIA PRIMATOLOGICA 28:52–59, 1977.

Vickery, B.H.; McRae, G.I. Effects of continuous treatment of male baboons with superagonists of LHRH. INTERNATIONAL JOURNAL OF FERTILITY 25:179–184, 1980.

Wickings, E.J.; Nieschlag, E. Testosterone production and metabolism in laboratory-maintained male rhesus monkeys. INTERNATIONAL JOURNAL OF FERTILITY 22:56–59, 1977.

Wickings, E.J.; Nieschlag, E. Serum levels of testicular and adrenal steroids after dexamethasone and hCG-administration in the laboratory-maintained rhesus monkey. ACTA ENDOCRINOLOGICA 87:650–658, 1978.

Wickings, E.J.; Nieschlag, E. Seasonality in endocrine and exocrine testicular function of the adult rhesus monkey (Macaca mulatta) maintained in a controlled laboratory environment. INTERNATIONAL JOURNAL OF ANDROLOGY 3:87–104, 1980a.

Wickings, E.J.; Nieschlag, E. Pituitary response to LHRH and TRH stimulation and peripheral steroid hormones in conscious and anesthetized adult male rhesus monkeys (Macaca mulatta). ACTA ENDOCRINOLOGICA 93:287–293, 1980b.

Wickings, E.J.; Nieschlag, E. Suppression of spermatogenesis over two years in rhesus monkeys actively immunized with follicle stimulating hormone. FERTILITY AND STERILITY 34:269–274, 1980c.

Wickings, E.J.; Nieschlag, E. Hypothalamic involvement in seasonal variations of the ultradian serum LH and testosterone patterns in the adult male rhesus monkey. BIOLOGY OF REPRODUCTION 24, SUPPLEMENT 1: Abstract 161, 1981.

Wickings, E.J.; Qazi, M.H.; Nieschlag, E. Determination of biologically active LH in the serum of male rhesus monkeys (*Macaca mulatta*). JOURNAL OF REPRODUCTION AND FERTILITY 57:497–504, 1979.

Wickings, E.J.; Hanker, J.P.; Nieschlag, E. Serum levels of biologically active LH following pituitary stimulation with LHRH and two analogues in the male rhesus monkey: Effect of season. JOURNAL OF ENDOCRINOLOGY 85:12P, 1980a.

Wickings, E.J.; Usadel, K.-H.; Dathe, G.; Nieschlag, E. The role of follicle stimulating hormone in testicular function of the mature rhesus monkey. ACTA ENDOCRINOLOGICA 95:117–128, 1980b.

Wickings, E.J.; Zaidi, P.; Nieschlag, E. Seminal parameters in rhesus monkeys under physiological conditions and in studies for male fertility control using FSH antibodies or LHRH-agonists. AMERICAN JOURNAL OF PRIMATOLOGY 1:203–210, 1981a.

Wickings, E.J.; Zaidi, P.; Nieschlag, E. Effects of chronic high-dose LHRH-agonist treatment on pituitary and testicular functions in rhesus monkeys. JOURNAL OF ANDROLOGY 2:72–79, 1981b.

Wickings, E.J.; Zaidi, P.; Brabant, G.; Nieschlag, E. Stimulation of pituitary and testicular functions with LH-RH agonist or pulsatile LHRH treatment in the rhesus monkey during the non-breeding season. JOURNAL OF REPRODUCTION AND FERTILITY 63:129–136, 1981c.

Wickler, W. Socio-sexual signals and their interspecific imitation among primates. Pp. 69–147 in PRIMATE ETHOLOGY. D. Morris, ed. London, Weidenfeld and Nicolson, 1967.

Wilson, M.I.; Brown, G.M.; Wilson, D. Annual and diurnal changes in plasma androgen and cortisol in adult male squirrel monkeys (*Saimiri sciureus*) studied longitudinally. ACTA ENDOCRINOLOGICA 87:424–433, 1978.

Yamaji, T.; Dierschke, D.J.; Hotchkiss, J.; Bhattacharya, A.M.; Surre, A.M.; Knobil, E. Estrogen induction of LH release in the rhesus monkey. ENDOCRINOLOGY 89:1034–1041, 1971.

Zaidi, P.; Wickings, E.J.; Arslan, M.; Nieschlag, E. Characterization and comparison of testicular LH/hCG receptors of rhesus monkeys (*Macaca mulatta*) and green monkeys (*Cercopithecus aethiops*). AMERICAN JOURNAL OF PRIMATOLOGY 2:285–290, 1982a.

Zaidi, P.; Wickings, E.J.; Nieschlag, E. The effects of ketamine HCl and barbiturate anesthesia on the metabolic clearance and production rates of testosterone in the male rhesus monkey (*Macaca mulatta*). JOURNAL OF STEROID BIOCHEMISTRY 16:463–466, 1982b.

Zamboni, L.; Conaway, C.H.; Van Pelt, L. Seasonal changes in production of semen in free-ranging rhesus monkeys. BIOLOGY OF REPRODUCTION 11:251–267, 1974.

Zuckerman, S.; Parkes, A.S. The effect of male hormone on a mature castrated male rhesus monkey. JOURNAL OF ANATOMY 72:277–279, 1938.

Spermatozoa
Collection, Evaluation, Metabolism, Freezing, and Artificial Insemination

David E. Wildt

National Zoological Park, Smithsonian Institution, Washington, D.C. 20008

INTRODUCTION

The study of reproductive function and propagation of numerous domesticated species has benefited from the techniques of semen collection, cryopreservation of spermatozoa, and artificial insemination. The adaptation of this technology to any nondomesticated mammal including the nonhuman primate is not a simple endeavor. Various studies have demonstrated the feasibility of collecting monkey and ape spermatozoa. Fresh spermatozoa also have been used for artificial insemination as an alternative to natural breeding. However, at this writing, there are no known reports of successful artificial breeding in monkeys or apes using previously frozen spermatozoa. Although stress probably accounts for at least a portion of this failure, other factors also play major roles. A strikingly low data base continues to exist concerning reproductive traits in nonhuman primates, including expected ejaculate norms and spermatozoal morphology, in vitro longevity, and metabolism. Certain inherent characteristics of nonhuman primate ejaculates also pose handling difficulties when conducting fertility evaluations, recovering maximal sperm numbers per ejaculate, or processing semen for freezing or artificial insemination.

This lack of information provides strong impetus for further research since the potential uses of semen collection, freezing, and artificial insemination have widespread and significant application. These advantages have been reviewed and are of both experimental and propagative benefit [Hendrickx et al, 1978; Wildt, 1985]. In major breeding programs semen evaluation allows male fertility comparisons and eventual improvement in genetic stocks as well as determination of capacitation requirements and spermatozoal survival time. The cryopreservation of spermatozoa ensures the perpetuation of outstanding sires or species which may be ecologically endangered and permits the long-distance shipment of selected male gametes. The advantages of artificial insemination include precise control of timed conceptions, prevention of venereal disease transmission, and a reduction in the number of males required in a breeding colony. Artificial breeding permits the more efficient use of species that may show seasonal fluctuations in fertility or sexual activity. It also is becoming increasingly apparent that certain laboratory-rearing conditions negatively influence adequate development of sexual behavior [Czaja et al, 1975]. Artificial insemination serves as an alternative for the breeding of socially dysfunctioning or incompatible animals.

This chapter reviews the available data concerning semen collection, handling, freezing, artificial insemination, and sperm metabolism in nonhuman primates. Emphasis has been placed on research areas that lack concentrated knowledge, in anticipation that interest in further investigative efforts will be stimulated.

SEMEN COLLECTION

Three methods have been employed to collect semen from nonhuman primates: electrostimulation, the artificial vagina, and postcopulatory vaginal aspiration.

Comparative Primate Biology, Volume 3: Reproduction and Development, pages 171–193

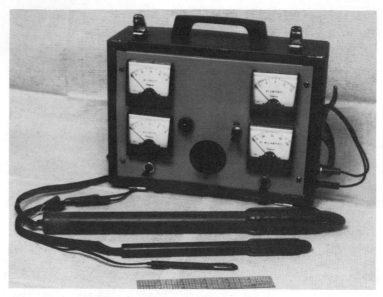

Fig. 1. An AC electrical stimulator with voltage and amperage gauges and variable rheostat (see text for more detail). Rectal probes with longitudinal electrode configuration are in foreground.

Electrostimulation

The most commonly applied procedure for collecting monkey and ape semen has been electroejaculation using either a penile electrode or rectal probe approach. Both techniques require an electrostimulator device of either alternating-current or direct-current type. A number of stimulator systems and circuitry diagrams have been described [Weisbroth and Young, 1965; Fussell et al, 1967; Gould et al, 1978]. Our laboratory uses a commercially available 60-Hz unit which requires a 110- to 120-volt alternating current (Fig. 1, P-T Electronics, Boring, OR). This stimulator is capable of delivering a continuous range of 0–60 volts using a variable transformer and has a 1-amp capacity. Also available is a direct-current stimulator (Fig. 2, Lane Manufacturers, Denver, CO) with battery pack capable of producing sufficient stimulus for electroejaculation. The latter system is principally used for field studies or in locations where alternating current is unavailable.

Most electrical stimulators manufactured for semen collection from domestic species can be adapted for use in nonhuman primates. Unfortunately, comparative evaluations of stimulator requirements are often confounded because most studies have not standardized basic traits which include stimulation current, frequency, voltage,

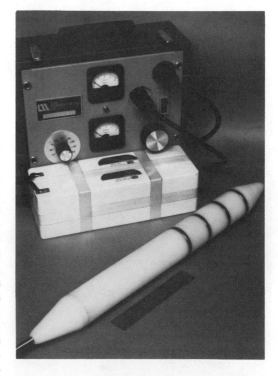

Fig. 2. A DC electrical stimulator with battery pack (see text for more detail). A rectal probe with ring electrodes is in foreground.

and wave form. Sine, square, and rectangular wave-form stimulators have been tested in monkeys and apes, and the sine type has generally proved the safest and most predictable [Warner et al, 1974; Gould et al, 1978]. At least two reports have emphasized the need to examine other traits including electrode/tissue interface resistance and current density at the electrode surface [Warner et al, 1974; Gould et al, 1978]. Thus, an index can be formulated for comparing equipment; for example, a stimulator producing lowest current density and still permitting semen collection would indicate a superior system.

The electrostimulator can be adapted to two specific methods for recovering spermatozoa, the penile electrode or rectal probe electroejaculation. Each has limitations and advantages; however, both require several precollection procedures. Food is withheld both the previous evening and the morning of collection. After restraint and/or anesthesia of the animal, the hair in the genital area is clipped and the area washed with a mild disinfectant (Fig. 3). Semen samples are easily contaminated by bacteria which rapidly cause deterioration of sperm viability when held in vitro. Removing the preputial hair reduces the degree of contamination by 67–98% [Roussel and Austin, 1968].

In the penile electrode approach, first introduced by Mastroianni and Manson in 1963, the unanesthetized animal generally is held on its back or placed in a restraint chair. One of two brass, copper, or aluminum foil electrodes are lubricated, positioned at the base of the penis, and connected to the positive electrode of the stimulator (Fig. 4). A negative electrode is then held against the ventral aspect of the glans penis. A warmed collecting vial is placed over the glans and intermittent, gradually increased current (1–45 volts) is discharged by the operator. In general these electrical charges are delivered at a frequency of 10–20 impulses per second for a duration of 25–50 milliseconds. Ejaculation is abrupt in macaque monkeys [Van Pelt and Keyser, 1970] and usually occurs without an erection and within 5 minutes following the initial stimulation [Settlage and Hendrickx, 1974a; Kraemer and Kuehl, 1980b]. Consecutive ejaculates can be obtained frequently; three to 12 sequential ejaculates were obtained from five rhesus monkeys during a 45- to 80-minute interval on a single day [Hendrickx et al, 1978]. For males collected on 2 consecutive days, sperm concentration per milliliter of ejaculate decreases on the second day, al-

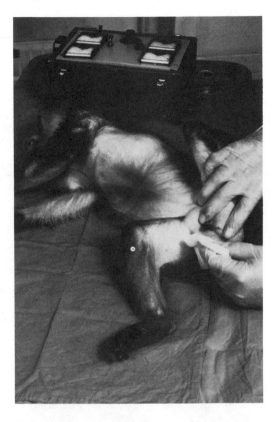

Fig. 3. Monkey is positioned in lateral recumbency and the genital area cleaned.

though ejaculate volume is greater, thereby increasing the total number of spermatozoa collected [Valerio et al, 1970].

A major disadvantage of the penile method is that the male is fully conscious, and thus susceptible to considerable discomfort from the electrical stimulation. The procedure has been employed extensively in macaques, 93% of which ejaculate in response to such stimulation [Valerio et al, 1969, 1970]. Considerable variability exists among individual males in current requirements to elicit ejaculation. Additionally, some macaque species (*M. fascicularis*) ejaculate at lower voltages than others (*M. mulatta*) [Valerio et al, 1969]. Behavioral conditioning also plays a role in males collected as frequently as three times weekly; some macaque males ejaculate in response to simple penile attachment of the electrodes in the absence of any applied current [Settlage and Hendrickx, 1974a]. No physical abnormalities are observed in stimulated macaques, unless excessive voltage (greater than

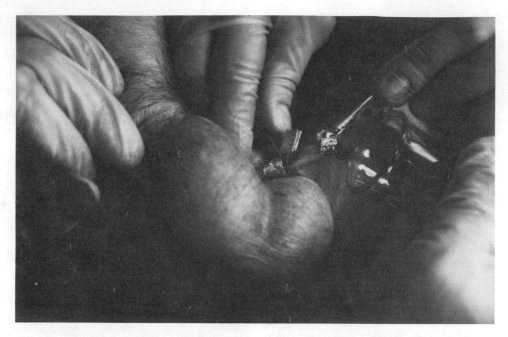

Fig. 4. Foil electrodes attached to the penile shaft for electrostimulation.

30–40 volts) is used. Complications involving superficial skin lesions can then result [Valerio et al, 1969; Settlage and Hendrickx, 1974a].

Semen also has been collected by rectal probe electroejaculation, first employed by Weisbroth and Young in 1965. In this procedure a rigid rectal probe containing silver, platinum, copper, or stainless steel electrodes [Warner et al, 1974; Gould et al, 1978] is used to deliver the current from an electrical stimulator (Fig. 1). The probes are most frequently constructed of plastic, Teflon, or lucite, and the electrodes are mounted on the probe surface in either a ring (Fig. 2) or a longitudinal configuration (Fig. 1). There is some controversy on whether the ring or longitudinal electrode design is more effective. In recent years there appears to be an increase in the use of longitudinal type, primarily because the latter produces less somatic stimulation and induced urination during electroejaculation. Electric current directions and patterns of rectal probe assemblies are available [Warner et al, 1974]. The size of the animal dictates the diameter of the rectal probe to be used (Table 1). Recently, a modified rectal approach was reported in which an electrode was mounted on a gloved finger and used to collect semen from macaques and baboons; however, the specifics of

the procedure and ejaculate traits were not provided [Brindley, 1981].

Small monkeys have been physically restrained for rectal probe electroejaculation [Kuehl and Dukelow, 1974; Denis et al, 1976]; however, in most cases semen is collected in lightly sedated [Gould et al, 1978] or anesthetized [Harrison, 1980b; Platz et al, 1980] males. The latter approach using ketamine hydrochloride (administered intramuscularly) is currently the method of choice. Atropine sulfate to control salivation and stabilize cardiovascular activity is not recommended since this drug has been reported to block seminal emission in several nonhuman primate species [Roussel and Austin, 1968; Warner et al, 1974; Gould et al, 1978]. Similarly, phenothiazine compounds such as acetylpromazine maleate and promazine hydrochloride to tranquilize or smooth anesthesia recovery are to be avoided since these drugs apparently inhibit erection and ejaculation [Warner et al, 1974; Gould et al, 1978] and increase the incidence of urination during electroejaculation.

For rectal probe electroejaculation, the male is placed supine, in lateral recumbency (Fig. 3), or face down in a canvas sling [Roussel and Austin, 1968; Harrison, 1980b], all positions that facilitate access to both the anal opening and the penis.

TABLE 1. Rectal Probe Diameters for Semen Collection From Nonhuman Primates

Species	Probe diameter (cm)
G. gorilla; P. pygmaeus; P. troglodytes; P. cynocephalus	2.5–3.0
H. lar; M. mulatta; M. fascicularis; M. speciosa; M. nemestrina; C. aethiops; T. gelada; E. patas; C. galeritus; C. apella	1.3
A. fusciceps; C. colobus	1.0
S. sciureus; S. nigricollis; C. jacchus; C. rubicundus; C. moloch; T. glis	0.6–0.7

Adapted from Kraemer and Kuehl [1980b].

Feces are removed from the rectum and the probe is moistened with sterile lubricating jelly (Fig. 5) and inserted into the rectum (Figs. 6, 7). The depth of insertion varies with species size and is such that the electrodes are positioned adjacent to the accessory sex organs. Occasionally, probe location may be varied during electroejaculation to obtain a more desired effect. Often longitudinal electrodes are mounted on only a portion of the probe, necessitating that the electrodes be positioned ventrally (against the accessory organs) during electroejaculation. The rectal probe is attached to the stimulator leads and the collection procedure initiated (Fig. 8).

Various electrical current regimens have been used [Warner et al, 1974; Gould et al, 1978; Platz et al, 1980]. The method used in our laboratory involves administering electrical stimuli in sets of ten serial stimulations applied at the same voltage and amperage. The stimuli are given in a 3-second on and 3-second off pattern, with a continuous rise in voltage from 0 volts to the desired peak, then returning to 0. Initial voltage is selected on the basis of the animal's response (predominantly leg extension; Figs. 9, 10) during stimulation. After the first ten stimulations at initial voltage, the next set of ten stimulations is increased 1 volt. After three sets (a total of 30 stimulations), the procedure is discontinued and the ejaculate evaluated. If additional ejaculate is required, a subsequent series of 30 stimulations (3 sets of 10 stimuli each) is administered. During the second series, the first ten stimulations are initiated at the intermediate voltage of the first series and increased in increments of 1 volt for each additional ten stimuli. In

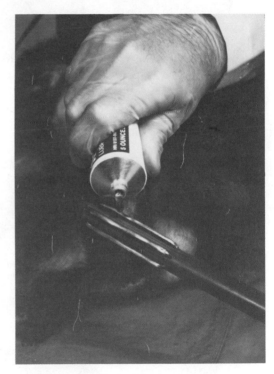

Fig. 5. Lubrication of the rectal probe prior to electrostimulation.

most species, ejaculation (Fig. 11) occurs at less than 8 volts or when alternating current is delivered at 0.25 mamp/mm² of electrode area [Gould et al, 1978]. Insertion of the probe too deeply into the rectum or the use of greater than 7–8 volts often results in urine contamination of the semen

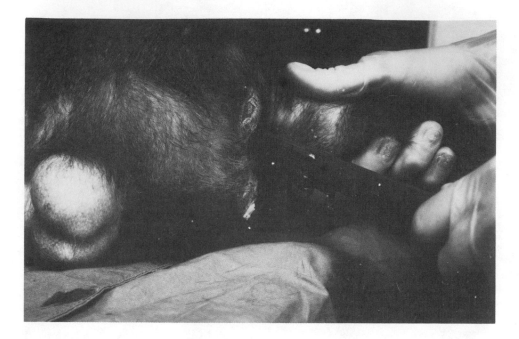

Fig. 6. Insertion of the rectal probe with the electrodes positioned ventrally.

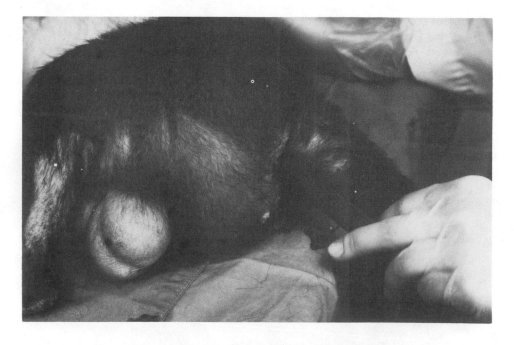

Fig. 7. Rectal probe inserted and held with slight ventral pressure.

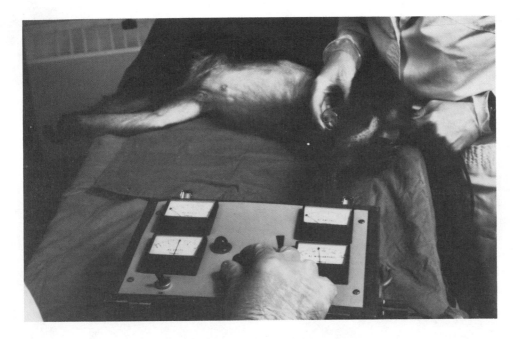

Fig. 8. Rectal probe electrical stimulation of the macaque monkey.

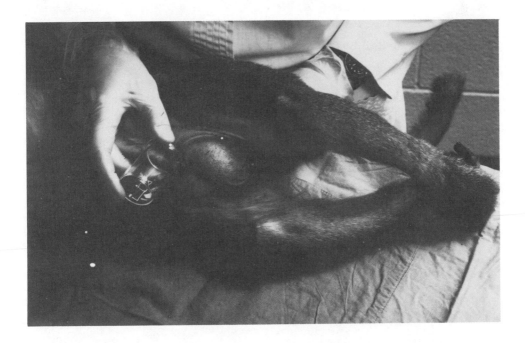

Fig. 9. Desired leg extension and position during rectal probe electroejaculation.

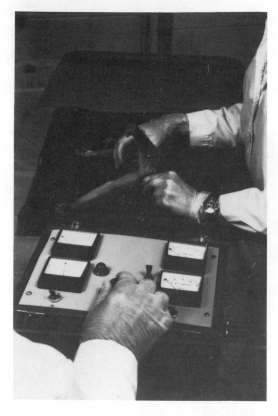

Fig. 10. Leg extension in the squirrel monkey during rectal probe electroejaculation.

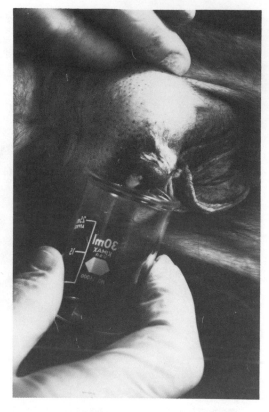

Fig. 11. Ejaculation in a macaque male with no simultaneous erection.

sample [Roussel and Austin, 1968]. Ejaculation using the rectal probe method is usually prolonged and can occur with erection (Fig. 12) or without erection (Fig. 11). Generally, 10 minutes of stimulation is required to ensure that the collection is complete [Van Pelt and Keyser, 1970]. A high proportion of monkeys (99% of macaques) [Harrison, 1980b] and apes ejaculate in response to rectal probe electroejaculation, apparently with little physical posttreatment effect. In one study following electroejaculation using a current density of 0.25 mamp/mm^2 of electrode surface area, protoscopic examinations of the rectal mucosa failed to reveal any damage beyond a mild, transient erythema [Gould et al, 1978]. The maximal frequency for rectal probe collection is unknown, although at least one study reported that collections could be conducted three times weekly without inducing a refractory response or affecting ejaculate quality [Denis et al, 1976].

Both the penile and rectal probe electroejaculation procedures, when used correctly, are safe. However, there is little specific information on libido or breeding ability of primates previously subjected to either treatment [Wildt, 1985]. Because of variations in equipment and routine procedures among laboratories, it is difficult to determine if ejaculate quality is influenced by collection technique. Ejaculates from various macaque species collected by either the penile or rectal probe method show no marked differences in ejaculate volume or sperm count per milliliter of ejaculate (Table 2). Further comparative investigations are necessary to determine the effect of these two collection procedures on ejaculate quality, particularly sperm morphology. Overall, many investigators prefer the rectal probe approach because it is more reliable, can be adapted to any size primate, and is less stressful, even though anesthesia is necessary [Fussel et al, 1967; Van

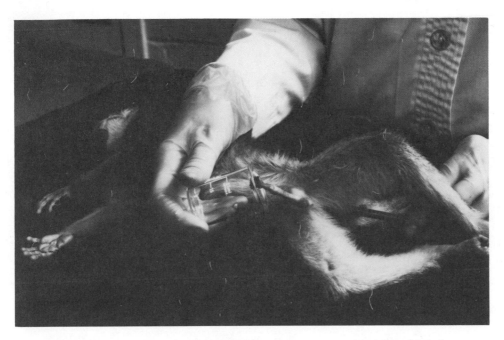

Fig. 12. Erection in a squirrel monkey subjected to rectal probe electrostimulation.

Pelt and Keyser, 1970; Gould et al, 1978; Harrison, 1980b].

Masturbation, the Artificial Vagina, and Vaginal Aspiration

Spontaneous masturbation occurs frequently among caged primates, and some individuals reportedly can be trained to provide a semen specimen on demand [Gould et al, 1978]. There is one report of conditioning a chimpanzee to ejaculate into an artificial vagina [Fussell et al, 1973] and another of a baboon ejaculating spontaneously under anesthesia [Kraemer and Vera Cruz, 1969]. Additionally, a moderate degree of success has been achieved in retrieving viable spermatozoa from the vagina of macaque females by aspirating postcopulation [Cho and Honjo, 1973]. There is little information on the quality of ejaculates obtained by natural versus artificial methods. However, one study noted repeated spontaneous ejaculation in a single baboon and these ejaculates were compared to those collected by electroejaculation [Kraemer and Vera Cruz, 1969]. The average semen volume of the animal that ejaculated spontaneously was significantly greater (about twofold) than the average of all samples collected by electroejaculation. Also the proportion of the total spermatozoa in the liquid fraction was greater in the spontaneous ejaculate than the electroejaculate.

SEMEN HANDLING AND GROSS APPEARANCE

Most monkey and ape ejaculates consist of two fractions, a liquid and coagulum (Fig. 13) component. The coagulum originates from the mixing of secretions of the cranial prostate with that of the seminal vesicle, the degree of firmness being related to the proportion of cranial prostatic fluid contributed [Roussel and Austin, 1967a]. The function of the coagulum, which comprises 55–68% of the ejaculate, is unknown but is thought to assist the sperm-rich fraction in maintaining contact against the external cervical os in the vagina, thereby promoting sperm transport [Settlage and Hendrickx, 1974b]. Most nonhuman primates produce ejaculate coagulum, although it may be that some species and certain individuals are less prone to this formation than others [Roussel and Austin, 1967a]. Furthermore, during electroejaculation the coagulum can be emitted before or after the liquid fraction [Weisbroth and Young, 1965]. Initially it

TABLE 2. Ejaculate Characteristics in Nonhuman Primates

Species	No. of ejaculates	Stimulation[a]	X̄ Ejaculate volume (ml)[b]	X̄ Sperm count/ml of ejaculate (×10⁶)[b]	X̄ % sperm motility	X̄ % abnormal sperm[b]	Reference
G. gorilla	5	RP	0.3 (0.2–0.6)	171	33	—	Warner et al, 1974
G. gorilla	2	RP	—	—	—	29	Seuanez et al, 1977
G. gorilla	3	RP	0.3 (0.1–0.5)	15 (2–28)	11 (2–20)	92 (90–95)	Platz et al, 1980
G. gorilla	12	RP	1.0 (0.2–2.6)	191 (15–1,106)	(0–80)	(75–98)	Wildt et al, unpublished
P. troglodytes	52	RP	1.1 (0.1–2.5)	548 (54–2,750)	42 (14–77)	—	Warner et al, 1974
P. troglodytes	11	AV	—	(280–1,330)	(70–95)	—	Fussell et al, 1973
P. troglodytes	19	RP	1.9 (0.5–6.2)	609 (230–1,269)	30 (10–60)	(16–57)	Roussel and Austin, 1968; Ackerman and Roussel, 1968
P. pygmaeus	8	RP	1.1 (0.2–3.2)	61	47	—	Warner et al, 1974
H. lar	13	RP	1.3 (0.5–4.0)	152 (51–350)	9 (0–20)	(31–58)	Roussel and Austin, 1968; Ackerman and Roussel, 1968
P. cynocephalus	42	RP	3.6	71	66	—	Kraemer and Vera Cruz, 1969
T. gelada	5	RP	1.0 (0.5–2.0)	503 (351–651)	21 (5–30)	19	Roussel and Austin, 1968; Ackerman and Roussel, 1968
M. nemestrina	4	RP	2.2	9 (2–20)	97	—	Weisbroth and Young, 1965
M. nemestrina	5	RP	1.2 (0.9–1.5)	6 (2–10)	67 (54–82)	—	Reznicek et al, 1968
M. mulatta	33	RP	1.1 (0.2–4.5)	1,069 (100–3,600)	58 (10–85)	(26–47)	Roussel and Austin, 1968; Ackerman and Roussel, 1968
M. mulatta	28	PE	2.5 (1.1–5.0)	410 (170–675)	—	22 (13–47)	Valerio et al, 1970
M. mulatta	100	PE	1.8 (1.2–5.0)	484 (100–1,500)	—	24 (8–72)	
M. mulatta	—	PE	0.2	1,516 (12–4,472)	72 (40–95)	20 (2–48)	Van Pelt and Keyser, 1970
M. mulatta	121	PE	—	668	—	—	Settlage and Hendrickx, 1974a

M. mulatta	—	PE	(1.4–7.2)	(68–122)	—	—	Zamboni et al, 1974
M. mulatta	249	RP	—	419	54	<5	Harrison et al, 1980b
M. mulatta	—	PE	—	359 (110–1,100)	62	36	Wickings et al, 1981
M. arctoides	22	RP	1.6 (0.4–4.0)	468 (214–1,268)	49 (10–80)	(10–50)	Roussel and Austin, 1968; Ackerman and Roussel, 1968
M. fascicularis	17	RP	1.2 (0.6–3.0)	458 (160–830)	57 (25–75)	(30–36)	Roussel and Austin, 1968; Ackerman and Roussel, 1968
M. fascicularis	—	PE	0.8 (0.1–6.0)	347 (110–1,120)	—	32 (19–66)	Valerio et al, 1970
M. cyclopis	24	PE	—	366 (78–1,220)	—	—	Peng et al, 1973
M. radiata	—	PE	0.8	204	41	32	Valerio and Dalgard, 1975
M. radiata	190	PE	(1.9–2.2)	1,105–1,251	(72–76)	—	Jayaraman, 1980
C. galeritus	2	RP	1.3 (1.1–1.5)	576 (542–609)	60 (55–65)	—	Roussel and Austin, 1968; Ackerman and Roussel, 1968
E. patas	21	RP	0.6 (0.4–1.0)	1,153 (251–3,600)	45 (10–70)	(25–56)	Roussel and Austin, 1968
C. aethiops	23	RP	0.9 (0.3–2.0)	440 (166–811)	39 (15–70)	(26–40)	Roussel and Austin, 1968; Ackerman and Roussel, 1968
C. aethiops	—	PE	1.2	145	58	24	Valerio and Dalgard, 1975
C. apella	15	RP	0.6 (0.3–1.0)	161 (56–740)	24 (10–50)	41	Roussel and Austin, 1968; Ackerman and Roussel, 1968
C. apella	42	PE	(0.5–0.7)	(169–341)	62 (10–93)	15–20	Bush et al, 1975
S. sciureus	—	RP	0.1	295	79	—	Lang, 1967
S. sciureus	15	RP	0.4 (0.2–1.5)	260 (81–311)	52 (40–80)	35–51	Roussel and Austin, 1968; Ackerman and Roussel, 1968
S. sciureus	78	RP	0.15 (0.1–0.2)	(322–533)	(64–68)	—	Denis et al, 1976
T. glis	4	RP	0.1 (0.1–0.1)	103 (90–117)	52 (50–60)	8	Roussel and Austin, 1968; Ackerman and Roussel, 1968

[a]RP = rectal probe; PE = penile electrode; AV = artificial vagina.
[b]Values in parentheses = ranges.

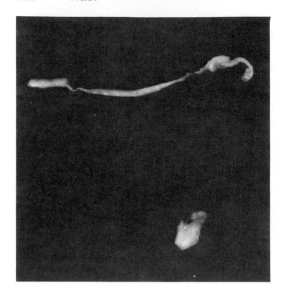

Fig. 13. Coagulum in the ejaculate of an electrostimulated macaque monkey.

was thought that a portion of the coagulum liquified [Roussel and Austin, 1967a], but later studies in macaques demonstrated that the coagulum contracted extruding an additional sperm-rich fraction [Van Pelt and Keyser, 1970; Settlage and Hendrickx, 1974b]. Such an occurrence is critical in achieving maximal sperm recovery because between 30% and 70% of the total number of ejaculated sperm are trapped in the coagulum [Hoskins and Patterson, 1967; Roussel and Austin, 1967a]. After maximum exudation has occurred it is important to separate both fractions as the coagulum acts as a sponge incorporating the surrounding sperm-rich liquid [Settlage and Hendrickx, 1974b].

Various methods have been developed, primarily in macaques, to decompose the coagulum, thus freeing spermatozoa. Compounds capable of dissolving fibrin coagula (Evans Blue, cysteinamine, acetylcysteine, and bromosulphalein) are ineffective in liquifying the ejaculate coagula of monkeys [Dukelow, 1970]. Some enzyme preparations (streptokinase-human plasminogen-streptodoronase, viper venom, 0.2–2% α-amylase, 0.5–1% peptidase, and α-chymotrypsin) either completely fail or cause partial dissolution but damage spermatozoal motility [Weisbroth and Young, 1965; Hoskins and Patterson, 1967; Roussel and Austin,

1967a; Denis et al, 1976] or morphological integrity [Settlage and Hendrickx, 1974b]. Trypsin (1–2% solution) or pronase (0.5–1% solution) added to the ejaculate and allowed to equilibrate at 37°C for 30 minutes promotes liquefaction supposedly without affecting spermatozoal quality [Roussel and Austin, 1967a,b; Valerio et al, 1970; Bush et al, 1975; Harrison, 1980b]. Trypsin concentrations greater than 2% can increase the incidence of sperm abnormalities [Bush et al, 1975]. The coagulum problem also can be partially circumvented by collecting the ejaculate directly into a washed, dilute saline solution or Eagle's medium already composed of a 1–2% trypsin or 1% pronase component [Hoskins and Patterson, 1967; Bush et al, 1975]. The ejaculate is incubated for 30 minutes and the sperm fraction separated from the diluting fluid by centrifugation. Additionally, if certain males are to be designated as long-term semen donors, it may be advantageous to surgically isolate the prostate, thereby permanently eliminating coagulum formation [Greer et al, 1968].

Not all primate coagula react similarly to enzyme digestion. Limited studies in species other than macaques indicate that enzymes may not be necessary for recovery of trapped spermatozoa. For example, squirrel monkey coagula incubated for 30–60 minutes at 37°C in a hydrated environment produce liquefaction with normal spermatozoal motility [Denis et al, 1976].

SEMEN EVALUATION

Under most laboratory conditions the ejaculate is evaluated immediately for volume, percent sperm motility, progressive motility, and sperm concentration. Progressive motility is used to subjectively assess the degree of forward movement of the spermatozoa, using a scale of 0 (lowest rating) to 5 (highest rating). An optional evaluative method includes assessing morphologic features of a given number of spermatozoa per ejaculate. Previous studies concerned with evaluating fertility in male nonhuman primates have primarily emphasized ejaculate volume, sperm concentration, and percent sperm motility because these traits have been positively correlated to conception rate [Valerio et al, 1970].

Table 2 summarizes the currently established ejaculate norms for monkeys and apes. Often a wide range in values is reported for a given species even within a single study. Much of this variation can be attributed to differences among laboratories in technique and subjective criteria. However, it is not unusual for ejaculate volume, sperm count, or percent sperm motility to vary considerably within a species or even between ejaculates from a single individual. Therefore, when assessing male fertility it is important to accumulate semen data on each male over a period of time. Macaque males used in an extensive breeding program have been subjected to fertility evaluations routinely at 60- to 90-day intervals [Valerio et al, 1970]. In our laboratory, males suspected of reproductive dysfunction are electroejaculated at least three times at 3- to 4-week intervals before final judgment of fertility status. Additionally, seasonal factors may influence ejaculate quality. Laboratory-maintained rhesus monkeys produce seasonal semen profiles, the highest-quality ejaculates being observed from October through December [Valerio and Dalgard, 1975]. Azoospermia from February to July is reported for this species [Valerio and Dalgard, 1975; Wickings et al, 1981], although long-term acclimation to colony environment can alleviate this condition [Valerio and Dalgard, 1975]. In contrast, seminal volume and sperm concentration and percent motility in bonnet macaques (*M. radiata*) appear unrelated to seasonal changes [Jayaraman et al, 1980].

In past studies insufficient emphasis has been placed on the traits of progressive sperm status and morphologic sperm forms. The percent motility factor is of questionable importance if sperm cells are showing circular or backward movement or no advanced progression. Likewise, spermatozoa could show forward motion but experience a high incidence of abnormal morphologic features. As the percent of abnormal cells increases, the quality of the semen sample decreases and consequently its potential fertilizing capacity is reduced. Table 2 illustrates the extremely marked differences within and among species in the degree of aberrant sperm morphology. There is little evidence to indicate that abnormal sperm numbers are influenced by the collection procedure used. For example, the ranges in mean percent abnormal sperm forms detected in rhesus monkeys collected by the penile electrode and rectal probe methods were 12–36% and <5–31%, respectively (Table 2). Because of captive-breeding difficulties and the endangered status of certain species, particularly

the gorilla, a recent interest in the significance of structural sperm defects has developed. As many as 29–90% of ejaculated sperm in certain gorillas display a bizarre shape, size, or feature that is clearly different from the expected normal type [Seuanez et al, 1977; Platz et al, 1980; Wildt et al, unpublished]. Of interest is the observation that many other nonhuman primates produce considerable numbers of aberrant-appearing sperm forms. Unfortunately, in most cases, the specific types of abnormalities observed have gone unreported. However, even in fertile men, 20–35% of spermatozoa have a structural defect [Afzelius, 1981], so the significance of similar finding in nonhuman primates and its precise relationship to fecundity remains to be determined.

SPERM METABOLISM

Following seminal fluid emission, sperm metabolism is largely a biodegradative process to support the function of progressive motility. Comparatively few studies on the glycolytic-respiratory process and its control have been reported in nonhuman primates, possibly owing to the low cell number in average ejaculates and the consequent difficulties encountered in measuring small amounts of metabolic end products [Peterson and Freund, 1969]. For this same reason few studies also have been conducted in the human, although the data base for man is considerably greater and potentially applicable to metabolic traits existing for most nonhuman primates. Mann and Lutwak-Mann [1981] have recently provided a comprehensive overview on the current understandings and theories of semen metabolism as it pertains to man and several domestic species. Ejaculated semen undergoes two metabolic processes, anaerobic glycolysis and aerobic respiration, the rates of these functions being proportional to spermatozoa concentration and motility.

Glycolytic fructolysis occurs only in the presence of fructose, the primary seminal sugar available to the spermatozoa. In the absence of oxygen, spermatozoa are no longer capable of utilizing endogenous substrates and must rely on anaerobic fructolysis to convert fructose to lactic acid. In human spermatozoa, a positive correlation generally exists between the rate of fructolysis and the degree of spermatozoal motility. Human spermatozoa supplemented with fructose and incubated anaerobically produce lactic acid at a continuous

TABLE 3. Concentration of Lactic Acid and Fructose in Sperm Fraction and Seminal Plasma Fraction Separated From Frozen-Thawed Nonhuman Primate Semen

| | | mg/100 ml semen | | | |
| | | Lactic acid | | Fructose | |
	No.	Sperm fraction	Plasma fraction	Sperm fraction	Plasma fraction
P. troglodytes	10	0.24	1.60	0.10	4.97
T. gelada	1	0.10	1.30	0	1.60
M. mulatta	23	0.32	1.38	0.14	7.55
M. arctoides	10	0.28	1.83	0	2.61
M. fascicularis	7	0.36	2.39	0.07	2.99
E. patas	19	0.34	1.94	0.18	3.15
C. aethiops	6	0.20	1.92	0.10	2.64
C. apella	3	0	0.04	0	5.63
S. sciureus	8	0.42	1.51	0	1.10
T.glis	1	2.15	1.80	0	0

Adapted from Ackerman and Roussel [1971].

rate for several hours at 37°C. However, if spermatozoal motility is inhibited (by the addition of a spermicide), fructolytic activity and the production of lactic acid are irreversibly lost.

The metabolic pathway for spermatozoal conversion of fructose to lactic acid was elucidated by Mann in 1964. Initially, fructose is phosphorylated to fructose-6-phosphate by hexokinase and adenosine triphosphate (ATP). A second phosphorylation step occurs to the fructose 1:6 diphosphate moiety made possible by the phosphofructokinase enzyme and additional ATP. Fructose 1:6 diphosphate is converted by aldolase to triose phosphate which undergoes oxidation to phosphoglyceric acid by glyceraldehyde-3-phosphate dehydrogenase. At this time a simultaneous reduction of nicotinamide adenine dinucleotide (NAD+) to NADH occurs. Phosphoglyceric acid is converted by enolase to phosphopyruvic acid, the latter losing phosphate to adenosine diphosphate (ADP), by pyruvic kinase. Pyruvic acid forms and is reduced by lactate dehydrogenase to lactic acid, the end product of anaerobic fructolysis. This final step is accompanied by a reoxidation of NADH to NAD+. At least three enzymes involved in this system (hexokinase, phosphofructokinase, pyruvate kinase) appear to regulate sperm fructolysis. For monkey spermatozoa, the greatest potential for enzymatic regulation of fructolysis is related to the kinetic and allosteric regulatory properties of phosphofructokinase [Hoskins et al, 1971].

Other sugars, in particular glucose and mannose, are phosphorylated by hexokinase. The latter enzyme varies in affinity for the various seminal sugars in the order of mannose > glucose > fructose. As a consequence, semen extended with a glucose-containing diluent (ie, egg yolk base) and then anaerobically incubated experiences an initial retardation in fructose utilization.

The levels of biochemical substrates in the seminal plasma of nonhuman primates has not been extensively examined. Fresh semen from bonnet macaques contains fructose concentrations averaging 14.9–15.8 mg/ml [Jayaraman et al, 1980], which are about sevenfold greater than the concentration reported for humans (2.5 mg/ml) [Mann and Lutwak-Mann, 1981] and three to four times greater than the levels detected in pig-tailed macaque monkeys (*M. nemestrina*) (3.7–5.5 mg/ml) [Reznichek et al, 1968]. Lactic acid content of fresh seminal fluid of this species ranges from 0.4 to 1.1 mg/ml [Reznichek et al, 1968]. Fructose and lactic acid levels also have been examined in monkey and ape ejaculates following cryopreservation [Ackerman and Roussel, 1971]. Semen samples were frozen, thawed, and centrifuged, and then analyses were made separately on the seminal plasma fraction and the sperm pellet resuspended in saline. Table 3 depicts the results from ten species and illustrates the marked species specificity in substrate concentrations. The latter also can be influenced by enzymatic approaches to digesting the coagulum of fresh ejaculates. Treatment of macaque coagulum for 1 hour with trypsin results in decreased fructose and increased lactic acid concentrations [Reznichek et al, 1968]. However, neither of these biochemical constituents nor others (citric acid, acid phosphatase, amylase, maltase, and total protein) in seminal fluid are apparently affected by normal seasonal changes, at least in one species of macaque [Jayaraman et al, 1980]

The respiratory function of ejaculated spermatozoa is active to a point in the absence of seminal plasma [Mann and Lutwak-Mann, 1981]. Numerous substances including lactic acid, pyruvic acid, acetic acid, sorbitol, long-chained fatty acids, and amino acids provide substrates for exogenous sperm respiration [Mann, 1964; Mills and Scott, 1969; Niel and Masters, 1972]. However, considerable species variation exists, and most work to date has been conducted in taxonomic groups other than nonhuman primates.

Spermatozoa are capable of retaining motility, provided oxygen is available even in the absence of seminal plasma or other metabolizable substrate. For many domestic species a coefficient for such respiration (denoted Z_{O_2}) is calculated based on the microliters of oxygen utilized by 10^8 spermatozoa per hour in vitro. Limited data are available for monkeys, although the Z_{O_2} for macaque spermatozoa has been reported as ranging from 10.5 to 14.7 $\mu l/10^8$ cell/hr [Ackerman and Roussel, 1971].

SEMEN PRESERVATION
Short-Term Preservation

Few data are available on the duration of viability of nonhuman primate spermatozoa in vitro. However, rhesus monkey spermatozoa collected by the penile electrode method and equilibrated in a nonglycerolated buffer have reduced motility in 3 hours and no motility by 24 hours after collection [Leverage et al, 1972]. In contrast, diluting semen (macaque, patas, African green monkey) with an egg yolk-glutamate-glycerol extender, cooling to 5°C over 2 hours, and holding at 5°C results in motility in all samples through at least 48 hours [Roussel and Austin, 1968]. In the latter study antibiotic also was added to semen to prolong in vitro motility. Motility longevity of diluted spermatozoa containing penicillin (1,000 IU/ml) is improved only slightly and nonsignificantly.

Chronic-Freeze Preservation

Various studies concerned with chronic-freeze preservation of nonhuman primate spermatozoa are summarized in Table 4. Generally, egg yolk, carbohydrate substrates, and glycerol in various proportions constitute the variety of cryoprotective diluents tested. Freezing procedures have basically involved adding collected semen to the diluent and freezing by 1) placing the diluted semen into ampules and solidifying in liquid nitrogen vapor, or 2) allowing the mixture to equilibrate to 4°C before pelleting on a solid block of dry ice. Both ampules and pellets are stored in liquid nitrogen. Little attention has been paid to methods to thaw frozen monkey semen. Frozen ampules have been thawed in a 5°C water bath over a 3-minute period [Roussel and Austin, 1967b]. Frozen semen in pellet form has been thawed in 0.9% saline warmed to 37° C [Denis et al, 1976]. Even less emphasis has been placed on the effects of initial sperm concentration on postfreezing viability, although in one report, optimal postthaw recoveries in the squirrel monkey were achieved when the ejaculate was diluted to 6-9 $\times$ 10^7 sperm cells/ml [Denis et al, 1976]. Generally, nonhuman primate spermatozoa retain some viability following freeze preservation, usually 50-88% of the original prefreeze motility status (Table 4). Recovery rates, which vary considerably, are related to techniques used and the immediate postcollection quality of the ejaculate. Duration of storage may be another significant factor as postthaw recovery of nonhuman primate spermatozoa is much less at 5-12 months after freezing than after only 3 days of frozen storage [Ackerman and Roussel, 1971]. In contrast, another study reported no differences in postthaw survival of macaque semen aliquots frozen for 24 hours or 20 weeks [Cho and Honjo, 1973].

The fertilizing capacity of these spermatozoa is unknown, since no live nonhuman primate offspring have resulted from artificial insemination with previously frozen spermatozoa. Electron microscopy reveals structural cellular alterations in macaque semen as a result of freezing. Such aberrant sperm morphology, which is not detected using light microscopy, includes loss of head and tail membrane integrity and mitochondrial spindle disintegration [Leverage et al, 1972; Cho et al, 1975]. Only one study has emphasized the effect of diluent constituents on postfreezing sperm viability in monkeys [Mahone and Dukelow, 1978]. Cynomolgus macaque semen was frozen in various concentrations of egg yolk and glycerol and in diluents with pH levels adjusted from 6.0 to 8.7. No significant difference was observed between spermatozoal motilities of diluent egg yoke con-

TABLE 4. Summary of Freezing Nonhuman Primate Spermatozoa

Species	Freezing diluent	Procedure	$\overline{X}$ Post-thaw % motility survival	Reference
M. mulatta *M. arctoides* *E. patas* *C. aethiops* *P. troglodytes*	20% egg yolk, 14% glycerol with sodium glutamate in distilled water	Trypsin-treated semen incubated in diluent (1:10) for 30 min at room temperature. Placed in glass ampules and frozen in liquid N_2 vapor over an 8-min period. Plunged into liquid N_2. Thawed in 5°C water bath within 3 min.	50 50 51 53 54	Roussel and Austin 1967b
P. papio	Same as Roussel and Austin, 1967b.	Same as Roussel and Austin, 1967b.	64.5	Kraemer and Vera Cruz, 1969
M. mulatta	20% egg yolk, 7% glycerol, with sodium citrate, sodium bicarbonate, and potassium phosphate	Semen incubated in nonglycerolated diluent for 30 min at 37°C. Added glycerol and then cooled at 1.3°C/min from 37 to 4°C, 5°C/min from 4 to −20°C, 10°C/min from −20 to −70°C. Plunged into liquid N_2.	68	Leverage et al, 1972
M. fascicularis	9.9% egg yolk, 27.3% glucose, 36.4% lactose, 18% raffinose mixed and centrifuged. Supernatant plus 5% glycerin used as diluent. pH adjusted with Tris buffer.	Semen equilibrated for 10 min at 37°C and then added diluent (5:1). Mixture precooled to 4°C for 30 min. Pellet frozen on dry ice and plunged into liquid N_2.	70.2 and 60.5 at 24 hr and 20 weeks, respectively, after storage in liquid N_2	Cho and Honjo, 1973
M. fascicularis	10–14% egg yolk, 11% lactose and 4–20% glycerol. pH adjusted with Tris buffer.	Semen equilibrated for 10 min at 37°C. Added diluent (4.5:1) and equilibrated at 4°C for 20 min. More diluent added (9:1) and equilibrated at 4°C for 25 min. Pellet frozen on dry ice and plunged into liquid N_2.	65 (20% egg yolk, 11% lactose, 4% glycerol, pH 7.2)	Mahone and Dukelow, 1978
S. sciureus	20% egg yolk, 11% lactose, 4% glycerol	Semen equilibrated for 55 min at 37°C. Diluent added (ratio dependent on sperm count) and equilibrated at 5°C for 20 min. More diluent added and equilibrated at 5°C for 25 min. Pellet frozen on dry ice and plunged into liquid N_2.	87.9	Denis et al, 1976

centrations from 10% to 40%. Progressive sperm motility was greater at a pH of 7.2 and and 8.0 than at 5.8, 6.5, and 8.7, and glycerol concentrations of 7% and 10% yielded optimal progressive motility after freezing. Again, species specificity may be a factor, since squirrel monkey semen has been shown to freeze poorly at glycerol concentrations greater than 4% [Denis et al, 1976].

ARTIFICIAL INSEMINATION

Most artificial insemination attempts have been made using fresh spermatozoa (Table 5). Four genera of nonhuman primates (squirrel monkey, macaque monkey, baboon, chimpanzee) have been successfully artificially inseminated [Kraemer and Kuehl, 1980a]; only the macaque, baboon, and chimpanzee have produced live offspring. The first artificial insemination successes in nonhuman primates concerned recovering fertilized ova after artificial semen deposition in monkeys containing intrauterine devices [Mastroianni and Rosseau, 1965] or treated with gonadotropic hormones [Bennett, 1967]. The first pregnancies resulting in viable offspring from artificial breeding were reported in the rhesus monkey [Dede and Plentl, 1966]. The artificial insemination of previously frozen monkey spermatozoa to date has not resulted in a term pregnancy. However, two independent studies in which macaque monkeys were inseminated with previously frozen spermatozoa resulted in three pregnancies which spontaneously aborted within 6–8 weeks of conception [Leverage et al, 1972; Honjo et al, 1975]. Although investigations employing frozen spermatozoa have been sparse and without success, other laboratories have demonstrated that artificial breeding, particularly in macaques using fresh spermatozoa, can be effective. Studies in macaques, baboons, and squirrel monkeys have all used semen collected by electroejaculation and deposited in the reproductive tract of physically restrained, unanesthetized females.

The most extensive and successful trials with artificial breeding in monkeys were reported by Czaja et al [1975]. In this study, rhesus spermatozoa were collected by the penile electrode approach and the raw semen diluted to about 2×10^8 live cells/ml with a 25% egg yolk–0.2 M Tris-buffered glucose extender. Naturally cycling females were selected for artificial insemination on the basis of perineal sex skin coloration. Each female was removed from the cage and physically restrained in a supine position on a table. A nasal speculum was used to spread the vaginal opening, exposing the cervical os. A blunted 5-cm, 18-gauge needle attached to a 250-μl syringe was manipulated through the cervix and into the uterus. A single insemination was made into each female using about 0.1 ml of extended semen containing a total of 2×10^7 live spermatozoa. Depending on the day of the cycle the insemination was performed, conception rates varied from 10% to 62.5% Of the total of 218 artificial inseminations performed, 87 (39.9%) produced pregnancies, which was higher than the rate for females naturally breeding.

A key to successful artificial insemination in nonhuman primates appears to be accurate determination of expected ovulation onset and thus time of insemination. It is apparent that adjusting the artificial breeding schedule to the female's cycle characteristics results in greater conception rates [Settlage et al, 1973]. A relationship also exists to seasonality even in monkeys maintained in consistent laboratory environments. Settlage et al [1973] obtained a conception rate of 25% following artificial insemination of rhesus monkeys during February, March, April, and September compared to a rate of 9% during May, June, and August. It is presumed that the decline in seasonal conception rate is due to anovulation or abnormal female gametes. To date, physical characteristics (ie, sex skin coloration and/or tumescence) have been used in baboons and certain macaque species to predict expected ovulation [Kraemer and Vera Cruz, 1972; Czaja et al, 1975] and thus estimate the time of insemination. However, urinary hormone concentrations [Hodges et al, 1979; Lasley et al, 1983] or direct laparoscopic examination of ovarian activity [Jewett and Dukelow, 1972; Wildt et al, 1977; Harrison, 1980a] could also be effective indices to accurately timing artificial breeding.

The site of seminal deposition also appears to significantly influence artificial breeding efficiency. Although in utero deposition of spermatozoa is probably most effective, insertion of an insemination needle transcervically is often difficult. It appears that depositing the spermatozoa into the cervix or at least against the cervical os increases the artificial insemination success rate. In one comparative study, conception rates of 4%, 19%, and 20% were achieved using intravaginal, cervical, and uterine inseminations, respectively

TABLE 5. Artificial Insemination Results in Nonhuman Primates

Species	Procedure	Results	Reference
M. mulatta	Used females exhibiting natural cycles or following ovulation induction with gonadotropins. Semen collected by penile electrode. Coagulum deposited in vagina with forceps, daily between 8th and 16th day of cycle.	2 pregnancies from artificial insemination during 15 cycles in which ovulation was induced; 4 pregnancies from artificial insemination during 33 cycles in which ovulation occurred spontaneously.	Dede and Plentl, 1966
S. sciureus	Used 5 females treated with gonadotropins for 9 days. Semen collected by rectal probe electroejaculation. Semen deposited intravaginally on the 10th or 11th day. Three monkeys sacrificed on 12th day.	16 fertilized eggs (1–4 cells) collected from 3 sacrificed monkeys. Other 2 females not pregnant.	Bennett, 1967
M. mulatta	Used naturally cycling females. Semen collected by penile electrode, diluted with buffer, washed twice by centrifugation. A volume of 0.2–1.0 ml was inseminated intraperitoneally into unanesthetized female midway between pubis and umbilicus and 1.5 cm lateral of midline. Inseminated 2–3 times on alternative days during midcycle.	3/8 females pregnant; 2 pregnancies terminated at 8 weeks, 1 offspring born alive.	Van Pelt, 1970
M. mulatta	Used naturally cycling females. Semen collected by penile electrode and held for 30 min at 37°C. Semen (7.5 × 10⁶ motile sperm) deposited in utero or intracervically either on the 11th through 14th day of cycle or on alternate days 10, 12, and 14 of cycle.	20% and 19% conception rate for in utero and intracervical methods, respectively.	Valerio and Dalgard, 1975

Species	Method	Results	Reference
P. cynocephalus	Used naturally cycling females. Semen collected by rectal probe electroejaculation. Females restrained in squeeze cage and 5-ml syringe used to deposit an average of 20×10^6 spermatozoa with 60% motility rating. Insemination performed 3 times on alternate days during maximal sex skin tumescence.	1 of 6 females became pregnant and delivered a live single offspring.	Kraemer and Vera Cruz, 1972
M. mulatta	Used naturally cycling females. Semen collected by penile electrode into 5-ml syringe. Syringe placed into vagina of unanesthetized female and ejaculate expelled against cervix. Insemination performed on days 10, 12, and 14 of cycle or every other day from 2 days before midcycle to 14 days before next anticipated menses.	21.3% conception rate based on 47 cycles of exposure to artificial insemination. Greater conception rate than obtained by natural mating.	Settlage et al, 1973
M. cyclopis	Used naturally cycling females. Semen collected by penile electrode and diluted in saline. Liquid and coagulum deposited in vagina once on day 10–14 of cycle.	1 pregnancy from insemination on day 14.	Peng et al, 1973
M. mulatta	Used naturally cycling females. Semen collected by penile electrode and diluted with egg yolk extender containing Tris-buffered glucose, streptomycin sulfate, penicillin, and buffered potassium. Unanesthetized females inseminated according to sex skin coloration variation with 2×10^7 live spermatozoa. Semen deposited in utero.	218 inseminations resulted in 87 pregnancies (39.9% conception rate).	Czaja et al, 1975
P. troglodytes	Used a naturally cycling female. Semen collected by masturbation. Entire ejaculate inseminated into cervical os of anesthetized female at a time based on genital sexual swelling.	1 viable female offspring produced in 244 days	Martin et al, 1977

[Valerio and Dalgard, 1975]. Pregnancies also have occurred as the result of novel artificial breeding approaches. Van Pelt [1970] introduced ejaculated sperm intraperitoneally into macaque females during midcycle and obtained three pregnancies, including a live birth.

CONCLUSIONS

It can be concluded that semen from most monkeys and apes can be readily collected using several artificial procedures. Electroejaculation is the most reliable and effective method; however, few studies have been conducted to examine the effects of this procedure on subsequent libido and breeding behavior. Although few data have been published concerning viability or fertilizable life of macaque spermatozoa in vitro, the sperm cell can withstand freeze preservation as evidenced by postthaw progressive motility. In general, ejaculates of nonhuman primates contain a moderately high proportion of spermatozoa with morphological defects. Furthermore, some ultrastructural damage due to cryopreservation has been reported but not extensively examined. Although no offspring have been born following artificial insemination with previously frozen spermatozoa, surprisingly few attempts have been made. In contrast, several studies utilizing fresh semen have illustrated the potential of artificial insemination in propagating monkeys and apes. In these cases, conception rates between artificially and naturally bred groups have been similar. Unfortunately, there is a lack of conclusive results on factors affecting sperm metabolism, handling ejaculate coagulum, the number of sperm required for conception, and the proper time of insemination. Hormonal therapies designed to artificially induce ovulation often produce less than definitive results, in part because of variations in hormonal potencies, injection regimens among laboratories, and a diversity in species tested, as well as differences in the endogenous endocrine balance in individuals at the onset of hormonal treatment. As a result, artificial insemination is probably more applicable to the naturally cycling/ovulating nonhuman primate. Consequently, methods of monitoring the cycle and estimating ovulation must be used with artificial insemination attempts.

The results suggest that increased research efforts are required to optimize the methods for artificial insemination using fresh or frozen-thawed spermatozoa. Further comparative studies are required to more definitively establish 1) ejaculate and fertility "norms" for each species; 2) type of insemination required (intravaginal, cervical, or uterine); 3) time and number of inseminations needed; 4) minimum spermatozoa numbers necessary to achieve conception; and 5) optimal diluents, equilibration intervals, and methods for freeze preservation of spermatozoa. Intensive emphasis should be placed on producing offspring using artificial insemination with previously frozen spermatozoa. Simultaneous studies need to be initiated also to investigate methods of evaluating male fertility including the ejaculate characteristics of spermatozoal motility, spermatozoa concentrations per ejaculate, and aberrant sperm morphology, as well as the relevance of more recent techniques for examining human semen quality (ie, sperm penetration assay [Yanagimachi et al, 1976; Karp et al, 1981] or cervical mucus penetration test [Alexander, 1981]). Finally, it should be realized that most artificial breeding successes to date have occurred in physically restrained females. Artificial insemination in larger monkeys and great apes will require chemical restraint. Neither the effects of anesthesia nor the induced stress of handling a nonhuman primate species on reproductive function is well understood, and both deserve further examination.

ACKNOWLEDGMENTS

The author thanks W. Richard Dukelow and Stephen J. O'Brien for their editorial comments, Jo Gayle Howard and Duane C. Kraemer for assistance in reviewing the chapter topic, and Stella Gregory for typing the manuscript. Portions of this paper were presented at the Lion-Tailed Macaque Symposium, May 19–22, 1982, sponsored by the Baltimore Zoological Society.

REFERENCES

Ackerman, D.R.; Roussel, J.D. Fructose, lactic acid and citric acid content of the semen of eleven subhuman primate species and of man. JOURNAL OF REPRODUCTION AND FERTILITY 17:563–566, 1968.
Ackerman, D.R.; Roussel, J.D. Citric acid, lactic acid and oxygen metabolism of frozen-thawed semen from four subhuman primate species. JOURNAL OF REPRODUCTION AND FERTILITY 27:441–443, 1971.

Afzelius, B.A. Abnormal human spermatozoa including comparative data from apes. AMERICAN JOURNAL OF PRIMATOLOGY 1:175–182, 1981.

Alexander, N.J. Evaluation of male infertility with an in vitro cervical mucus penetration test. FERTILITY AND STERILITY 36:201–208, 1981.

Bennett, J.P. Artificial insemination of the squirrel monkey. JOURNAL OF ENDOCRINOLOGY 37:473–474, 1967.

Brindley, G.S. Electroejaculation: Its technique, neurological implications and uses. JOURNAL OF NEUROLOGY, NEUROSURGERY AND PSYCHIATRY 44:9–18, 1981.

Bush, D.E.; Russell, L.H.; Flowers, A.L.; Sorensen, A.M. Semen evaluation in capuchin monkeys (Cebus apella). LABORATORY ANIMAL SCIENCE 25:588–593, 1975.

Cho, F.; Honjo, S. A simplified method for collecting and preserving cynomolgus macaque semen. JAPANESE JOURNAL OF MEDICAL SCIENCE AND BIOLOGY 26:261–268, 1973.

Cho, F.; Honjo, S.; Makita, T. Fertility of frozen-preserved spermatozoa of cynomolgus monkeys. Pp. 125–133 in CONTEMPORARY PRIMATOLOGY, INTERNATIONAL CONGRESS OF PRIMATOLOGY. S. Kondo; M. Kawai; A. Ehara, eds. Basel, Karger, 1975.

Czaja, J.A.; Eisle, S.G.; Goy, R.W. Cyclical changes in the sexual skin of female rhesus. Relationships to mating behavior and successful artificial insemination. FEDERATION PROCEEDINGS 34:1680–1684, 1975.

Dede, J.A.; Plentl, A.A. Induced ovulation and artificial insemination in a rhesus colony. FERTILITY AND STERILITY 17:757–764, 1966.

Denis, L.T.; Poindexter, A.N.; Ritter, M.B.; Seager, S.W.J.; Deter, R.L. Freeze preservation of squirrel monkey sperm for use in timed fertilization studies. FERTILITY AND STERILITY 27:723–729, 1976.

Dukelow, W.R. Reproductive physiology of primates. PROCEEDINGS OF THE AMERICAN ASSOCIATION OF ZOO VETERINARIANS, Michigan State University, East Lansing, 1970.

Fussell, E.N.; Franklin, L.E.; Frantz, R.C. Collection of chimpanzee semen with an artificial vagina. LABORATORY ANIMAL SCIENCE 23:252–255, 1973.

Fussell, E.N., Roussel, J.D.; Austin, C.R. Use of the rectal probe method for electrical ejaculation of apes, monkeys and a prosimian. LABORATORY ANIMAL CARE 17:528–530, 1967.

Gould, K.G.; Warner, H.; Martin, D.E. Rectal probe electroejaculation of primates. JOURNAL OF MEDICAL PRIMATOLOGY 7:213–222, 1978.

Greer, W.E., Roussel, J.D.; Austin, C.R. Prevention of coagulation in monkey semen by surgery. JOURNAL OF REPRODUCTION AND FERTILITY 15:153–155, 1968.

Harrison, R.M. Laparoscopy in monkeys and apes. Pp. 73–94 in ANIMAL LAPAROSCOPY. R.M. Harrison; D.E. Wildt, eds. Baltimore, Williams and Wilkins, 1980a.

Harrison, R.M. Semen parameters in Macaca mulatta: Ejaculates from random and selected monkeys. JOURNAL OF MEDICAL PRIMATOLOGY 9:265–273, 1980b.

Hendrickx, A.G.; Thompson, R.S.; Hess, D.L.; Prahalada, S. Artificial insemination and a note on pregnancy detection in the nonhuman primate. SYMPOSIUM OF THE ZOOLOGICAL SOCIETY OF LONDON 43:219–240, 1978.

Hodges, J.K.; Czekala, N.M.; Lasley, B.L. Estrogen and luteinizing hormone secretion in diverse primate species from simplified urinary analysis. JOURNAL OF MEDICAL PRIMATOLOGY 8:349–364, 1979.

Hoskins, D.D.; Patterson, D.L. Prevention of coagulum formation with recovery of motile spermatozoa from rhesus monkey semen. JOURNAL OF REPRODUCTION AND FERTILITY 13:337–340, 1967.

Hoskins, D.D.; Stephens, D.T.; Casillas, E.R. Enzymic control of fructolysis in primate spermatozoa. BIOCHIMICA BIOPHYSICA ACTA 237:227–238, 1971.

Jayaraman, S.; Hurkadli, K.S.; Sheth, A.R. Lack of seasonal changes in biochemical constituents of bonnet monkey semen. ARCHIVES OF ANDROLOGY 4:327–330, 1980.

Jewett, D.A.; Dukelow, W.R. Serial observations of follicular morphology near ovulation in Macaca fascicularis. JOURNAL OF REPRODUCTION AND FERTILITY 31:287–290, 1972.

Karp, L.E.; Williamson, R.A.; Moore, D.E.; Shy, K.K.; Plymate, S.R.; Smith, W.D. Sperm penetration assay: Useful test in evaluation of male fertility. OBSTETRICS AND GYNECOLOGY 57:620–623, 1981.

Kraemer, D.C.; Kuehl, T.J. Artificial insemination of nonhuman primates. Pp. 1133–1134 in CURRENT THERAPY IN THERIOGENOLOGY. D. Morrow, ed. Philadelphia, Saunders, 1980a.

Kraemer, D.C.; Kuehl, T.J. Semen collection and evaluation of breeding soundness in nonhuman primates. Pp. 1134–1137 in CURRENT THERAPY IN THERIOGENOLOGY. D. Morrow, ed. Philadelphia, Saunders, 1980b.

Kraemer, D.C.; Vera Cruz, N.C. Collection, gross characteristics and freezing of baboon semen. JOURNAL OF REPRODUCTION AND FERTILITY 20:345–348, 1969.

Kraemer, D.C.; Vera Cruz, N.C. Breeding baboons for laboratory use. Pp. 42–47 in BREEDING PRIMATES. W.I.B. Beveridge, ed. Basel, Karger, 1972.

Kuehl, T.J.; Dukelow, W.R. A restraint device for electroejaculation of squirrel monkeys (*Saimiri sciureus*). LABORATORY ANIMAL SCIENCE 24:364–366, 1974.

Lang, C.M. A technique for the collection of semen from squirrel monkeys (*Saimiri sciureus*) by electroejaculation. LABORATORY ANIMAL CARE 17:218–221, 1967.

Lasley, B.L.; Czekala, N.M.; Lindburg, D.G. Urinary estrogen profiles in the lion tailed macaque. Pp. 149–159 in THE LION-TAILED MACAQUE: STATUS AND CONSERVATION. P.G. Heltne, ed. Alan R. Liss, 1985.

Leverage, W.E.; Valerio, D.A.; Schultz, A.P.; Kingsbury, E.; Dorey, C. Comparative study on the freeze preservation of spermatozoa, primate, bovine and human. LABORATORY ANIMAL SCIENCE 22:882–889, 1972.

Mahone, J.P.; Dukelow, W.R. Semen preservation in *Macaca fascicularis*. LABORATORY ANIMAL SCIENCE 28:556–561, 1978.

Mann, T. BIOCHEMISTRY OF SEMEN AND THE MALE REPRODUCTIVE TRACT. London, Methuen, 1964.

Mann, T.; Lutwak-Mann, C. MALE REPRODUCTIVE FUNCTION AND SEMEN. New York, Springer-Verlag, 1981.

Martin, D.E.; Graham, C.E.; Gould, K.C. Successful pregnancy in the chimpanzee using artificial insemination. SYMPOSIUM ON ARTIFICIAL BREEDING OF NON-DOMESTIC ANIMALS, 1977.

Mastroianni, L.; Manson, W.A. Collection of monkey semen by electroejaculation. PROCEEDINGS OF THE SOCIETY FOR EXPERIMENTAL BIOLOGY AND MEDICINE 112:1025–1027, 1963.

Mastroianni, L.; Rosseau, C.U. Influence of the intrauterine coil on ovum transport and sperm distribution in the monkey. AMERICAN JOURNAL OF OBSTETRICS AND GYNECOLOGY 93:416–420, 1965.

Mills, S.C.; Scott, T.W. Metabolism of fatty acids by testicular and ejaculated ram spermatozoa. JOURNAL OF REPRODUCTION AND FERTILITY 18:367–369, 1969.

Niel, A.R.; Masters, C.J. Metabolism of fatty acids by bovine spermatozoa. BIOCHEMISTRY JOURNAL 127:375–385, 1972.

Peng, M.; Lai, Y.; Yang, C.; Chiang, H.; New, A.E.; Chang, C. Reproductive parameters of the Taiwan monkey (*Macaca cyclopis*). PRIMATES 14:201–213, 1973.

Petersen, R.N.; Freund, M. Glycolysis of washed suspensions of human spermatozoa. BIOLOGY OF REPRODUCTION 1:238–246, 1969.

Platz, C.C.; Wildt, D.E.; Bridges, C.H.; Seager, S.W.J.; Whitlock, B.S. Electroejaculation and semen analysis in a male lowland gorilla. PRIMATES 21:130–132, 1980.

Reznichek, R.C.; Roussel, J.D.; Mangelson, N.L.; Kado, R.T.; Cockett, A.T.K. Some morphologic and biochemical observations of semen in nemestrina monkeys destined for space flight. FERTILITY AND STERILITY 19:376–381, 1968.

Roussel, J.D.; Austin, C.R. Enzymic liquefaction of primate semen. INTERNATIONAL JOURNAL OF FERTILITY 12:288–290, 1967a.

Roussel, J.D.; Austin, C.R. Preservation of primate spermatozoa by freezing. JOURNAL OF REPRODUCTION AND FERTILITY 13:333–335, 1967b.

Roussel, J.D.; Austin, C.R. Improved electroejaculation of primates. JOURNAL OF THE INSTITUTE OF ANIMAL TECHNICIANS 19:22–32, 1968.

Settlage, D.S.F.; Hendrickx, A.G. Electroejaculation technique in *Macaca mulatta* (rhesus monkeys). FERTILITY AND STERILITY 25:157–159, 1974a.

Settlage, D.S.F.; Hendrickx, A.G. Observations on coagulum characteristics of the rhesus monkey electroejaculate. BIOLOGY OF REPRODUCTION 11:619–623, 1974b.

Settlage, D.S.F.; Swan, S.; Hendrickx, A.G. Comparison of artificial insemination with natural mating technique in rhesus monkeys, *Macaca mulatta*. JOURNAL OF REPRODUCTION AND FERTILITY 32:129–132, 1973.

Seuanez, H.N.; Carothers, A.D.; Martin, D.E.; Short, R.V. Morphological abnormalities in spermatozoa of man and great apes. NATURE 270:345–347, 1977.

Valerio, D.A.; Dalgard, D.W. Experiences in the laboratory breeding of nonhuman primates. LABORATORY ANIMAL HANDBOOKS 6:49–62, 1975.

Valerio, D.A.; Ellis, E.B.; Clark, M.L.; Thompson, G.E. Collection of semen from macaques by electroejaculation. LABORATORY ANIMAL CARE 19:250–252, 1969.

Valerio, D.A.; Leverage, W.E.; Munster, J.H. Semen evaluation in macaques. LABORATORY ANIMAL CARE 20:734–740, 1970.

Valerio, D.A.; Leverage, W.E.; Bensenhaver, J.C.; Thornett, H.D. The analysis of male fertility, artificial insemination and natural matings in the laboratory breeding of macaques. Pp. 515–525 in MEDICAL PRIMATOLOGY. E.I. Goldsmith; J. Moor-Jankowski, eds. Basel, Karger, 1971.

Van Pelt, L.F. Intraperitoneal insemination of *Macaca mulatta*. FERTILITY AND STERILITY 21:159–162, 1970.

Van Pelt, L.F.; Keyser, P.E. Observations on semen collection and quality in macaques. LABORATORY ANIMAL CARE 20:726–733, 1970.

Warner, H.; Martin, D.E.; Keeling, M.E. Electroejaculation of the great apes. ANNALS OF BIOMEDICAL ENGINEERING 2:419–432, 1974.

Weisbroth, S.; Young, F.A. The collection of primate semen by electroejaculation. FERTILITY AND STERILITY 16:229–235, 1965.

Wickings, E.J.; Zaidi, P.; Nieschlag, E. Seminal parameters in rhesus monkeys under physiological conditions and in studies for male fertility control using FSH antibodies or LH-RH-agonists. AMERICAN JOURNAL OF PRIMATOLOGY 1:203–210, 1981.

Wildt, D.E. Reproductive techniques of potential use in the artificial propagation of nonhuman primates. Pp. 161–194 in THE LION-TAILED MACAQUE: STATUS AND CONSERVATION. P.G. Heltne, ed. Alan R. Liss, 1985.

Wildt, D.E.; Doyle, L.L.; Stone, S.C.; Harrison, R.M. Correlation of perineal swelling with serum ovarian hormone levels, vaginal cytology and ovarian follicular development during the baboon reproductive cycle. PRIMATES 18:261–270, 1977.

Yanagimachi, R.; Yanagimachi, H.; Rodgers, B.J. The use of zona-free animal ova as a test-system for the assessment of the fertilizing capacity of human spermatozoa. BIOLOGY OF REPRODUCTION 15:471–476, 1976.

Zamboni, L.; Conaway, C.H.; Van Pelt, L. Seasonal changes in production of semen in free-ranging rhesus monkeys. BIOLOGY OF REPRODUCTION 11:251–267, 1974.

Gametogenesis

T.G. Baker

School of Medical Sciences, University of Bradford, Bradford BD7 1DP, United Kingdom

INTRODUCTION

During the past 30 years a considerable amount of knowledge has been accumulated on the anatomy, physiology, and biochemistry of mammalian reproduction. This is especially true of studies relating to the ovary [eg, Franchi et al, 1962; Baker, 1972a; Zuckerman and Baker, 1977; Jones, 1978; Peters and McNatty, 1980]. It is therefore surprising that few of these studies have been concerned with the ovary in nonhuman primates, especially when one considers that many tens of thousands of primates have been used in biomedical research [Yager and Judge, 1967; Baker, 1972b, 1977]. As Koering [1974] has pointed out, one of the major constraints to the use of primates has been the paucity of species available in the major primate research centers in Europe, the United States, and the Soviet Union [Diczfalusy and Standley, 1972; Prasad and Anand Kumar, 1977]. Other constraints include the enormous expenditure required to import, quarantine, and maintain a colony of primates, and especially the provision of expensive animal facilities to minimize the transfer of pathogenic microorganisms (zoonoses) between animals and personnel [Ruch, 1959; Fiennes, 1967]. These problems have recently been compounded by difficulties in obtaining many of the primate species owing to the stringent export regulations imposed by the countries providing the animals in an attempt to prevent extinction or severe reduction in numbers of many species. The future use of primates may depend on the production of animals in captivity which would have the added advantage of minimizing the transmission of pathogens to man.

The aim of the present review must be to encourage further studies on gametogenesis in primates. That such studies are important in biomedical research is now widely accepted since the extrapolation of data from laboratory rodents to primates is rarely justified. Gametogenesis in primates differs from that in many other mammalian classes, and the response of germ cells to such exogenous factors as ionizing radiations and drugs is also markedly different [Baker, 1978; Baker and Neal, 1977].

DEFINITIONS OF TERMS

The term gametogenesis describes the events leading to the formation of the gametes; oogenesis can be defined as the formation, development, and maturation of the female gamete [Holmes, 1979]. The term germ cell is nonspecific and applies to male and female sex cells at all stages in their development, whereas primordial germ cells (also called gonocytes) are only found in the embryo before sex differentiation. By contrast, oogonia occur after the sexual differentiation of the ovary and they are capable of repeated mitotic divisions before entering the prophase of the first meiotic division, when they are termed primary oocytes. The term ovum is correctly applied only to the germ cell that has extruded two polar bodies after completing both meiotic divisions. Consequently it is the secondary oocyte at the metaphase of meiosis II which, in most mammalian species, is shed from the ripe follicle at ovulation [Rothschild, 1956; Austin and Walton, 1960]. For most species it is therefore incorrect to speak of unfertilized ova since the postmetaphase stages of the second meiotic division are completed only after fertilization by a spermatozoon. Thus the word egg is usefully retained since it applies equally to follicular and ovulated oocytes and also to early postfertilization stages [Baker, 1972a].

Spermatogonia are analogous to oogonia: they are the main "stem" cells in the testis and undergo mitotic divisions throughout life (cf oogonia; see below). Spermatocytes are the cellular stages in-

Comparative Primate Biology, Volume 3: Reproduction and Development, pages 195–213
© 1986 Alan R. Liss, Inc.

volved with meiosis whereas spermatozoa are analogous to ova. There is an additional stage in gametogenesis in the male, namely the spermatid which is a stage in the differentiation of the secondary spermatocyte into a spermatozoon [Steinberger and Steinberger, 1972]. This process of differentiation is called spermiogenesis (cf spermatogenesis, which is analogous to oogenesis).

EMBRYOLOGY OF THE GONAD

The only primate species in which gonadal development has been subjected to intensive embryological studies are the rhesus monkey and man [Witschi, 1948; Gillman, 1948; van Wagenen and Simpson, 1965]. In view of the close similarity of early embryonic development in the primates that have been investigated, it would seem reasonable to suppose that gonadal differentiation follows the same pattern in the majority of primate species. It will be shown later that this supposition is at least partly true since the timing and cytology of gametogenesis in postnatal primates is comparable in spite of variations in the duration of gestation and of the length of the prepubertal period [Egozcue, 1969].

Primordial Germ Cells

The precise origin of the primordial germ cells in primates is open to conjecture although in Amphibia their lineage can be traced from the fertilized egg (as "germinal cytoplasm" rich in RNA) through successive cleavage divisions to an area of the grey crescent in the blastula [Blackler, 1966]. It is well established that destruction of the primordial germ cells in these lower vertebrates leads to complete sterility, and there is much convincing circumstantial evidence to show that this is also true in mammals including primates [Franchi et al,

1962; Baker, 1972a; Zuckerman and Baker, 1977; Baker and Eastwood, 1983].

In mammals the primordial germ cells are recognized by their large size, nearly spherical shape, and by means of certain histochemical reactions (eg, alkaline phosphatase, esterases, glycogen). By using a combination of these techniques, Pinkerton et al [1961] have successfully demonstrated that human primordial germ cells are the sole progenitors of oogonia which in turn give rise to oocytes. Furthermore, Kennelly and Foote [1966], using tritiated thymidine incorporation in the rabbit, have shown that ovulated eggs arise from primordial germ cells which incorporated the radioisotope in the embryo [Zuckerman and Baker, 1977; Baker and Eastwood, 1983]. These studies confirm the continuity of the germ cell line from embryo to adult (Fig. 1) [Baker and Eastwood, 1983].

The earliest stage in primate embryogenesis in which primordial germ cells can be recognized is in the yolk sac of the 12 somite stage embryo in man [Witschi, 1948] (Fig. 2). These large, round cells subsequently migrate up the yolk sac stalk and around the allantois to enter the embryo caudally adjacent to the hindgut. Migration continues via the gut and its mesentery [Witschi, 1948, for human embryos; Butler, 1971, for the Senegal galago], until the primordial germ cells reach the genital ridges (Fig. 3).

The migration of the primordial germ cells is an active process involving amoeboid movements of the cells and possibly lytic enzymes to perforate membranes. Unlike the migratory processes in some lower vertebrates (eg, birds and reptiles [Franchi et al, 1962]), there is no evidence for the transport of germ cells via the blood stream in mammals [Tarkowski, 1970]. Evidence from in

TABLE 1. Ages at Which Germ Cells, Gonads, and Sex Ducts Develop in the Human Fetus

Age of embryo	Morphological event
24 days	First primordial germ cells recognizable
During the 4th week	Mesonephric tubules form
25–30 days	Primordia of Wolffian ducts form
31–35 days	Primordia of sex glands appear as thickening of coelomic epithelium
28–35 days	Migration of germ cells to gonadal primordia
44–48 days	Mullerian duct appears

From Peters and McNatty [1980].

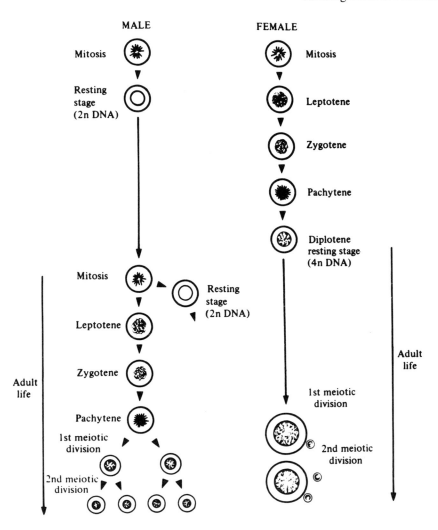

Fig. 1. Life cycles of male and female germ cells. [From Byskov, 1982.]

vitro studies supports the view of Witschi [1970] that the genital ridges produce a chemotactic substance ("telopheron") to attract the primordial germ cells [Blandau, 1969; Czolowska, 1969]. However, a proportion of these cells may fail to reach the presumptive gonadal anlagen and may give rise to germ cell tumors or accessory gonadal tissue.

The Sexually Indifferent Gonad

Van Wagenen and Simpson [1965] compared the development of the gonad in the rhesus monkey and man. In both species primordial germ cells colonized the genital ridges at about 33 days postconception (Tables 1 and 2). At this time the genital ridges are forming on the inner borders of the mesonephros as thickenings of the surface epithelium with a denser "knot" of underlying stroma (mesenchyme). The latter contains cords of epithelial cells which seem to be continuous with the surface epithelium. The development of the genital ridges continues slowly, and the primordial germ cells associate with the medullary cords. The attachment of the genital ridge to the mesonephros becomes more pendulous until (around 36 days postconception) a rudimentary gonad can be recognized [van Wagenen and Simpson, 1965].

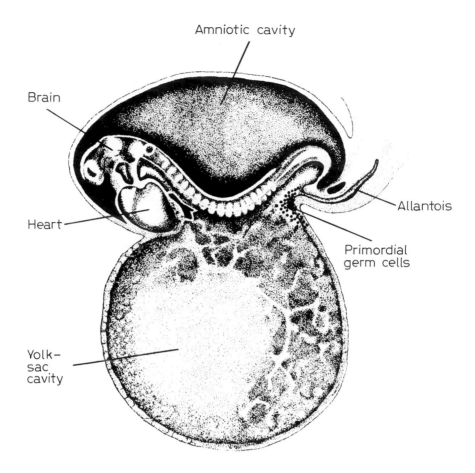

Fig. 2. Reconstruction of a 24-day human embryo showing the primordial germ cells (black dots). [Redrawn after Witschi, 1948.]

Sexual Differentiation of the Gonad

The indifferent gonad consists of a coelomic epithelium, an underlying stroma, primordial germ cells, and a potential ingress of cellular material from the mesonephros. During sexual differentiation these materials are assembled into either a testis or an ovary [Gillman, 1948; Franchi et al, 1962]. In reality these changes initially consist in the formation of a testis or the lack of testicular development [Gillman, 1948].

There can be little doubt that sexual differentiation is controlled largely by the presence or absence of a Y chromosome in the cells of the gonad since the Y chromosome is strongly male-deter-mining in mammals [Jacobs, 1966; Tarkowski, 1970; Fechheimer, 1970; Burgoyne, 1981]. It would seem that the Y chromosome exerts its effect via the H-Y antigen [Ohno, 1979]. However, this primary mechanism can be negated by some autosomal or X-linked genes (eg, testicular feminization, sex-reversal, etc [Simpson, 1976; Burgoyne, 1981]), and various exogenous and endogenous factors can modify gonadal development leading to varying degrees of intersexuality [Overzier, 1963]. Intersexuality seems to be rare in nonhuman primates; the only cases in the literature appear to be bilaterial ovotestis [Sullivan and Drobeck, 1966] and gonadal agenesis [Koford et al, 1966; Wilson, 1972].

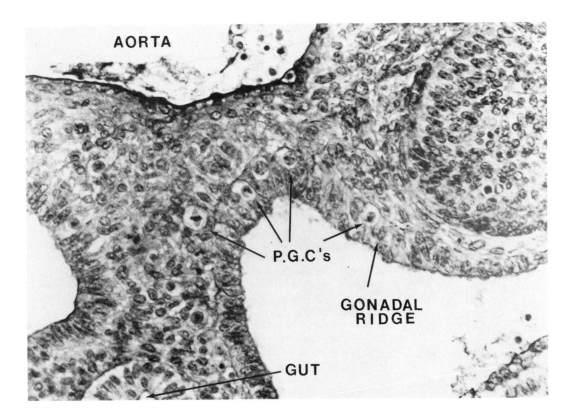

Fig. 3. Section of human embryo at about 31 days postconception showing primordial germ cells in the gut mesentery and gonadal anlagen. [From Witschi, 1948.]

Testis. Sexual differentiation of the gonad occurs in rhesus monkey and human embryos between the 36th and 42nd days after conception [Gillman, 1948; van Wagenen and Simpson, 1965; Baker and Eastwood, 1983]. If the gonad develops into a testis, the germ cells enter the medullary cords to form the presumptive seminiferous tubules and the development of a band of connective tissue (tunica albuginea) prevents differentiation of the cortex. Subsequently the primordial germ cells rapidly proliferate by mitosis but become quiescent (as gonocytes or prospermatogonia) shortly before birth (Table 3).

An early feature of testicular differentiation is the formation of islands of interstitial (Leydig) cells between adjacent seminiferous tubules. These Leydig cells produce androgens in response to the stimulus of chorionic gonadotropin (hCG in man; mCG in monkeys) [Zondek and Zondek, 1965, 1979; Abramovich et al, 1974; Baker and Scrimgeour, 1980, 1981]. Fetal androgens, largely of testicular origin, are essential for the development of the Wolffian ducts to complete the male reproductive system (Fig. 4). In the absence of androgens (or of the enzyme 5α-reductase which converts testosterone to dihydrotestosterone [Simpson, 1976; Williams, 1981]), the male ducts fail to develop, resulting in a phenotypic female with inguinal testes (testicular feminization [Simpson, 1976]).

The distribution of Leydig cells in the fetal testis seems to be affected by the levels of chorionic gonadotropin produced by the placenta. Thus around the time of birth in the human testis [Zondek and Zondek, 1965; Abramovich et al, 1974]

TABLE 2. Sequence of Development of the Macaque Embryonic and Fetal Ovary

Conception age	Characteristics
31 days	No ventromedian thickening of mesothelium over mesonephric body
33–34 days	*Genital ridge present*; thickened mesothelium and cords of similar small cells extend into mesenchyme; a few enlarged cells (primordial germ cells) between cords beneath surface mesothelium
36–42 days	*Undifferentiated gonad* (or presumptive ovary, because testis is identifiable at 38–40 days); elongate body overlying mesenophros, compactly cellular with suggestion of cords; mesovarium formed
46–50 days	*Definitive ovary*, in cross section spade-shaped with crenated outline; a few larger cells, possibly sex cells, scattered throughout; primary tunica albuginea consists of loose tissue and is interrupted by epithelial cords continuous with surface; development of fimbria of uterine tube
56–65 days	*Definitive cortex established*; tunica albuginea testis indistinct and transient
70–82 days	*Inner cortex divided into lobules* by invasion of connective tissue; decreased epithelial components in medulla; sex cells in deeper parts of lobules enlarged and in prophase of meiosis; at periphery of cortex, subepithelial cells remain small, constituting *small-cell zone*
90–105 days	*Outward progression of meiotic activity* through two-thirds of cortex; lobulation maximally distinct; lobules subdivided into smaller units; enlarging oocytes at corticomedullary junction approach size of those in primordial follicles
110–130 days	*A few primordial follicles* present, increasing gradually in number; prophase of meiosis has extended outward into subepithelial cords; medulla free of epithelial components
132–136 days	*Multiple primordial follicles*; formation of tunica albuginea ovarii
140–155 days	*Primordial follicles occupy more than half of cortex*; centrally a few follicles with single layer of cuboidal granulosa and an occasional vesicular follicle may be present; meiotic activity extending to periphery of cortex with enlargement of cells in small-cell zone; accumulation of degeneration products at corticomedullary junction
Perinatal days 153–181	*Oocytes in surface epithelium, in subepithelial cords* perforating tunica albuginea ovarii, and in remnants of primitive cortical lobules; increased atresia with formation of highly vascularized masses of epithelioid cells; occasional vesicular follicles; increased connective tissue in tunica albuginea ovarii and throughout ovary
Postnatal months 3–6	Small vesicular follicles are more common than in perinatal period

From van Wagenen and Simpson [1965].

and rhesus monkey (Baker, unpublished observations), only a small proportion of the interstitial tissue can be detected and the incidence remains low until shortly before puberty (ca 2.75–3 years of age in the macaque [van Wagenen and Simpson, 1965]). This apparent relationship between the amount of Leydig tissue and chorionic gonadotropin should be treated with some caution, however, since the testis is increasing in size during the period of "regression" of interstitial cells. Further-

more, anencephalic human fetuses frequently show a considerable reduction in the extent of the Leydig tissue, irrespective of the level of hCG, indicating that fetal FSH and LH can at least influence the maintenance of the tissue [Baker and Scrimgeour, 1980, 1981].

Ovary. Sexual differentiation of the ovary occurs around day 46 postconception in the rhesus monkey, which is some 4–6 days later than in human

TABLE 3. Comparison of Embryonic and Fetal Development of the Human and Macaque Testes

Characteristics	Human		Monkey	
	Ovulation age (days)	Crown-rump length (mm)	Conception age (days)	Crown-rump length (mm)
Definitive testis	42	23	38	<17.5
Mesorchium formed	48–52	31–32	44–50	19–35
Seminiferous tubules				
Distinct from tunica albuginea	48	31	50	35
Outlined distinctly by basal membrane	44–48	25–31	50	35
Convolutions peripheral	99–113	111–130	110	141
Convolutions throughout length	113–127	130–150	132	182
Sustentacular cells				
Radial orientation	42	23	40–50	175–350
Nuclei basal; cytoplasm fills lumen	Remain dispersed in human		70–85	<111
Nuclei again dispersed			Birth–4 mo PN	200+
Spermatogonia				
Few distinguishable	48	31	50–54	35–48
Increased in number; some strikingly larger	74	44	90	113
Basal	87–97	90–120	85–90	111–113
Glandular interstitial cells				
Few identifiable	52–55	32–37	50–51	35–48
Differentiated; maximal number	71–99	60–120	85–90	111–113
Fewer; loss of differentiation	99–127	120–150	90–100	113–131
Sparse; indistinct outline	173–birth	270–400	90–95	131–160
Tunica albuginea				
Present; irregular width	42–44	23–25	38	<17.5
Uniform width; distinct from tubules	48	31	44	19
Transformation to connective tissue; pale, edematous	55–61	37–44	50	35
Differentiation of fibrous and vascular layers	99–113	120–150	100	131
Connective tissue				
Increase between tubules	113–127	120–150	110	141
Lobulation; septa formed	127–169	170–220	125–168	170–200
Straight and rete tubules				
Strands of cells	53	32	54–70	<48
Patent tubules	173+	270+	70–110	<111

From van Wagenen and Simpson [1965].

202

OVARY   TESTIS

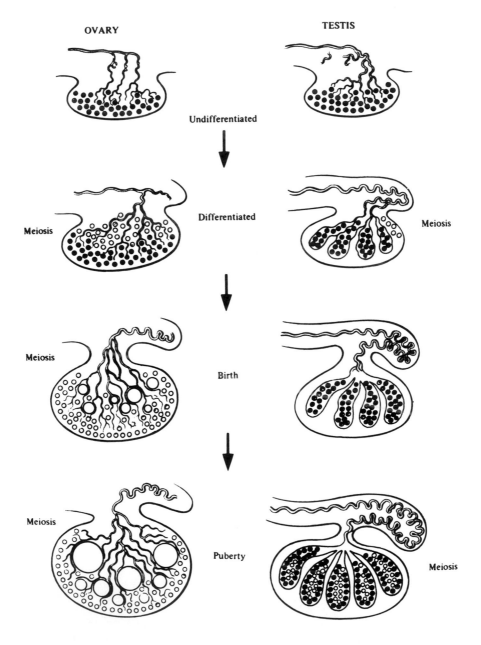

Undifferentiated

Differentiated

Meiosis   Meiosis

Meiosis   Meiosis

Meiosis   Birth

Puberty   Meiosis

Fig. 4. The sexual differentiation of the gonad into an ovary or a testis. [From Byskov, 1982.]

embryos [van Wagenen and Simpson, 1965; Baker, 1972a,b; Baker and Eastwood, 1983]. The primordial germ cells remain in the cortex, become associated with cells derived from the coelomic epithelium of the gonad, and enlarge to become oogonia. A tunica albuginea ovari either fails to form at this time (macaque) or is rudimentary (human), and the medulla remains small until after birth [Gillman, 1948; Baker, 1963, 1966b, 1972a; van Wagenen and Simpson, 1965; Katzberg, 1967].

Interstitial cells are far less obvious than in the male.

As in the testis, the ovary contains two populations of mitotically active "stem cells," the primordial germ cells, which appear to undergo a few divisions, and their successors the oogonia, which undergo many divisions before entering the prophase of meiosis to become oocytes (see below). The germ cells become associated with somatic cells (pregranulosa cells) derived from the coelomic epithelium [Gillman, 1948; Merchant-Larios, 1978] and/or rete ovari [Byskov, 1979].

THE OVARY IN FETAL LIFE

Meiosis

In both rhesus monkey and human embryos the definitive ovary is first recognizable around 56 days postconception [Baker, 1963, 1966b; van Wagenen and Simpson, 1965]. At this stage the cortex is well developed but the medulla is still rudimentary. The cortex contains numerous oogonia, both at interphase and undergoing mitosis. With the onset of the second month of gestation a small proportion (ca 5% in both species) of the germ cells complete their final premeiotic division followed by DNA synthesis in preparation for meiosis. Such cells generally resemble oogonia but their nuclear chromatin is condensed to form areas of fibrillar material [Baker and Franchi, 1967a, 1972a]. Cells of this description are believed to be at the preleptotene stage of meiotic prophase and represent the transition phase from oogonia to oocytes [Baker, 1963, 1966b].

The leptotene stage of meiotic prophase is characterized by the presence within the nucleus of the normal diploid number of chromosomal threads (46 in man; 42 in macaques). During zygotene the homologous maternal and paternal threads associate in pairs, the pairing process (synapsis) commencing at any point along the length of the threads. With the onset of the pachytene stage, synapsis is completed and the haploid number of paired threads (synaptonemal complexes) is found in the nucleus (Fig. 5). It should be pointed out, however, that the apparent reduction in chromosomal number is due solely to the association of threads into pairs; the reduction division resulting in a truly haploid condition is not completed until ovulation. The lateral arms of the synaptonemal complex each consist of two chromosomal threads in such tight apposition that only one thread can

usually be detected with the electron microscope [Baker and Franchi, 1972a]. But in oocytes which on grounds of size and complexity of cytoplasmic organelles are judged to be at late pachytene, the lateral arms seem to split longitudinally to reveal the component threads [Baker and Franchi, 1967a]. This tetrad of four chromatids, arranged in two pairs (bivalents), undergoes "crossing over" (and exchange of parts of homologous chromosomes) during the early part of the diplotene stage. The process of meiosis is not synchronized in primate ovaries: oogonia and oocytes at all stages of meiotic prophase coexist in the ovary until around the time of birth when the prediplotene stages are eliminated [Baker, 1963, 1966b].

In general terms, the earliest stages of oogenesis (oogonia and oocytes in meiotic prophase) are found in the superficial regions of the ovarian cortex whereas the more mature germ cells (pachytene and follicular oocytes) occur near the corticomedullary border [Ohno et al, 1962; Baker, 1963, 1966b; van Wagenen and Simpson, 1965].

The Number of Germ Cells

The ovary enlarges dramatically during embryonic and fetal life. Part of this growth phase is due to an increase in the somatic constituents of the gland, but the major component derives from the marked increase in the number and volume of the germ cells as they pass through mitosis and meiosis [Baker, 1963, 1966b]. The overall total population of germ cells in the monkey increases from about 310,000 at the second month after fertilization to a maximum of some 3,518,000 during the fifth month (cf human ovary: 600,000 and 6,800,000, respectively; Fig. 6). This marked increase in the number of germ cells clearly reflects the high rate of mitosis in oogonia, since there is no evidence that germ cells arise from other cell lines in the fetal ovary. Between the fifth month postconception and the time of birth the population of oocytes declines by some 65% to 2,000,000 in the human ovary, and 910,000 in the monkey. This decline is due partly to the elimination of enormous numbers of germ cells by atresia and also to the eventual cessation of mitosis by oogonia [Baker, 1963, 1966b] (Fig. 6). Atresia affects germ cells at all stages in their maturation: oogonia degenerate at interphase or during an abortive division, whereas oocytes undergo pyknosis and eosinophilia at any stage of meiotic prophase (but particularly pachytene and diplotene). The consequence of prenatal

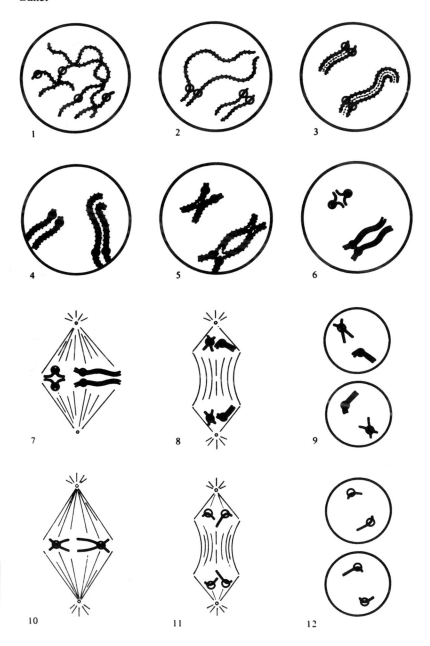

Fig. 5. Diagram showing the behavior of chromosomes during meiosis. For simplicity only two pairs of chromosomes are depicted—a short pair with terminal pairing, and a long set with intermediate synapsis. Only the nuclei are shown; the cytoplasm of the cells has been disregarded. 1) Leptotene; 2) zygotene; 3) pachytene; 4) late pachytene showing tetrad (two pairs of bivalents); 5) diplotene; 6) diakinesis; 7) metaphase I; 8) late anaphase I; 9) telophase I (idealized); 10) metaphase II; 11) anaphase II; 12) telophase II (ovum and polar body). [From Baker, 1982.]

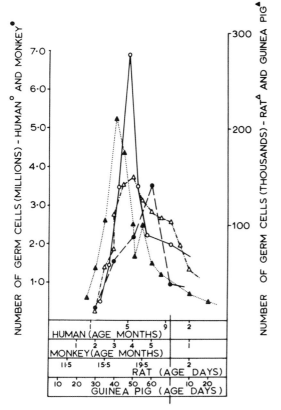

Fig. 6. Fluctuations in the number of germ cells in the ovaries of embryonic and fetal rats, guinea pigs, monkeys, and human beings. [From Baker, 1972a.]

Simpson, 1965; Katzberg, 1967]. It is noteworthy that the changes occurring in the ovary between the fifth month after fertilization and the time of birth (1 month interval in monkey; 4.5 months in man) are almost identical in terms of the developmental changes and reduction in numbers of the prediplotene stages. It may be inferred, therefore, that the process of oogenesis in the monkey is accelerated (or in the human it is retarded), such that the ovaries of both species have reached the same developmental stage at birth. The appearance of the ovary at birth is similar in all the primates that have been examined, but so far studies of oogenesis have been completed only for man and macaque [Katzberg, 1967; Baker, 1972b].

The "Resting" Stage of Meiotic Prophase in Oocytes and Initiation of Follicular Growth

The prediplotene stages of meiotic prophase occur for at most a few months during fetal life, and the stages of preovulatory maturation within the graafian follicle (diakinesis to metaphase II) for less than 48 hours in each reproductive cycle [Edwards, 1966, 1980]. The stage of oogenesis of greatest interest in terms of the effects of exogenous substances (drugs, radiation, etc) on the ovary is thus the period of arrested development, since it occurs for a prolonged period of time (up to 50 years in man; 25 years in some other species of primate [Baker, 1972b, 1978]).

Early in juvenile life oocytes at diplotene are enclosed within primordial follicles composed of a single layer of flattened granulosa cells. Such follicles account for 90% of the oocyte population at all ages from before birth to senescence. The remaining 10% of the oocyte population are enclosed either in follicles with a single layer of cuboidal granulosa cells, or within multilayered or graafian follicles [Green and Zuckerman, 1951; Baker, 1966a]. It is doubtful, however, that such follicles in the juvenile ovary ever undergo ovulation: their oocytes usually undergo hyalinization or fragmentation at a time when pyknosis and eosinophilia affect the membrana granulosa [Ingram, 1962]. It is only after puberty that follicular growth normally culminates in ovulation (see chapter by Koering, this volume).

The question thus arises as to what factor(s) control the "switching on" of the process of follicular growth. In other words, what initiates mitosis in granulosa cells and the synthesis of the mucopolysaccharide layer (zona pellucida) which sepa-

atresia is to eliminate all the prediplotene germ cell stages by shortly after birth so that only follicular oocytes at diplotene survive. The population of germ cells in the ovary at birth is thus finite and can only be reduced with increasing age by atresia and ovulation because no "stem cells" remain to make good deficiencies in the population (Fig. 6). It is clear, therefore, that any agent that kills germ cells (eg, radiation) has a permanent and irrevocable effect in reducing the number of germ cells [Baker, 1966a, 1971a,c].

The time at which the prediplotene stages in germ cell differentiation are eliminated from the ovary appears to be fixed for most mammalian species [Baker, 1972a]. In man, the baboon, and the rhesus monkey it occurs within a few days of birth [Baker, 1963, 1966b; van Wagenen and rates the oocyte from the membrana granulosa? Little is known of these processes in primate ovaries [see Koering, 1969, and this volume]. However, studies of mouse ovaries in organ culture and in vivo clearly demonstrate that the size of the oocyte is one important factor and that for a short period of time gonadotropic hormones have to be present [Eshkol et al, 1971; Baker and Neal, 1973, 1974]. Furthermore, anencephalic human fetuses (in which the hypothalamus is damaged or absent) do not release gonadotropic hormones from their pituitary glands and thus their ovaries are devoid of follicles beyond the earliest primordial stage [Baker and Scrimgeour, 1980, 1981]. It is possible, therefore, that the initial "trigger" for follicular development arises in the oocyte; this stimulus then passes to the granulosa cells, which (in man and macaque) respond to a "surge" of gonadotropic hormones shortly before birth.

It was once held that the oocyte was a truly inactive or "resting" cell in that it was incapable of synthesizing protein or RNA. Thus histochemical studies failed to reveal significant amounts of RNA in oocytes of monkeys (*Macaca mulatta* and loris [Seschacher and Bagga, 1963]), although follicle cells contained RNA [Guraya, 1966; see also Jacoby, 1962]. No one would deny that the oocyte contains ribosomes, mitochondria, and other organelles for the cell to carry out the basic metabolic processes associated with its nutrition and respiration [Hope, 1965; Baker, 1972a; Bjersing, 1977], but it was previously held that the cell synthesized none of the "yolky" material which accounts for the rapid growth phase [Raven, 1961].

More recent studies have demonstrated that rhesus monkey and rodent oocytes incorporate radioactive precursors of RNA at many stages in their morphogenesis up to the stage where they are enclosed within multilayered follicles [Oakberg, 1967]. Nuclear RNA synthesis is first detected at the pachytene stage of meiotic prophase and increases dramatically during the diplotene stage, especially in oocytes within primordial follicles [Baker et al, 1969]. Tritiated uridine is incorporated specifically by the chromosomes and by nucleoli, and subsequently passes out of the nucleus into the cytoplasm (presumably as ribosomal RNA [Baker et al, 1969]). With the onset of follicular growth the degree of chromosomal labeling with [^{3}H]uridine gradually decreases to a very low level in graafian follicles (mouse [Oakberg, 1967]; rab-

bit [Odeblad and Magnusson, 1954; see also Baker et al, 1969; Baker, 1972a]).

The use of high-resolution autoradiography has related the incorporation of [^{3}H]uridine to chromosomal structure. Primordial oocytes of monkeys incorporate the isotope into dense fibrillar and granular material lateral to the "cores" of chromosomes at diplotene. This material represents the "loop matrix" (ribonucleoprotein [Baker and Franchi, 1967b]), which is organized into loops analogous to those on the lampbrush chromosomes of Amphibia [Gall and Callan, 1962; Miller, 1965], and known to be a site of high synthetic activity [Ficq et al, 1959; Gall, 1958]. Lampbrush chromosomes have been detected by means of electron microscopy in oocytes of women and the rhesus monkey [Baker and Franchi, 1967a,b; 1972a,b] and are believed to be of almost universal occurrence in mammals [Baker and Franchi, 1967c].

The large quantities of ribonucleoprotein synthesized by lampbrush chromosomes could have a multiplicity of function in addition to the usual metabolic processes. There is evidence in Amphibia that some of the RNA is stored until after fertilization to act as the early organizer of the embryo [Davidson, 1968; Rinaldi and Monroy, 1969]. If such a regulatory mechanism exists in primates (and so far there is little evidence for or against this hypothesis), it would corroborate E.B. Wilson's [1925] classical view that organogenesis and/or embryonic induction commences during oogenesis. At a simpler level, one may postulate that informational RNA passing from oocyte to granulosa cells is the "trigger" initiating growth of the follicle. These concepts are clearly of importance to our knowledge of oogenesis and embryology and require testing on various mammalian species, including primates. At the present time one can only conclude that oocytes in primates have the potential for protein synthesis and make large quantities of RNA. In any event, the concept of a "resting" phase in oogenesis is clearly no longer tenable.

Origin of the Definitive Oocytes and the Process of Atresia

It was shown previously that the earliest recognizable germinal cells (primordial germ cells) give rise to oogonia, and that these two cell types are the only ovarian "stem cells" before birth. Oogonia and oocytes are often observed close to or

within the so-called germinal (coelomic) epithelium, but experiments involving the uptake of silver particles and radioactive substances have
shown that epithelial cells are never transformed
into germ cells [Chiquoine, 1960; Rudkin and
Greich, 1962; Kennelly and Foote, 1966]. The
results of numerous experimental procedures have
failed to detect any evidence for the "neoforma-
tion" of germ cells in mammals at any age [Fran-
chi et al, 1962; Baker, 1972a]. Moreover, studies
of fluctuations in the size of the population of germ
cells, and of their radiosensitivity, provide strong
evidence for the generally held view that the female is born with a finite "stock" of oocytes which
gradually becomes depleted with increasing age.
Thus in the rhesus monkey, for example, some 2.5
million germ cells are eliminated between the fifth
month postconception and birth and a further
800,000 cells undergo atresia before puberty. The
number of oocytes continues to decline throughout
adult life (owing to ovulation, as well as atresia),
and few oocytes survive in animals believed to be
aged 20 years or more [Green and Zuckerman,
1951, 1954; van Wagenen and Simpson, 1965;
Baker, 1966a].

The factors underlying atresia remain obscure,
although pituitary control of the process seems
certain. Removal of the pituitary gland, or treatment with stilbestrol, considerably diminishes the
rate of atresia of follicular oocytes, whereas treatment with pregnant mare serum gonadotropin
(PMSG), follicle-stimulating hormone (FSH), or
radiation increases the number of oocytes that
undergo degeneration [Williams, 1956; Jones and
Krohn, 1961; Beaumont, 1969; Weir and Rowlands, 1977]. Atresia may be related to genetic
abnormalities in germ cells, to chiasma frequency,
or to the time in the "production line" when the
germ cell reaches diplotene [Henderson and Edwards, 1968; Cohen, 1971]. It has been suggested
that atresia of oocytes during the juvenile period
in the monkey is necessary so that granulosa and/
or thecal cells may be transformed into interstitial
cells to enable one follicle to achieve "full maturation at or after puberty" (presumably in terms of
circulating steroid hormones [Sturgis, 1961]).
Clearly many more studies of atresia in primates
will have to be undertaken before the mechanism
of this important process can be understood [In-
gram, 1962; Weir and Rowlands, 1977; Koering,
this volume].

Oogenesis in Prosimian Primates

All of the processes described previously in this
review seem to occur in the Prosimiae as in the
other species of primates that have been studied
[Butler, 1971]. But the elimination of the prediplotene stage of meiosis is incomplete or absent. The
ovaries of *Galago*, *Loris*, *Nycticebus*, *Daubentonia*, and *Perodicticus* thus contain "nests" of
germ cells within the ovarian cortex which super-
ficially resemble seminiferous tubules of the testis.
Each "nest" contains cells that can be identified as
oogonia (both at interphase and undergoing mitosis), as well as oocytes at stages from leptotene to
diplotene [Rao, 1927; Gérard, 1920, 1932; Gérard
and Herlant, 1953; Brambell, 1956; Butler, 1964,
1969, 1971; Petter-Rousseaux and Bourlière, 1965;
Anand Kumar, 1966, 1968, 1974; Duke, 1967;
Ioannou, 1967]. There can be little doubt that these
cells are oogonia and oocytes since they are similar
in appearance (with both light and electron micro-
scopes) to comparable cells in ovaries of fetal
primates [Butler, 1969, 1971]. What has been disputed, however, is the origin and function of these
germinal cells. Few contemporary students would
accept the thesis [Gérard, 1920, 1932] that such
cells arise in the "germinal" (coelomic) epithelium
and move into the cortex along with the epithelial
cords. It seems highly probable that the oogonia
were formed from primordial germ cells in the
embryo but were not eliminated by the wave of
atresia affecting the ovary around the time of birth
(see above). Support for this view derives from
the observation that oogonia occasionally persist
at the hilar region in the ovaries of cats [Brambell,
1956].

Even if we accept the view that germ cells within
cortical "nests" are an embryological curiosity
persisting into adult life [Brambell, 1956], there
still remains the problem as to their function and/
or fate. It is now well established that oogonia in
the germinal "nests" give rise to oocytes at leptotene; indeed, meiosis can proceed as far as the
diplotene stage of prophase [Butler, 1964, 1969,
1971; Ioannou, 1967; Anand Kumar, 1968, 1974].
What is not established, however, is that any of
these cells leave the "nests" to become part of the
definitive stock of oocytes in primordial follicles.
Autoradiographs of the ovaries of animals that had
been injected with [^{3}H]thymidine contain oogonia
labeled during interphase, and oocytes labeled at
preleptotene. Although large numbers of germ cells

within the cortical "tubules" were labeled, none of the definitive follicular oocytes (outside of nests) seem to incorporate the isotope. The fact that labeled follicular oocytes have not been detected in the ovaries of Loris, Galago, and Nycticebus is thus a strong indication that the "stock" of oocytes in these species (like those in other mammals) is fixed at birth with no contribution from the primitive nest cells during postnatal life [Ioannou, 1967; David et al, 1974; Anand Kumar, 1974].

There can be little doubt, however, that the number of germ cells within the cortical nests fluctuates with the phases of the reproductive cycle [Anand Kumar, 1966]. The population of oogonia and oocytes in the slender loris increases from about 11,000 during anestrous to 164,000 at estrous. If pregnancy ensues the number continues to rise to some 172,000 and then declines to around the anestrous level during lactation. A similar decline in the population, with high numbers of atretic germ cells, occurs in the absence of pregnancy. These fluctuations in the number of nest cells are almost certainly controlled by pituitary hormones although steroids may act as the local intermediate. Thus the population of germ cells in anestral lorises is increased following injections of estrogen [Anand Kumar, 1966, 1974], but there is no evidence for a comparable increase in primordial follicles. If the problem of postnatal oogenesis in prosimian primates is to be resolved, counts will need to be made of the numbers of definitive follicular oocytes throughout life.

ADULT OVARIES: FOLLICULAR GROWTH AND THE COMPLETION OF MEIOSIS IN THE OOCYTE

These topics are dealt with in detail by Koering (this volume). Suffice it to say that once initiated shortly before birth, follicular growth continues spontaneously throughout reproductive life until the supply of oocytes becomes severely depleted at the menopause. Gonadotropic hormones are certainly involved in the terminal stages of this process, but the mechanism of control of the earlier stages is disputed [Baker, 1972a; Zuckerman and Baker, 1977; Peters and McNatty, 1980; Edwards, 1980].

The preovulatory maturation of the oocyte from the diplotene stage of meiotic prophase to metaphase II (at which time ovulation occurs) is only completed in the mature graafian follicle in re-

sponse to the midcycle "surge" of gonadotropic hormones [Baker, 1972a; Zuckerman and Baker, 1977; Peters and McNatty, 1980]. Thus the oocyte at diplotene has a very long life, potentially around 50+ years in the human female and around 20+ years in the rhesus monkey [Baker, 1972a; van Wagenen and Simpson, 1965, 1973; Edwards, 1980].

THE TESTIS IN JUVENILE MACAQUES

The regression in the development of the testis that commenced in late fetal life continues for up to 9 months after birth. The testis increases somewhat in size owing mainly to the lengthening and convolution of the tubules in which gonocytes are sparse. But toward the end of this early juvenile phase the gonocytes enlarge in size, their nuclei become round and turgid, and their cytoplasm becomes more extensive and complex. These cells show features typical of spermatogonia in the mature testis and become increasingly common from the 11th month postpartum to 1 year 11 months [van Wagenen and Simpson, 1954; Baker and Beaumont, unpublished observations]. The spermatogonia arise only from preexisting gonocytes: there is no evidence of a common origin of germinal and Sertoli cells [Green and Bernstein, 1970; van Wagenen and Simpson, 1954].

Spermatocytes first appear in the seminiferous tubules of animals aged about 3 years: they are larger than spermatogonia and undergo meiosis from leptotene to telophase II without an intervening period of arrested development (cf oocytes). By this time the tubules are approaching the dimensions found in the adult, although they are still devoid of a lumen; this appears during the early part of the third year, when the spermatids and spermatozoa first occur. The tubules accumulate cellular debris at this time, because the lumina of the tubules are still not open to the rete tubules. The duct system becomes patent at about the time of puberty, which can occur in male rhesus monkeys aged 3–3.5 years, although in most the production of a normal ejaculate and the chances of mating in the wild is probably delayed until about 1 year later [Vandenbergh, 1971].

The development of the testis in man and rhesus monkey is remarkably similar, even to the diameter of the tubules and the appearance of individual cell types [Charny et al, 1952; van Wagenen and Simpson, 1954, 1965] (Table 3). The most noteworthy difference between the species is the time span during which the foregoing developmental changes occur. Thus in the testis of the monkey before puberty these take about 3–3.5 years [Conaway and Sade, 1965], whereas those in man occur within 11–15 years [van Wagenen and Simpson, 1965]. A further difference is that the spermatogenic cycle in postpubertal men continues throughout the year at a reasonably constant level, whereas that in the monkey undergoes seasonal fluctuations in parallel to seasonal breeding [Conaway and Sade, 1965; Vandenbergh and Vessey, 1968; Vandenbergh, 1971].

THE TESTIS AFTER PUBERTY

The anatomy and physiology of the adult testis is considered in an earlier chapter by Wickings et al (this volume).

CONCLUSIONS

Germ cells arise outside of the embryo and are first identified in the wall of the yolk sac. They subsequently migrate by an active (amoeboid-type) process to colonize the developing gonadal ridges. After a period of mitotic activity the primordial germ cells enlarge (to become oogonia or "gonocytes" in the male) at the time that sexual differentiation of the gonad occurs. At this time the germ cells are associated with somatic cells derived from the surface (coelomic) epithelium and/or the mesonephros.

Sexual differentiation of the gonad occurs between about the 36th and 42nd days after conception and initially consists in the formation of a testis or the lack of such changes. Male germ cells enter the medullary cords to form seminiferous tubules, and a tunica albuginea forms to prevent further development of the cortex. By contrast, if an ovary develops, the germ cells remain in the cortex, which develops at the expense of the medulla.

In both sexes, germ cells initially proliferate by mitosis before becoming quiescent (male) or entering meiosis (female). The rapid growth phase in testicular development, together with the degeneration of some male gonocytes, results in a paucity of germ cells in the seminiferous tubules until shortly before puberty. The testis has extensive intertubular islands of Leydig cells. These androgen-producing interstitial cells fluctuate in number

with the changing levels of hCG to become sparse until the peripubertal period.

Ovarian development is characterized by an ever increasing number of germ cells (oogonia; oocytes at varying stages of meiotic prophase) until the fifth month of gestation in man and the rhesus monkey, after which the size of the germ cell population decreases with increasing age. In spite of differences in the length of gestation, most of the prediplotene stages of first meiotic prophase are eliminated by the time of birth. Thereafter the ovary contains only follicular oocytes at diplotene. However, some of the graafian follicles found shortly after the midcycle LH surge in the adult will proceed from the diplotene stage to metaphase II when ovulation occurs. Errors in meiosis, leading to phenotypic changes, are common in man but seem to be rare in nonhuman primates.

The oocyte at diplotene contains diffuse chromosomes reminiscent of the lampbrush chromosomes found in lower vertebrates. Such chromosomes produce large quantities of RNA to direct their own growth and metabolism and perhaps to act as a "trigger" for the development of the follicle and its zona pellucida. Some of the RNA may also be stored to act as the early organizer of embryonic development after fertilization has occurred.

The ovaries of most postnatal primates are devoid of germinal "stem" cells, and hence any agent which destroys oocytes (and the "natural" process of atresia) has a permanent and irrevocable effect. This is not true in male primates where spermatogonia persist basally in the seminiferous tubules throughout life to give rise to generations of spermatocytes, spermatids, and hence to spermatozoa. Another potential exception to the general rule is the ovary in prosimian primates where "nests" of oogonia and prediplotene oocytes persist through adult life. There can be little doubt that the number of germ cells per "nest" fluctuates with the phases of the reproductive cycle and pregnancy due to changes in the levels of circulating steroid hormones. However, studies using autoradiographic labeling with [3H]thymidine indicate that the nest cells are likely to be only an embryological curiosity: there is no evidence that such cells ever contribute to the population of definitive (follicular) oocytes.

The reasons for the enormous loss of female (and to some extent male) germ cells by a degenerative process (atresia) remain largely obscure although the loss of follicular oocytes is related to the levels of gonadotropic and/or steroid hormones. Many agents can accelerate the rate of loss (estrogens, X-irradiation, certain drugs) while other factors reduce the rate of atresia (androgens, hypophysectomy, genetic factors).

The majority of the studies that have provided the above information have been confined to rhesus monkeys and man together with limited studies of isolated stages in prosimian primates and the baboon. There is thus a clear need for detailed investigations to be carried out for a wide variety of primates.

ACKNOWLEDGMENTS

The author's own research on gametogenesis in primates was supported by grants from the Ford Foundation, Population Council, Medical Research Council (U.K.), the Wellcome Trust, and the Universities of Bradford, Birmingham, and Edinburgh.

REFERENCES

Abramovich, D.R.; Baker, T.G.; Neal, P. Effect of human chorionic gonadotrophin on testosterone secretion by the foetal human testis in organ culture. JOURNAL OF ENDOCRINOLOGY 60:179–185, 1974.

Anand Kumar, T.C. Effects of sex-steroids on the reproductive organs of the female loris. Second International Congress on Hormonal Steroids. EXCERPTA MEDICA INTERNATIONAL CONGRESS SERIES 132:369–370, 1966.

Anand Kumar, T.C. Oogenesis in lorises: *Loris tardigradus lydekkerianus* and *Nycticebus coucang.* PROCEEDINGS OF THE ROYAL SOCIETY, Series B, 169:167–176, 1968.

Anand Kumar, T.C. Oogenesis in adult prosimian primates. CONTRIBUTIONS TO PRIMATOLOGY 3:82–96, 1974.

Austin, C.R.; Walton, A. Fertilization. Pp. 310–416 in MARSHALL'S PHYSIOLOGY OF REPRODUCTION, Vol. 1, Pt. 2. A.S. Parkes, ed. London, Longmans, 1960.

Baker, T.G. A quantitative and cytological study of germ cells in human ovaries. PROCEEDINGS OF THE ROYAL SOCIETY, Series B, 158:417–433, 1963.

Baker, T.G. The sensitivity of oocytes in post-natal rhesus monkeys to X-irradiation. JOURNAL OF REPRODUCTION AND FERTILITY 12:183–192, 1966a.

Baker, T.G. A quantitative and cytological study of oogenesis in the rhesus monkey. JOURNAL OF ANATOMY (LONDON) 100:761–776, 1966b.

Baker, T.G. Comparative aspects of the effects of radiation during oogenesis. MUTATION RESEARCH 1:9–22, 1971a.

Baker, T.G. Electron microscopy of the primary and secondary oocyte. Pp. 7–27 in ADVANCES IN THE BIOSCIENCES, Vol. 5. G. Raspé, ed. Oxford, Pergamon, 1971b.

Baker, T.G. Radiosensitivity of mammalian oocytes with particular reference to the human female. AMERICAN JOURNAL OF OBSTETRICS AND GYNECOLOGY 110:746:761, 1971c.

Baker, T.G. Oogenesis and ovarian development. Pp. 398–437 in REPRODUCTIVE BIOLOGY. H. Balin; S.R. Glasser, eds. Amsterdam, Excerpta Medica, 1972a.

Baker, T.G. Gametogenesis. In: Symposium on the use of non-human primates in research on problems of human reproduction (WHO), Sukhumi, U.S.S.R. ACTA ENDOCRINOLOGICA SUPPLEMENT 166:18–45, 1972b.

Baker, T.G. Current status of research on the primate ovary. Pp. 142–148 in USE OF NON-HUMAN PRIMATES IN BIO-MEDICAL RESEARCH. M.R.N. Prasad; T.C. Anand Kumar, eds. New Delhi, Indian National Science Academy, 1977.

Baker, T.G. Effects of ionizing radiations on mammalian oogenesis: A model for chemical effects. ENVIRONMENTAL HEALTH PERSPECTIVES 24:31–37, 1978.

Baker, T.G. Oogenesis and ovulation. Pp. 17–45 in REPRODUCTION IN MAMMALS, 2nd Ed., Vol. 1. C.R. Austin; R.V. Short, eds. Cambridge, Cambridge University Press, 1982.

Baker, T.G.; Eastwood, J. Origin and differentiation of germ cells in man. BIBLIOTHECA ANATOMICA 24:67–76, 1983.

Baker, T.G.; Franchi, L.L. The fine structure of oogonia and oocytes in human ovaries. JOURNAL OF CELL SCIENCE 2:213–224, 1967a.

Baker, T.G.; Franchi, L.L. The structure of the chromosomes in human primordial oocytes. CHROMOSOMA (BERLIN) 22:358–377, 1967b.

Baker, T.G.; Franchi, L.L. The fine structure of chromosomes in bovine primordial oocytes. JOURNAL OF REPRODUCTION AND FERTILITY 14:511–513, 1967c.

Baker, T.G.; Franchi, L.L. The fine structure of oogonia and oocytes in the rhesus monkey (*Macaca mulatta*). ZEITSCHRIFT FÜR ZELLFORSCHUNG UND MIKROSKOPISCHE ANATOMIE 126:53–74, 1972a.

Baker, T.G.; Franchi, L.L. Electron microscope studies of radiation-induced degeneration in oocytes of sexually mature rhesus monkeys. ZEITSCHRIFT FÜR ZELLFORSCHUNG UND MIKROSKOPISCHE ANATOMIE 133:435–454, 1972b.

Baker, T.G.; Neal, P. Initiation and control of meiosis and follicular growth in ovaries of the mouse. ANNALES DE BIOLOGIE ANIMALE, BIOCHIMIE, BIOPHYSIQUE 13:137–144, 1973.

Baker, T.G.; Neal, P. Oogenesis in human fetal ovaries maintained in organ culture. JOURNAL OF ANATOMY (LONDON) 118:591–604, 1974.

Baker, T.G.; Neal, P. Action of ionizing radiations on the mammalian ovary. Pp. 1–58 in THE OVARY, 2nd Ed., Vol. 3. S. Zuckerman; B.J. Weir, eds. New York, Academic Press, 1977.

Baker, T.G.; Scrimgeour, J.B. Development of the gonad in normal and anencephalic human fetuses. JOURNAL OF REPRODUCTION AND FERTILITY 60:193–199, 1980.

Baker, T.G.; Scrimgeour, J.B. Development of the gonads in anencephalic human fetuses. Pp. 13–25 in FUNCTIONAL MORPHOLOGY OF THE HUMAN OVARY. J.R.T. Coutts, ed. Lancaster, MTP Press Ltd., 1981.

Baker, T.G.; Beaumont, H.M.; Franchi, L.L. The uptake of tritiated uridine and phenylalanine by the ovaries of rats and monkeys. JOURNAL OF CELL SCIENCE 4:655–675, 1969.

Beaumont, H.M. Effect of hormonal environment on the radiosensitivity of oocytes. Pp. 943–953 in RADIATION BIOLOGY OF THE FETAL AND JUVENILE MAMMAL Washington, U.S. Atomic Energy Commission, CONF-690501, 1969.

Bjersing, L. Ovarian histochemistry Pp. 303–391 in THE OVARY, 2nd Ed., Vol. 1. S. Zuckerman; B.J. Weir, eds. New York, Academic Press, 1977.

Blackler, A.W. Embryonic sex cells of Amphibia. Pp. 9–28 in ADVANCES IN REPRODUCTIVE PHYSIOLOGY. Vol. 1. A. McLaren, ed. London, Logos–Academic Press, 1966.

Blandau, R.J. Observations on living oogonia and oocytes from human embryonic and fetal ovaries. AMERICAN JOURNAL OF OBSTETRICS AND GYNECOLOGY 104:310–319, 1969.

Brambell, F.W.R. Ovarian changes. Pp. 397–544 in MARSHALL'S PHYSIOLOGY OF REPRODUCTION, Vol. 1, Pt. 1. A.S. Parkes, ed. London, Longmans, 1956.

Burgoyne, P.S. The genetics of sex development. Pp. 1–31 in BASIC REPRODUCTION MEDICINE, Vol. 1. D. Hamilton; F. Naftolin, eds. Cambridge, MA, MIT Press, 1981.

Butler, H. The reproductive biology of a strepsirhine (Galago senegalensis senegalensis). INTERNATIONAL REVIEW OF GENERAL AND EXPERIMENTAL ZOOLOGY 1:241–296, 1964.

Butler, H. Post-puberal oogenesis in Prosimiae. Pp. 15–21 in RECENT ADVANCES IN PRIMATOLOGY, Vol. 2. H.O. Hofer, ed. Basel, Karger, 1969.

Butler, H. Oogenesis and folliculogenesis. Pp. 243–268 in COMPARATIVE REPRODUCTION OF NON-HUMAN PRIMATES. E.S.E. Hafez, ed. Springfield, IL, Thomas, 1971.

Byskov, A.G. Regulation of meiosis in mammals. ANNALES DE BIOLOGIE ANIMALE, BIOCHIMIE, BIOPHYSIQUE 19:1251–1261, 1979.

Byskov, A.G. Primordial germ cells and regulation of meiosis. Pp. 1–16 in REPRODUCTION IN MAMMALS, 2nd Ed., Vol. 1. C.R. Austin; R.V. Short, eds. Cambridge, Cambridge University Press, 1982.

Charny, C.W.; Conston, A.S.; Meranze, D.R. Testicular developmental histology. ANNALS OF THE NEW YORK ACADEMY OF SCIENCE 55:597–608, 1952.

Chiquoine, A.D. Electron microscope observations on the vitally stained ovary of the mouse. ANATOMICAL RECORD 136:176, 1960.

Cohen, J. The comparative physiology of gamete populations. ADVANCES IN COMPARATIVE PHYSIOLOGY AND BIOCHEMISTRY 4:267–379, 1971.

Conaway, C.H.; Sade, D.S. The seasonal spermatogenic cycle in free ranging rhesus monkeys. FOLIA PRIMATOLOGICA 3:1–12, 1965.

Czolowska, R. Observations on the origin of "germinal cytoplasm" in Xenopus laevis. JOURNAL OF EMBRYOLOGY AND EXPERIMENTAL MORPHOLOGY 22:229–251, 1969.

David, G.F.X.; Anand Kumar, T.C.; Baker, T.G. Uptake of tritiated thymidine by primordial germinal cells in the ovaries of the adult slender loris. JOURNAL OF REPRODUCTION AND FERTILITY 41:447–451, 1974.

Davidson, E.H. GENE ACTIVITY IN EARLY DEVELOPMENT. New York, Academic Press, 1968.

Diczfalusy, E.; Standley, C.C. The use of non-human primates in research on human reproduction. WHO Symposium, Sukhumi. ACTA ENDOCRINOLOGICA SUPPLEMENT 166, 1972.

Duke, K.L. Ovogenic activity of the fetal type in the ovary of the adult slow loris Nycticebus coucang. FOLIA PRIMATOLOGICA 7:150–154, 1967.

Edwards, R.G. Mammalian eggs in the laboratory. SCIENTIFIC AMERICAN 215:72–81, 1966.

Edwards, R.G. CONCEPTION IN THE HUMAN FEMALE. London, Academic Press, 1980.

Egozcue, J. Meiosis in five Macaca species. FOLIA PRIMATOLOGICA 11:1–16, 1969.

Eshkol, A.; Lunenfeld, B.; Peters, H. Ovarian development in infant mice. Pp. 249–258 in GONADOTROPHINS AND OVARIAN DEVELOPMENT. W.R. Butt; A.C. Crooke; M. Ryle, eds. Edinburgh, Livingstone, 1971.

Fechheimer, N.S. Genetic aspects of testicular development and function. Pp. 1–40 in THE TESTIS, Vol. 3. A.D. Johnson; W.R. Gomes; N.L. Vandemark, eds. New York, Academic Press, 1970.

Ficq, A.; Pavan, C.; Brachet, J. Metabolic processes in chromosomes. EXPERIMENTAL CELL RESEARCH SUPPLEMENT 6:105–114, 1959.

Fiennes, R.N. ZOONOSES OF PRIMATES. London, Weidenfeld and Nicolson, 1967.

Franchi, L.L.; Mandl, A.M.; Zuckerman, S. The development of the ovary and the process of oogenesis. Pp. 1–88 in THE OVARY, Vol. 1. S. Zuckerman; A.M. Mandl; P. Eckstein, eds. London, Academic Press, 1962.

Gall, J.G. Chromosomal differentiation. Pp. 103–135 in THE CHEMICAL BASIS OF DEVELOPMENT. W.D. McElroy; B. Glass, eds. Baltimore, Johns Hopkins, 1958.

Gall, J.G.; Callan, H.G. ^{3}H-uridine incorporation in lampbrush chromosomes. PROCEEDINGS OF THE NATIONAL ACADEMY OF SCIENCES, 48:562–570, 1962.

Gérard, P. Contribution à l'étude de l'ovaire des Mammifères. L'ovaire de *Galago mossambicus* (Young). ARCHIVES DE BIOLOGIE 30:357–391, 1920.

Gérard, P. Etude sur l'ovogenèse et l'ontogenèse chez les lémuriens du genre *Galago*. ARCHIVES DE BIOLOGIE 43:93–151, 1932.

Gérard, P.; Herlant, M. Sur la persistance de phénomènes d'oogenèse chez les lémuriens adultes. ARCHIVES DE BIOLOGIE 64:97–111, 1953.

Gillman, J. The development of the gonads in man, with a consideration of the role of fetal endocrines and the histogenesis of ovarian tumours. CONTRIBUTIONS TO EMBRYOLOGY, CARNEGIE INSTITUTION OF WASHINGTON 32:81–131, 1948.

Green, E.L.; Bernstein, S.E. Do cells outside the testes participate in repopulating the germ cells after irradiation? Negative results. INTERNATIONAL JOURNAL OF RADIATION BIOLOGY 17:87–92, 1970.

Green, S.H., Zuckerman, S. The number of oocytes in the mature rhesus monkey (*Macaca mulatta*). JOURNAL OF ENDOCRINOLOGY 7:194–202, 1951.

Green, S.H., Zuckerman, S. Further observations on oocyte numbers in mature rhesus monkeys (*Macaca mulatta*). JOURNAL OF ENDOCRINOLOGY 10:284–290, 1954.

Guraya, S.S. A histochemical study of rhesus monkey ovary. ACTA MORPHOLOGICA NEERLANDO-SCANDINAVICA 4:395–406, 1966.

Henderson, S.A.; Edwards, R.G. Chiasma frequency and maternal age in mammals. NATURE (LONDON) 218:22–28, 1968.

Holmes, S. HENDERSON'S DICTIONARY OF BIOLOGICAL TERMS, 4th Ed. London, Longmans, 1979.

Hope, J. The fine structure of the developing follicle of the rhesus monkey. JOURNAL OF ULTRASTRUCTURE RESEARCH 12:592–610, 1965.

Ingram, D.L. Atresia. Pp. 247–274 in THE OVARY, Vol. 1. S. Zuckerman; A.M. Mandl; P. Eckstein, Ed. London, Academic Press, 1962.

Ioannou, J.M. Oogenesis in adult prosimians. JOURNAL OF EMBRYOLOGY AND EXPERIMENTAL MORPHOLOGY 17:139–145, 1967.

Jacobs, P.A. Abnormalities of the sex chromosomes in man. Pp. 61–91 in ADVANCES IN REPRODUCTIVE PHYSIOLOGY, Vol. 1. A. McLaren, ed. London, Logos–Academic Press, 1966.

Jacoby, F. Ovarian histochemistry. Pp. 189–246 in THE OVARY, Vol. 1. S. Zuckerman; A.M. Mandl; P. Eckstein, eds. London, Academic Press, 1962.

Jones, E.C.; Krohn, P.L. The effect of hypophysectomy on age changes in the ovaries of mice. JOURNAL OF ENDOCRINOLOGY 21:497–509, 1961.

Jones, R.E. THE VERTEBRATE OVARY. New York, Plenum, 1978.

Katzberg, A.A. The developing ovum in the baboon. Pp. 217–234 in THE BABOON IN MEDICAL RESEARCH. H. Vagtborg, ed. London, University of Texas Press, 1967.

Kennelly, J.J.; Foote, R.H. Oocytogenesis in rabbits. The role of neogenesis in the formation of the definitive ova and the stability of oocyte DNA measured with tritiated thymidine. AMERICAN JOURNAL OF ANATOMY 118:573–590, 1966.

Koering, M.J. Cyclic changes in ovarian morphology during the menstrual cycle in *Macaca mulatta*. AMERICAN JOURNAL OF ANATOMY 126:73–101, 1969.

Koering, M.J. Comparative morphology of the primate ovary. CONTRIBUTIONS TO PRIMATOLOGY 3:38–81, 1974.

Koford, C.B.; Faber, PA; Windle, F. Twins and teratisms in rhesus monkeys. FOLIA PRIMATOLOGICA 4:221–226, 1966.

Merchant-Larios, H. Ovarian differentiation. Pp. 47–77 in THE VERTEBRATE OVARY. R.E. Jones, ed. New York, Plenum, 1978.

Miller, O.L. Fine structure of lampbrush chromosomes. NATIONAL CANCER INSTITUTE MONOGRAPHS 18:79–99, 1965.

Oakberg, E.F. H^3-uridine labelling of mouse oocytes. ARCHIVES D'ANATOMIE MICROSCOPIQUE ET DE MORPHOLOGIE EXPERIMENTALE 56:3–4, 1967.

Odeblad, E.; Magnusson, G. An autoradiographic study on the intracellular accumulation of radioactive phosphate in the egg cell of the mouse. ACTA ENDOCRINOLOGICA 17:290–293, 1954.

Ohno, S. MAJOR SEX-DETERMINING GENES. Berlin, Springer Verlag, 1979.

Ohno, S.; Klinger, H.P.; Atkin, N.B. Human oogenesis. CYTOGENETICS 1:42–51, 1962.

Overzier, C., ed. INTERSEXUALITY. London, Academic Press, 1963.

Peters, H.; MacNatty, K.P. THE OVARY. London, Paul Elek, 1980.

Petter-Rousseaux, A.; Bourlière, F. Persistance des phénomènes d'ovogénèse chez l'adulte de *Daubentonia madagascariensis* (Prosimii, Lemuriformes). FOLIA PRIMATOLOGICA 3:241–244, 1965.

Pinkerton, J.H.M.; McKay, D.G.; Adams, E.C.; Hertig, A.T. Development of the human ovary—a study using histochemical techniques. OBSTETRICS AND GYNECOLOGY 18:152–181, 1961.

Prasad, M.R.N.; Anand Kumar, T.C. USE OF NON-HUMAN PRIMATES IN BIOMEDICAL RESEARCH. New Delhi, Indian National Science Academy, 1977.

Rao, C.R.N. On the structure of the ovary and the ovarian ovum of *Loris lydekkerianus* Cabr. QUARTERLY JOURNAL OF MICROSCOPICAL SCIENCE 71:57–74, 1927.

Raven, C.P. OOGENESIS: THE STORAGE OF DEVELOPMENTAL INFORMATION. Oxford, Pergamon, 1961.

Rinaldi, A.M.; Monroy, A. Polyribosome formation and RNA synthesis in the early post-fertilization stages of the sea urchin egg. DEVELOPMENTAL BIOLOGY 19:73–86, 1969.

Rothschild, Lord. FERTILIZATION. London, Methuen, 1956.

Ruch, T.C. DISEASES OF LABORATORY PRIMATES. Philadelphia, Saunders, 1959.

Rudkin, G.T.; Griech, H.A. On the persistence of oocyte nuclei from fetus to maturity in the laboratory mouse. JOURNAL OF CELL BIOLOGY 12:169–175, 1962.

Seshacher, B.R.; Bagga, S. Cytochemistry of the oocyte of *Loris tardigradus lydekkerianus* (Cabr). JOURNAL OF MORPHOLOGY 113:119–138, 1963.

Simpson, J.L. DISORDERS OF SEXUAL DIFFERENTIATION. New York, Academic Press, 1976.

Steinberger, E.; Steinberger, A. Testis: Basic and clinical aspects. Pp. 144–267 in REPRODUCTIVE BIOLOGY. H. Balin; S.R. Glasser, ed. Amsterdam, Excerpta Medica, 1972.

Sturgis, S.H. Factors influencing ovulation and atresia of ovarian follicles. P. 213 in CONTROL OF OVULATION. C.L. Villee, ed. Oxford, Pergamon, 1961.

Sullivan, D.J.; Drobeck, H.P. True hermaphroditism in a rhesus monkey. FOLIA PRIMATOLOGICA 4:309–317, 1966.

Tarkowski, A.K. Germ cells in natural and experimental chimeras in mammals. PHILOSOPHICAL TRANSACTIONS OF THE ROYAL SOCIETY, SERIES B 259:107–112, 1970.

Vandenbergh, J.G. Reproductive adaptations in macaques. Pp. 103–118 in ADVANCES IN REPRODUCTIVE PHYSIOLOGY, Vol. 5. M.W. Bishop, ed. London, Logos–Academic Press, 1971.

Vandenbergh, J.G.; Vessey, S. Seasonal breeding of free-ranging rhesus monkeys and related ecological factors. JOURNAL OF REPRODUCTION AND FERTILITY 15:71–79, 1968.

van Wagenen, G.; Simpson, M.E. Testicular development in the rhesus monkey. ANATOMICAL RECORD 118:231–252, 1954.

van Wagenen, G.; Simpson, M.E. EMBRYOLOGY OF THE OVARY AND TESTIS: *HOMO SAPIENS* AND *MACACA MULATTA*. New Haven, Yale University Press, 1965.

van Wagenen, G.; Simpson, M.E. POSTNATAL DEVELOPMENT OF THE OVARY IN *HOMO SAPIENS* AND *MACACA MULATTA* AND INDUCTION OF OVULATION IN THE MACAQUE. New Haven, Yale University Press, 1973.

Weir, B.J.; Rowlands, I.W. Ovulation and atresia. Pp. 265–284 in THE OVARY, 2nd Ed., Vol. 1. S. Zuckerman; B.J. Weir, eds. New York, Academic Press, 1977.

Williams, P.C. The history and fate of redundant follicles. Pp. 59–68 in CIBA FOUNDATION COLLOQUIA ON AGEING, Vol. 2. G.E.W. Wolstenholme; E.C.P. Millar, eds. London, Churchill, 1956.

Williams, R.H. TEXTBOOK OF ENDOCRINOLOGY, 6th Ed. Philadelphia, Saunders, 1981.

Wilson, E.B. THE CELL IN DEVELOPMENT AND HEREDITY. New York, Macmillan, 1925.

Wilson, J.G. Abnormalities of intrauterine development in non-human primates. In: The use of non-human primates in research on human reproduction. E. Diczfalusy; C.C. Standley, eds. ACTA ENDOCRINOLOGIA SUPPLEMENT 166:261–191, 1972.

Witschi, E. Migration of the germ cells of human embryos from the yolk sac to the primitive gonadal folds. CONTRIBUTIONS TO EMBRYOLOGY OF THE CARNEGIE INSTITUTION OF WASHINGTON 32:67–80, 1948.

Witschi, E. Embryology of the testis. Pp. 3–10 in THE TESTIS, Vol. 1. E. Rosemburg; C.A. Paulsen, ed. New York, Plenum, 1970.

Yager, R.H.; Judge, F.J. Questionnaire on animals used for research in 1966. INSTITUTE OF LABORATORY ANIMAL RESOURCES 11:2–5, 1967.

Zondek, L.H.; Zondek, T. Observations on the testis in anencephaly with special reference to the Leydig cells. BIOLOGY OF THE NEONATE 8:329–347, 1965.

Zondek, T.; Zondek, L.H. FETAL ENDOCRINOLOGY. Basel, Karger, 1979.

Zuckerman, S.; Baker, T.G. The development of the ovary and the process of oogenesis. Pp. 41–67 in THE OVARY, 2nd Ed., Vol. 1. S. Zuckerman; B.J. Weir, eds. New York, Academic Press, 1977.

Ovarian Architecture During Follicle Maturation

Marilyn J. Koering

Department of Anatomy, George Washington University Medical Center, Washington, D.C. 20037

INTRODUCTION

A unique characteristic of most primates is the ability to select one dominant ovarian follicle from a cohort of developing follicles. This cyclic process of follicle development and maturation is the major controlling factor in regulating the ovarian cycle via the hypothalamic-pituitary axis [Knobil et al, 1980; Wildt et al, 1981] and is therefore the basis for adult reproductive activity. Those species classified as primates have been given their position in taxonomy [Simpson, 1945] without adequate information on the genital tract morphology [Mossman, 1953]. It is interesting to observe how little is known about ovaries of various primate genera [Brambell, 1960; Young, 1961; Mossman and Duke, 1973; Harrison and Weir, 1977]. In only three of the 18 genera of Old World monkeys have the ovaries been examined in detail. However, it is likely that among primates, variations in structure/function relationships will be found to be minimal when more species are thoroughly investigated.

In all primate ovaries studied, the basic components are similar. The follicle is the entity from which the majority of other hormonally active compartments are derived. The corpus luteum results from the ruptured dominant follicle, and certain types of interstitial gland cells arise from atretic follicles. Since all primates, except certain Strepsirhini, are monotocous and have a single corpus luteum, the major ovarian differences are seen in the amounts of interstitial gland tissue and in accessory luteal tissue. On the basis of these possible variations, it has been shown that those species of higher rank, such as members of the Hominidae and Pongidae, have ovarian morphology that is most closely related [Wislocki, 1932]. Similarly, the ovaries of the Cercopithecidae are more closely related structurally to those of the Hominidae than the Cebidae.

One of the major concerns in the past has been the lack of sufficient information for an understanding of the mechanisms and interactions that are responsible for cyclic ovarian activity. Such knowledge is required for artificial control of the cycle, which is critical in correcting infertility problems in captive nonhuman primates as well as in women. Just as relevant is having the capability to inhibit the process when such regulation is required.

Major investigative inroads have recently led to new insight into the intricate hormonal associations involved in ovarian activity, but many questions regarding structure-function relationships remain unanswered. Since the architecture of the ovary constantly changes throughout the cycle, with the growth and demise of follicles predominating in the first half of the cycle and the formation, maturation and decline of the corpus luteum occurring during the latter half, it is essential to know the status of follicles throughout the cycle because the follicles are the basic controlling units. The morphological transformations observed in follicle development are the visualized result of the response of the follicular cells' molecular composition to the microenvironment. As they become more receptive to certain stimuli, they synthesize and release specific hormones that also can affect their microscopic structure.

The most recent studies on folliculogenesis have focused on how the dominant follicle is selected and what occurs to and within the preovulatory follicle. A challenging aspect yet to be unraveled is the sequence of events that occur prior to the selection of the dominant follicle. From what type of cohort is the dominant follicle selected? Once

Comparative Primate Biology, Volume 3: Reproduction and Development, pages 215–262
© 1986 Alan R. Liss, Inc.

follicle growth is initiated, is it a continuous process?

The deficiency in these morphological data continues because of the difficulty in analyzing total ovaries throughout the stages of the cycle and in relating these data to the changes in production of hypothalamic-pituitary and ovarian hormones. However, some of this information can be obtained by concentrated investigation of certain nonhuman primates. Macaque monkeys have been utilized in most studies; they are ideal because of their ovarian cyclicity and availability and the ease of performing certain necessary manipulations. Complementing some of these results have been a few studies on the human female. The data presented here will attempt to summarize what is known about follicular ovarian architecture during recruitment and selection of the dominant follicle in primates.

STRUCTURAL FEATURES OF FOLLICLES

General Remarks

The follicular components of the primate ovary that are responsible for regulating reproductive activity are the developing preantral and antral follicles. These maturing structures vary in number with age and stages of the cycle and are the precursors of the corpus luteum, atretic follicles, and certain types of interstitial gland tissue. Follicles in all stages of development are present in ovaries from infancy to menopause, and their presence signifies various degrees of follicular activity. Although it is difficult to assess the precise state of reproductive activity by examining the ovary, whether it be during the breeding season of the lower primates or in the more frequent cycles of the higher primates, the presence of certain types of follicles and their derivatives can give some insight into the state of ovarian function. Therefore a review of the morphological characteristics of distinct follicular stages that occur from the initiation of growth and throughout follicle maturation will be most relevant before examining how these developmental stages relate to time in the cycle.

The terminology that will be used to describe the various types of follicles is consistent with previous studies [Koering, 1969, 1983; Balboni, 1976]. In the literature a greater variety of classification schemes are found for preantral than for antral follicles [Block, 1951a; Hertig and Barton, 1973; Dvořák and Tesařík, 1980; Gougeon, 1979, 1981b; Peters and McNatty, 1980]. This variation in terminology presents a problem when results from different studies are evaluated. Therefore it

is critical that follicles of similar descriptions be compared, irrespective of their classification. The term "preantral follicle" can refer to all follicles prior to antrum formation and therefore can include the primordial follicles. However, primordial follicles that are surrounded by a single layer of squamous granulosa cells and are in a dormant stage are most often identified as a separate group. Growing follicles without antra and with one or more layers of cuboidal granulosa cells are usually called preantral follicles, and all follicles with an antrum are referred to as antral follicles.

Dormant and Developing Follicles

Primordial Follicles. In all ovaries, the primordial and smallest preantral follicles are located at the periphery of the ovary (Figs. 19, 21) and are easily recognized microscopically by their oocyte with its distinct nucleus (Fig. 1). Primordial follicles have a single layer of flattened cells surrounding the oocyte (Fig. 1), whose nucleus is in the diplotene prophase stage of meiosis [Baker, 1979]. The thin granulosa cell layer is recognized by the flattened nuclei. The cytoplasm of these cells blends in with the adjacent connective tissue (Fig. 1). At the ultrastructural level, the granulosa cell cytoplasm is composed of various organelles, and peripheral to

---

Fig. 1. The cortex of an ovary from a rhesus monkey showing numerous primordial and preantral follicles. The primordial follicles (1) lie more peripheral in the cortex than the other larger developing preantral follicles and are characterized by their prominent oocytes. A follicle (2) in the initial stages of growth is composed of a single layer of cuboidal cells surrounding the oocyte. Further development is characterized by an increase in the number of granulosa cells. This causes new layers to form, which are at first incomplete layers (3), resulting in nonspherical follicles. In the two larger preantral follicles which are 160 (4) and 180 μm (5) in diameter, the zona pellucida surrounds the oocyte. 167×.

Fig. 2. A portion of a primordial follicle from a cynomolgus monkey. In the oocyte are seen part of the nucleus (N) and some mitochondria (M) in the ooplasm. Lying adjacent to the oocyte is a flattened portion of one of the surrounding granulosa cells. Both of these cell types have projections (between arrows) that are compressed in the extracellular space. The granulosa cell cytoplasm contains mitochondria, ribosomes, rough endoplasmic reticulum, and a lipid droplet (D), and rests on a basement membrane (B). The surrounding connective tissue has a preponderance of collagen fiber bundles cut in cross section. 8,700×.

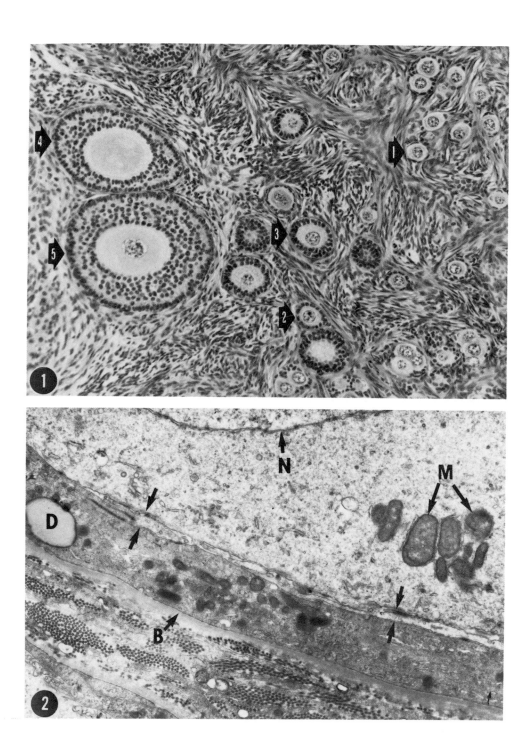

this layer of cells is a basement membrane (Fig. 2). At this stage, primordial follicles are similar in the rhesus monkey [Hope, 1965; van Wagenen and Simpson, 1973] and the human [Hertig and Adams, 1967; Peters and McNatty, 1980; Dvořák and Tesařík, 1980]. Projections can form from both the granulosa and the oocyte cell membranes, and they become compressed in the adjacent extracellular space (Fig. 2). In some areas, junctions are seen (Fig. 2) [Hertig and Barton, 1973] similar to those described in other nonprimate species [Anderson, 1979].

Preantral Follicles. Once growth is initiated, each granulosa cell becomes cuboidal (Fig. 1) because of compression from the increasing number of adjacent granulosa cells. As even more cells are formed, some of them are forced from the single layer into a second layer (Fig. 1), resulting in an incomplete second layer for a limited period of time [Koering, 1983]. Also responsible for some of the unequal distribution of granulosa cells, giving an elongated follicle, is likely to be pressure exerted by surrounding structures. This is most easily seen in large preantral follicles (Fig. 1). During the development of the granulosa cells, maturing changes also occur in the oocyte [Hertig and Barton, 1973]. The zona pellucida also begins to form soon after the initiation of growth [Peters and McNatty, 1980] and is well defined in the larger preantral follicles (Fig. 1). The granulosa cells forming the basal layer of such follicles have cytoplasm composed of mitochondria, Golgi, ribosomes, and endoplasmic reticulum (Fig. 3), features associated with protein synthesis. Similar morphology was seen in squirrel monkey preantral follicles [Hertig et al, 1971]. Such granulosa cells rest on a basement membrane which is in direct contact with bundles of collagen fibers (Fig. 3). In preantral follicles 125 μm in diameter, the oocyte contains increased numbers of mitochondria, Golgi, and cortical granules (Fig. 4) when compared to primordial follicle oocytes (Fig. 2). There are also numerous membrane projections into the zona pellucida. Similar relationships have been described previously in the rhesus monkey [Hope, 1965], *Cebus albifrons* [Barton and Hertig, 1975], squirrel monkey [Hertig and Barton, 1973], chimpanzee [Barton and Hertig, 1972], and human [Baca and Zamboni, 1967; Zamboni, 1970; Hertig and Barton, 1973].

When preantral follicles in the rhesus monkey attain a diameter of 200–250 μm, the amount of follicular fluid begins to increase, resulting in the separation of granulosa cells (Fig. 5) and the initial formation of antra, which eventually coalesce into a single fluid-filled antrum. In the granulosa cells located centrally in the transforming preantral follicle, the cytoplasm is more abundant (Fig. 6) and filled with organelles (Figs. 6, 7) [Balboni, 1976; Dvořák and Tesařík, 1980]. These cells appear to be more active in protein synthesis than those at the periphery (Fig. 3).

Antral Follicles. As the amount of follicular fluid continues to increase, the oocyte and its surrounding granulosa cells retain an attachment to the follicle wall (Fig. 8), so that the oocyte comes to occupy an eccentric position in the follicle. In many follicles larger than 1 mm, the granulosa cells forming the wall are often loosely arranged near the lumen (Fig. 9). These cells have numerous mitochondria and do not appear similar to steroid-secreting cells found in the corpus luteum [Adams and Hertig, 1969; Gillim et al, 1969; Crisp et al, 1970; Koering et al, 1973a] or to other steroid-secreting cells [Christensen and Gillim, 1969].

After a certain stage of the cycle in anthropoids, only one follicle normally goes on to ovulate, and the competing follicles begin to degenerate. In the normal primate cycle, the presence of this dominant follicle can be verified by laparoscopy and by determining peripheral and ovarian vein levels of estradiol [diZerega and Hodgen, 1981]. The dominant follicle eventually attains a diameter in vivo of about 10 mm in rhesus monkeys [Betteridge et al, 1970; Clark et al, 1979a] and at least 20 mm in women [Bomsel-Helmreich et al, 1979; O'Herlihy

---

Fig. 3. Portions of several granulosa cells composing the basal layer of a 100-μm preantral follicle from a cynomolgus monkey. Each cell has an irregular-shaped nucleus, mitochondria, Golgi, ribosomes, and rough endoplasmic reticulum. A lipid droplet (D) is seen in one of the cells. The granulosa cells rest on the underlying basement membrane (B) adjacent to collagen fibers, which are seen in longitudinal (L), cross (C), and oblique (O) section. 8,160×.

Fig. 4. A portion of an oocyte and its zona pellucida in a 125-μm preantral follicle from a cynomolgus monkey. The oocyte has numerous mitochondria (M), cortical granules (C), Golgi (G), and numerous projections into the zona pellucida. 8,760×.

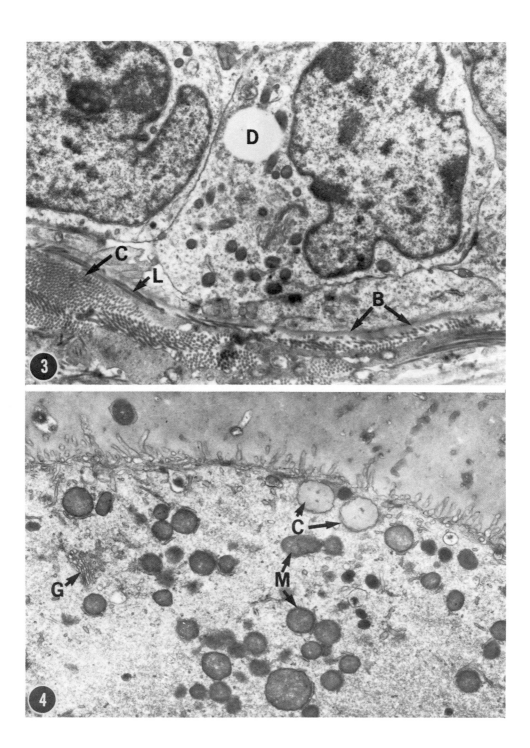

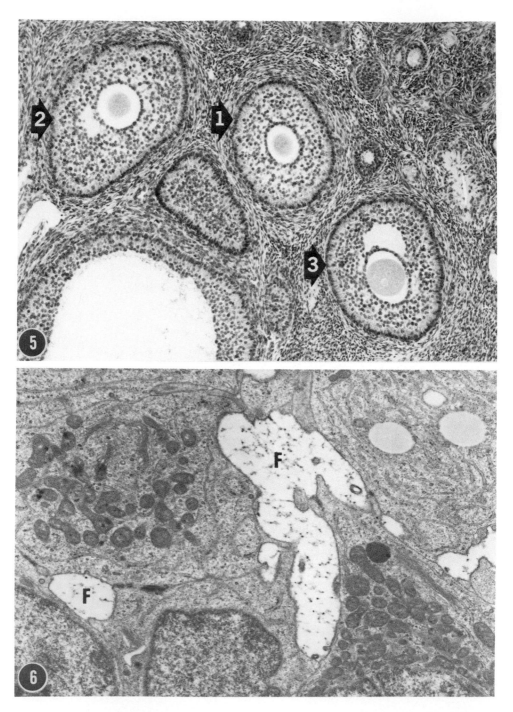

Fig. 5. A section through the cortex of an ovary from a rhesus monkey showing three follicles in the process of transformation from the preantral to the antral condition. Two of the follicles are sectioned peripheral to their center and therefore only show a small portion of the oocyte. One of these (1) depicts the initial accumulation of follicular fluid, which is responsible for the spaces between granulosa cells. The fluid continues to increase in amount, forming distinct spaces, as seen in the adjacent follicle (2). As the process continues, an antral follicle (3) results. 110×.

Fig. 6. Granulosa cells from a 250-μm rhesus monkey follicle in the process of antrum formation. These cells are located in the innermost region of the follicle, and the majority have an abundance of cytoplasm with numerous organelles. The extracellular space contains a precipitate from the follicular fluid (F). 11,020×.

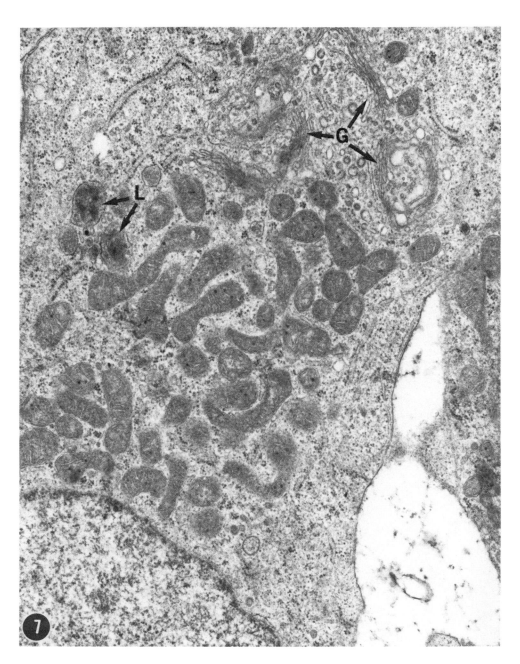

Fig. 7. Portions of two granulosa cells from the same follicle seen in Figure 6. There is an abundance of mitochondria and a few lysosomes (L). Free ribosomes are distributed throughout the cytoplasm, and Golgi (G) is associated with coated vesicles. 21,420×.

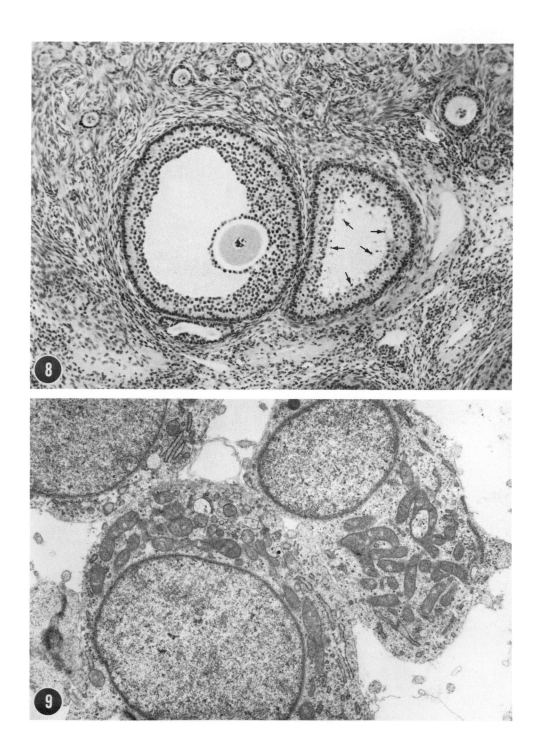

et al, 1980; Hillier et al, 1981]. In ovaries prepared for light-microscopic examination, these measurements are smaller, as seen in the rhesus monkey [Koering, 1969], howler and spider monkeys [Dempsey, 1939], and the human [Block, 1951a,b], owing to tissue shrinkage. The wall of the dominant follicle is composed of theca interna cells separated from the granulosa cells by a basement membrane. In the rhesus monkey the theca interna is thin [Hartman and Corner, 1941; Koering, 1969; Koering et al, 1982a], except in the areas where there is slight folding (Fig. 10). The theca interna cells are large in comparison to granulosa cells, have an abundant blood supply, and appear more like steroid-secreting cells. The granulosa cells are smaller (Fig. 10) and have cytoplasmic morphology resembling that of protein-secreting cells, as was previously observed by Crisp and Channing [1972]. This structural arrangement is of interest when making a correlation with the functions of the dominant follicles.

One of the main activities of the ovary during the latter part of the follicular phase of the cycle is the synthesis and release of estradiol. This was first verified in the human by Zander et al [1959] and was later correlated with the appearance of the dominant follicle [Baird and Fraser, 1974]. It is now believed that both the theca interna and the granulosa cells are involved in the in vivo synthesis, but the contributions of each may vary depending on the state of maturation.

In order to determine what is occurring, both morphologically and physiologically, during the final maturation of the dominant follicle, various techniques have been utilized. The goal of these methods is to capture the follicle in its immediate state of activity at a specific time. These techniques include 1) analyzing ovarian vein blood output, follicular fluid aspirates, and the morphological architecture, and 2) providing an environment for in vitro maintenance of follicular cells that will allow mimicking of in vivo activity.

Some of the most recent hormonal information shows elevations of estradiol occurring as soon as the dominant follicle is selected and attaining a peak of over 3,000 pg/ml prior to ovulation [di-Zerega and Hodgen, 1981; Goodman and Hodgen, 1983]. To obtain more insight into the viability of a follicle, the hormonal composition of follicular aspirates has been correlated with the morphological status of the granulosa and theca interna cells [Bomsel-Helmreich et al, 1979; Brailly et al, 1981; Westergaard et al, 1982]. The content of steroids in the fluid varies in relation to follicular size and state of activity [Bomsel-Helmreich et al, 1979; McNatty et al, 1976b] and therefore can serve as an indicator of follicular growth. In addition, follicular fluid contains numerous nonsteroidal factors [Channing et al, 1982].

Examination of granulosa cells from the dominant follicle in women shows that up to 2% of the cells could have pyknotic nuclei [Bomsel-Helmreich et al, 1979]. This is also true of macaques (Fig. 10) [Koering et al, 1982a]. These studies reveal that a number of degenerating cells can be present in a healthy preovulatory follicle.

From in vitro preparations, it is known that theca interna cell preparations can secrete androstenedione [McNatty et al, 1979c; McNatty, 1982]. This steroid is believed to be mobilized across the basement membrane of the follicle and metabolized by granulosa cells to estradiol [Fowler et al, 1978; Hillier, 1981]. During the preovulatory period, the activity of the aromatase system increases in granulosa cells [Hillier et al, 1982]. Since granulosa cells are involved mainly in metabolism of androstenedione, which requires the synthesis of an aromatase enzyme, the lack of steroid-secreting intracellular machinery (Fig. 9) is not surprising. This two-cell interaction is most likely responsible for synthesizing the estradiol present in follicular fluid [McNatty and Baird, 1978] and also enhances the follicular output of estradiol from the preovulatory follicle [McNatty et al, 1979c].

However, theca interna cells also have aromatase enzymes [Vernon et al, 1983], and these cells may be responsible for estradiol present in the ovarian vein [Channing and Coudert, 1976] prior to the

Fig. 8. A section through the cortex of an ovary from a rhesus monkey, with a 400-μm developing antral follicle lying adjacent to a portion of a follicle in early atresia. The degenerating follicle is characterized by the presence of pyknotic nuclei (arrows) in granulosa cells lining the lumen. 123×.

Fig. 9. Portions of three granulosa cells on the luminal aspect of the wall of a 1-mm developing antral follicle from a pigtailed monkey. Each cell has a spheroidal nucleus, an abundance of mitochondria, ribosomes, and rough endoplasmic reticulum. 7,940×.

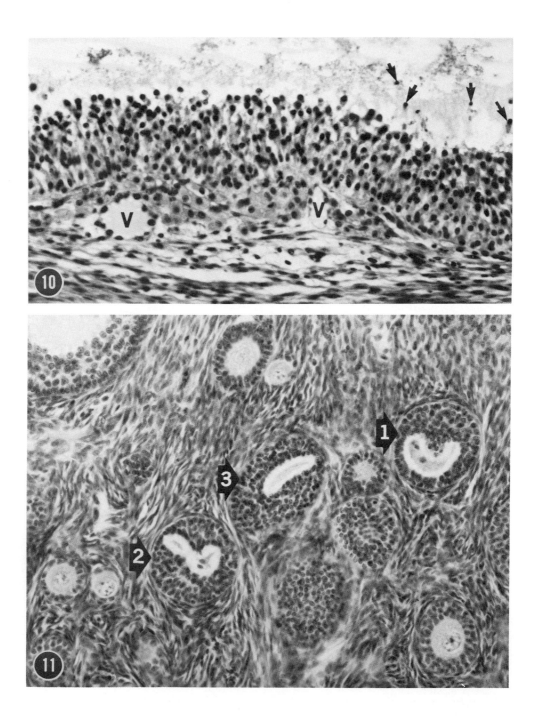

preovulatory period. The aromatase system is controlled by follicle-stimulating hormone (FSH), and in smaller antral follicles the activity of this system is low [Hillier et al, 1981]. It therefore appears that the site of follicular estrogen output varies according to the requirements for maintaining a normal cycle, and the follicle is flexible enough to respond to such needs.

In addition, granulosa cells are involved in the production of a variety of nonsteroidal factors that function in concert with the other hormones in regulating follicle development and oocyte maturation. Among these are inhibin [Channing et al, 1978], oocyte maturation inhibitor, luteinization stimulator and inhibitor [Channing et al, 1982], and prostaglandins [Armstrong, 1981].

These data on the preovulatory follicle are derived from a combination of various scientific methods, each having its own advantages. When evaluating studies on follicular maturation, the results must be considered in relation to the techniques utilized. In vitro data indicate a cell's capabilities in the absence of associated in vivo mechanisms, whereas preserved cells maintain their state at the time of removal from an in vivo environment but are limited as to direct functional activity. The utmost benefit derives from the use of many techniques to supply a variety of data that can complement or reinforce each other and thus make their interpretation more valid.

Fig. 10. A portion of the wall of a dominant follicle from a cynomolgus monkey. The theca interna varies in thickness, with two blood vessels (V) in a region with numerous thecal cells. The granulosa is about eight layers thick. Some luminal granulosa cells have pyknotic nuclei (arrows). 400×.

Fig. 11. A section through the cortex of an ovary from a rhesus monkey showing numerous preantral follicles. Three of the follicles are in states of atresia. One shows partial collapse (1) of the zona pellucida and inclusion of cells within the oocyte. Progressive degeneration is characterized by further enfolding of the zona pellucida and greater reduction of the oocyte (2, 3). Pyknosis is not seen in the granulosa cells composing these follicles. 250×.

Atretic Follicles

Normal Degeneration. The majority of primordial and developing follicles in an ovary are destined to degenerate. It seems reasonable to assume that certain molecular changes occur within these follicles that signal their demise, prior to any morphological signs of regression. However, when examining sectioned ovaries, structural criteria are used to classify the follicles. For preantral follicles, the most useful indicator is signs of necrosis in the oocyte, as the granulosa cells appear normal [Vermande-Van Eck, 1956; Himelstein-Braw et al, 1976; Byskov, 1979; Gougeon, 1981b; Koering, 1983] (Fig. 11). However, oocytes can be distorted as a result of poor tissue preparation, most often from inadequate preservation (Fig. 12).

In antral follicles, the most utilized sign of early regression is the presence of pyknotic nuclear degeneration in the granulosa cells lining the lumen (Fig. 13). This nuclear change has been used for many years in recognizing cellular degeneration [Leuchtenberger, 1950; Alfert, 1955] and has become an acceptable means of characterizing follicle atresia [Sturgis, 1949; Koering, 1969; Byskov, 1979]. As degeneration progresses, the nuclei of more granulosa cells become pyknotic until no normal cells remain (Fig. 13). The follicle then begins to collapse, and the components of the basement membrane accumulate into a thickened band called the glassy membrane. Eventually, this elongated structure will be the only visual sign of previous follicles (Fig. 13). The theca interna usually degenerates, and the area reverts to the appearance of the surrounding stroma. However, in most primates, two exceptions to this routine atretic process have been observed. In one, the granulosa cells luteinize to form an accessory corpus luteum [Corner, 1940; Koering, 1969]. In the other, the cells in the area of the theca interna hypertrophy and form one type of interstitial gland tissue [Mossman and Duke, 1973; Koering, 1974].

Interstitial Gland Tissue. This tissue can form from various ovarian sources [Koering, 1974], but the type seen in most ovaries at one time or another originates from the cells in the theca interna of follicles in various stages of degeneration. As an atretic follicle collapses, the cells are forced into a cordlike arrangement with components of the basement membrane forming an inner band (Figs. 14, 15).

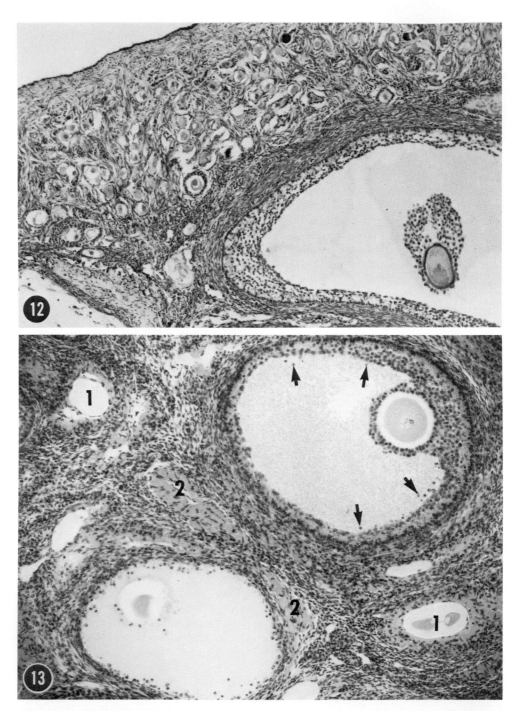

Fig. 12. A section through a portion of an ovary from a 1½- year-old rhesus monkey. The fixative was neutral buffered Formalin. Note the destruction of the oocytes in the primordial follicles and the lack of detail in granulosa cells of antral follicles, making proper classification of the status of the follicles difficult. 115×.

Fig. 13. A section through a portion of the cortex of an ovary from an adult rhesus monkey. The larger (550-μm) antral follicle is in early atresia and has a few granulosa cells with pyknotic nuclei (arrows) lining the lumen. The smaller follicle is in a later stage of atresia, having no normal granulosa cells. The remains of numerous other degenerate follicles are identified by their residual lumen (1) and/or the presence of their collapsed thickened basement membrane (2). [From Koering, 1969; reprinted with permission.]

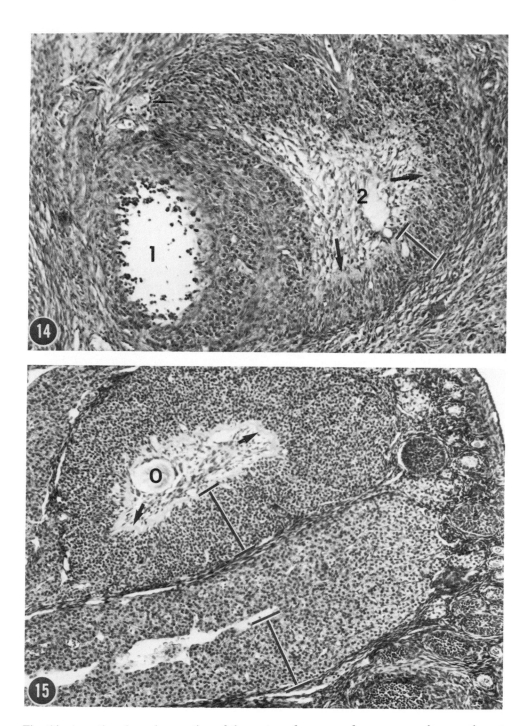

Fig. 14. A section through a portion of the cortex of an ovary from a cynomolgus monkey at ovulation, showing two follicles (1,2) in the later stages of atresia. One follicle (2) has collapsed. Its original basement membrane is represented by an inner band (arrows) of connective tissue (glassy membrane), which is surrounded by cords of interstitial gland tissue (bar). In the adjacent follicle (1), the area of the theca interna is similar, but some granulosa cells with pyknotic nuclei are still present in the follicle lumen. 137×.

Fig. 15. A section through the cortex of an ovary from a squirrel monkey. Some primordial follicles are present in the outer cortex. The atretic follicles are responsible for the formation of the interstitial gland tissue (bars) that now occupies the theca interna area. A degenerate oocyte (O) and the former granulosa cell basement membrane (arrows) are seen in one of the follicles. In the other, only the interstitial gland cells in the theca interna are present. 115×.

In Old World monkeys and women, the presence of interstitial gland tissue is variable. In the gibbon it is abundant during the luteal phase of the cycle [Dempsey, 1940]. In rhesus monkeys [Sturgis, 1949; Koering, 1969, 1979] and cynomolgus monkeys (Fig. 14), it is prevalent at ovulation, whereas in women it is seen during late pregnancy [Mossman et al, 1964]. The role of this secretory-like tissue in follicle development is not understood, but its presence at distinct times during follicular activity suggests that it may play a role in the process. The most recent studies on normal theca interna cells in developing follicles in anthropoids demonstrate their ability to secrete androgens and estrogen [Channing and Coudert, 1976; McNatty et al, 1979a; Vernon et al, 1983]. However, during atresia, they retain their ability to synthesize androgens [McNatty et al, 1979a; Brailly et al, 1982] but lose much of their ability to synthesize estradiol [McNatty et al, 1979a; Brailly et al, 1981].

Interstitial gland tissue is most abundant in New World monkeys [Koering, 1974], and recent evidence suggests that its occurrence may be correlated with the breeding season [Diamond et al, 1983] (Figs. 29, 31). It is present in spider and howler monkeys [Dempsey, 1939] and squirrel monkeys [Hertig et al, 1971] (Figs. 15, 31, 37).

Polyovular Follicles

Developing follicles with one or more oocytes have been described in several primate species [Hartman, 1926; Săglik, 1938; David and Ramaswami, 1971; Mossman and Duke, 1973; Peters, 1978; Harrison and Weir, 1977]. Speculations as to their origin have been numerous, but today the most widely accepted explanation is that they are the result of incomplete separation of Pflüger's tubes during development, as previously described [Hartman, 1926; Peters, 1978].

Some investigators believe that they may be stimulated by hormones, as suggested in the monkey [Lloyd and Rubenstein, 1941; Graham and Bradley, 1971] and human [Bacsich, 1949; Jones, 1968]. It was also initially postulated that polyovular follicles were prevalent only in infant and prepubertal groups [Hartman, 1926]. However, it has been shown that polyovular primordial follicles are present in some individuals throughout their reproductive years [Hartman, 1926; Green and Zuckerman, 1947; Harrison, 1949; van Wagenen and Simpson, 1973; Gougeon, 1981a; Koering, 1983]. They can develop into medium-size follicles that can contain oocytes of similar size (Fig. 16) or of unequal size (Fig. 17).

Whether polyovular follicles continue to develop and go on to ovulate is not known. But if this does occur, twinning is a possibility [Hartman, 1926; Jones, 1968]. Twinning occurs most frequently (88% of pregnancies) in the marmoset, and a corpus luteum is present in each ovary [Wislocki, 1939]. If one ovary is removed, twin births can still occur (and two corpora lutea are present) [Gengozian and Merritt, 1970]. Otherwise, twinning is minimal in primates, and there is little evidence to suggest that more than one oocyte is released from a single follicle [Brambell, 1960]. It is believed that oocytes in such follicles undergo asynchronous maturation, as shown in women [Gougeon, 1981a]; in no mammalian species is this known to be a mechanism for increasing the number of eggs ovulated [Mossman and Duke, 1973].

Vascularization and Innervation

Development, maintenance, and stimulation of follicle cells are accomplished by the transport of the essential nutrients and hormones to the follicles. This is achieved by the vasculature with possibly some direct transfer from cells in the immediate vicinity. Just as important as having a means for importation is having a mechanism that is capable of mobilizing the follicular secretory products into the general circulation. Along with these vessels and in the surrounding connective tissue are numerous autonomic nerves [Brambell, 1960; Jacobowitz and Wallach, 1967]. It has been shown over the years that blood flow to a tissue or organ increases as its activity is accelerated. The controlling factors for regulating the flow are hormones [Reynolds, 1973; Niswender et al, 1976] and the innervation [Keller, 1966] that is respon-

Fig. 16. A section through a rhesus monkey ovary that has developing preantral and antral follicles. Some of the follicles have more than one oocyte of equal size. 120×.

Fig. 17. A section through a rhesus monkey ovary that has developing preantral and antral follicles. The two larger follicles have at least two oocytes, but each is in a different stage of maturation. 117×.

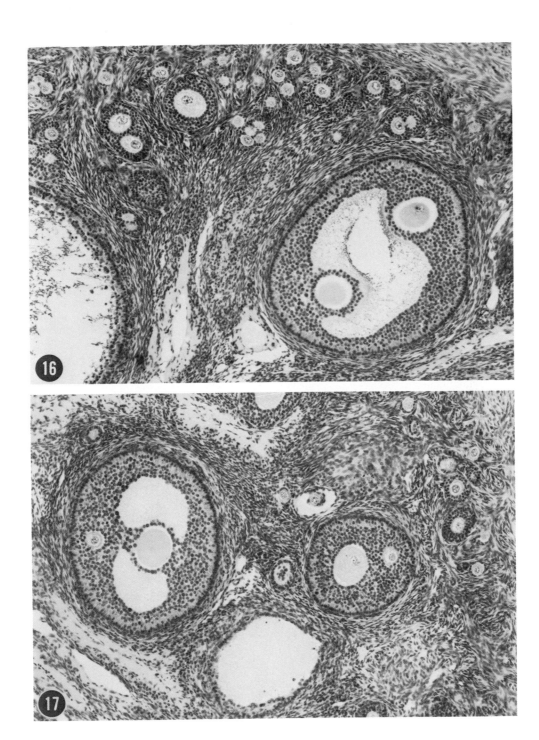

sible for the release of neurotransmitters [Goldman, 1966].

During follicle development, when the theca interna is well established, blood vessels of various sizes can be seen throughout the theca. Recent data show that blood vessels occupy about 25% of the theca interna area in smaller antral follicles but that this increases to 48% in the dominant follicle [Zeleznik, 1982]. The vessels form a wreath [Gillet et al, 1980] around the preovulatory follicle (Fig. 10), and they are most evident 24 hours prior to ovulation [Jewett and Dukelow, 1971, 1972]. After follicle rupture, these same vessels penetrate through the basement membrane [Gillet et al, 1980] and are responsible for supplying blood to the newly formed corpus luteum. As the corpus luteum develops, the vessels sprout and form an extensive network with numerous anastomoses [Reynolds, 1973].

Lymphatic vessels are also distributed throughout the ovary and are most easily seen in the medulla in ovaries of all ages (Fig. 30) or stages of activity (Fig. 32). Lymphatic capillaries form a meshwork similar to the blood vessels in human ovaries [Gillet et al, 1980]. It is believed by some investigators that the role of lymphatics in ovarian activity is mainly limited to serving as the primary route for protein molecules that escape the blood vessels [Reynolds, 1973], but their role can vary with the cyclic hormonal changes [Gillet et al, 1980]. However, the wide distribution of these vessels [Peters and McNatty, 1980] would suggest that they are influential in maintaining the microenvironment.

The nerves identified in the ovary not only innervate the vessels but also are responsible for stimulation of smooth muscle [Owman et al, 1975]. Smooth muscle fibers that are located around follicles in the theca externa in the human [Brambell, 1960; Okamura et al, 1972] may play some role in mechanical control of the follicle wall [Owman et al, 1975]. Although such a mechanism may have some function in ovulation, it appears that it is not essential for follicle rupture [Espey, 1978; Burden and Lawrence, 1980].

FOLLICULOGENESIS AND OVULATION
Ovarian Cycle

The primary purpose of folliculogenesis is to produce an oocyte that can be released from the ovary and will be capable of fertilization. The ovarian cycle is the period of time during which certain follicles are recruited to form a pool from which a dominant follicle is selected. This follicle then ruptures, and the cells in its wall form a corpus luteum that secretes hormones involved in inhibiting follicle growth and preparing the uterus for embryo nidation. Only a portion of this interval is devoted to active follicle maturation, but the sequence is probably the same in all primate species, with variation occurring only in the length of time before the series of events is repeated. In most nonprimate species, folliculogenesis is initiated following pregnancy and lactation and ultimately results in another pregnancy.

In many of the higher primates and those restricted to the limitations of captivity, pregnancy does not occur after every ovulation [Dukelow et al, 1979; Hess et al, 1979]. In such individuals, regular ovarian cycles occur, as can be determined by the repetition of hormonal patterns (Fig. 18), behavior, and vaginal and uterine changes. Except in the human, there is a definite relationship to the seasons, which results in distinct breeding periods [Corner, 1932; Van Horn and Eaton, 1979; Jarosz et al, 1977; Omar and De Vos, 1971; Riesen et al, 1971] based at least partially on photoperiods [Van Horn, 1980; Wehrenberg and Dyrenfurth, 1983; Bowers and Elton, 1982]. In the human, various additional external and neural stimuli can also affect the cycle.

It is generally accepted that New World nonhuman primates have shorter ovarian cycles than Old World primates. In the marmoset, mean cycle length is 15–23 days [Harding et al, 1982], which is similar to that of capuchin monkeys, with a 20-day cycle [Nagle et al, 1979], and the owl monkey, with a 15-day cycle [Bonney et al, 1979]. In contrast, some Old World macaque monkeys have a 28-day cycle [Monroe et al, 1970; Kirton et al, 1970; Stabenfeldt, and Hendrickx, 1973b], and the patas monkey has a 30-day cycle [Sly et al, 1983]. In higher anthropoids, variation exists from 28 days in women [Neill et al, 1967] to 33 days in gorillas [Nadler et al, 1983].

The following sections review the information available on the structural aspects of follicle formation during the primate ovarian cycle. Since the most thorough data have been obtained from macaques and women, these will receive major emphasis. This discussion will be followed by the most recent information on platyrrhines and strepsirhines.

Cercopithecoidea and Hominoidea

Primordial Follicle Population. The total number of primordial follicles in adult cycling monkeys (Figs. 19, 20) and women varies greatly [Koering, 1983; Block, 1952], but in most monkeys this non-proliferating pool of follicles usually composes about 80% of the follicle population [Zuckerman, 1951; Vermande-Van Eck, 1956; Koering, 1983]. When comparing right and left ovaries, the number of primordial follicles is similar in monkeys [Green and Zuckerman, 1954; Vermande-Van Eck, 1956; Burton, 1981; Koering, 1983] and women [Block, 1952]. However, some of this variability between individuals can be attributed to age, as fewer oocytes are present in older ovaries [Green and Zuckerman, 1951; Block, 1952; Gougeon, 1981b], but major differences in numbers are also found between individuals at birth [Block, 1953], suggesting that such variations are a normal phenomenon. The pool of oocytes present at birth seems to be sufficient to support the length of a female's reproductive life [Green and Zuckerman, 1951; Baker, 1963], considering that there are no massive waves of atresia. It also appears that great numbers of oocytes are lost between birth and puberty in primates [Block, 1952; van Wagenen and Simpson, 1965, 1973]. This is true in nonprimates, where statistical modeling has shown that a major depletion in primordial follicles occurs prior to the onset of cyclic ovarian activity [Faddy et al, 1983].

Initiation of Growth. Initiation of preantral follicle growth is seen soon after birth [van Wagenen and Simpson, 1973; Lintern-Moore et al, 1974]. Whether a stimulus is necessary to trigger this growth or there is a removal of a local inhibitor remains unclear. It remains doubtful whether gonadotropins alter follicle growth [Peters et al, 1973], as deactivation of gonadotropins by antigonadotropins has no effect [Eshkol et al, 1970]. Other possible stimulants are androgens, as previously shown in macaques [Green and Zuckerman, 1947]. Whatever the cause, only a few primordial follicles are affected at any one time, since adjacent follicles are rarely in the same state of development (Fig. 1) [Koering, 1983]. Those primordial follicles that first begin to grow are usually located closest to the medulla (Fig. 21), suggesting that a positive influence is derived from the more central microenvironment. In addition, it seems reasonable to suggest that the triggering mechanism may be within the

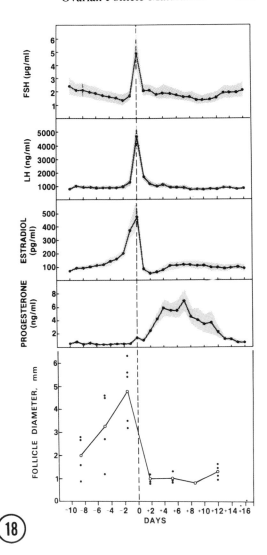

Fig. 18. Peripheral levels of gonadotropin, estradiol, and progesterone throughout the 28-day menstrual cycle of the rhesus monkey [adapted from Hodgen et al, 1976] and their relationship to the largest developing follicle in an ovary [adapted from Koering, 1969]. All data have been adjusted to the time of the LH surge.

oocyte. Once initiation of growth occurs, the granulosa cells of preantral follicles become capable of synthesizing proteins, as indicated by the presence in the cytoplasm of organelles associated with protein synthesis (Fig. 2). The secretory product may inhibit growth of the adjacent follicle [Faddy et al, 1983].

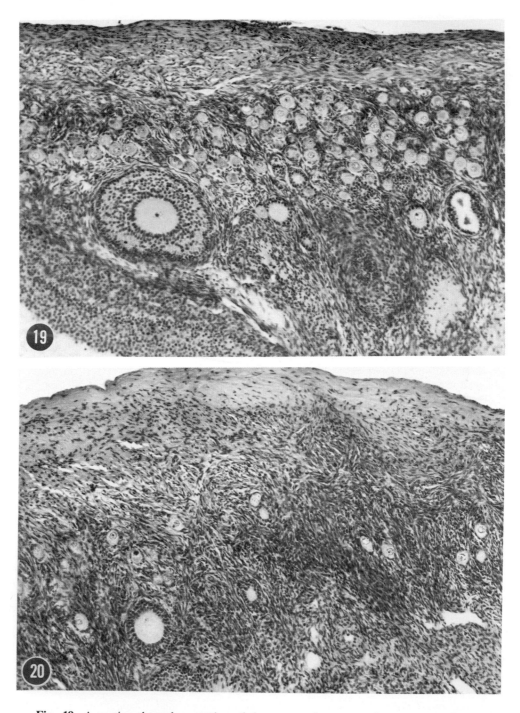

Fig. 19. A section through a portion of the cortex of an ovary from a cynomolgus monkey during the early follicular phase of the cycle. There is an abundance of primordial follicles and a 200-μm preantral follicle. 125×.

Fig. 20. A section through a portion of the cortex of an ovary from another cynomolgus monkey during the early follicular phase of the cycle. There are few primordial follicles in this ovary compared to that in Figure 19. 130×.

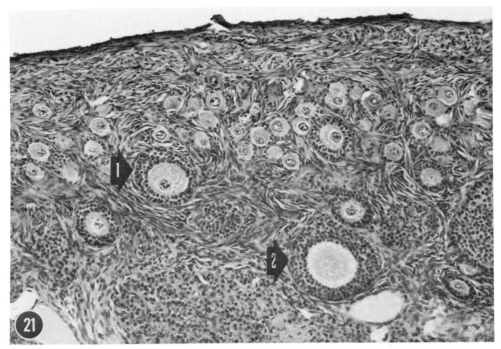

Fig. 21. A section through a portion of the cortex of a rhesus monkey during the midfollicular phase of the cycle. The primordial follicles are more peripheral, whereas growing preantral follicles are located toward the medulla. The developing preantral follicles are of various sizes, and no adjacent developing follicles are similar in size. The two largest follicles are 100 μm (1) and 150 μm (2) in diameter. 150×.

Since preantral follicles of various sizes are distributed throughout the ovary (Fig. 21), it is possible that the initiation of new growth occurs continuously, with a few follicles starting to grow every few days, and is not related to the cycle [Peters et al, 1975]. However, once this growth begins, the length of time it takes to produce an antral follicle remains unknown for primates.

A factor influencing the number of growing follicles in the nonprimate is the size of the primordial pool. The larger the number of primordial follicles in an ovary, the greater the number of developing follicles [Krarup et al, 1969; Peters, 1979]. Whether there is a similar relationship in primates has not been determined because of limited sample sizes [Block, 1952; Koering, 1983]. The other factors that possibly induce and maintain preantral follicle growth remain just as elusive.

The growth of the preantral follicle itself is related to the size of its oocyte. There are two distinct growth phases (Fig. 22), and a linear relationship exists between them. Until an oocyte attains a diameter of 80–90 μm, it increases in size more rapidly in relation to the follicle than it does after that size is attained. Subsequently, the oocyte grows much more slowly in relation to the increase in follicle size. Identical biphasic growth was previously observed in the baboon [Zuckerman and Parkes, 1932], gibbon [Dempsey, 1940], rhesus monkey [Green and Zuckerman, 1947], langur [Burton, 1981], and human [Lintern-Moore et al, 1974; Gougeon, 1981b].

Preantral Follicle Development. To be sure that a preantral follicle has initiated its growth, it should have at least one layer of cuboidal granulosa cells (Fig. 1), equivalent to a diameter of at least 20–40 μm. Such follicles are present in all ovaries throughout the 28-day cycle [Koering, 1983]. In order to obtain some insight into the distribution and possible variability in numbers of all other developing preantral follicles, they will be grouped according to size increments. When mean percentages are obtained for five stages of the cycle, comparisons can be made (Fig. 23). Follicles with a diameter greater than 60 μm are always more abundant during the periovulatory period (Fig. 23). For follicles between 100 and 200 μm in diameter, a significant increase of at least $P < 0.05$ exists

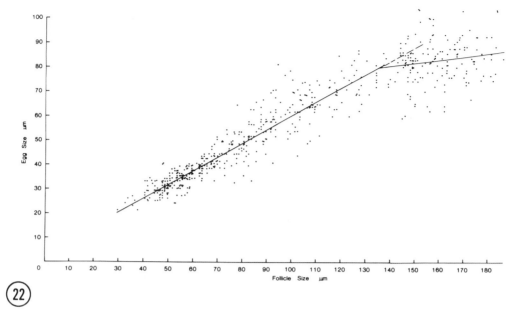

(22)

Fig. 22. The relationship between the size of the follicle and the size of the oocyte. Each dot represents a measured follicle, and its position is determined by its size and that of its oocyte. [From Koering, 1983; reprinted by permission.]

when compared to the other four stages. This suggests that preantral follicles 100 μm in diameter and above are sensitive to some factor in their microenvironment that is stimulating them to increase in size at this time. Although this investigation [Koering, 1983] gives a static view of preantral follicle development, it should in no way be inferred that growth is totally inhibited during the other stages. Another study, utilizing a labeling procedure, has revealed that preantral follicle growth does take place during certain portions of the follicular and luteal phases of the cycle [Zeleznik et al, 1980]. The increase in the percentage of preantral follicles that occurs during the periovulatory period is similar to that observed in mice [Pedersen, 1970]. These data imply that preantral follicle growth is an ongoing process throughout the cycle. It is possible that the largest follicles in this pool form a cohort, as they become antral follicles, from which the next dominant follicle will be selected following luteal phase inhibition [Koering, 1969; Hess and Resko, 1973; Resko et al, 1974].

The periovulatory increase in larger preantral follicles seen in the rhesus monkey (Fig. 23) [Koering, 1983] may have been present in prior data [Green and Zuckerman, 1951; Block, 1951b] but was not detected for numerous reasons. Among these are the methods selected to categorize the individuals in relation to time in the cycle, as well as the manner in which follicles are classified. Both of these factors may have been too imprecise to demonstrate an elevation. In a recent study [Koering, 1983], the ovaries were grouped according to their total morphological architecture [Koering, 1969] as well as to their ovarian vein progesterone levels [Resko et al, 1975]. In earlier investigations [Green and Zuckerman, 1951, 1954], rhesus monkeys were assigned to their stages (days 1–9, 10–18, 19–28) solely on the basis of menstrual cycle records, and developing preantral follicles of all sizes were assigned to a single group. As a result, no differences in number were identified among the three stages. Other variations in data collection also exist that make it difficult to compare final analyses between these studies. In the human, Block [1951a] concentrated on follicles less than 100 μm in diameter, as he alleged that larger preantral follicles were too few for adequate sampling. His results showed an elevation in the number of grow-

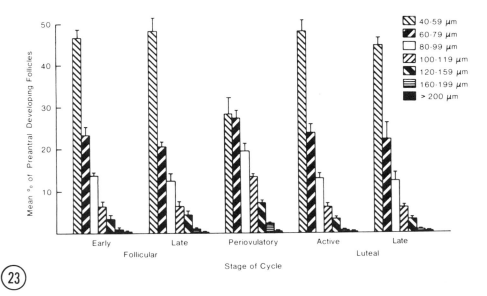

Fig. 23. The relationship between the mean percentage of preantral developing follicles of various sizes during five stages of the cycle for the rhesus monkey. There is a significant decrease in the 100- to 119-μm group (P < 0.005), the 120- to 159-μm group (P < 0.05), and the 160- to 199-μm group (P < 0.005) during the periovulatory period as compared to the other four stages. The decrease in the 40- to 59-μm group during this period is due to the increase in the other size groups.

ing preantral follicles < 100 μm in diameter following ovulation. In contrast, another analysis of human ovaries [Gougeon, 1982] excluded preantral follicles less than 115 μm in diameter but showed that there was an influx of follicles greater than 115 μm during the early luteal phase [Gougeon, 1982].

Antral Follicle Development. Antral follicles are present in various sizes and states of activity throughout the regular cycle. When comparing follicular changes as reported in different studies, it is critical that the method of follicle classification and the type of tissue preparation be considered. The size of follicles can be estimated by the number of granulosa cells, the number of granulosa cell layers, or the cross diameters [Koering, 1983]. Any such quantitative measurements will vary between species (the human preovulatory follicle is larger than that of the rhesus monkey) but will depend even more on how the tissue was treated prior to examination.

With the advent of better laparoscopy techniques, many investigations are now using in situ specimens, which give the most realistic size values. In contrast, histologically prepared samples

possess more shrinkage artifacts. When comparing follicle sizes, this variation must be considered. It is quite possible that fixed antral follicles 1 mm in diameter in the monkey may be equivalent to 4-mm follicles in nonpreserved human ovaries [McNatty et al, 1983]. However, the most thorough studies now available on follicle development throughout the cycle have been done on sectioned ovaries. Therefore, this investigative approach will be used as the basis for determining the sequence of events leading to follicle maturation.

To elucidate the fluctuations that occur during this approximately 28-day interval, antral follicles will be grouped into size categories: small, less than 500 μm in diameter; medium, 500–1,000 μm (1 mm) in diameter; and large, greater than 1 mm in diameter. Using this classification, the greatest mean percentage of developing follicles is always the small size (Fig. 24) during the rhesus monkey menstrual cycle. The decrease seen in this size group during the preovulatory period is compensated by the increase in percentage of atretic follicles that have formed interstitial gland tissue (Fig. 24). The next most abundant group is the developing medium-size follicles; it is also in this size

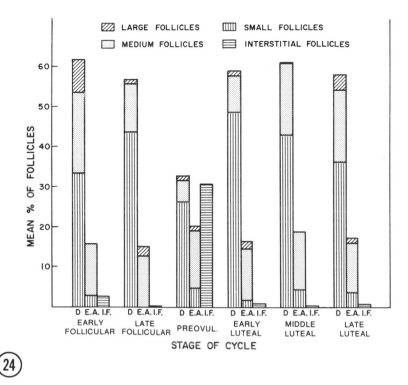

(24)

Fig. 24. The relationship between the mean percentage of various types and sizes of antral follicles during six stages of the cycle. Within each stage the follicles are classified as developing (D), early atretic (E.A.), and atretic follicles that formed interstitital gland tissue (I.F.). Large follicles are > 1 mm, medium follicles are 0.50–1.0 mm, and small follicles are < 0.5 mm. [Modified from Koering, 1969.]

group that early atresia is most prevalent (Fig. 24). Large follicles (> 1 mm in diameter) vary in size and number throughout the cycle (Fig. 24).

In attempting to integrate the available information on the status of antral follicles and hormonal interactions, discussion will center on the major stages of the ovarian cycle. The interval in which larger-size antral follicles are absent occurs when corpus luteum activity dominates the ovarian environment [Koering, 1969]. In the rhesus monkey at this time, the largest follicles are usually just under 1 mm in diameter [Koering, 1969; Clark et al, 1979b]. In women, the largest developing follicles are less than 5 mm in diameter [McNatty et al, 1983], which is considered a small size for unfixed human follicles, and there are few of them. The fluid from these follicles has high levels of aromatizable androgens and low levels of estradiol, which makes it similar to that of atretic follicles. How-

ever, the granulosa cells are highly responsive to FSH in terms of aromatase activity, and these follicles could therefore be considered likely candidates for the next dominant follicle [McNatty et al, 1983]. Whether any of these follicles are truly capable of becoming a healthy follicle with a fertilizable oocyte remains unclear [McNatty et al, 1979b]. When progesterone levels decrease [Resko et al, 1974; Goodman et al, 1977] and FSH increases [Ross et al, 1970], mitosis is resumed [Gougeon, 1979] and larger antral follicles appear [Koering, 1969]. This progesterone-dominated inhibition of follicle growth can be overcome by giving supraphysiological doses of gonadotropins to rhesus monkeys in the presence of an active corpus luteum. The ovaries respond by producing multiple ovulatory dominant follicles [diZerega and Hodgen, 1980b; Zeleznik and Resko, 1980], showing that a certain number of follicles are capable of responding to the hormonal stimulation. Although it has been shown that the intercycle FSH elevation is not essential for the initiation of follicle growth [diZerega et al, 1980a], it is a normal event [Nass et al, 1981], but whether it acts as a stimulatory or a facilitatory agent remains in question.

When evaluating macaque ovaries from the late-luteal phase, results indicate that the status of developing follicles is similar in both ovaries of a pair [Koering, 1969], even though ovarian vein progesterone levels are significantly different between the right and left ovaries [Marut and Hodgen, 1982]. Early studies indicated that there is no consistent pattern as to which side will produce the next dominant follicle [Hartman, 1932], but evidence now shows that in 70% of the cycles the next dominant follicle appears on the side opposite the corpus luteum [Williams and Hodgen, 1983]. This may be related to cycle length of the intraovarian environment. Closer evaluation of more recent data suggests that an intraovarian gradient plays a role in inhibiting the resumption of follicle growth in the areas closest to the regressing corpus luteum [diZerega and Hodgen, 1982]. Therefore, morphologically, follicles in the ovary not affected by diffusing progesterone have a similar chance in the competition for production of the next dominant follicle.

During the early follicular phase of the cycle, there is an increase in the percentage of follicles greater than 1 mm in diameter (Fig. 24). By day 4, there is an increase in the percentage of medium-size follicles in the ovary that is destined to produce the new dominant follicle (Fig. 25). It has been shown that following luteectomy, the dominant follicle occurs 95% of the time in the ovary on the opposite side [Goodman et al, 1977]. This observation provides a means to predict with some certainty which ovary will produce the next dominant follicle prior to the selection process. Therefore differences in the status of follicles in this favored ovary, when compared to the opposite side, give insight into what happens during recruitment of the dominant follicle [Koering et al, 1982b]. In this study, there was an increase in the percentage of medium-size follicles during the early follicular phase, suggesting that the dominant follicle is probably a member of this size group and is not one of the 1-mm follicles that were present during the end of the luteal phase of the cycle. If supraphysiological doses of gonadotropins are administered at this time, more than one preovulatory follicle will develop [diZerega and Hodgen, 1980a], indicating that more than one follicle is capable of sequestering amounts of hormone sufficient for stimulation. In contrast, if normal levels of FSH are suppressed by inhibin administration, the larger developing follicles lack proper cellular components [Stouffer and Hodgen, 1980]. Even though follicle development culminates in the rupture of a dominant follicle in these monkeys, the resulting corpus luteum is defective in that it cannot maintain a normal luteal phase. This implies that FSH not only is the main stimulatory hormone for the pool of follicles from which a normal follicle is selected, but is also responsible for providing proper stimulation to produce enough granulosa cells [Channing et al, 1981] that in turn are capable of producing an adequate corpus luteum.

After morphological selection has taken place, the dominant follicle secretes increased amounts of estrogen, which is attested to by the asymmetry seen between the right and left ovarian vein blood samples [diZerega et al, 1980b]. At the same time, there is an increase in the percentage of medium-size follicles that have become atretic (Fig. 25a). When only menstrual cycle data are used as the basis for categorizing monkeys instead of luteectomy, there is also a suggestion that a similar turnover of medium-size follicles has occurred in the ovary with the dominant follicle (Fig. 25b). Once the dominant follicle has control of the microenvironment, supraphysiological levels of gonadotropins fail to stimulate additional follicles [diZerega and Hodgen, 1980a], suggesting that the dominant follicle participates in the suppression of the responsiveness of other developing follicles to gonadotropins.

Profiles of the follicular status of two monkeys examined 8 days after luteectomy show that a dominant follicle is present (Fig. 26) and that there is a competing follicle of equal size lying adjacent to it. Whether these two follicles originated from neighboring areas or were pushed together because of their large size has not been determined. The latter hypothesis seems more likely, since smaller follicles in the same stage of development are rarely in the same location (Fig. 26). There is also a variation in numbers of developing and atretic follicles between the two ovaries (Fig. 26), which implies that not all follicles react identically at a specific time, even though they have similar spatial distribution throughout the ovaries.

After selection, the dominant follicle takes con-

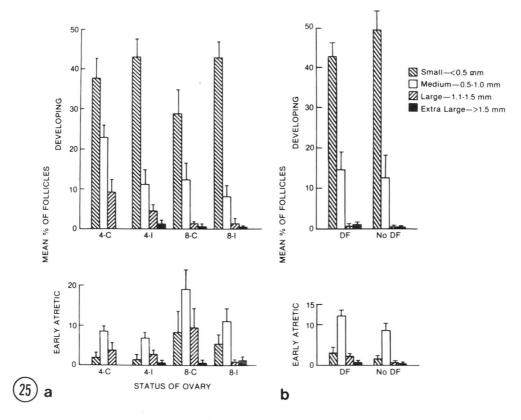

Fig. 25. The relationship of the mean percentage of developing and early atretic follicles from four size groups during the follicular phase of the cycle in the rhesus monkey. a) Comparison of the results obtained 4 and 8 days after luteectomy from either the ovary taken from the same side that had the corpus luteum removed (ipsilateral—I) or the opposite side (contralateral—C). There was a significant increase (P < 0.05) in the mean percentage of developing medium size follicles in the 4-C group. [From Koering et al, 1982; reprinted with permission.] b) The results obtained from the monkeys in the follicular stage of the cycle seen in Figure 24. The original data were reevaluated, placing the ovaries of a pair with a definitive dominant follicle in one group.

trol of ovarian activity as witnessed by the increased degree of hormonal asymmetry, not only elevated ovarian vein estradiol output but also androstenedione and progesterone, which occurs 3 days prior to the luteinizing hormone (LH) surge [diZerega et al, 1980b]. During this period, the largest developing follicles present in macaques are most often maintained at sizes below 1 mm in diameter [Koering, 1969]. When examining the architecture of these macaque ovaries just prior to rupture, there is an abundance of interstitial gland tissue located in the area of the theca interna of most atretic follicles (Fig. 14) [Koering, 1969, 1974]. If these cells have retained their ability to

synthesize androstenedione and estrogen, as seen in less degenerate follicles [Brailly et al, 1982], they may be contributing to the elevated hormone levels present in the ovarian vein [diZerega et al, 1980b] and performing some role in the ovulatory process [Sturgis, 1949].

Atresia. The majority of developing follicles are lost through the atretic process. In ovaries of regularly cycling rhesus monkeys, atretic follicles are always present [Koering, 1969, 1983] (Fig. 24). In preantral follicles [Koering, 1983] and in antral follicles less than 0.5 mm in diameter (Fig. 24), degeneration is minimal. The greatest percentage

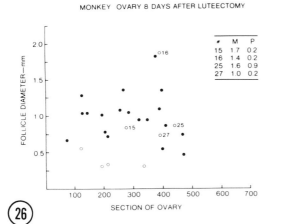
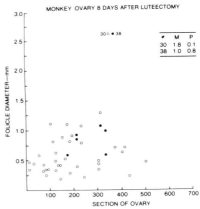

Fig. 26. The spatial distribution of developing (○) and early atretic (●) follicles throughout two ovaries 8 days after luteectomy. A dominant follicle (#16 and #30) has been selected in each ovary. The mitotic (M) and pyknotic (P) indices are shown for the follicles that are numbered. [Modified from Koering et al, 1982.]

of atretic antral follicles are in the medium-size (0.5–1.00 mm) group (Figs. 24, 25), suggesting that the majority of developing follicles attain this size and then degenerate. However, one or more of these follicles manages to escape (Fig. 26) and reach a greater diameter, but only one of these finally survives (Fig. 26).

A significant decrease in the developing medium-size follicle pool occurs during the early follicular phase of the cycle (Fig. 25) and is coincident with selection of the dominant follicle [Koering et al, 1982b] (Fig. 25). It is also possible that the majority of these medium-size early atretic follicles compose the pool of follicles that are responsible for the formation of the increased amount of interstitial gland tissue present at ovulation (Fig. 24).

Soon after selection of the dominant follicle takes place, the majority of competing follicles larger than 1 mm in diameter become atretic (Fig. 26), resulting in an increase in the percentage of large atretic follicles (Fig. 24). The exact cause of this degeneration is not known, although most evidence implies a change in the hormonal environment. It is believed that a decrease in gonadotropin output, which reflects an estradiol elevation, is responsible for the degeneration of these large follicles [Clark et al, 1979a; Zeleznik, 1982]. It has been shown that although nonovulatory follicles are responsive to FSH [Hillier et al, 1981], they do not obtain sufficient exposure. In in vivo situations, this can result not only from low circulatory levels of FSH, but also from poor circulation to the area. So the arrangement of the vasculature may also be responsible for determining which follicle survives [Zeleznik et al, 1981].

However, the ultimate effect of atresia is death of the granulosa cells. This results from their inability to obtain nutrients required for their routine cellular needs. Even though a cell may not be performing its ascribed function as it relates to overall activity, that is not sufficient reason for its physical demise. Therefore, it is unlikely that the lack of any stimulatory hormone could be responsible; more likely it is a specific block of the cells' ability to obtain nutrients or possibly some type of toxic influence.

Dynamics of Follicle Growth. The sequence of events in follicle development that leads to the rupture of a single follicle includes the initiation of growth, recruitment of a cohort, selection of the follicle, and its maturation. Best understood are the morphology and hormonal interactions necessary for the selection and maturation of this preovulatory follicle. Much less is known about the earlier stages.

The future dominant follicle begins the maturation process by responding to changes in its microenvironment; the nature of these changes remains unclear, but they permit it to begin to

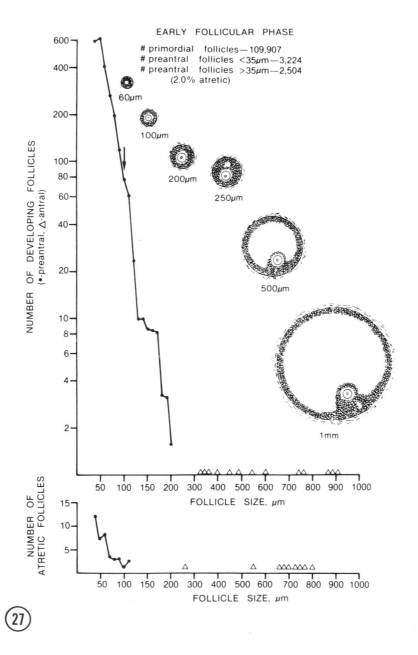

Fig. 27. Summary of the follicular architecture in a rhesus monkey (2210R) ovary during the early follicular phase of the cycle. These graphs depict the relationship between the number of developing or early atretic preantral and antral follicles and their size. The arrow identifies the group of preantral follicles that are 100 μm in diameter. The diagrams show the morphological characteristics of follicles at the various sizes.

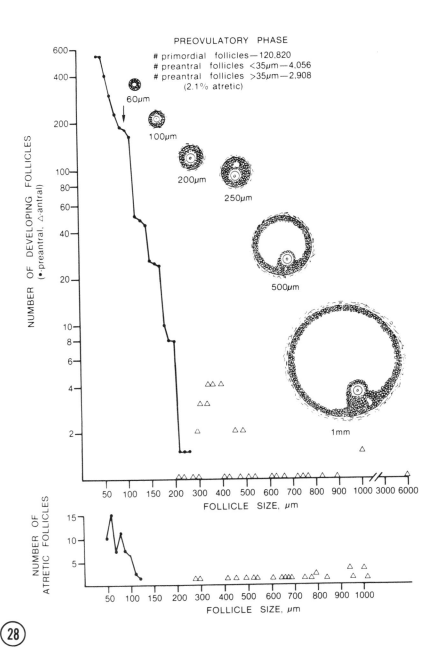

Fig. 28. Summary of the follicular architecture of a rhesus monkey (2207L) ovary during the preovulatory phase of the cycle. These graphs depict the relationship between the number of developing or early atretic preantral and antral follicles and their size. The arrow identifies the group of preantral follicles that are 100 μm in diameter. The diagrams show the morphological characteristics of follicles at the various sizes. Compare with Figure 27.

grow. In macaques this follicle becomes a member of a cohort of follicles of which the majority will become atretic prior to attaining a diameter of 1 mm. The size of this cohort varies in direct proportion to the number of primordial follicles in the ovary. It has been shown in mice [Peters, 1979; Faddy et al, 1983] that the greater the number of primordial follicles in the reserve pool, the greater the number of growing follicles. Although some evidence supports this observation in primates [Block, 1952; Gougeon, 1981b; Koering, 1983], it has not been properly evaluated owing to limitations in sample size. As preantral follicles increase in diameter, they decrease in number (Figs. 27, 28), suggesting that the members of any initial cohort may progress at different rates, since the loss in number cannot be accounted for by atresia in either monkeys [Koering, 1983] or mice [Faddy et al, 1983]. It has been shown that in rodents some follicles begin to grow daily and that their growth is continuous until they either become atretic or ovulate [Pedersen, 1970].

When the growing preantral follicles attain a diameter of about 100 μm, they become responsive to one or more of the hormones present during the periovulatory period. This is supported by morphological evidence that shows a significant increase at this time in the percentage of follicles of this size and larger, in both macaques (Figs. 23, 28) [Koering, 1983] and women [Gougeon, 1982]. A similar observation was previously made in rodents [Pedersen, 1970; Hirshfield and Midgley, 1978]. These larger developing preantral follicles begin to form an antrum when they attain a diameter of 200–250 μm in the monkey (Figs. 27, 28) and human [Gougeon, 1979], probably during the periovulatory period.

During the luteal phase of the cycle the majority of follicles present in the rhesus monkey are developing [Koering, 1983] (Fig. 24), but mitosis is decreased and antral follicles are maintained below 1 mm in diameter [Koering, 1969]. However, preantral follicles continue their growth, as shown by their mitotic activity [Zeleznik et al, 1980]. Possibly, in this pool of larger preantral and antral follicles is the next dominant follicle. When progesterone levels decline, mitosis is resumed in the larger antral follicles, and they increase in size [Koering, 1969].

In rhesus monkeys and women, the interval from the corpus luteum demise until the next ovulation is about 12–14 days. Similarly, this same length of time is required before the next LH surge if the dominant follicle is destroyed prior to ovulation or if the active corpus luteum is removed [Goodman et al, 1977]. When follicle growth was interrupted 4 days into the follicle growth phase, 12–14 days were also required for the next LH surge to occur [Goodman et al, 1982]. These latter two rhesus monkey studies clearly show that a minimum of 12 days is necessary for the selection and maturation of a dominant follicle. In contrast, if the ovary with the dominant follicle is removed 8 days into the growth phase, the period to the next LH surge is extended to 18 days [Koering et al, 1982b]. This implies that after selection has occurred, the microenvironment inhibits the initiation of follicle recruitment. Whether this is due to the inability of the proper follicle to respond at this time or the state of the hypothalamic-pituitary axis is such that it does not immediately react to the ovarian hormonal change is not known.

These studies substantiate that 12–14 days are required in macaques for selection and follicle maturation if the ovarian environment is such that the follicles can respond. The dominant follicle is then selected prior to day 8. This competition for dominance probably occurs within the pool of 0.5–1 mm size antral follicles [Koering et al, 1982b], since this is the size group that shows a major percentage increase (Fig. 25) and is the same group in which atresia is most prevalent after selection of the dominant follicle (Figs. 25, 27, 28). During the follicular phase of the cycle, when intricate hormonal interactions involving the dominant follicle predominate, the growing preantral follicles continue their development (Fig. 23) under the influence of appropriate hormones as they become available to them. The larger antral follicles show their major response during the ovulatory period [Koering, 1983].

Platyrrhini

Callithricidae. Members of this family include the marmosets and tamarins. There is new interest in these because of their possible role in scientific investigations. However, very little is known about the morphological architecture of their ovaries, especially in relation to the variations in their breeding and hormonal patterns. The marmoset first became of scientific interest because it was a primate that normally produced two young at a time [Hill, 1926]; later it was more thoroughly investigated by Wislocki [1939]. More recently, the common marmoset, *Callithrix jacchus*, has been utilized in scientific studies, and its cycle length was determined to be 16.4 days [Hearn et al, 1978]. The follicular phase is about 8.8 days, and following ovulation, the newly formed corpus luteum secretes estradiol as well as progesterone [Hearn et al, 1978]. During the luteal phase, numerous accessory corpora lutea are also present [Koering, 1974] as well as some antral follicles [Wislocki, 1939] that appear to be of similar size [Wislocki, 1939] to those seen in other primates [Koering, 1969]. When colony-bred marmosets were studied, the cycle length increased to 29 [Hearn, 1983] or 30 days [Harding et al, 1982], and progesterone levels were elevated for about 19 or 22 days, respectively, leaving a follicular phase length similar to that previously observed [Hearn et al, 1978].

In another callithricid, the cotton-top tamarin (*Saguinus oedipus*), cycle length was shown to be 23 days [Brand, 1981; French et al, 1983], which is an increase over the 15 days previously described [Preslock et al, 1973]. These extended cycle periods in both species have been attributed to possible stress [Harding et al, 1982; Brand, 1981], but this is now questioned [French et al, 1983].

Cebidae. This family includes the owl (*Aotus*), capuchin (*Cebus*), spider (*Ateles*), howler (*Alouatta*), and squirrel (*Saimiri*) monkeys, all of which have shorter cycles than do Old World monkeys. In addition, this group also has more interstitial gland tissue [Dempsey, 1939; Koering, 1974], although some variations in relation to overall reproductive activity are now found to exist as more morphological and hormonal correlations are being made (Figs. 29, 31).

In the owl monkey, hormone levels display cyclic patterns of about 16 days with no clear distinction between follicular and luteal phases [Bonney et al, 1979; Dixson, 1983]. In contrast, hormonal levels in the capuchin monkey show that estradiol peaks between days 7 and 9 and that cycle length is about 21 days [Nagle et al, 1979; Nagle and Denari, 1983].

The spider monkey has a cycle length estimated at 26–27 days [Goodman and Wislocki, 1935] based on vaginal washings, and 20–22 days if changes in urinary estrogens are used [Hodges et al, 1981]. The information available on follicle formation in this monkey [Dempsey, 1939] is limited to the description of the larger follicles. In howler monkeys, the largest preantral follicles have only two or three layers of granulosa cells, whereas in the

spider monkey they attain a diameter of 0.3–0.4 mm before an antrum forms. In both species, developing follicles are maintained at 1 mm in diameter during the luteal phase and attain 4 mm during the early follicular phase [Dempsey, 1939]. The atretic follicles contribute to the interstitial gland tissue that characterizes the ovary. This tissue derived from the theca interna should not be confused with accessory corpora lutea [Koering, 1974].

The squirrel monkey exhibits greater cyclic variability, 7–25 days [Butler, 1974]. However, this variation may possibly be attributed to lack of consideration of an inherent breeding season and also to the manner of evaluating the cyclic changes. These monkeys are known to have a distinct breeding season that occurs between December and April in the northern hemisphere [Kuehl and Dukelow, 1975], and this is the time that cyclic ovarian events occur, possibly explaining the major differences seen in ovaries that were randomly examined and not related to the season or cycle (Figs. 29, 31). During the breeding season the ovaries show follicular activity with minimal amounts of interstitial gland tissue (Fig. 29) [Hertig et al, 1971], whereas during the nonbreeding season there are fewer developing and smaller-size antral follicles, and the ovaries are filled with interstitial gland tissue, most of it derived from atretic follicles (Fig. 15).

More precise cycle length data have been obtained by using hormone levels during the breeding period, rather than changes in vaginal cytology [Lang, 1967; Srivastava et al, 1970]. Such studies show that monkeys of Peruvian origin have a 9-day cycle length [Wolf et al, 1977; Ghosh et al, 1982]. This was supported by behavioral evidence revealing an 8-day periodicity between receptive intervals [Wilson, 1977]. In captive squirrel monkeys of Bolivian origin, cycle length during the breeding season (December–March) varied from 6 to 12 days [Diamond et al, 1983]. It is interesting to note that even during the breeding season some monkeys have low estradiol levels and no peaks, similar to the pattern characterizing the nonbreeding season [Diamond et al, 1983]. The follicles present during this nonbreeding period are receptive to an increase in either dose or duration of FSH [Kuehl and Dukelow, 1975]. This suggests that a decreased responsiveness of the ovary to FSH occurs and is a possible cause for anovulation [Jarosz et al, 1977].

It should be remembered that the estradiol and progesterone levels in squirrel monkeys are 10–15 times greater [Diamond et al, 1983; Dukelow,

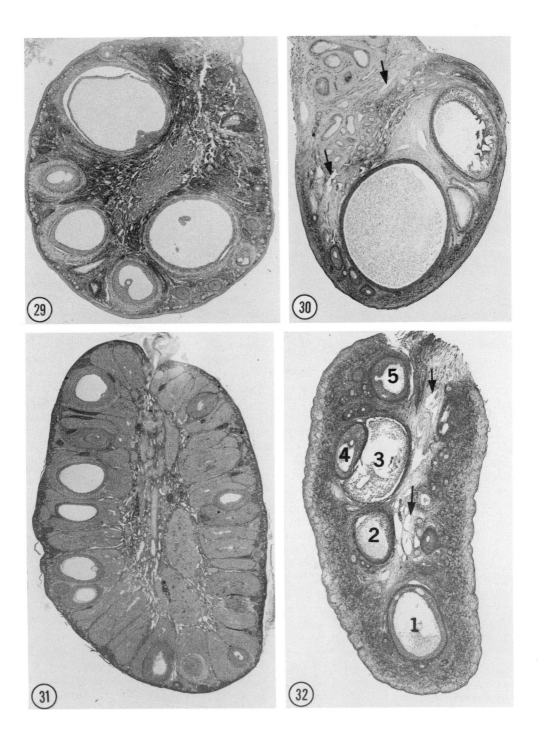

1983] than those reported in Old World monkeys [Knobil, 1974; Dailey and Neill, 1981] and women [Ross et al, 1970; Sherman and Korenman, 1975] and can be correlated with the amount of glandular tissue that is present during most of the year (Figs. 15, 31) [Koering, 1974]. The need for such elevated levels may be attributed to the inherent requirement of this species to compensate for a receptor-mediated decrease in sensitivity to progesterone [Chrousos et al, 1982].

Strepsirhini

Little information is available on follicular maturation in this group. Most studies have focused on cycle length, behavior, and breeding patterns. In the wild, where the majority of investigations have been conducted, there are distinct reproductive seasons that are believed to be influenced by photoperiods [Van Horn, 1980].

Galago senegalensis senegalensis has at least two restricted mating periods [Butler, 1960] in the wild. Estimates of cycle length vary depending on the facet of the reproductive cycle being measured. When comparing the status of follicles before and after ovulation, there is a decrease in the number of larger developing follicles following ovulation [Butler, 1960]. Further evaluation of the ovaries reveals that antral follicles up to 600 μm in diameter are present, but in varying degrees of atresia [Butler, 1967]. Gestation is estimated at 120 days [Van Horn and Eaton, 1979], and evidence suggests that postpartum estrus follows [Butler, 1960].

In *Galago crassicaudatus*, data support a single breeding season [Van Horn and Eaton, 1979]. However, in captivity they can be bred throughout the year [Buettner-Janusch, 1964], with cycle lengths of 44 days. During the interval, estradiol begins to rise 5–7 days before the 6-day behavioral estrous period. Progesterone begins to rise as estradiol declines and then peaks midway through the 24-day luteal phase [Van Horn and Eaton, 1979], suggesting that typical follicular development takes place.

As in the other members of this group, breeding seasons are observed in *Loris tardigradus* in the wild [Van Horn and Eaton, 1979]. They have two estrous cycles separated by an anestrous period of 164 days [Manley, 1966]. About 56% of the pregnancies produce twins, and two corpora lutea are present, suggesting the rupture of two follicles [Ramaswami and Anand Kumar, 1965]. During anestrus, pregnancy, and lactation, medium-size antral follicles are seen [Ramaswami and Anand Kumar, 1965].

In both galagos and lorises, oogenesis persists into adult life [Anand Kumar, 1974], which differs from the situation in other primates [Brambell, 1960; Zuckerman, 1951; Baker, 1963, 1966]. This is supported by the observation that different stages of mitosis or meiotic prophase are seen in germ cells without a definitive layer of granulosa cells [Anand Kumar, 1974].

Lemur catta and *Lemur variegatus* [Van Horn and Eaton, 1979; Shideler and Lasley, 1982] have up to three spontaneous ovulations, making them seasonally polyestrous. *Lemur variegatus* has a 40-day interval between ovulations [Bogart et al, 1977], and these sequences usually occur during December–March. Estrogen profiles show a gradual increase in estrogen over a 4-day period, and mating is restricted to the final day, when levels sharply decline [Shideler and Lasley, 1982]. In *Lemur catta*, cycle length was also about 40 days [Van Horn and Eaton, 1979].

Fig. 29. A section through an adult squirrel monkey ovary that has numerous developing follicles but few atretic follicles and minimal amounts of interstitial gland tissue. 17×.

Fig. 30. A section through a rhesus monkey ovary at day 23 of an anovulatory cycle. A 2.5-mm developing follicle is present, and lymphatics (arrows) are prevalent in the medulla. 13.5×.

Fig. 31. A section through an adult squirrel monkey ovary having some small developing antral follicles and an abundance of interstitial gland tissue formed from atretic follicles. Compare to Figure 29. 11.5×.

Fig. 32. A section through an ovary from a 1½-year-old rhesus monkey. There is an abundance of primordial follicles in the cortex and three developing (1,4,5) and two atretic (2,3) antral follicles. The largest developing follicle is 900 μm in diameter, and the largest atretic follicle is 1.2 mm in diameter. Numerous lymphatic vessels (arrows) are seen in the medulla. 20×.

FOLLICULOGENESIS AND ANOVULATION
The Ovarian Cycle

Anovulation occurs in primates when the hormonal environment is not sufficient to support follicle maturation and ovulation during a specified time interval. This is accepted as a normal occurrence in numerous adult nonhuman primates with distinct breeding seasons [Van Horn, 1980; Shideler and Lasley, 1982]. It is also a characteristic feature in infants and in prepubertal and most postpartum individuals. At these stages of reproductive life, there are sufficient numbers of primordial follicles present [van Wagenen and Simpson, 1973] to permit recruitment and selection of a dominant follicle, but gonadotropin levels are insufficient to permit follicle development that will culminate in ovulation [Knobil, 1980; Williams and Hodgen, 1983].

In contrast, anovulation becomes more of an abnormality if the primate has adapted to regular cycles based on lunar photoperiods and ovulation is missed during a cycle. In many of the higher-level primates and those adapting to their captive environment, there appear to be more regular monthly ovarian cycles if cycle lengths are based on hormonal profiles. In the human female, regular cycles throughout the year have always been described [Cowgill et al, 1962; Dewan et al, 1978], whereas in macaques, ovulations can be limited to certain seasons [Van Horn, 1980]. Anovulation was first suggested as an event in the normal adult monkey by Heape [1894] and was later verified by Corner [1923] and Allen [1927]. In monkeys, this inhibition of follicle rupture was related to seasonal change [Van Herwerden, 1906], which later was seen to be more frequent in the summer in most rhesus monkeys [Hartman, 1932]. During the same season, variability in cycle length was also observed [Riesen et al, 1971]. In human studies, the regularity of cycles was based on menstrual periods and did not necessarily reflect the true ovarian status, as ovulation may not occur during every cycle [Döring, 1969]. Lack of ovulation in the human female may also be related to various hormonal abnormalities that present themselves as polycystic ovarian disease [Goldzieher, 1981], premature ovarian failure [Coulam, 1982], and luteal phase defect [Strott et al, 1970].

In anovulatory cycles in the rhesus monkey, developing follicles are often above 1 mm in diameter (Fig. 30). Early atretic follicles of similar size are also often present [Koering, 1969], suggesting that numerous developing follicles have been recruited and one possibly selected but that the hormonal milieu necessary for the final stages of maturation has not been achieved. This is supported by hormonal assays showing that the anovulation seen during the summer in rhesus macaques is associated with low estradiol secretion, which results in lack of gonadotropin surges [Dailey and Neill, 1981]. Since all these monkeys have had normal ovulatory cycles previously and large follicles can be present, it would seem reasonable to assume that the hormonally based defect lies in the late follicular stages of the cycle. It is known that FSH support is essential for the final maturation process [diZerega et al, 1981] and that LH is required for the rupture [Jones, 1968], so irregularities in this sequence could result in anovulation [Schenken and Hodgen, 1983].

Juvenile and Pubertal Periods

Because ovulation does not occur during these periods, one might believe that the ovary is in a resting state, which is an incorrect assumption. In both rhesus macaque and human infants there is a continuum of follicular development [Block, 1952, 1953; van Wagenen and Simpson, 1965, 1973; Peters et al, 1978], but no follicle attains preovulatory status. Activity is maintained throughout the juvenile period [Peters et al, 1978], and it is during this time that the majority of primordial follicles are lost through atresia [Himelstein-Braw et al, 1976]. During this period, follicles continue to be maintained at 1 mm (Fig. 32), and detectable levels of estradiol are present [Dierschke et al, 1974].

Once the rhesus monkey attains menarche and cyclic uterine activity is initiated, anovulation continues for up to a year, as witnessed by Corner [1923] and Allen [1927]. The question arose later as to whether the ovary or the hypothalamic-pituitary mechanism was the major site for inhibiting the final maturation process, since numerous developing follicles were present in ovaries of such individuals [Grinsted and Peters, 1979]. Data reveal that rhesus monkeys will ovulate after treatment with exogenous gonadotropins [Weiss et al, 1976a]. This suggests that the controlling site is not the ovary but the hypothalamic-pituitary axis, which possibly lacks adequate sensitivity to steroid feedback [Reiter and Grumbach, 1982]. More elegant studies have shown that the initial stimulation of the cycles culminating in ovulation is related to the status of maturation of the neuroendocrine system [Knobil, 1980]. It is the pulsatile release of gonadotropin-releasing hormone (GnRH) that is responsible for activation of cyclic follicle development [Wildt et al, 1980]. Using adult rhesus monkeys that had bilateral lesions in the region of the arcuate nucleus of the hypothalamus, a pulse of GnRH every 3 hours gave a result similar to that seen in perimenarchial monkeys; a pulse every 2 hours produced anovulatory cycles similar to the postmenarchial period, whereas a pulse every hour supported routine ovulatory cycles [Pohl et al, 1983]. Accompanying the development of this hypothalamic responsiveness is the establishment of asymmetrical ovarian activity [Williams et al, 1982].

Pregnancy and Lactation

In most primates, folliculogenesis throughout pregnancy and lactation is maintained in a status similar to that occurring during the luteal phase of the cycle [Greenwald, 1978]; that is, no follicles attain dominance. In the earliest stages of pregnancy, the microenvironment of the luteal phase is maintained owing to the rescue of the corpus luteum, which is known to inhibit the resumption of the folliculogenic process [Govan, 1968]. Experimental evidence shows that continued administration of human chorionic gonadotropin (hCG) after the initiation of the demise of the corpus luteum can only temporarily revive it [Neill and Knobil, 1972]. This sequence mimics the normal activity seen during early pregnancy [Knobil, 1973]. The lack of responsiveness that follows has now been attributed to a desensitization of the luteal cells to the hormone [diZerega and Hodgen, 1983]. At this time, which is about day 25 of pregnancy, ovariectomy does not jeopardize pregnancy in the rhesus monkey [Hartman, 1941], although a drop in estradiol occurs [Atkinson et al, 1975]. A similar result was observed in women, where after day 40–50, pregnancy is maintained after corpus luteum removal [Melinkoff, 1950; Csapo et al, 1972]. However, in the marmoset the corpus luteum is necessary for nearly one-third of gestation [Chambers and Hearn, 1979].

If pregnancy is terminated on day 21 in the rhesus monkey, about 40 days are required for the next spontaneous ovulation to occur, suggesting that such an interval is necessary to obtain a preovulatory follicle [diZerega and Hodgen, 1979]. However, this time period can be reduced to 12 days by administration of exogenous gonadotropin stimulation [diZerega et al, 1979]. This implies that follicles are present that are sensitive to these

hormones, but whether these force-grown follicles are normal is not known.

At day 40 of pregnancy in the rhesus monkey, developing follicles approaching 1 mm in diameter are present (Fig. 33), and early atretic follicles of medium size are the most abundant, which is characteristic in other stages in this monkey (Figs. 24, 25). This is similar to observations in New World monkeys [Dempsey, 1939] and in women [Govan, 1968].

During this stage of pregnancy, the corpus luteum enters a period of lesser activity [Koering et al, 1973a], with the cells having few or no hCG receptors both in women [Rao et al, 1977] and monkeys [diZerega and Hodgen, 1983]. However, the luteal cells still secrete some progesterone and relaxin [Nixon et al, 1983]. Also present at this time in the ovaries of New World monkeys (Fig. 37) [Dempsey, 1939; Koering, 1974], gibbons [Săglik, 1938], and women [Govan, 1968] is interstitial gland tissue derived from atretic follicles.

Throughout pregnancy, the profile of hormones varies between species. There is generally not a sharp rise in progesterone levels in certain Old World monkeys [Hodgen et al, 1972; Stabenfeldt and Hendrickx, 1972; Albrecht and Townsley, 1976], but in the human [Tulchinsky et al, 1972] and marmoset [Chambers and Hearn, 1979], levels increase following the first quarter of gestation.

During late pregnancy, increased morphological activity is seen in the ovaries. This was first documented in the corpus luteum, which appears structurally revived in macaques [Koering et al, 1973b; Gulyas, 1974; Hodgen et al, 1977; Chandrashekar et al, 1980] and women [Crisp et al, 1973], and was shown to be involved in progesterone output [LeMaire et al, 1968, 1970; Koering et al, 1973b]. The causes of the rejuvenation of this structure and its function in the overall endocrine interactions are not understood. When luteal cells from such corpora lutea are evaluated to determine their capabilities, results indicate that they are not responsive to prolactin [Goldsmith et al, 1978], but show an increased binding to hCG [Rao et al, 1978; diZerega and Hodgen, 1983]. Data also reveal that ovarian vein blood from the ovary with the corpus luteum contains relaxin [Weiss et al, 1976b], and if the corpus luteum is removed, relaxin levels quickly decline [Nixon et al, 1983]. In the monkey, follicles appear to increase in size during this stage, some becoming greater than 1 mm in diameter (Fig. 34); this is accompanied by early atresia of follicles of the same size. Similar

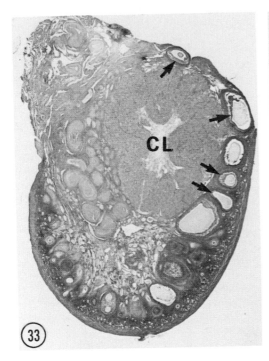

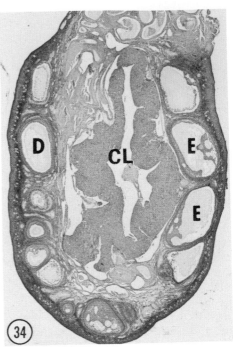

Fig. 33. A section through a rhesus monkey ovary at day 48 of pregnancy. The corpus luteum (CL) and a few developing follicles (arrows) under 1 mm are present. 12×.

Fig. 34. A section through a rhesus monkey ovary at day 157 of pregnancy. The corpus luteum (CL) and one developing (D) and two early atretic (E) follicles above 1 mm are present. The clear areas surrounding the luteal tissue represent blood and lymphatic vessels. 12×.

observations were made in the baboon [Zuckerman and Parkes, 1932] and the human [Govan, 1970; Dekel et al, 1977]. However, in the rhesus monkey and baboon, no elevations of progesterone were seen at parturition [Hodgen et al, 1972; Albrecht and Townsley, 1976]; however, in the mangabey [Stabenfeldt and Hendrickx, 1973a] and human [Tulchinsky et al, 1972], progesterone levels continue to rise.

Also during late pregnancy, interstitial gland tissue can be quite abundant (Figs. 35, 36) and has been described in the human [Nelson and Greene, 1958; Mossman et al, 1964; Maqueo and Goldzieher, 1966]. This probably reflects a hormonal response by the atretic follicles [Koering, 1969]. This tissue is also extremely abundant in New World monkeys [Dempsey, 1939; Săglik, 1938; Hertig et al, 1971].

Following parturition, spontaneous ovulatory menstrual cycles do not resume until 2–4 months postpartum in nonnursing [Goodman and Hodgen, 1978] and 7–8 months in nursing Old World monkeys [Hartman, 1932] and New World monkeys [Dempsey, 1939]. The cause for this postpartum infertility has been attributed to both inadequate gonadotropin secretion and ovarian refractoriness to proper gonadotropin stimulation [Williams et al, 1979]. In contrast, lactation does not interfere with ovulation in marmosets (*Callithrix jacchus*) [Epple and Katz, 1983], and the interval between births may be only 5 days longer than the normal gestation length [Chambers and Hearn, 1979].

Most recent evidence supports the hypothesis that the functional integrity of the hypothalamic-pituitary system has been desensitized and that ovarian responsiveness is normal. These conclusions are based on results obtained from administering estradiol at a dose known to be effective in eliciting gonadotropin surges in cycling macaque monkeys; no response was obtained when given through 180 days in nursing females and 35–49 days in nonnursing females [Williams et al, 1979]. This view is further supported by exogenous gonadotropin treatment in a regimen that normally stimulates follicle growth and which induces follicle development and ovulation within 12 days following parturition [diZerega et al, 1979]. These data attest to a hypothalamic-pituitary deficiency [Plant et al, 1980] rather than an inherent ovarian nonresponsiveness.

An ovary from a 180-day lactating mother can contain numerous developing follicles about 1 mm in diameter (Fig. 38); at least one follicle 1.4 mm in diameter is in early atresia, and the original corpus luteum has regressed. However, if a mother with such an ovary then weans the infant, about 40 days are required until the next spontaneous ovulation occurs [Williams and Hodgen, 1983], which seems lengthy in light of the follicular status of the ovaries (Fig. 38). This suggests that the numerous developing follicles that are present are not being properly stimulated to allow for selection of a dominant follicle, or that these follicles are inherently incapable of responding and a new follicle must be recruited, which requires 40 days.

SUMMARY

The data on primate follicle development obtained during the past few years have clarified numerous aspects of the process, but most of these studies have been limited to macaques, with some valuable data on the final stages in women. Since the majority of primates are monotocous, making them unique among mammals, it is quite possible that the basic mechanisms involved in follicle recruitment and selection are similar in all primates. Their ability to select a single dominant follicle from a developing pool that includes the components of two morphologically separate ovaries reflects a most intricate, hormonally controlled process. In marmosets, where twinning is the norm, each ovary produces a single dominant follicle, which again shows control of the hormonal mechanism within each ovary.

A combination of techniques has been used to obtain the recent information on selection and maturation of the dominant follicle. These include evaluating the structural changes in ovarian follicular architecture and identifying variations in hormonal patterns and follicles after various manipulative procedures involving hemiovariectomy, luteectomy, administration of exogenous hormones, and tissue incubation. Recent studies on the human ovary have supplied valuable insight into the activities of the larger antral follicles, but the opportunities for manipulative studies in the human female are limited, which encourages investigators to pursue most experimental research on nonhuman primates.

The major question remaining, about which very little is known, is recruitment of the dominant follicle. What are the important factors required for the initiation and control of early preantral growth? Since their stimulation is not effected by gonadotropins, the next likely candidates are the steroid hormones. Other possible factors that also need further investigation include prolactin, releasing hormones, and prostaglandins.

The role of prolactin in the luteotropic process in nonprimates has been well established [Greenwald and Rothchild, 1968; Meites et al, 1972], but its involvement in higher primate ovarian activity has been believed to be minor. This view has now been challenged because of its possible involvement in corpus luteum function in women during the normal 28-day cycle [McNatty et al, 1974]. Hyperprolactinemia is known to cause suppression of gonadal function [Lachelin et al, 1977], which can be characterized overtly by luteal-phase defect [Strott et al, 1970]. It now appears that high levels of prolactin have a major influence on normal follicle development prior to selection of the dominant follicle [Kauppila et al, 1982; Ylikorkala and Kauppila, 1981].

When high levels of prolactin are found in human follicular fluid, there are an accompanying marked reduction in FSH accumulation, low estradiol levels, and fewer numbers of granulosa cells [McNatty, 1979]. These could easily account for the luteal-phase defect. These data therefore suggest an involvement of prolactin in folliculogenesis. More insight into the mechanism of action was highlighted after introduction of prolactin to immature rat granulosa cell cultures primed with FSH [Dorrington and Gore-Langton, 1981]. Their results indicated that after 24 hours, prolactin inhibited the FSH-induced aromatase activity, again implying that prolactin can play a role in follicle development. These data and prolactin's concomitant pulsatile release with luteinizing hormone in women [Cetel and Yen, 1983] should stimulate

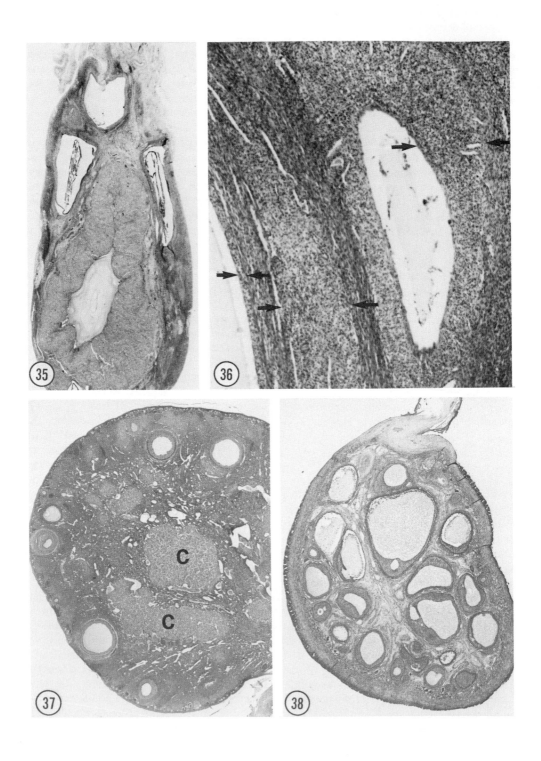

more investigation into the extent of its contribution to the mechanism of folliculogenesis. The high prolactin levels during lactation resulting from the suckling stimulus probably account for the inhibition of ovulation seen in monkeys [Maneckjee et al, 1976] and women [Delvoye et al, 1978].

Another factor having a possible role in follicle growth is gonadotropin-releasing hormone (GnRH). This hypothalamic neuropeptide, whose major effect is stimulation of specific cells in the pituitary gland, also has receptor sites on ovarian granulosa and luteal cells [Hsueh and Jones, 1981]. Because GnRH becomes diluted significantly in the peripheral circulation, this would lead one to believe that its role in ovarian activity would be insignificant. Therefore what the ovary may be recognizing are GnRH-like peptides secreted by extrahypothalamic tissues [Hsueh and Jones, 1981]. The use of GnRH as an ovulation-inducing agent has been only partially successful, although it is now known that ovulation can be successfully triggered by a precise pulsatile administration [Knobil, 1980]. Continuous activation of GnRH receptors by a constant delivery of GnRH results in reduced synthesis and secretion of gonadotropins [Clayton and Catt, 1981]. However, when a GnRH agonist was administered to normally cycling women [Baumann et al, 1980] and monkeys [Werlin and Hodgen, 1983], ovulation was inhibited and was accompanied by decreased pituitary responsiveness to GnRH. In contrast, sequential daily doses also have been shown to induce ovulation in women [Kletzky et al, 1982; Yen, 1983], with pulsatile pharmacologic doses causing multiple preovulatory follicles [Liu et al, 1983].

When cultured rodent granulosa cells were treated with GnRH, there was a direct inhibitory effect both on estrogen production [Hsueh and Jones, 1981] and on the formation of surface receptors [Clayton and Catt, 1981]. In women, a GnRH agonist also affects granulosa cell activity by inhibiting progesterone secretion [Tureck et al, 1982]. Clearly, the data show that GnRH plays a role in folliculogenesis via the pituitary, but whether it has a direct role in controlling follicular cell activity in vivo is unclear, and the results should be interpreted with care [Sopelak et al, 1983; Hodgen, 1983].

Also influencing the folliculogenic process are prostaglandins. These fatty acids are known to play a role in follicular rupture in primates [Wallach et al, 1975], but whether any of the prostaglandins have additional functional activities has not been clarified. When isolated granulosa cells from 4- to 6-mm human follicles were exposed to prostaglandin E, adenyl cyclase activity increased [Armstrong, 1981]. This was also previously observed in the monkey [Channing, 1972], which suggests that it can mimic gonadotropin activity, possibly even in the very early stages of follicle growth prior to the appearance of pituitary gonadotropin receptors [Armstrong, 1981]. The theca interna cells of human follicles are also capable of producing both prostaglandins E and $F_{2\alpha}$ [Plunkett et al, 1975].

Although numerous questions have been answered, many still remain, and certain of these must be finally addressed in a primate model. Not only will the results aid in the control of primate fertility, but they may even be the key to the prevention of extinction of some species. The scarcity of certain primates, such as the great apes;

Fig. 35. A section through a human ovary at day 165 of pregnancy showing the corpus luteum and three large follicles. The material seen in the follicle lumen is the granulosa cell layer that has moved from the periphery of the follicle (probably an artifact). $5\times$.

Fig. 36. A portion of the same ovary seen in Figure 36. Interstitial gland tissue (between arrows) is seen in the wall of the degenerating antral follicle, in the totally collapsed atretic follicle, and in the partially collapsed atretic follicle. $52\times$.

Fig. 37. A section through an ovary from a pregnant squirrel monkey. Four developing follicles range at their widest diameter between 600 and 800 μm. Portions (C) of the corpus luteum are located between masses of interstitial gland tissue. The clear, small, irregular-shaped structures throughout the section are blood vessels and lymphatics. $11.5\times$.

Fig. 38. A section through an ovary from a postpartum lactating cynomologus monkey 180 days after delivery. Numerous antral follicles are present. The largest follicle is 1.4 mm in diameter and is in early atresia. $14\times$.

the threatened existence of others, such as the marmosets; and the unusual ovarian morphology of the New World monkeys make data acquisition most challenging but also expensive. However, these various constraints should not discourage investigators from probing the ovarian biology of these primates, for it is only through further scientific investigation that basic new knowledge will be obtained.

ACKNOWLEDGMENTS

The author acknowledges the following grants from the National Institutes of Health utilized in obtaining the original previously published and new data: 2T1GM-723, T01-HD-00104, RR-00163 (Wisconsin Regional Primate Research Center), RR-00167 (Oregon Primate Research Center), R01-HD-03087, and N01-HD-7-2835.

The author is most grateful to Dr. H.W. Mossman for his critical reading of this manuscript, to Marian Thor for her editorial contributions, and to Sandra Kosha for her secretarial assistance.

REFERENCES

Adams, E.C; Hertig, A.T. Studies on the human corpus luteum. I. Observations on the ultrastructure of development and regression of the luteal cells during the menstrual cycle. JOURNAL OF CELL BIOLOGY 41:696–715, 1969.

Albrecht, E.D.; Townsley, J.D. Serum progesterone in the pregnant baboon (*Papio papio*). BIOLOGY OF REPRODUCTION 14:610–612, 1976.

Alfert, M. Changes in the staining capacity of nuclear components during cell degeneration. BIOLOGICAL BULLETIN 109:1–12, 1955.

Allen, E. The menstrual cycle of the monkey, *Macacus rhesus:* Observations on normal animals, the effects of removal of the ovaries and the effects of injections of ovarian and placental extracts into the spayed animals. CONTRIBUTIONS TO EMBRYOLOGY 19:1–44, 1927.

Anand Kumar, T.C. Oogenesis in adult prosimian primates. Pp. 82–96 in CONTRIBUTIONS TO PRIMATOLOGY, Vol. 3. W.P. Luckett, ed. Basel, Karger, 1974.

Anderson, E. Follicular morphology. Pp. 91–105 in OVARIAN FOLLICULAR DEVELOPMENT AND FUNCTION. A.R. Midgley; W.A. Sadler, eds. New York, Raven, 1979.

Armstrong, D.T. Prostaglandins and follicular functions. JOURNAL OF REPRODUCTION AND FERTILITY 62:283–291, 1981.

Atkinson, L.E.; Hotchkiss, J.; Fritz, G.R.; Surve, A.H.; Neill, J.D.; Knobil, E. Circulating levels of steroids and chorionic gonadotropin during pregnancy in the rhesus monkey, with special attention to the rescue of the corpus luteum in early pregnancy. BIOLOGY OF REPRODUCTION 12:335–345, 1975.

Baca, M.; Zamboni, L. The fine structure of human follicular oocytes. JOURNAL OF ULTRASTRUCTURE RESEARCH 19:354–381, 1967.

Bacsich, P. Multinuclear ova and multiovular follicles in the young human ovary and their probable endocrinological significance. JOURNAL OF ENDOCRINOLOGY 6:i–ii, 1949.

Baird, D.T.; Fraser, I.S. Blood production and ovarian secretion rates of estradiol-17β and estrone in women throughout the menstrual cycle. JOURNAL OF CLINICAL ENDOCRINOLOGY AND METABOLISM 38:1009–1017, 1974.

Baker, T.G. A quantitative and cytological study of germ cells in human ovaries. PROCEEDINGS OF THE ROYAL SOCIETY, LONDON, SERIES B 158:417–433, 1963.

Baker, T.G. A qualitative and cytological study of oogenesis in the rhesus monkey. JOURNAL OF ANATOMY 100:761–776, 1966.

Baker, T.G. The control of oogenesis in mammals. Pp. 353–364 in OVARIAN FOLLICULAR DEVELOPMENT AND FUNCTION. A.R. Midgley; W.A. Sadler, eds. New York, Raven, 1979.

Balboni, G.C. Histology of the ovary. Pp. 1–24 in THE ENDOCRINE FUNCTION OF THE HUMAN OVARY. V.H.T. Jones; M. Serio; G. Giusti, eds. New York, Academic Press, 1976.

Barton, B.R.; Hertig, A.T. Ultrastructure of annulate lamellae in primary oocytes of chimpanzees (*Pan troglodytes*). BIOLOGY OF REPRODUCTION 6:98–108, 1972.

Barton, B.R.; Hertig, A.T. Ultrastructure of quiescent oocytes of *Cebus albifrons*. JOURNAL OF ANATOMY 120:227–238, 1975.

Baumann, R.; Kuhl, H.; Taubert, H.-D.; Sandow, J. Ovulation inhibition by daily i.m. administration of a highly active LH-RH analog [D-Ser(TBU)⁶-LH-RH-(1-9)-nonapeptide-ethylamide]. CONTRACEPTION 21:191–196, 1980.

Betteridge, K.J.; Kelly, W.A.; Marston, J.H. Morphology of the rhesus monkey ovary near the time of ovulation. JOURNAL OF REPRODUCTION AND FERTILITY 22:453–459, 1970.

Block, E. Quantitative morphological investigations of the follicular system in women. Methods of quantitative determination. ACTA ANATOMICA 12:267–285, 1951a.

Block, E. Quantitative morphological investigations of the follicular system in women. Variations in the different phases of the sexual cycle. ACTA ENDO-

CRINOLOGICA 8:33–54, 1951b.

Block, E. Quantitative morphological investigations of the follicular system in women. Variations at different ages. ACTA ANATOMICA 14:108–123, 1952.

Block, E. A quantitative morphological investigation of the follicular system in newborn female infants. ACTA ANATOMICA 17:201–206, 1953.

Bogart, M.H.; Kumamoto, A.T.; Lasley, B.L. A comparison of the reproductive cycle of three species of *Lemur*. FOLIA PRIMATOLOGICA 28:134–143, 1977.

Bomsel-Helmreich, O.; Gougeon, A.; Thebault, A.; Saltarelli, D.; Milgrom, E.; Frydman, R.; Papiernik, E. Healthy and atretic human follicles in the preovulatory phase: Differences in evolution of follicular morphology and steroid content of follicular fluid. JOURNAL OF CLINICAL ENDOCRINOLOGY AND METABOLISM 48:686–694, 1979.

Bonney, R.C.; Dixson, A.F.; Fleming, D. Cyclic changes in the circulating and urinary levels of ovarian steroids in the adult female owl monkey (*Aotus trivirgatus*). JOURNAL OF REPRODUCTION AND FERTILITY 56:271–280, 1979.

Bowers, C.L.; Elton, R.H. Synchronization of menstrual cycles in pigtailed macaques using photoperiod. JOURNAL OF MEDICAL PRIMATOLOGY 11:252–256, 1982.

Brailly, S.; Gougeon, A.; Milgrom, E.; Bomsel-Helmreich, O.; Papiernik, E. Androgens and progestins in the human ovarian follicle: Differences in the evolution of preovulatory, healthy nonovulatory, and atretic follicles. JOURNAL OF CLINICAL ENDOCRINOLOGY AND METABOLISM 53:128–134, 1981.

Brailly, S.; Gougeon, A.; Milgrom, E.; Bomsel-Helmreich, O.; Papiernik, E. Importance of changes in the transformation of progestin into androgen during preovulatory development and atresia of human follicles. Pp. 180–187 in FOLLICULAR MATURATION AND OVULATION. R. Rolland; E.V. van Hall; S.G. Hillier; K.P. McNatty; J. Schoemaker, eds. Amsterdam, Excerpta Medica, 1982.

Brambell, F.W.R. Ovarian changes. Pp. 397–542 in MARSHALL'S PHYSIOLOGY OF REPRODUCTION, Vol. I. A.S. Parkes, ed. London, Longmans, 1960.

Brand, H.M. Urinary oestrogen excretion in the female cotton-topped tamarin (*Saguinus oedipus oedipus*). JOURNAL OF REPRODUCTION AND FERTILITY 62:467–473, 1981.

Buettner-Janusch, J. The breeding of galagos in captivity and some notes on their behavior. FOLIA PRIMATOLOGICA 2:93–110, 1964.

Burden, H.W.; Lawrence, I.E. Nerve supply of the ovary. Pp. 99–105 in BIOLOGY OF THE OVARY. P.M. Motta; E.S.E. Hafez, eds. Boston, Martinus Nijhoff, 1980.

Burton, G.J. Ovarian morphology of the dusky leaf monkey (*Presbytis obscura*): Follicular development and atresia. JOURNAL OF ANATOMY 133:443–458, 1981.

Butler, H. Some notes on the breeding cycle of the Senegal galago *Galago senegalensis senegalensis* in the Sudan. PROCEEDINGS OF THE ZOOLOGICAL SOCIETY OF LONDON 135:423–430, 1960.

Butler, H. The oestrus cycle of the Senegal bush baby (*Galago senegalensis senegalensis*) in the Sudan. JOURNAL OF ZOOLOGY LONDON 151:143–162, 1967.

Butler, H. Evolutionary trends in primate sex cycles. Pp. 2–35 in CONTRIBUTIONS TO PRIMATOLOGY, Vol. 3. W.P. Luckett, ed. Basel, Karger, 1974.

Byskov, A.G. Atresia. Pp. 41–57 in OVARIAN FOLLICULAR DEVELOPMENT AND FUNCTION. A.R. Midgley; W.A. Sadler, eds. New York, Raven, 1979.

Cetel, N.S.; Yen, S.S.C. Concomitant pulsatile release of prolactin and luteinizing hormone in hypogonadal women. JOURNAL OF CLINICAL ENDOCRINOLOGY AND METABOLISM 56:1313–1315, 1983.

Chambers, P.L.; Hearn, J.P. Peripheral plasma levels of progesterone, oestradiol-17β, oestrone, testosterone, androstenedione and chorionic gonadotropin during pregnancy in the marmoset monkey, *Callithrix jacchus*. JOURNAL OF REPRODUCTION AND FERTILITY 56:23–32, 1979.

Chandrashekar, V.; Wolf, R.C.; Dierschke, D.J.; Sholl, S.A.; Bridson, W.E.; Clark, J.R. Serum progesterone and corpus luteum function in pregnant pigtailed monkeys (*Macaca nemestrina*). STEROIDS 36:483–495, 1980.

Channing, C.P. Stimulatory effects of prostaglandins upon luteinization of rhesus monkey granulosa cell cultures. PROSTAGLANDINS 2:331–349, 1972.

Channing, C.P.; Coudert, S.P. Contribution of granulosa cells and follicular fluid to ovarian estrogen secretion in the rhesus monkey in vivo. ENDOCRINOLOGY 98:590–597, 1976.

Channing, C.P.; Anderson, L.D.; Batta, S.K. Follicular growth and development. CLINICS IN OBSTETRICS AND GYNECOLOGY 5:375–389, 1978.

Channing, C.P.; Anderson, L.D.; Hoover, D.J.; Gagliano, P.; Hodgen, G. Inhibitory effects of porcine follicular fluid on monkey serum FSH levels and follicular maturation. BIOLOGY OF REPRODUCTION 25:885–903, 1981.

Channing, C.P.; Anderson, L.D.; Hoover, D.J.; Kolena, J.; Osteen, K.G.; Pomerantz, S.H.; Tanabe, K. The role of nonsteroidal regulators in control of oocyte and follicular maturation. RECENT PROGRESS IN HORMONE RESEARCH 38:331–408, 1982.

Christensen, A.K.; Gillim, S.W. The correlation of fine structure and function in steroid-secreting cells, with emphasis on those of the gonads. Pp. 415–488 in THE GONADS. K.W. McKerns, ed. New York, Appleton-Century-Crofts, 1969.

Chrousos, G.P.; Renquist, D.; Brandon, D.; Barnard, D.; Fowler, D.; Loriaux, D.L.; Lipsett, M.B. The squirrel monkey: Receptor-mediated end-organ resistance to progesterone? JOURNAL OF CLINICAL ENDOCRINOLOGY AND METABOLISM 55:364–368, 1982.

Clark, J.R.; Dierschke, D.J.; Wolf, R.C. Estrogen-induced follicular atresia in rhesus monkeys. Pp. 71–74 in OVARIAN FOLLICULAR DEVELOPMENT AND FUNCTION. A.R. Midgley; W.A. Sadler, eds. New York, Raven, 1979a.

Clark, J.R.; Dierschke, D.J.; Meller, P.A.; Wolf, R.C. Hormonal regulation of ovarian folliculogenesis in rhesus monkeys. II. Serum concentrations of estradiol 17β and follicle stimulating hormone associated with growth and identification of the preovulatory follicle. BIOLOGY OF REPRODUCTION 21:497–503, 1979b.

Clayton, R.N.; Catt, K.J. Gonadotropin-releasing hormone receptors: Characterization, physiological regulation, and relationship to reproductive function. ENDOCRINE REVIEWS 2:186–209, 1981.

Corner, G.W. Ovulation and menstruation in Macacus rhesus. CONTRIBUTIONS TO EMBRYOLOGY 15:73–101, 1923.

Corner, G.W. The menstrual cycle of the Malayan monkey, Macaca iris. ANATOMICAL RECORD 52:401–410, 1932.

Corner, G.W. Accessory corpora lutea in the ovary of the monkey Macaca rhesus. ANALES DE LA FACULTAD DE MEDICINA DE MONTEVIDEO 25:553–560, 1940.

Coulam, C.B. Premature gonadal failure. FERTILITY AND STERILITY 38:645–655, 1982.

Cowgill, U.M.; Bishop, A.; Andrew, R.J.; Hutchinson, G.E. An apparent lunar periodicity in the sexual cycle of certain prosimians. PROCEEDINGS OF THE NATIONAL ACADEMY OF SCIENCES USA 48:238–241, 1962.

Crisp, T.M.; Channing, C.P. Fine structural events correlated with progestin secretion during luteinization of rhesus monkey granulosa cells in culture. BIOLOGY OF REPRODUCTION 7:55–72, 1972.

Crisp, T.M.; Dessouky, D.A.; Denys, F.R. The fine structure of the human corpus luteum of early pregnancy and during the progestational phase of the menstrual cycle. AMERICAN JOURNAL OF ANATOMY 127:37–70, 1970.

Crisp, T.M.; Dessouky, D.A.; Denys, F.R. The fine structure of the human corpus luteum of term pregnancy. AMERICAN JOURNAL OF OBSTETRICS AND GYNECOLOGY 115:901–911, 1973.

Csapo, A.I.; Pulkkinen, M.O.; Ruttner, B.; Sauvage, J.P.; Wiest, W.G. The significance of the human corpus luteum in pregnancy maintenance. AMERICAN JOURNAL OF OBSTETRICS AND GYNECOLOGY 112:1061–1067, 1972.

Dailey, R.A.; Neill, J.D. Seasonal variation in reproductive hormones of rhesus monkeys: Anovulatory and short luteal phase menstrual cycles. BIOLOGY OF REPRODUCTION 25:560–567, 1981.

David, G.F.X.; Ramaswami, L.S. Reproductive systems of the North Indian langur (Presbytis entellus entellus Dufresne). JOURNAL OF MORPHOLOGY 135:99–130, 1971.

Dekel, N.; David, M.P.; Yedwab, G.A.; Kraicer, P.F. Follicular development during late human pregnancy. INTERNATIONAL JOURNAL OF FERTILITY 22:24–29, 1977.

Delvoye, P.; Demaegd, M.; Uwayitu-Nyampeta; Robyn, C. Serum prolactin, gonadotropins, and estradiol in menstruating and amenorrheic mothers during two years' lactation. AMERICAN JOURNAL OF OBSTETRICS AND GYNECOLOGY 130:635–639, 1978.

Dempsey, E.W. The reproductive cycle of New World monkeys. AMERICAN JOURNAL OF ANATOMY 64:381–397, 1939.

Dempsey, E.W. The structure of the reproductive tract in the female gibbon. AMERICAN JOURNAL OF ANATOMY 67:229–253, 1940.

Dewan, E.M.; Menkin, M.F.; Rock, J. Effect of photic stimulation on the human menstrual cycle. PHOTOCHEMISTRY AND PHOTOBIOLOGY 27:581–585, 1978.

Diamond, E.J.; Aksel, S.; Hazelton, J.M.; Jennings, R.A.; Abee, C.R. Seasonal changes of serum concentration of estradiol and progesterone in Bolivian squirrel monkeys (Saimiri sciureus) AMERICAN JOURNAL OF PRIMATOLOGY, 6:103–113, 1984.

Dierschke, D.J.; Karsch, F.J.; Weick, R.F.; Weiss, G.; Hotchkiss, J.; Knobil, E. Hypothalamic-pituitary regulation of puberty: Feedback control of gonadotropin secretion in the rhesus monkey. Pp. 104–114 in CONTROL OF THE ONSET OF PUBERTY. M.M. Grumbach; G.D. Grave; F.E. Mayer, eds. New York, Wiley, 1974.

Dixson, A.F. The owl monkey (Aotus trivirgatus). Pp. 71–114 in REPRODUCTION IN NEW WORLD PRIMATES. J. Hearn, ed. Boston, MTP Press, 1983.

diZerega, G.S. LH/hCG receptor desensitization in the monkey corpus luteum during pregnancy. SOCIETY FOR THE STUDY OF REPRODUCTION. Abstract 9, 1981.

diZerega, G.S.; Hodgen, G.D. Pregnancy-associated ovarian refractoriness to gonadotropin: A myth. AMERICAN JOURNAL OF OBSTETRICS AND GYNECOLOGY 134:819–822, 1979.

diZerega, G.S.; Hodgen, G.D. The primate ovarian cycle: Suppression of human menopausal gonadotropin-induced follicular growth in the presence of the dominant follicle. JOURNAL OF CLINICAL ENDOCRINOLOGY AND METABOLISM 50:819–825, 1980a.

diZerega, G.S.; Hodgen, G.D. Cessation of folliculogenesis during the primate luteal phase. JOURNAL OF CLINICAL ENDOCRINOLOGY AND METABOLISM 51:158–160, 1980b.

diZerega, G.S.; Hodgen, G.D. Folliculogenesis in the primate ovarian cycle. ENDOCRINE REVIEWS 2:27–49, 1981.

diZerega, G.S.; Hodgen, G.D. The interovarian progesterone gradient: A spatial and temporal regulator of folliculogenesis in the primate ovarian cycle. JOURNAL OF CLINICAL ENDOCRINOLOGY AND METABOLISM 54:495–499, 1982.

diZerega, G.S.; Williams, R.F.; Morin, M.L.; Hodgen, G.D. Anovulation after pregnancy termination: Ovarian versus hypothalamic-pituitary factors. JOURNAL OF CLINICAL ENDOCRINOLOGY AND METABOLISM 49:594–599, 1979.

diZerega, G.S.; Nixon, W.E.; Hodgen, G.D. Intercycle serum follicle-stimulating hormone elevations: Significance in recruitment and selection of the dominant follicle and assessment of corpus luteum normalcy. JOURNAL OF CLINICAL ENDOCRINOLOGY AND METABOLISM 50:1046–1048, 1980a.

diZerega, G.S.; Marut, E.L.; Turner, C.K.; Hodgen, G.D. Asymmetrical ovarian function during recruitment and selection of the dominant follicle in the menstrual cycle of the rhesus monkey. JOURNAL OF CLINICAL ENDOCRINOLOGY AND METABOLISM 51:698–701, 1980b.

diZerega, G.S.; Turner, C.K.; Stouffer, R.L.; Anderson, L.D.; Channing, C.P.; Hodgen, G.D. Suppression of follicle-stimulating hormone-dependent folliculogenesis during the primate ovarian cycle. JOURNAL OF CLINICAL ENDOCRINOLOGY AND METABOLISM 52:451–456, 1981.

Döring, G.K. The incidence of anovular cycles in women. JOURNAL OF REPRODUCTION AND FERTILITY, SUPPLEMENT 6:77–81, 1969.

Dorrington, J.; Gore-Langton, R.E. Prolactin inhibits oestrogen synthesis in the ovary. NATURE 290:600–602, 1981.

Dukelow, W.R. The squirrel monkey. Pp. 149–180 in REPRODUCTION IN NEW WORLD PRIMATES. J. Hearn, ed. Boston, MTP Press, 1983.

Dukelow, W.R.; Grauwiler, J.; Brüggemann, S. Characteristics of the menstrual cycle in nonhuman primates. I. Similarities and dissimilarities between Macaca fascicularis and Macaca arctoides. JOURNAL OF MEDICAL PRIMATOLOGY 8:39–47, 1979.

Dvořák, M.; Tesařík, J. Ultrastructure of human ovarian follicles. Pp. 121–137 in BIOLOGY OF THE OVARY. P.M. Motta; E.S.E. Hafez, eds. Boston,

Martinus Nijhoff, 1980.

Epple, J.; Katz, Y. The saddle back tamarin and other tamarins. Pp. 115–148 in REPRODUCTION IN NEW WORLD PRIMATES. J. Hearn, ed. Boston, MTP Press, 1983.

Eshkol, A.; Lunenfeld, B.; Peters, H. Ovarian development in infant mice. Dependence on gonadotrophic hormones. Pp. 249–258 in GONADOTROPINS AND OVARIAN DEVELOPMENT. E.R. Butt; A.C. Crooke; M. Ryle, eds. London, Livingstone, 1970.

Espey, L.L. Ovarian contractility and its relationship to ovulation: A review. BIOLOGY OF REPRODUCTION 19:540–551, 1978.

Faddy, M.J.; Gosden, R.G.; Edwards, R.G. Ovarian follicle dynamics in mice: A comparative study of three inbred stains and a F_1 hybrid. JOURNAL OF ENDOCRINOLOGY 96:23–33, 1983.

Fowler, R.E.; Fox, N.L.; Edwards, R.G.; Steptoe, P.C. Steroid production from 17α-hydroxypregnenolone and dehydroepiandrosterone by human granulosa cells in vitro. JOURNAL OF REPRODUCTION AND FERTILITY 54:109–117, 1978.

French, J.A.; Abbott, D.H.; Scheffler, G.; Robinson, J.A.; Goy, R.W. Cyclic excretion of urinary oestrogens in female tamarins (Saguinus oedipus). JOURNAL OF REPRODUCTION AND FERTILITY 68:177–184, 1983.

Gengozian, N.; Merritt, C.B. Effect of unilateral ovariectomy on twinning frequency in the marmoset. JOURNAL OF REPRODUCTION AND FERTILITY 23:509–512, 1970.

Ghosh, M.; Hutz, R.J.; Dukelow, W.R. Serum estradiol 17β, progesterone, and relative luteinizing hormone levels in Saimiri sciureus: Cyclic variations and the effect of laparoscopy and follicular aspiration. JOURNAL OF MEDICAL PRIMATOLOGY 11:312–318, 1982.

Gillet, J.Y.; Maillet, R.; Gautier, C. Blood and lymph supply of the ovary. Pp. 86–98 in BIOLOGY OF THE OVARY. P.M. Motta, E.S.E. Hafez, eds. Boston, Martinus Nijhoff, 1980.

Gillim, S.W.; Christensen, A.K.; McLennan, C.E. Fine structure of the human menstrual corpus luteum at its stage of maximum secretory activity. AMERICAN JOURNAL OF ANATOMY 126:409–428, 1969.

Goldman, H. Catecholamine-induced redistribution of blood flow in the unanesthetized rat. AMERICAN JOURNAL OF PHYSIOLOGY 210:1419–1423, 1966.

Goldsmith, L.T.; Hochman, J.A.; Weiss, G. Effect of human placental lactogen upon the human corpus luteum of late pregnancy. GYNECOLOGICAL AND OBSTETRICAL INVESTIGATION 9:210–218, 1978.

Goldzieher, J.W. Polycystic ovarian disease. FERTILITY AND STERILITY 35:371–394, 1981.

Goodman, A.L.; Hodgen, G.D. Post partum patterns of circulating FSH, LH, prolactin, estradiol, and progesterone in nonsuckling cynomolgus monkeys. STEROIDS 31:731–744, 1978.

Goodman, A.L.; Hodgen, G.D. The ovarian triad of the primate ovarian cycle. RECENT PROGRESS IN HORMONE RESEARCH 39:1, 1983.

Goodman, A.L.; Nixon, W.E.; Johnson, D.K.; Hodgen, G.D. Regulation of folliculogenesis in the cycling rhesus monkey: Selection of the dominant follicle. ENDOCRINOLOGY 100:155–161, 1977.

Goodman, A.L.; Koering, M.J.; Nixon, W.E.; Williams, R.F.; Hodgen, G.D. Follicle dominance and ovarian asymmetry after luteectomy in rhesus monkeys. AMERICAN JOURNAL OF PHYSIOLOGY 243:E325–E331, 1982.

Goodman, L.; Wislocki, G.B. Cyclical uterine bleeding in a New World monkey (Ateles geoffroyi). ANATOMICAL RECORD 61:379–381, 1935.

Gougeon, A. Qualitative changes in medium and large antral follicles in the human ovary during the menstrual cycle. ANNALES DE BIOLOGIE ANIMALE BIOCHIMIE ET BIOPHYSIQUE 19:1461–1468, 1979.

Gougeon, A. Frequent occurrence of multiovular follicles and multinuclear oocytes in the adult human ovary. FERTILITY AND STERILITY 35:417–422, 1981a.

Gougeon, A. Cinétique de la croissance et de l'involution des follicules ovariens pendant le cycle menstruel chez la femme. Thèse de doctorat d'état es sciences naturelles, University of Paris, 1981b.

Gougeon, A. Rate of follicular growth in the human ovary. Pp. 155–163 in FOLLICULAR MATURATION AND OVULATION. R. Rolland; E.V. van Hall; S.G. Hillier; K.P. McNatty; J. Schoemaker, eds. Amsterdam, Excerpta Medica, 1982.

Govan, A.D.T. The human ovary in early pregnancy. JOURNAL OF ENDOCRINOLOGY 40:421–428, 1968.

Govan, A.D.T. Ovarian follicular activity in late pregnancy. JOURNAL OF ENDOCRINOLOGY 48:235–241, 1970.

Graham, C.E.; Bradley, C.F. Polyovular follicles in squirrel monkeys after prolonged diethylstilboestrol treatment. JOURNAL OF REPRODUCTION AND FERTILITY 27:181–185, 1971.

Green, S.H.; Zuckerman, S. A comparison of the growth of the ovum and follicle in normal rhesus monkeys, and in monkeys treated with oestrogens and androgens. JOURNAL OF ENDOCRINOLOGY 5:207–219, 1947.

Green, S.H.; Zuckerman, S. The number of oocytes in the mature rhesus monkey (Macaca mulatta). JOURNAL OF ENDOCRINOLOGY 7:194–202, 1951.

Green, S.H.; Zuckerman, S. Further observations on oocyte numbers in mature rhesus monkeys (Macaca mulatta). JOURNAL OF ENDOCRINOLOGY 10:284–290, 1954.

Greenwald, G.S. Follicular activity in the mammalian ovary. Pp. 639–689 in VERTEBRATE OVARY. R.E. Jones, ed. New York, Plenum, 1978.

Greenwald, G.S.; Rothchild, I. Formation and maintenance of corpora lutea in laboratory mammals, JOURNAL OF ANIMAL SCIENCE 27 SUPPLEMENT I:139–162, 1968.

Grinsted, J.; Peters, H. The human ovary during puberty. ANNALES DE BIOLOGIE ANIMALE BIOCHIMIE ET BIOPHYSIQUE 19:1455–1460, 1979.

Gulyas, B.J. The corpus luteum of the rhesus monkey (Macaca mulatta) during late pregnancy. An electron microscopic study. AMERICAN JOURNAL OF ANATOMY 139:95–122, 1974.

Harding, R.D.; Hulme, M.J.; Lunn, S.F.; Henderson, C.; Aitken, R.J. Plasma progesterone levels throughout the ovarian cycle of the common marmoset (Callithrix jacchus). JOURNAL OF MEDICAL PRIMATOLOGY 11:43–51, 1982.

Harrison, R.J. Multiovular follicles in the ovaries of lower primates. NATURE 164:409–410, 1949.

Harrison, R.J.; Weir, B. Structure of the mammalian ovary. Pp. 113–218 in THE OVARY, Vol. I. S. Zuckerman; B. Weir, eds. New York, Academic Press, 1977.

Hartman, C.G. Polynuclear ova and polyovular follicles in the opossum and other mammals, with special reference to the problem of fecundity. AMERICAN JOURNAL OF ANATOMY 37:1–51, 1926.

Hartman, C.G. Studies in the reproduction of the monkey Macacus (Pithecus) rhesus, with special reference to menstruation and pregnancy. CONTRIBUTIONS TO EMBRYOLOGY 23:1–161, 1932.

Hartman, C.G. Non-effect of ovariectomy on the twenty-fifth day of pregnancy in the rhesus monkey. PROCEEDINGS OF THE SOCIETY FOR EXPERIMENTAL BIOLOGY AND MEDICINE 48:221–223, 1941.

Hartman, C.G.; Corner, G.W. The first maturation division of the macaque ovum. CONTRIBUTIONS TO EMBRYOLOGY 29:1–6, 1941.

Heape, W. The menstruation of Semnopithecus entellus. PHILOSOPHICAL TRANSACTIONS OF THE ROYAL SOCIETY 185B:411–471, 1894.

Hearn, J.P. The common marmoset (Callithrix jacchus). Pp. 181–216 in REPRODUCTION IN NEW WORLD PRIMATES. J. Hearn, ed. Boston, MTP Press, 1983.

Hearn, J.P.; Abbott, D.H.; Chambers, P.C.; Hodges, J.K.; Lunn, S.F. Use of the common marmoset, Callithrix jacchus, in reproductive research. PRIMATE MEDICINE 10:40–49, 1978.

Hertig, A.T.; Adams, E.C. Studies on the human oocyte and its follicle. I. Ultrastructural and histochemical observations on the primordial follicle stage. JOURNAL OF CELL BIOLOGY 34:647–675, 1967.

Hertig, A.T.; Barton, B.R. Fine structure of mammalian oocytes and ova. Pp. 317–348 in HANDBOOK OF PHYSIOLOGY, Section 7, ENDOCRINOLOGY, Vol. II, FEMALE REPRODUCTIVE SYSTEM. R.O. Greep; E.B. Astwood, eds. Washington, American Physiological Society, 1973.

Hertig, A.T.; King, N.W. Jr.; Barton, B.R.; Johnson, L.D.; Mackey, J.J.; Bates, C. Observations on the ovary of the squirrel monkey, *Saimiri sciureus*, using the light and electron microscope. Pp. 472–503 in MEDICAL PRIMATOLOGY. E.I. Goldsmith; J. Moor-Jankowski, eds. Basel, Karger, 1971.

Hess, D.L.; Resko, J.A. The effects of progesterone on the patterns of testosterone and estradiol concentrations in the systemic plasma of the female rhesus monkey during the intermenstrual period. ENDOCRINOLOGY 92:446–453, 1973.

Hess, D.L.; Hendrickx, A.G.; Stabenfeldt, G.H. Reproductive and hormonal patterns in the African green monkey (*Cercopithecus aethiops*). JOURNAL OF MEDICAL PRIMATOLOGY 8:273–281, 1979.

Hill, J.P. Demonstration of the embryologia varia (development of *Hapale jacchus*). JOURNAL OF ANATOMY 60:486–487, 1926.

Hillier, S.G. Regulation of follicular oestrogen biosynthesis: A survey of current concepts. JOURNAL OF ENDOCRINOLOGY 89:3P–18P, 1981.

Hillier, S.G.; Reichert, L.E.; Van Hall, E.V. Control of preovulatory follicular estrogen biosynthesis in the human ovary. JOURNAL OF CLINICAL ENDOCRINOLOGY AND METABOLISM 52:847–856, 1981.

Hillier, S.G.; Van Hall, E.V.; Van den Boogaard, A.J.M.; De Zwart, F.A.; Keyzer, R. Activation and modulation of the granulosa cell aromatase system: Experimental studies with rat and human ovaries. Pp. 51–70 in FOLLICULAR MATURATION AND OVULATION. R. Rolland; E.V. van Hall; S.G. Hillier; K.P. McNatty; J. Schoemaker, eds. Amsterdam, Excerpta Medica, 1982.

Himelstein-Braw, R.; Byskov. A.G.; Peters, H.; Faber, M. Follicular atresia in the infant human ovary. JOURNAL OF REPRODUCTION AND FERTILITY 46:55–59, 1976.

Hirshfield, A.N.; Midgley, A.R. Morphometric analysis of follicular development in the rat. BIOLOGY OF REPRODUCTION 19:597–605, 1978.

Hodgen, G.D. Releasing hormones as diagnostic and therapeutic agents. FERTILITY AND STERILITY 39:592–593, 1983.

Hodgen, G.D.; Dufau, M.L.; Catt, K.J.; Tullner, W.W. Estrogens, progesterone and chorionic gonadotropin in pregnant rhesus monkeys. ENDOCRINOLOGY 91:896–900, 1972.

Hodgen, G.D.; Stouffer, R.L.; Barber, D.L.; Nixon, W.E. Serum estradiol and progesterone during pregnancy and the status of the corpus luteum at delivery in cynomolgus monkeys (*Macaca fascicularis*). STEROIDS 30:295–301, 1977.

Hodges, J.K.; Gulick, B.A.; Czekala, N.M.; Lasley, B.L. Comparison of urinary oestrogen excretion in South American primates. JOURNAL OF REPRODUCTION AND FERTILITY 61:83–90, 1981.

Hope, J. The fine structure of the developing follicle of the rhesus monkey. JOURNAL OF ULTRASTRUCTURE RESEARCH 12:592–610, 1965.

Hsueh, A.J.W.; Jones, P.B.C. Extrapituitary actions of gonadotropin-releasing hormone. ENDOCRINE REVIEWS 2:437–461, 1981.

Jacobowitz, D.; Wallach, E.E. Histochemical and chemical studies of the autonomic innervation of the ovary. ENDOCRINOLOGY 81:1132–1139, 1967.

Jarosz, S.J.; Kuehl, T.J.; Dukelow, W.R. Vaginal cytology, induced ovulation and gestation in the squirrel monkey (*Saimiri sciureus*). BIOLOGY OF REPRODUCTION 16:97–103, 1977.

Jewett, D.A.; Dukelow, W.R. Follicular morphology in *Macaca fascicularis*. FOLIA PRIMATOLOGICA 16:216–220, 1971.

Jewett, D.A.; Dukelow, W.R. Serial observations of follicular morphology near ovulation in *Macaca fascicularis*. JOURNAL OF REPRODUCTION AND FERTILITY 31:287–290, 1972.

Jones, G.S. Induction of ovulation. ANNUAL REVIEW OF MEDICINE 19:351–372, 1968.

Kauppila, A.; Leinonen, P.; Vihko, R.; Ylostalo, P. Metoclopramide-induced hyperprolactinemia impairs ovarian follicle maturation and corpus luteum function in women. JOURNAL OF CLINICAL ENDOCRINOLOGY AND METABOLISM 54:955–960, 1982.

Keller, L. Observation on ovarian nerves. ZEITSCHRIFT FÜR ZELLFORSCHUNG UND MIKROSKOPISCHE ANATOMIE. ABTEILUNG HISTOCHEMIE 69:284–287, 1966.

Kirton, K.T.; Niswender, G.G.; Midgley, A.R.; Jaffe, R.B.; Forbes, A.D. Serum luteinizing hormone and progesterone concentration during the menstrual cycle of the rhesus monkey. JOURNAL OF CLINICAL ENDOCRINOLOGY AND METABOLISM 30:105–110, 1970.

Kletzky, O.A.; Davajan, V.; Mishell, D.R. The effect of gonadotropin-releasing hormone on ovarian estradiol secretion. AMERICAN JOURNAL OF OBSTETRICS AND GYNECOLOGY 142:427–431, 1982.

Knobil, E. On the regulation of the primate corpus luteum. BIOLOGY OF REPRODUCTION 8:246–258, 1973.

Knobil, E. On the control of gonadotropin secretion in the rhesus monkey. RECENT PROGRESS IN HOR-

MONE RESEARCH 30:1–46, 1974.

Knobil, E. The neuroendocrine control of the menstrual cycle. RECENT PROGRESS IN HORMONE RESEARCH 36:53–88, 1980.

Knobil, E.; Plant, T.M.; Wildt, L.; Belchetz, P.E.; Marshall, G. Control of the rhesus monkey menstrual cycle: Permissive role of hypothalamic gonadotropin-releasing hormone. SCIENCE 207:1371–1373, 1980.

Koering, M.J. Cyclic changes in ovarian morphology during the menstrual cycle in *Macaca mulatta*. AMERICAN JOURNAL OF ANATOMY 126:73–101, 1969.

Koering, M.J. Comparative morphology of the primate ovary. Pp. 38–81 in CONTRIBUTIONS TO PRIMATOLOGY, Vol. 3. W.P. Luckett, ed. Basel, Karger, 1974.

Koering, M.J. Folliculogenesis in primates: Process of maturation and atresia. Pp. 187–199 in ANIMAL MODELS FOR RESEARCH ON CONTRACEPTION AND FERTILITY. N.J. Alexander, ed. Hagerstown, MD, Harper and Row, 1979.

Koering, M.J. Preantral follicle development during the menstrual cycle in the *Macaca mulatta* ovary. AMERICAN JOURNAL OF ANATOMY 166:429–443, 1983.

Koering, M.J.; Wolf, R.C.; Meyer, R.K. Morphological changes in the corpus luteum correlated with progestin levels in the rhesus monkey during early pregnancy. BIOLOGY OF REPRODUCTION 9:254–271, 1973a.

Koering, M.J.; Wolf, R.C.; Meyer, R.K. Morphological and functional evidence for corpus luteum activity during late pregnancy in the rhesus monkey. ENDOCRINOLOGY 93:686–693, 1973b.

Koering, M.J.; Goodman, A.L.; Williams, R.F.; Hodgen, G.D. Granulosa cell pyknosis in the dominant follicle of monkeys. FERTILITY AND STERILITY 37:837–844, 1982a.

Koering, M.J.; Baehler, E.A.; Goodman, A.L.; Hodgen, G.D. Developing morphological asymmetry of ovarian follicular maturation in monkeys. BIOLOGY OF REPRODUCTION 27:989–998, 1982b.

Krarup, T.; Pedersen, T.; Faber, M. Regulation of oocyte growth in the mouse ovary. NATURE 224:187–188, 1969.

Kuehl, T.J.; Dukelow, W.R. Ovulation induction during the anovulatory season in *Saimiri sciureus*. JOURNAL OF MEDICAL PRIMATOLOGY 4:23–31, 1975.

Lachelin, G.C.L.; Abu-Fadil, S.; Yen, S.S.G. Functional delineation of hyperprolactinemic-amenorrhea. JOURNAL OF CLINICAL ENDOCRINOLOGY AND METABOLISM 44:1163–1174, 1977.

Lang, C.M. The estrous cycle of the squirrel monkey (*Saimiri sciureus*). LABORATORY ANIMAL CARE 17:442–451, 1967.

LeMaire, W.J.; Rice, B.F.; Savard, K. Steroid hormone formation in the human ovary. V. Synthesis of progesterone in vitro in corpora lutea during the reproductive cycle. JOURNAL OF CLINICAL ENDOCRINOLOGY AND METABOLISM 28:1249–1256, 1968.

LeMaire, W.J.; Conly, P.W.; Moffett, A.; Cleveland, W.W. Plasma progesterone secretion by the corpus luteum of term pregnancy. AMERICAN JOURNAL OF OBSTETRICS AND GYNECOLOGY 108:132–134, 1970.

Leuchtenberger, C. A cytochemical study of pycnotic nuclear degeneration. CHROMOSOMA 3:449–473, 1950.

Lintern-Moore, S.; Peters, H.; Moore, G.P.M.; Faber, M. Follicular development in the infant human ovary. JOURNAL OF REPRODUCTION AND FERTILITY 39:53–64, 1974.

Liu, J.H.; Durfee, R.; Muse, K.; Yen, S.S.C. Induction of multiple ovulation by pulsatile administration of gonadotropin-releasing hormone. FERTILITY AND STERILITY 40:18–22, 1983.

Lloyd, R.S.; Rubenstein, B.B. Multiple ova in the follicles of juvenile monkeys. ENDOCRINOLOGY 29:1008–1014, 1941.

Maneckjee, R.; Srinath, B.R.; Moudgal, N.R. Prolactin suppresses release of luteinising hormone during lactation in the monkey. NATURE 262:507–508, 1976.

Manley, G.H. Reproduction in lorisoid primates. Pp. 493–500 in COMPARATIVE BIOLOGY OF REPRODUCTION IN MAMMALS. I.W. Rowlands, ed. New York, Academic Press, 1966.

Maqueo, M.; Goldzieher, J.W. Hormone-induced alterations of ovarian morphology. FERTILITY AND STERILITY 17:676–683, 1966.

Marut, E.L.; Hodgen, G.D. Asymmetric secretion of principal ovarian venous steroids in the primate luteal phase. STEROIDS 39:461–469, 1982.

McNatty, K.P. Relationship between plasma prolactin and the endocrine microenvironment of the developing human antral follicle. FERTILITY AND STERILITY 32:433–438, 1979.

McNatty, K.P. Ovarian follicular development from the onset of luteal regression in humans and sheep. Pp. 1–18 in FOLLICULAR MATURATION AND OVULATION. R. Rolland; E.V van Hall; S.G. Hillier; K.P. McNatty; J. Schoemaker, eds. Amsterdam, Excerpta Medica, 1982.

McNatty, K.P.; Baird, D.T. Relationship between follicle-stimulating hormone, androstenedione and oestradiol in human follicular fluid. JOURNAL OF ENDOCRINOLOGY 76:527–531, 1978.

McNatty, K.P.; Sawers, R.S.; McNeilly, A.S. A possible role for prolactin in control of steroid secretion by the human Graafian follicle. NATURE 250:653–655, 1974.

McNatty, K.P.; Makris, A.; DeGrazia, C.; Osathan-ondh, R.; Ryan, K.J. The production of progesterone, androgens, and estrogens by granulosa cells, thecal tissue, and stromal tissue from human ovaries in vitro. JOURNAL OF CLINICAL ENDOCRINOLOGY AND METABOLISM 49:687–699, 1979a.

McNatty, K.P.; Smith, D.M.; Makris, A.; Osathan-ondh, R.; Ryan, K.J. The microenvironment of the human antral follicle: Interrelationships among the steroid levels in antral fluid, the population of granulosa cells, and the status of the oocyte in vivo and in vitro. JOURNAL OF CLINICAL ENDOCRINOLOGY AND METABOLISM 49:851–860, 1979b.

McNatty, K.P.; Makris, A.; Reinhold, V.N.; DeGrazia, C.; Osathanondh, R.; Ryan, K.J. Metabolism of androstenedione by human ovarian tissues in vitro with particular reference to reductase and aromatase activity. STEROIDS 34:429–443, 1979c.

McNatty, K.P.; Hillier, S.G.; Van den Boogaard, A.M.J.; Trimbos-Kemper, T.C.M.; Reichert, L.E.; Van Hall, E.V. Follicular development during the luteal phase of the human menstrual cycle. JOURNAL OF CLINICAL ENDOCRINOLOGY AND METABOLISM 56:1022–1031, 1983.

Meites, J.; Lu, K.H.; Wuttke, W.; Welsch, C.W.; Nagasawa, H.; Quadri, S.K. Recent studies on functions and control of prolactin secretion in rats. RECENT PROGRESS IN HORMONE RESEARCH 28:471–516, 1972.

Melinkoff, E. Questionable necessity of the corpus luteum. AMERICAN JOURNAL OF OBSTETRICS AND GYNECOLOGY 60:437–439, 1950.

Monroe, S.E.; Atkinson, L.E.; Knobil, E. Patterns of circulating luteinizing hormone and their relation to plasma progesterone levels during the menstrual cycle of the rhesus monkey. ENDOCRINOLOGY 87:453–455, 1970.

Mossman, H.W. The genital system and the fetal membranes as criteria for mammalian phylogeny and taxonomy. JOURNAL OF MAMMALOGY 34:289–298, 1953.

Mossman, H.W.; Duke, K.L. COMPARATIVE MORPHOLOGY OF THE MAMMALIAN OVARY. Madison, University of Wisconsin Press, 1973.

Mossman, H.W.; Koering, M.J.; Ferry, D. Cyclic changes of interstitial gland tissue of the human ovary. AMERICAN JOURNAL OF ANATOMY 115:235–256, 1964.

Nadler, R.D.; Collins, D.C.; Miller, L.C.; Graham, C.E. Menstrual cycle patterns of hormones and sexual behavior in gorillas. HORMONES AND BEHAVIOR 17:1–17, 1983.

Nagle, C.A.; Denari, J.H. The cebus monkey (Cebus apella). Pp. 39–67 in REPRODUCTION IN NEW WORLD PRIMATES. J. Hearn, ed., Boston, MTP Press, 1983.

Nagle, C.A.; Denari, J.H.; Quiroga, S.; Riarte, A.; Merlo, A.; Germino, N.I.; Gómez-Argaña, F.; Rosner, J.M. The plasma pattern of ovarian steroids during the menstrual cycle in capuchin monkeys (Cebus apella). BIOLOGY OF REPRODUCTION 21:979–983, 1979.

Nass, T.E.; Dierschke, D.J.; Clark, J.R.; Wolf, R.C. The role of FSH and the corpus luteum in folliculogenesis and ovulation in rhesus monkeys. Pp. 135–140 in DYNAMICS OF OVARIAN FUNCTION. N.B. Schwartz; M. Hunzicker-Dunn, eds. New York, Raven, 1981.

Neill, J.D.; Knobil, E. On the nature of the initial luteotropic stimulus of pregnancy in the rhesus monkey. ENDOCRINOLOGY 90:34–38, 1972.

Neill, J.D.; Johansson, E.D.B.; Datta, J.K.; Knobil, E. Relationship between the plasma levels of luteinizing hormone and progesterone during the normal menstrual cycle. JOURNAL OF CLINICAL ENDOCRINOLOGY AND METABOLISM 27:1167–1173, 1967.

Nelson, W.W.; Greene, R.R. Some observations on the histology of the human ovary during pregnancy. AMERICAN JOURNAL OF OBSTETRICS AND GYNECOLOGY 76:66–90, 1958.

Niswender, G.D.; Reimers, T.J.; Diekman, M.A.; Nett, T.M. Blood flow: A mediator of ovarian function. BIOLOGY OF REPRODUCTION 14:64–81, 1976.

Nixon, W.E.; Reid, R.; Abouhozaifa, B.; Williams, R.F.; Steinetz, B.G.; Hodgen, G.D. Origin and regulation of relaxin secretion in monkeys: Effects of chorionic gonadotropin, luteectomy, fetectomy and placentectomy. Pp. 427–431 in FACTORS REGULATING OVARIAN FUNCTION. G.S. Greenwald; P. Terranova, eds. New York, Raven, 1983.

O'Herlihy, C.; De Crespigny, L.C.; Lopata, A.; Johnston, I.; Hoult, I.; Robinson, H. Preovulatory follicular size: A comparison of ultrasound and laparoscopic measurements. FERTILITY AND STERILITY 34:24–26, 1980.

Okamura, H.; Virutamasen, P.; Wright, K.H.; Wallach, E.E. Ovarian smooth muscle in the human being, rabbit and cat. Histochemical and electron microscopic study. AMERICAN JOURNAL OF OBSTETRICS AND GYNECOLOGY 112:183–191, 1972.

Omar, A.; De Vos, A. The annual reproductive cycle of an African monkey (Cercopithecus mitis kolbi Neuman). FOLIA PRIMATOLOGICA 16:206–215, 1971.

Owman, C.; Sjöberg, N.-O.; Svensson, K.-G.; Walles, B. Autonomic nerves mediating contractility in the human Graafian follicle. JOURNAL OF REPRODUCTION AND FERTILITY 45:553–556, 1975.

Pedersen, T. Follicle kinetics in the ovary of the cyclic mouse. ACTA ENDOCRINOLOGICA 64:304–323, 1970.

Peters, H. Folliculogenesis in mammals. Pp. 121–144 in THE VERTEBRATE OVARY. R.E. Jones, ed. New York, Plenum, 1978.

Peters, H. Some aspects of early follicular development. Pp. 1–13 in OVARIAN FOLLICULAR DEVELOPMENT AND FUNCTION. A.R. Midgley; W.A. Sadler, eds. New York, Raven, 1979.

Peters, H.; McNatty, K.P. THE OVARY. Berkeley, University of California Press, 1980.

Peters, H.; Byskov, A.G., Faber, M. Intraovarian regulation of follicle growth in the immature mouse. Pp. 20–23 in THE DEVELOPMENT AND MATURATION OF THE OVARY AND ITS FUNCTIONS. International Congress Series No. 267, H. Peters, ed. Amsterdam, Excerpta Medica, 1973.

Peters, H.; Byskov, A.G.; Himelstein-Braw, R.; Faber, M. Follicular growth: The basic event in the mouse and human ovary. JOURNAL OF REPRODUCTION AND FERTILITY 45:559–566, 1975.

Peters, H.; Byskov, A.G.; Grinsted, J. Follicular growth in fetal and prepubertal ovaries of humans and other primates. CLINICS IN ENDOCRINOLOGY AND METABOLISM 7:469–485, 1978.

Plant, T.M.; Schallenberger, E.; Hess, D.L.; McCormack, J.T.; Dufy-Barbe, L.; Knobil, E. Influence of suckling on gonadotropin secretion in the female rhesus monkey (Macaca mulatta). BIOLOGY OF REPRODUCTION 23:760–766, 1980.

Plunkett, E.R.; Moon, Y.S.; Zamecnik, J.; Armstrong, D.T. Preliminary evidence of a role for prostaglandin F in human follicular function. AMERICAN JOURNAL OF OBSTETRICS AND GYNECOLOGY 123:391–397, 1975.

Pohl, C.R.; Richardson, D.W.; Hutchison, J.S.; Germak, J.A.; Knobil, E. Hypophysiotropic signal frequency and the functioning of the pituitary-ovarian system in the rhesus monkey. ENDOCRINOLOGY 112:2076–2080, 1983.

Preslock, J.P.; Hampton, S.H.; Hampton, J.K. Cyclic variations of serum progestins and immunoreactive estrogens in marmosets. ENDOCRINOLOGY 92:1096–1101, 1973.

Ramaswami, L.S.; Anand Kumar, T.C. Some aspects of reproduction of the female slender loris, Loris tardigradus lydekkerianus Cabr. ACTA ZOOLOGICA STOCKHOLM 46:257–273, 1965.

Rao, C.V.; Griffin, L.P.; Carman, F.R. Gonadotropin receptors in human corpora lutea of the menstrual cycle and pregnancy. AMERICAN JOURNAL OF OBSTETRICS AND GYNECOLOGY 128:146–153, 1977.

Rao, C.V.; Sanfilippo, J.; Carman, F.R. Gonadotropin receptors in human corpora lutea of term pregnancies. AMERICAN JOURNAL OF OBSTETRICS AND GYNECOLOGY 132:581–583, 1978.

Reiter, E.O.; Grumbach, M.M. Neuroendocrine control mechanisms and the onset of puberty. ANNUAL REVIEWS OF PHYSIOLOGY 44:595–613, 1982.

Resko, J.A.; Norman, R.L; Niswender, G.D.; Spies, H.G. The relationship between progestins and gonadotropins during the late luteal phase of the menstrual cycle in rhesus monkeys. ENDOCRINOLOGY 94:128–135, 1974.

Resko, J.A.; Koering, M.J.; Goy, R.W.; Phoenix, C.H. Preovulatory progestins: Observations on their source in rhesus monkeys. JOURNAL OF CLINICAL ENDOCRINOLOGY AND METABOLISM 41:120–125, 1975.

Reynolds, S.R.M. Blood and lymph vascular systems of the ovary. Pp. 261–316 in HANDBOOK OF PHYSIOLOGY, Section 7, Vol. II. FEMALE REPRODUCTIVE SYSTEM. R.O. Greep; E.B. Astwood, eds. Washington, American Physiological Society, 1973.

Riesen, J.W.; Meyer, R.K.; Wolf, R.C. The effect of season on occurrence of ovulation in the rhesus monkey. BIOLOGY OF REPRODUCTION 5:111–114, 1971.

Ross, G.T.; Cargille, C.M.; Lipsett, M.B.; Rayford, P.L.; Marshall, J.R.; Strott, C.A.; Rodbard, D. Pituitary and gonadal hormones during spontaneous and induced ovulatory cycles. RECENT PROGRESS IN HORMONE RESEARCH 26:1–48, 1970.

Säglik, S. Ovaries of gorilla, chimpanzee, organ-utan and gibbon. CONTRIBUTIONS TO EMBRYOLOGY 27:179–199, 1938.

Schenken, R.S.; Hodgen, G.D. Follicle stimulating hormone induced ovarian hyperstimulation in monkeys: Blockade of the luteinizing hormone surge. JOURNAL OF CLINICAL ENDOCRINOLOGY AND METABOLISM 57:50–55, 1983.

Shideler, S.E.; Lasley, B.L. A comparison of primate ovarian cycles. AMERICAN JOURNAL OF PRIMATOLOGY SUPPLEMENT 1:171–180, 1982.

Simpson, G.G. The principles of classification and a classification of mammals. BULLETIN OF THE AMERICAN MUSEUM OF NATURAL HISTORY 85:1–350, 1945.

Sly, D.L.; Harbaugh, S.W.; London, W.T.; Rice, J.M. Reproductive performance of a laboratory breeding colony of patas monkeys (Erythrocebus patas). AMERICAN JOURNAL OF PRIMATOLOGY 4:23–32, 1983.

Sopelak, V.M.; Williams, R.F.; Hodgen, G.D. Ovarian and pituitary responsiveness of monkeys to GnRH and a GnRH agonist during the early and late follicular phase. Pp. 245–249 in FACTORS REGULATING OVARIAN FUNCTION. G.S. Greenwald; P.F. Terranova, eds. New York, Raven, 1983.

Srivastava, P.K.; Cavazos, F.; Lucas, F.V. Biology of reproduction in the squirrel monkey (Saimiri sciureus): I. The estrous cycle. PRIMATES 11:125–134, 1970.

Stabenfeldt, G.H.; Hendrickx, A.G. Progesterone levels in the bonnet monkey (Macaca radiata) during the menstrual cycle and pregnancy. ENDOCRINOL-

OGY 91:614–619, 1972.

Stabenfeldt, G.H.; Hendrickx, A.G. Progesterone levels in the sooty mangabey (*Cercocebus atys*) during the menstrual cycle, pregnancy and parturition. JOURNAL OF MEDICAL PRIMATOLOGY 2:1–10, 1973a.

Stabenfeldt, G.H.; Hendrickx, A.G. Progesterone studies in the *Macaca fascicularis*. ENDOCRINOLOGY 92:1296–1300, 1973b.

Stouffer, R.L.; Hodgen, G.D. Induction of luteal phase defects in rhesus monkeys by follicular fluid administration at the onset of the menstrual cycle. JOURNAL OF CLINICAL ENDOCRINOLOGY AND METABOLISM 51:669–671, 1980.

Strott, C.A.; Cargille, C.M.; Ross, G.T.; Lipsett, M.B. The short luteal phase. JOURNAL OF CLINICAL ENDOCRINOLOGY AND METABOLISM 30:246–251, 1970.

Sturgis, S.H. Rate and significance of atresia of the ovarian follicle of the rhesus monkey. CONTRIBUTIONS TO EMBRYOLOGY 33:69–80, 1949.

Tulchinsky, D.; Hobel, C.J.: Yeager, E.; Marshall, J.R. Plasma estrone, estradiol, estriol. progesterone, and 17-hydroxyprogesterone in human pregnancy. AMERICAN JOURNAL OF OBSTETRICS AND GYNECOLOGY 112:1095–1100, 1972.

Tureck, R.W.; Mastroianni, L.; Blasco, L.; Strauss, J.F. Inhibition of human granulosa cell progesterone secretion by a gonadotropin-releasing hormone agonist. JOURNAL OF CLINICAL ENDOCRINOLOGY AND METABOLISM 54:1078–1080, 1982.

Van Herwerden, M. Beitrag zur Kenntnis des menstrullen Cyklus. MONATSCHRIFT FÜR GEBURTS UND GYNAKOLOGIE 24:730–748, 1906.

Van Horn, R.N. Seasonal reproductive patterns in primates. PROGRESS IN REPRODUCTIVE BIOLOGY 5:181–221, 1980.

Van Horn, R.N.; Eaton, G.G. Reproductive physiology and behavior in prosimians. Pp. 79–122 in THE STUDY OF PROSIMIAN BEHAVIOR. G.A. Doyle; R.D. Martin, eds. New York, Academic Press, 1979.

van Wagenen, G.; Simpson, M.E. EMBRYOLOGY OF THE OVARY AND TESTIS IN *HOMO SAPIENS* AND *MACACA MULATTA*. New Haven, CT, Yale University Press, 1965.

van Wagenen, G.; Simpson, M.E. POSTNATAL DEVELOPMENT OF THE OVARY IN *HOMO SAPIENS* AND *MACACA MULATTA*. New Haven, CT, Yale University Press, 1973.

Vermande-Van Eck, G.J. Neo-ovogenesis in the adult monkey. ANATOMICAL RECORD 125:207–224, 1956.

Vernon, M.W.; Dierschke, D.J.; Sholl, S.A.; Wolf, R.C. Ovarian aromatase activity in granulosa and theca cells of rhesus monkey. BIOLOGY OF REPRODUCTION 28:342–349, 1983.

Wallach, E.E.; Bronson, R.; Hamada, Y.; Wright, K.H.; Stevens, V.C. Effectiveness of prostaglandin $F_{2\alpha}$ in restoration of HMG-HCG induced ovulation in indomethacin-treated rhesus monkeys. PROSTAGLANDINS 10:129–138, 1975.

Wehrenberg, W.B.; Dyrenfurth, I. Photoperiod and ovulatory menstrual cycles in female macaque monkeys. JOURNAL OF REPRODUCTION AND FERTILITY 68:119–122, 1983.

Weiss, G.; Rifkin, I.; Atkinson, L.E. Induction of ovulation in premenarchial rhesus monkeys with human gonadotropins. BIOLOGY OF REPRODUCTION 14:401–404, 1976a.

Weiss, G.; O'Byrne, E.M.; Steinetz, B.G. Relaxin: A product of the human corpus luteum of pregnancy. SCIENCE 194:948–949, 1976b.

Werlin, L.B.; Hodgen, G.D. Gonadotropin-releasing hormone agonist suppresses ovulation, menses, and endometriosis in monkeys: An individualized, intermittent regimen. JOURNAL OF CLINICAL ENDOCRINOLOGY AND METABOLISM 56:844–848, 1983.

Westergaard, L.; McNatty, K.P.; Christensen, I.; Larsen, J.K.; Byskov, A.G. Flow cytometric deoxyribonucleic acid analysis of granulosa cells aspirated from human ovarian follicles. A new method to distinguish healthy and atretic ovarian follicles. JOURNAL OF CLINICAL ENDOCRINOLOGY AND METABOLISM 55:693–698, 1982.

Wildt, L.; Marshall, G.; Knobil, E. Experimental induction of puberty in the infantile female rhesus monkey. SCIENCE 207:1373–1375, 1980.

Wildt, L.; Hausler, A.; Hutchison, J.S.; Marshall, G.; Knobil, E. Estradiol as a gonadotropin releasing hormone in the rhesus monkey. ENDOCRINOLOGY 108:2011–2013, 1981.

Williams, R.F.; Hodgen, G.D. Initiation of the primate ovarian cycle with emphasis on perimenarchial and postpartum events. Pp. 1–55 in REPRODUCTIVE PHYSIOLOGY IV, INTERNATIONAL REVIEW OF PHYSIOLOGY, Vol. 27. R.O. Greep, ed. Baltimore, University Park Press, 1983.

Williams, R.F.; Johnson, D.K.; Hodgen, G.D. Resumption of estrogen-induced gonadotropin surges in postpartum monkeys. JOURNAL OF CLINICAL ENDOCRINOLOGY AND METABOLISM 49:422–428, 1979.

Williams, R.F.; Turner, C.K.; Hodgen, G.D. The late pubertal cascade in perimenarchial monkeys: Onset of asymmetrical ovarian estradiol secretion and bioassayable luteinizing hormone release. JOURNAL OF CLINICAL ENDOCRINOLOGY AND METABOLISM 55:660–665, 1982.

Wilson, M.I. Characterization of the oestrous cycle and mating season of squirrel monkeys from copulatory behavior. JOURNAL OF REPRODUCTION AND FERTILITY 51:57–63, 1977.

Wislocki, G.B. On the female reproductive tract of the

gorilla with a comparison of that of other primates. CONTRIBUTIONS TO EMBRYOLOGY 23:165–204, 1932.

Wislocki, G.B. Observations on twinning in marmosets. AMERICAN JOURNAL OF ANATOMY 64:445–483, 1939.

Wolf, R.C.; O'Connor, R.F.; Robinson, J.A. Cyclic changes in plasma progestins and estrogens in squirrel monkeys. BIOLOGY OF REPRODUCTION 17:228–231, 1977.

Yen, S.S.C. Clinical applications of gonadotropin-releasing hormone and gonadotropin-releasing hormone analogs. FERTILITY AND STERILITY 39:257–266, 1983.

Ylikorkala, O.; Kauppila, A. The effects of the ovulatory cycle of metoclopramide-induced increased prolactin levels during follicular development. FERTILITY AND STERILITY 35:588–589, 1981.

Young, W.C. The mammalian ovary. Pp. 449–496 in SEX AND INTERNAL SECRETIONS, Vol. I. W.C. Young, ed. Baltimore, Williams and Wilkins, 1961.

Zamboni, L. Ultrastructure of mammalian oocytes and ova. BIOLOGY OF REPRODUCTION SUPPLEMENT 2:44–63, 1970.

Zander, J.; Brendle, E.; Munstermann, A.-M; Diczfalusy, E.; Martinsen, B.; Tillinger, K.-G. Identification and estimation of oestradiol-17β and oestrone in human ovaries. ACTA OBSTETRICA ET GYNAECOLOGICA SCANDINAVICA 38:724–736, 1959.

Zeleznik, A.J. Factors governing the selection of the preovulatory follicle in the rhesus monkey. Pp. 37–50 in FOLLICULAR MATURATION AND OVULATION. R. Rolland; E.V. van Hall; S.G. Hillier; K.P. McNatty; J. Schoemaker, eds. Amsterdam, Excerpta Medica, 1982.

Zeleznik, A.J.; Resko, J.A. Progesterone does not inhibit gonadotropin-induced follicular maturation in the female rhesus monkey (*Macaca mulatta*). ENDOCRINOLOGY 106:1820–1826, 1980.

Zeleznik, A.J.; Wildt, L.; Schuler, H.M. Characterization of ovarian folliculogenesis during the luteal phase of the menstrual cycle in rhesus monkeys using [^{3}H]thymidine autoradiography. ENDOCRINOLOGY 107:982–988, 1980.

Zeleznik, A.J.; Schuler, H.M.; Reichert, L.E. Jr. Gonadotropin-binding sites in the rhesus monkey ovary: Role of the vasculature in the selective distribution of human chorionic gonadotropin to the preovulatory follicle. ENDOCRINOLOGY 109:356–362, 1981.

Zuckerman, S. The number of oocytes in the mature ovary. RECENT PROGRESS IN HORMONE RESEARCH 6:63–109, 1951.

Zuckerman, S.; Parkes, A.S. The menstrual cycle of the primates. Part V. The cycle of the baboon. PROCEEDINGS OF THE ZOOLOGICAL SOCIETY OF LONDON, 139–192, 1932.

Ovulation and Corpus Luteum Formation

W. Richard Dukelow, Bi-qin Fan, and A.G. Sacco

Endocrine Research Center, Michigan State University, East Lansing, Michigan 48824 (W.R.D., B.F.), and Department of Obstetrics and Gynecology, Wayne State University, Detroit, Michigan 48202 (A.G.S.)

INTRODUCTION

The events leading to ovulation in terms of follicular morphological development and endocrinology have been treated thoroughly in the previous chapter of this volume by Dr. Koering. The selection of the dominant follicle and its subsequent growth have been defined by Hodgen [1982] and diZerega and Hodgen [1981]. The present review will treat the development of the follicle immediately prior to the time of ovulation, the ovulation process itself, and the formation and initiation of progesterone secretion by the corpus luteum. Also, because of the frequent clinical application and the research need to induce ovulation in many primates, both human and nonhuman, special attention will be paid to methods of ovulation induction and control of the time of ovulation.

Ovum and Follicular Morphology

As the time of ovulation approaches, the dominant follicle is characterized by increasing protrusion from the surface of the ovary and increased vascularity. The major volume of the follicle is a fluid-filled space called the antrum which is lined with a layer of granulosa cells that will eventually combine with cells from the theca interna layer to form the corpus luteum after ovulation. At the base of the follicle a small pedestal of cumulus cells (the cumulus oophorus) projects from the follicle wall, and the cumulus cells surround the oocyte within the follicular antrum. The basic morphology of the vestments of the egg consist of three: a loosely packed layer of large granulosa cells, an inner layer of small compact cells that constitute the corona radiata, and the mucopolysaccharide layer that immediately surrounds the ovum itself and is termed the zona pellucida. Upon ovulation the egg and the surrounding vestments will be expelled from the follicle and the cumulus cells will assist in enabling the egg to be picked up by wavelike action of the cilia that are located on the fimbriated end of the oviduct. These outer vestments will also serve in the transport of the egg down the oviduct [Gaddum-Rosse et al, 1973]. These cell layers also must be penetrated by the sperm, and specific sperm enzymes have been identified from the sperm acrosome that allow penetration of each cellular layer (see Dukelow and Yorozu, this volume).

All of these events, including the growth of the follicle, the capacitation of the sperm, the growth of cilia to influence egg transport, and the muscular action of the female reproductive tract, are under the control of the endocrine system. Thus, in a carefully orchestrated series of events the reproductive tract is prepared for the initiation of ovulation and the start of the reproductive process.

Preovulatory Events on the Ovarian Surface

The preovulatory events on the ovarian surface immediately prior to ovulation have been summarized by Dukelow [1983a,b]. The changes on the ovarian surface during the last 24–36 hours prior to ovulation have been laparoscopically described most extensively in the cynomolgus macaque (*Macaca fascicularis*) [Jewett and Dukelow, 1971, 1972, 1973; Rawson and Dukelow, 1973; Dukelow et al, 1972; Dukelow, 1975]. In this species very discrete morphological changes occur in a fixed sequence just prior to ovulation. By examination of these changes one can predict the time of ovulation, and this can then be used in timed-

Comparative Primate Biology, Volume 3: Reproduction and Development, pages 263–275

mating procedures or to study basic aspects of ovulation, capacitation, and fertilization. The site of the developing follicle can be identified on the surface of the ovary 2 days prior to ovulation by a generalized swelling and darkening of a part of the ovarian surface and an increase of about 35% in the total size of the ovary. For research purposes such studies are best carried out under laparoscopic examination [Dukelow and Ariga, 1976]. Within 30 hours of ovulation a stellate pattern of blood vessels occurs on the follicular surface, and by 8–10 hours before ovulation the blood vessels have become more pronounced and the follicular cone or stigma is established. At this time the oviductal fimbria moves to envelop the developing follicle and to prepare for the pickup of the ovum from the ovarian surface. Two to 3 hours before ovulation a lightening at the base of the follicle occurs, probably indicating the start of luteinization and the source of preovulatory progesterone.

A comparison of this development has been made with the squirrel monkey (*Saimiri sciureus*) and the galago (*Galago senegalensis*) [Harrison and Dukelow, 1974; Dukelow et al, 1973]. In the squirrel monkey similar vascular patterns are observed but ovulation is preceded by much more extensive hemorrhaging at the base of the follicle, and, accordingly, discrete blood vessel patterns are difficult to observe. In the galago a very pronounced protrusion of the follicle occurs from the ovarian surface, and the follicular vessels can be observed at the base of the follicle and occasionally near the apex. The formation of clear areas (the stigmata) is not evident in either the squirrel monkey or the galago as in the cynomolgus macaque. Basically similar patterns of periovulatory follicular development have been described in the Japanese macaque (*Macaca fuscata*), the baboon, and the chimpanzee [Nigi, 1977a,b; Wildt et al, 1977; Graham, 1981; Graham et al, 1973]. The increase of vasculature on the preovulatory follicle was confirmed by Zeleznik et al [1981]. These workers also showed an increase in human chorionic gonadotropin binding sites on day 9 of the cycle which are particularly heavy in the dominant follicle about to ovulate. This work was done in the rhesus monkey. Nagle et al [1980] described follicular development in the capuchin monkey (*Cebus apella*). Again a stellate pattern of small blood vessels was noted. These became more pronounced about 24 hours before ovulation and concomitant with the highest level of estradiol and at the time of a slight increase in the level of proges-

terone. A network of small vessels was uniformly spread across the follicular wall. These workers reported that 10 hours before ovulation, and with a decreasing pattern of estradiol and an increasing level of progesterone, the follicle showed a conical aspect with hemorrhages occurring in the follicular wall. The follicular wall seemed to have an increased pressure caused by contraction of the ovary at the base of the follicle. Ovulation time in this species was characterized by a tight adherence of the fimbria of the oviduct to the follicular surface, and this was maintained for at least 2 hours. The movement of the fimbria to the dominant follicle in the cynomolgus macaque is similar to the pattern seen in the human. In the rhesus monkey the fimbria is normally found more closely surounding one pole of the ovary in a caplike fashion, and in the pig-tailed macaque (*M. nemestrina*) the fimbrial position is intermediate between that of the rhesus and the cynomolgus macaque.

Preovulatory follicle diameter varies according to body size in primates. In humans this measurement is about 10 mm. Corresponding values for other primates are: gorilla, 7 mm; rhesus, 6.3–6.6 mm; baboon, 6 mm; gibbon, 5–6 mm; New World monkeys, 5–6 mm; tree shrews, tupia, and tarsiers, 1 mm. The quantity of granulosa cells is similar in all these species with the follicle size difference primarily due to the secretion of fluid into the antrum. The theca interna layer of the follicle is usually 2–4 cells in depth and this layer is best developed in gibbons and tree shrews [Dempsey, 1939; Duke and Luckett, 1955]. The size of the total ovary is generally proportional to body size except in the playrrhine species, in which the ovaries are disproportionately large. The bonnet macaque (*M. radiata*) shows unusual follicular development which is characterized by invaginations or folding of the follicular wall into the follicular antrum. Ovulation does occur from these follicles [Barnes et al, 1978].

Timing of Ovulation

The earliest interest in detecting the time of ovulation in nonhuman primates was related to the desire for selecting the optimal day for mating to achieve the highest pregnancy rate. By this standard, Hartman [1933] reported that the mean and modal ovulation date for the rhesus monkey was day 13 of the cycle. This method of estimating the day of ovulation based on the previous cycle length is not totally inaccurate and is routinely used in many breeding colonies to achieve pregnancy. Brüggemann and Dukelow [1980], using the stump-tailed macaque (*M. arctoides*), showed that the highest conception rate occurred after matings on day 11 of the cycle. Dukelow et al [1973] reported that in the cynomolgus macaque (*M. fascicularis*) ovulation normally occurs on day 13 when the animals have a cycle length from 25 to 28 days. In animals with a cycle length from 31 to 34 days, ovulation occurred on day 14.8. In the pig-tailed macaque (*M. nemestrina*) Blakley et al [1981] reported the start of the luteal phase (ie, ovulation) to be from 17.6 to 19.2 days in an animal with a mean cycle length of 32.8 days. The day of cynomolgus macaque ovulation has been computed on a regression equation from a corrected regression line [Fig. 4, Dukelow, 1977] to be $Y = 0.307 (X) + 5.12$ (where Y equals the day of ovulation and X equals the cycle length). Despite such calculations, wide variations can occur and ovulation has been observed in this species as early as day 12 of a 37-day cycle and as late as day 17 of a 24-day cycle. Another method of calculating ovulation time is based on the ratio between the day of ovulation and the animal's previous cycle length. This is normally determined from timed-mating studies and has been termed the DB/CL ratio (day of breeding/cycle length ratio) [Dukelow and Brüggemann, 1979]. Using this type of calculation the mean DB/CL ratio for successful pregnancies and short time mating was 0.45, 0.41, and 0.46 for the cynomolgus, stumptail, and rhesus macaque, respectively. A similar value of 0.46 was calculated for the pig-tailed macaque [Blakley et al, 1981], and for the only known seven timed matings in the chimpanzee a value of 0.58 was found (personal communication, Dr. David Martin, Yerkes Regional Primate Research Center).

With the advent of radioimmunoassay and rapid hormone assays, attempts have been made to predict ovulation time on the basis of the estrogen peak preceding the luteinizing hormone (LH) peak which in turn precedes ovulation. In the rhesus monkey Weick et al [1973] reported a sharp rise in estradiol accompanying the initial increase of LH and noted that the estradiol peak preceded the LH peak by 9–15 hours. Progesterone was not detected in peripheral plasma until 15 hours after the LH began to rise, and it reached a small peak within 6 hours of the LH peak. The earliest evidence for ovulation was obtained 28 hours after the LH peak, and the mean time of ovulation was 37 hours after the LH peak. It is interesting that most researchers now carrying out research on in vitro fertilization

of human eggs find the optimal time for recovery of eggs by follicular aspiration to be 32–38 hours after the administration of an LH source. Similarly, in in vitro fertilization of squirrel monkeys, optimal results were obtained when eggs were exposed to sperm 37 hours after administration of hCG as the LH source [Chan et al, 1982]. In the baboon, Shaikh et al [1982] reported that the mean interval from the estradiol peak to ovulation was 41.4 ± 2.3 hours and the interval from the estradiol peak to the LH peak was 17.3 ± 2.0 hours. In the capuchin monkey (*Cebus apella*) the estradiol peak preceded ovulation by 10–24 hours, and 12 hours after the estradiol peak there was a rise in plasma progesterone [Nagle et al, 1980].

Some species show a sex skin turgescence which represents an indirect indication of estrogen secretion in the female. Unfortunately, the end of turgescence (deturgescence) is quite variable. In the baboon the average number of days from start of deturgescence after ovulation was 2.07 ± 0.14 with a range of 0–5 days [Shaikh et al, 1982]. In the pig-tailed macaque the mean time from peak turgescence to ovulation was 6.3 ± 1.1 days [Blakley et al, 1981]. Czaja et al [1975] considered cyclical color changes in the sex skin of rhesus monkeys (another measure of estrogen output) and used this criterion to determine the date of artificial insemination. Reasonable results were obtained, but this method remains to be verified.

In the chimpanzee the sexual swelling detumescence seems to be closely related functionally with ovulation, and the last day of maximum swelling is generally defined as the day of ovulation [Graham, 1981]. Graham has also compared the time of LH peak and with sexual swelling and found that the midcycle rise of LH started on the day before and peaked on the day of ovulation. Similarly, Blakley et al [1977] found a correlation between ovulation and the beginning of detumescence both by laparoscopic observation and by measuring progesterone levels. Stevens et al [1970] studied 12 baboons (*Papio anubis*) and found that a turgescence peak occurred 3–4 days after the midcycle urinary estrogen peak. They found an LH peak in plasma and urine on the same day as the urinary estrogen peak, suggesting that ovulation might be expected to occur 2–3 days before detumescence. A similar finding was found for *Papio cynocephalus* by Kling and Westfahl [1978]. Nadler [1975] reported increased copulatory activity in the gorilla during the period of maximal swelling, and since the LH peak always occurs on the second day of such labial swelling [Nadler et al, 1979], this suggests that ovulation occurs on the third day of labial swelling in this species.

Among the New World species the time of ovulation is more difficult to determine because of the lack of a definite menstrual cycle. In these species ovulation is assumed to occur at about midcycle, and most breeding programs are based on that supposition. Changes in vaginal cornification or in the external genitalia are not evident in most of these species and are of little help in assessing the time of ovulation. It is in these species that ovulation is often induced using gonadotropic or steroid hormones; this subject will be treated later.

The length of the ovarian cycle of the marmoset has been reported by Hearn [1983] to be 28.6 ± 1.0 days. The length of the cycle of the capuchin monkey (*Cebus apella*) is 21.0 ± 1.1 days [Nagle et al, 1979] and in the squirrel monkey 8–10 days [Jarosz et al, 1977].

OVULATION

Biochemical and Biophysical Changes in the Follicle

Little is known of the biochemical and biophysical changes in the follicle of the nonhuman primate although this subject has been extensively researched in other animals, particularly the pig and the rabbit. Obviously there are major changes that occur immediately prior to ovulation, some of which have been mentioned above. These involve changes in the vasculature of the follicle, the appearance of an avascular area known as the macula pellucida or stigma, the formation of small blood clots near the stigma, some extravasation of blood, and finally the rupture of the follicle and expulsion of the oocyte. It is well established that the follicle wall weakens just prior to rupture, and this is evident in studies of the nonhuman primate follicle as well. Early workers believed that the increasing size of the antrum would lead to increased pressure within the follicle which ultimately would lead to the rupture of the follicle itself. Other theories of ovulation have examined the role of contractility of ovarian tissue near the base of the follicle and, particularly, the enzymatic activity in the follicle wall itself. Others have likened ovulation to an inflammatory response [Espey, 1980] and indeed there do appear to be similarities between these two natural phenemena. The process of ovulation has been reviewed by Rondell [1970], Parr [1975], and Espey [1978]. It now appears that there is no significant increase in the intrafollicular pressure at ovulation and, in fact, there is actually a decrease in pressure immediately prior to ovulation.

There is, however, a marked increase in the distensibility of the follicular wall just prior to ovulation, and this probably results in a thinning of the follicular wall and greater ease of rupture. Analysis of the mechanics of rupture illustrate that even a relatively small change in distensibility can produce an unstable follicle which will rupture at normal pressure.

The collagen component of the follicular wall appears to be of major significance in giving structural strength to the follicle. At the time of ovulation the normal bonding of collagen fibrils is disrupted in such a fashion as to reduce tension, and the tissue is then stretched. This suggests the involvement of an enzymatic agent and a collagenaselike enzyme has been identified in follicular-wall tissue and is activated at the time of ovulation. LH is the stimulating gonadotropin that triggers ovulation but it is difficult to envision a direct effect of LH on enzyme activity in the follicular wall. More likely the LH stimulates steroid secretion (there is an increased secretion of progesterone as well as estrogen within the follicle).

It is likely that other enzymes, hormones, or biochemical compounds are involved in the ovulation process. Since very little of this work has been done with nonhuman primates the reader is referred to the previously mentioned reviews for a more extensive discussion of ovulation mechanics in laboratory animals.

The Morphology of Ovulation

In his comprehensive review of ovulation mechanisms, Lipner [1974] described hyperemia induced by the LH surge that is preliminary to the final increase in follicular volume. This hyperemia is brought about by a change in capillary permeability which allows plasma to enter the follicular antrum swelling the dispensible follicle until its degraded wall can no longer contain the gradually increasing fluid volume. When rupture then occurs, the oocyte and its attendant cumulus cells are expelled and the stigma is plugged by clotted serum as the antrum refills with plasma . These morphological changes are in accord with the previously mentioned biochemical and biophysical changes that occur in other laboratory species. In the human, Okamura et al [1980] described the apical wall ultrastructurally in 16 human follicles at various stages of development. In the mature follicles the fibroblastic cytoplasm was well developed, was rich in lysosomelike granules, and contained peripheral multivesicular structures. Intercellular collagen fibers were sparse. This suggested that the collagen fibers were digested by the content of the liposomal granules and multivesicular structures, thus aiding follicular rupture. In the cynomolgus macaque, Rawson and Dukelow [1973] described laparoscopic observation of ovulation. The characteristic preovulatory follicle had a large protruding stigma as ovulation approached. The total time required for ovum expulsion was short, 30 seconds, which was approximately the time reported by Blandau [1955] for ovulation in the rat. The adherence of the egg mass to the ovarian surface and the strength of this adhesion, which was tenacious, may be of importance in the mechanism of transfer of the ovum to the oviduct, and one can speculate that the sweeping motion of the fimbria over the ovarian surface occurs in primates as in the other species showing this characteristic—ie, the rabbit. In the cynomolgus macaque after ovulation has occurred, complete rupture of the blood vessels on the surface of the follicle does not occur and, in fact, some of the follicular blood vessels can still be seen in the newly formed corpus luteum [Jewett and Dukelow, 1972]. In the Japanese macaque (*M. fuscata*) just prior to ovulation, the follicular dome wall becomes very thin and the cytoplasm of the granulosa cells and theca interna cells is flattened as if pressed against the follicular wall [Nigi, 1978]. At the bottom of the follicle this worker observed a few small folds on the follicular wall, a phenomenon also observed in the bonnet macaque (*M. radiata*) [Barnes et al, 1978]. In the squirrel monkey the preovulatory follicle has a clear, gelatinous dome, and indentation of the dome was found to be characteristic of the time immediately after ovulation. Because of the hemorrhaging in this species at the time of ovulation, postovulatory follicles are more easily discernible than in macaque species [Dukelow et al, 1973; Harrison and Dukelow, 1974].

Ovulation between the left and right ovary appears random despite occasional reports to the contrary. Dukelow [1977] reported on ovulations observed laparoscopically in 138 cycles of the cynomolgus macaque. In this case ovulation occurred in the left ovary 62.6% of the time, and no significant effect was noted on cycle length relative to the ovulatory status of the previous cycle or the occurrence of ovulation on the same ovary in consecutive cycles.

OVULATION INDUCTION

Steroid Involvement in Ovulation Induction

The steroid involvement in the normal ovulatory process has been extensively covered in the chap-

ters in this volume by Drs. Robinson and Koering. Accordingly, this section will deal only with steroidal effects involved in the artificial induction of ovulation. This will also consider the effects of season on the ovulatory process in some nonhuman primates since this occurrence necessitates the use of exogenous hormones (steroids and gonadotropins) to induce follicular maturation and ovulation.

The purpose of exogenous administration of steroids is to stimulate or mimic the events that occur in the normal cycle. In the normal cycle of most macaque species (see chapter by Robinson, this volume) the estradiol initiates an LH rise, and an increased level of serum progesterone occurs several hours before the LH peak but after the initiation of the LH surge. In the stump-tailed macaque [Wilks et al, 1980] a secondary follicle-stimulating hormone (FSH) surge occurs 2–3 days after the LH peak. The significance of this second FSH surge is not certain, but it may enhance postovulatory progesterone and estrogen synthesis. The history of a 25-year effort to induce ovulation in the rhesus monkey has been published by van Wagenen [1968]. Normally even with the use of steroids to induce follicular development, gonadotropins are included in the regimen to induce the ovulation itself. Spies and Niswender [1972] utilized 0.5 mg of progesterone daily in the rhesus monkey to block ovulation. This effectively blocks the LH surge. When the progesterone was stopped and estradiol administered, the monkeys exhibited a rise in LH and ovulation. Use of antiestrogens also blocked ovulation in three of five animals. These data suggest that injections of progesterone could be utilized in this fashion to synchronize the reproductive cycles of a number of laboratory and domestic species of animals and, of course, is one of the underlying principles of the use of contraceptive pills.

The occurrence of seasonal responses to ovulation induction regimens has been found in a number of primate species. The rhesus macaque shows a distinct seasonal effect on the occurrence of ovulation [Riesen et al, 1971]. Five of 24 menstrual cycles were ovulatory during the summer and 30 of 31 during the winter. This seasonality is not uniformly present in all rhesus monkeys but is of such a degree that it must be considered in breeding programs or studies of basic reproductive phenomena. Seasonal responses in the squirrel monkey are even more pronounced [Harrison and Dukelow, 1973]. Natural seasonality occurs when the animals receive an ovulatory regimen of 5 days of 5 mg of progesterone (to mimic the luteal phase) followed by 4 days of follicle-stimulating hormone and a single injection of human chorionic gonadotropin. In the northern hemisphere such a regimen results in cessation of ovulation during July, August, and September [Dukelow et al, 1981]. Attempts to overcome this seasonality have involved varying the dose of FSH-hCG, and the sequential or combined use of estradiol or progesterone pretreatments [Kuehl and Dukelow, 1975]. The administration of sequential estradiol and progesterone pretreatments to more closely mimic the natural cycle before the FSH-hCG treatment resulted in 22.4% ovulation. When the estradiol and progesterone were given in combinations of changing proportions (increasing progesterone), 16.7% of the animals ovulated. While these results were impressive, it was found that merely increasing the level of FSH from 1 mg to 2 mg per day or from a 4-day regimen to a 5-day regimen resulted in much higher levels of ovulation. The use of these ovulation induction regimens coupled with natural mating resulted in pregnancy [Jarosz et al, 1977].

Protein Hormone Involvement in Ovulation Induction

Dr. Gertrude van Wagenen and her associates spent over 25 years in developing a method for gonadotropic induction of ovulation in the rhesus macaque. This was summarized in her lecture before the American Fertility Society [van Wagenen, 1968]. A wide variety of domestic animal source gonadotropins were utilized with varying degrees of success, and even with the discovery of the FSH-like action of pregnant mare serum (PMS) by H.H. Cole in the early 1940s this failed to provide an answer to ovulation induction in the macaque. Following reports by Knobil et al [1956] of a species specificity for growth hormone in nonhuman primates, van Wagenen and her associates then utilized pituitaries recovered from rhesus monkeys to induce ovulation with very pronounced results. Today we recognize that while a variety of FSH sources can be utilized to stimulate follicular growth in nonhuman primates, there appears to be a species-specific requirement for the source of luteinizing hormone (LH) to actually induce the ovulation. Accordingly, most of the hormones used in nonhuman primates (and in humans) derive from primate sources. The most common primate sources of follicle-stimulating hormone (FSH) are human menopausal gonadotropin (hMG) or pituitary compounds from human or nonhuman primate sources. For the induction of ovulation, human chorionic gonadotropin (hCG) is most commonly used. In addition, clomiphene citrate, a nonsteroidal compound with FSH action, is utilized in both human and nonhuman primates although the ease of controlling the exact ovulation time is more difficult.

During the 1960s a variety of FSH-LH-hCG regimens were utilized in rhesus monkeys [Simpson and van Wagenen, 1962; Mastroianni et al, 1967; Wan and Balin, 1969; Dede and Plentl, 1966], with varying degrees of success. These various regimens were repeated by McArthur [1973]. There was no response in the animals treated with the low-dose regimen of Dede and Plentl [1966] and polycystic ovary formation, rather than ovulation, occurred in all of the animals treated by the methods of the other researchers. McArthur then tried a "staircase" regimen of increasing levels of hMG and monitored estrogen excreted in the urine.

Once the urinary estrogen excretion reached the normal preovulatory level of 6.8 mg for 24 hours, the hMG treatment was stopped and the estrogen level allowed to fall. Then a single injection of 500 IU of hCG was given to induce ovulation. By this method two of 12 trials resulted in failure, but ten single ovulations were induced. McArthur did find that the dose of hMG required to induce follicular growth and estrogen secretion varied markedly from animal to animal. In the baboon some early studies reported the effect of norethindronemestranol, hCG hMG, and clomiphene citrate in baboons [Kraemer et al, 1968]. In these studies animals that had just recently been brought from the wild were treated to prevent amenorrhea that came about through the transition to captivity. They found that erratic menstrual function can be regularized in part by cyclic estrogen-progestin therapy but failed to show a consistent relationship between cycle stability and conception rate. The use of hMG and hCG in baboons reportedly gave single ovulations, which was in contrast with other earlier reports of multiple ovulations with these same compounds. hMG-hCG has been shown to induce morphological changes in the maturation of the baboon ovum, and causes some defects of the zona pellucida [Katzberg and Hendrickx, 1966, 1968]. Roussel et al [1968] tested the effect of hMG at doses equivalent to 37.5 or 75 IU FSH followed by 2,000 IU of hCG in the stump-tailed macaque (*M. arctoides*), the patas monkey (*Erythrocebus patas*), and the African green monkey

(*Cercopithecus aethiops*). Administration of hMG daily for 4–6 days produced multiple follicular development, and, following hCG, some ovulations were obtained. There was clear evidence of overstimulation of the ovaries, with large numbers of follicles expanded to abnormally large size. Many follicles failed to ovulate, and follicles examined in histological sections presented signs of atresia. Repeated courses of treatment with hMG led to a refractory state of the ovaries which failed to respond to administered hCG and apparently became acyclic. The time of administration of the hCG is also important. Williams and Hodgen [1980] administered 1,000 IU of hGC to rhesus monkeys during the late follicular phase, either on day 9 or day 11. If the hCG was given coincidentally with the natural gonadotropin surge, no pharmacological effects were induced. However, when administered before the initiation of the spontaneous FSH and LH surges, the HCG induced apparent atresia of the dominant follicle, arrest of cyclic ovarian function lasting more than 3 weeks, and, in half the monkeys, an altered modulation of tonic FSH secretion independent of LH release where serum FSH levels persisted about threefold above normal.

In the squirrel monkey ovulation induction can be induced by a wide variety of regimens and has recently been reviewed [Dukelow, 1983c, 1985]. The original work in this area derived from studies with common laboratory and domestic species and utilized pregnant mare serum (PMS) supplemented with hCG to induce ovulation. Although the number of animals is small, the work of Bennett [1967] decisively showed that multiple ovulation could be induced using a regimen of 200 IU of PMS and a subsequent hCG injection. It was evident that follicular growth and ovulation could be induced by this method and furthermore that "superovulation" (ie, the ovulation of more than a single egg in each ovulation) could be achieved with high and continuous doses of PMS. Unfortunately animals soon became refractory to PMS, and thus the use of this ovulatory regimen could not be repeatedly used in the same animal. The refractoriness to PMS and production of antibodies against this protein hormone thus greatly limit its usefulness not only in the squirrel monkey but in other species as well.

Because of the cost of the animals involved and the necessity of maintaining squirrel monkeys over longer periods of time in reproductive research situations, studies were undertaken to develop techniques that would allow the production of single or double ovulations in the squirrel monkey without refractoriness to the regimen. A secondary factor was concern over the normality of oocytes that were produced by superovulation regimens, and it was believed by workers at that time that ova resulting from single or double ovulation would be more normal then superovulated oocytes. The results of these studies were published [Dukelow, 1970]. These studies repeated the superovulation-PMS trials of Bennett [1967] with equal results, but also demonstrated that 1 mg of domestic animal source pituitary FSH administered daily for 4 days with a single injection of 250–500 IU of hCG on the fourth day would result in ovulation in about 60% of the animals. hMG-hCG was also used in the squirrel monkey and ovulation was induced, but again the hyperstimulation phenomena was observed. In subsequent studies [Dukelow, 1979] the minimum effective dose of human chorionic gonadotropin following a 4-day administration of 1 mg of domestic animal FSH was reported and the minimum effective dose was found to be between 100 and 250 IU. This treatment, then, of 4 days FSH and a single injection of 250 IU of hCG has been used continuously in this author's laboratory over the past 15 years with virtually no change in its efficacy. Its use has been confirmed in the squirrel monkey by others [Travis and Holmes, 1974] as well as being used in a variety of other laboratory, domestic, and zoo animals. A summary of a 7-year period of the use of this regimen has been published [Dukelow et al, 1981]. It was found that the regimen can be repeated over several years with no refractoriness to the gonadotropins. Using the regimen described above, squirrel monkeys have been ovulated 20 or more times (at intervals of 3 weeks or more) with no significant effect on the percentage of animals ovulating or the number of ovulations per animal. There was an increase in the percent of animals responding with follicular growth after the fifth induction. The reason for the lack of refractoriness (antigonadotropic antibodies?) perhaps reflects the low dosage used or the lack of a suitable adjuvant to enhance antibody response. In the initial use of this regimen a 5-day pretreatment of 5 mg of progesterone daily was used to mimic the luteal phase of the cycle. While the progesterone pretreatment is not essential, a significant difference was noted in the percentage of animals ovulating when the pretreatment was used. There did appear to be a slight suppressive effect of progesterone pretreatment on follicular growth but not on the percentage of the animals ovulating or the number of ovulations per animal.

The level of hCG used to induce ovulation has been a matter of concern to some scientists and clinicians with many species of animals. A rabbit will ovulate in response to as little as 25 IU of hCG, and most nonhuman primates will ovulate in response to 100–1,000 IU of hCG. In the human, 5,000–10,000 IU hCG is commonly used clinically and as many as 20,000 IU hCG has been reported in the literature. Because of concern over possible antigenicity of high levels of hCG and some work which has indicated that hCG administered to rabbits to induce ovulation resulted in 9.7% chromosomally defective 6-day-old blastocysts [Fujimoto et al, 1974], it is important that minimum effective dose curves be determined for hCG if the regimen is to be used repeatedly in primate animals. To date this has only been done in the squirrel monkey.

The squirrel monkey is a seasonal reproducer [Harrison and Dukelow, 1973], and this seasonality is reflected in the response to the FSH-hCG ovulation induction regimen mentioned. Kuehl and Dukelow [1975] demonstrated that the seasonal effect could be overcome by doubling the dose of FSH from 1 to 2 mg per day or by extending the 1-mg dosage to 5 days instead of 4. Varying the dose of hGC had no effect on ovulation in the anovulatory season. Furthermore, the seasonal effect could be overcome by administration of estradiol and progesterone in various combinations that have been mentioned previously. Ovulation induced out of season results in oocytes that are capable of being fertilized in vitro [Kuehl and Dukelow, 1979] and in vivo [Jarosz et al, 1977], and the latter has resulted in normal pregnancy and birth.

Interestingly, direct injection of hCG into mature ovarian follicles of the squirrel monkey resulted in ovulation in 45% of the animals treated whereas using purified ovine LH, ovulation was observed in 55% of the animals similarly treated. None of the control animals receiving saline injections ovulated. This would suggest that the species-specificity requirement for an LH source might be due to an extrafollicular mechanism. Similar studies carried out in the cynomolgus macaque did not result in ovulation but did result in a 55% increase in menstrual cycle length [Rawson and Dukelow, 1978].

The use of LH-releasing hormone (LHRH) to elicit and LH response been reported in a variety of nonhuman primates and in humans [Yen et al, 1972]. Interestingly, an insensitivity to this compound has been reported in the rhesus and bonnet macaque [Ehara et al, 1972; Shah et al, 1976]. In contrast, Norman and Spies [1979] found that female fetuses, infants, and prepubertal animals can release LH in response to LHRH. Baboons and chimpanzees also respond to LHRH [Koyama, 1976; Hobson and Fuller, 1977; Graham et al, 1979]. Also the ring-tailed lemur (Lemur catta) responds to LHRH. It has also been demonstrated in the chimpanzee that LHRH antagonists can block gonadotropin release [Gosselin et al, 1979].

Since a major action of contraceptive steroids has been the blocking of ovulation, it is only natural that induced ovulation (and natural ovulation) should be studied in nonhuman primates using various antiprogestational agents. Much of this work is beyond the scope this review, but it should be mentioned that ovulation in rhesus monkeys has been suppressed by intranasal administration of progesterone or norethisterone [Anand Kumar et al, 1977]. Additionally, the ovulation induction regimen (FSH-hCG) previously described for use in the squirrel monkey has been used to test the effect of megestrol acetate with a dose-response blockage of ovulation [Harrison and Dukelow, 1971]. Using a dose (500 mg per day) that completely blocks ovulation in the squirrel monkey, ovulation was not blocked in the cynomolgus macaque [Harrison et al, 1974]. Similarly, synthetic TPAL (threonyl-prolyl-arginyl-lysine), a polypeptide reported to occur naturally in the hamster, has been tested at two doses for antiovulatory activity in the squirrel monkey. This treatment did not alter the ovulatory responses in the primates [Kuehl and Dukelow, 1978], but emphasizes the usefulness of the induced ovulatory nonhuman primate as a test system.

Prostaglandin Involvement in Ovulation

In recent years the role of prostaglandins, particularly of the E series, has received increasing attention in laboratory animals. To date very little has been done utilizing prostaglandins to induce ovulation, but one very pronounced finding was reported by Batta et al [1978a]. These workers used PMS and hCG in combination with three prostaglandins, PGE_1, PGE_2, and $PGF_{2\alpha}$ in an attempt to develop a reliable method for inducing superovulation in the rhesus monkey. The best results were obtained following daily injection of 100 IU PMS on cycle days 4, 5, 6, and 7, followed by 200 IU PMS on days 8, 9, 10, and 11. Four thousand IU of hCG was given on day 12, and 5 mg of the selected prostaglandin on day 13. Using the PGE_1 and PGE_2 treatments, 1–29 ovulations were obtained in each of 38 animals and only one animal failed to ovulate after initial exposure to this regimen. Most of the ovulations occurred between 24 and 48 hours after prostaglandin injection. Using $PGF_{2\alpha}$ resulted in very poor ovulation induction. In a subsequent paper Batta et al [1978b] studied the effect of administration of PGE_1 and PGE_2 on plasma FSH and LH concentrations. The rhesus monkeys were ovarectomized and treated with estradiol to suppress endogenous gonadotropin levels before the experiments. The administration of vehicle had no effect on LH or FSH secretion. On the other hand, PGE_1 (5 mg) brought about dramatic elevations in LH within 5 minutes and the high plasma concentrations were maintained for at least 60 minutes. Similarly, 5 mg of PGE_2 brought about rapid elevation of LH concentrations. FSH levels were not markedly altered by either of the the two prostaglandins. $PGF_{2\alpha}$ had no effect on plasma LH or FSH concentrations. These data demonstrated the ability of the prostaglandins of the E series to elevate the plasma LH and support other studies suggesting a possible role in gonadotropin induction of ovulation.

CORPUS LUTEUM FORMATION AND SECRETION

The secretion of progesterone by luteal tissue has been dealt with extensively in other chapters in this volume, as have the morphological aspects of corpus luteum formation. Accordingly, the subject will be treated only briefly in this chapter as a natural sequela following the eruptive ovulatory process.

Morphological Considerations

In his studies on the histological ovarian changes in the Japanese macaque (*M. fuscata*) Nigi [1978] indicated that the luteinization probably starts prior to ovulation, confirming similar studies in the cynomolgus macaque. In the Japanese macaque the formation of the corpus luteum progresses gradually during the first 40 hours after ovulation and then accelerates. Invasion of the granulosa cell layer by the blood capillaries was seen 15 hours after ovulation. Mitotic figures were observed in granulosa and theca interna cells until 43–47 hours after ovulation. This author has detailed the invasion of blood capillaries into the ovarian tissue.

References have already been made to the unusual ovarian histology of the bonnet macaque [Barnes et al, 1978]. The evidence available indicates that ovulation from these follicles results with their full inflation with blood plasma, and that the corpora lutea formed from this follicle are not different from those observed in other macaque species except for large numbers of granulocytes found in the interstium. Two types of luteal regression were observed and in one case a vascular stigma resembling a fresh ovulation stigma was found over an aberrant corpus luteum. The structural characteristics of the corpus luteum at the time of implantation and early pregnancy has been described by Booher et al [1981]. This study documents the changes in the luteal cells that occur after there are elevations in the levels of circulating progesterone and estrogen which are induced by the embryos. These changes in the granulosa lutein cells suggest an immediate use of existing precursor reserves and lipid droplets, possibly for the production of progesterone, followed by a reduction in the capacity of these cells to accumulate and process steroid precursor. These cells also show evidence of synthesis of a secretory protein. Structural changes in the thecal lutein cell during this time suggest an increased capacity for steroid synthesis, perhaps of estrogen, and an increased accumulation of steroid precursor by the cells.

In the owl monkey (*Aotus trivirgatus*) corpora lutea could not be identified with certainty either by form, stigmata, or histology, nor could they be differentiated from interstitial masses [Hertig et al, 1976]. The mature ovary has large multilobulated masses of luteinized interstitial tissue which occupy the medula and the cortex. Other New World monkeys also show dispersed luteal tissue throughout the ovarian stroma. This has been reported in the squirrel monkey. In the capuchin monkey (*Cebus apella*) two types of luteal tissue have been described, but apparently with the presence of a more classic corpus luteum. There is an indication that persistent corpora lutea from previous cycles may appear [Nagle et al, 1980].

Progesterone Secretion

Once the corpus luteum is formed, progesterone secretion is stimulated by luteinizing hormone either endogenously within the animal or by exogenous administration. The corpus luteum will continue to function until pregnancy is established and the functional corpus luteum and ovary are required for at least a month in macaque pregnancies. If implantation does not occur the corpus luteum will regress and progesterone levels will drop, as occurs in the human. In the rhesus monkey this drop of progesterone occurs even if the LH level remains high [Neill et al, 1967; Kirton et al, 1970]. During this period of time follicles will start to develop [Koering, 1969].

The exact mechanism that causes the luteolysis of the corpus luteum is uncertain. In studies on domestic and laboratory animals a wide variety of mechanisms have been proposed for the luteolytic factor and in many of these species prostaglandin F_{2a} is the luteolytic agent. This is not the case in nonhuman primates, and Knobil [1973] has indicated that estrogen may be the luteolytic agent in the rhesus monkey, as it is in the rabbit. Estrogen-induced luteal regression has been further studied in the rhesus monkey by Schoonmaker et al [1982] and in the baboon by Westfahl and Kling [1982].

CONCLUSIONS

The control of ovulation and the formation of the corpus luteum in the nonhuman primate is similar to that found in other laboratory and domestic species and in man. A delicate balance of pituitary protein hormones released under the influence of hypothalamic factor meshes with the steroids produced from the gonads to bring about the development, maturation, and release of the egg at a time when other hormonal effects are influencing cyclical development within the reproductive tract and muscle-contractive mechanisms which move the ovulated egg from the ovarian surface to the oviduct itself in preparation for fertilization. While very few comparative studies have been done across the primate families, there do appear to be common mechanisms in this process with variations occurring only in the morphology of the developing follicle and ovary, and the corpus luteum that is ultimately formed.

There are seasonal effects in many nonhuman primates that alter this ovulation process, and we are just now beginning to understand some of the mechanisms by which seasonal effects are manifest in altering hormonal levels to influence ovulation. Ovulation can be induced in nonhuman primates, and in man, by a wide variety of techniques of which the most productive appear to be the use of protein hormones either natural to the primate or of primate origin such as hMG and hCG.

The development of our understanding of these hypotheses has been greatly stimulated in the past 15–20 years primarily owing to interest in human contraception and means of altering the normal reproductive process to avoid various types of infertility. In the future, many types of nonhuman primates will be utilized to further define these important aspects of primate (human and nonhuman) physiology.

REFERENCES

Anand Kumar, T.C.; David, G.F.X.; Puri, V. Ovulation in rhesus monkeys suppressed by intranasal administration of progesterone and norethisterone. NATURE 270:532–534, 1977.

Barnes, R.D.; Lasley, B.L.; Hendrickx, A.G. Midcycle ovarian histology of the bonnet monkey, *Macaca radiata*. BIOLOGY OF REPRODUCTION 18:537–553, 1978.

Batta, S.K.; Stark, R.A.; Brackett, B.G. Ovulation induction by gonadotropin and prostaglandin treatments of rhesus monkeys and observations of the ova. BIOLOGY OF REPRODUCTION 18:264–278, 1978a.

Batta, S.K.; Niswender, G.D.; Brackett, B.G. Elevation of rhesus monkey plasma luteinizing hormone levels in response to E series prostaglandin. PROSTAGLANDINS 16:835–846, 1978b.

Bennett, J.P. The induction of ovulation in the squirrel monkey (*Saimiri sciureus*) with pregnant mares serum (PMS) and human chorionic gonadotrophin (HCG). JOURNAL OF REPRODUCTION AND FERTILITY 13:357–359, 1967.

Blakley, G.A.; Beamer, T.W.; Dukelow, W.R. Characteristics of the menstrual cycle in nonhuman primates. IV. Timed mating in *Macaca nemestrina*. LABORATORY ANIMAL SCIENCE 27:352–355, 1977.

Blandau, R.J. Ovulation in the rat. 16mm film. Seattle, University of Washington Film Service, 1955.

Booher, C.; Enders, A.C.; Hendrickx, A.G.; Hess, D.L. Structural characteristics of the corpus luteum during implantation in the rhesus monkey (*Macaca mulatta*). AMERICAN JOURNAL OF ANATOMY 160:17–36, 1981.

Brüggemann, S.; Dukelow, W.R. Characteristics of the menstrual cycle in nonhuman primates. III. Timed mating in *Macaca arctoides*. JOURNAL OF MEDICAL PRIMATOLOGY 9:213–221, 1980.

Chan, P.J.; Hutz, R.J.; Dukelow, W.R. Nonhuman primate in vitro fertilization: Seasonality, cumulus cells, cyclic nucleotides, ribonucleic acid and viability assays. FERTILITY AND STERILITY 38:609–615, 1982.

Czaja, J.A.; Eisele, S.G.; Goy, R.W. Cyclical changes in the sexual skin of female rhesus: Relationships to mating behavior and successful artificial insemination. FEDERATION PROCEEDING 34:1680–1684, 1975.

Dede, J.A.; Plentl, A.A. Induced ovulation and artificial insemination in a rhesus colony. FERTILITY AND STERILITY 17:757–764, 1966.

Dempsey, E.W. The reproductive cycle of New World monkeys. AMERICAN JOURNAL OF ANATOMY 64:381–398, 1939.

diZerega, G.S.; Hodgen, G.D. Folliculogenesis in the primate ovarian cycle. ENDOCRINE REVIEWS 2:27–49, 1981.

Duke, K.L.; Luckett, W.P. Histological observations on the ovary of several species of tree shrews (family Tupaiidae). ANATOMICAL RECORD 151:450, 1965.

Dukelow, W.R. Induction and timing of single and multiple ovulations in the squirrel monkey (Saimiri sciureus). JOURNAL OF REPRODUCTION AND FERTILITY 22:303–309, 1970.

Dukelow, W.R. The morphology of follicular development and ovulation in nonhuman primates. JOURNAL OF REPRODUCTION AND FERTILITY SUPPLEMENT 22:23–51, 1975.

Dukelow, W.R. Ovulatory cycle characteristics in Macaca fascicularis. JOURNAL OF MEDICAL PRIMATOLOGY 6:33–42, 1977.

Dukelow, W.R. Human chorionic gonadotropin: Induction of ovulation in the squirrel monkey. SCIENCE 206:234–235, 1979.

Dukelow, W.R. The nonhuman primate as a reproductive model for man. Pp. 79–105 in NONHUMAN PRIMATE MODELS FOR HUMAN DISEASES. W.R. Dukelow, ed. Boca Raton, FL, CRC Press, 1983a.

Dukelow, W.R. Ovum recovery and embryo transfer in primates. Pp. 165–174 in MAMMALIAN EGG TRANSFER. C.E. Adams, ed. Boca Raton, FL, CRC Press, 1983b.

Dukelow, W.R. The squirrel monkey (Saimiri sciureus). Pp. 149–179 in REPRODUCTION IN NEW WORLD PRIMATES. J.P. Hearn, ed. Lancaster, U.K., MTP Press, 1983c.

Dukelow, W.R. Reproductive cyclicity and breeding. Pp. 169–190 in HANDBOOK OF SQUIRREL MONKEY RESEARCH. L.A. Rosenblum; C.L. Coe, eds. New York, Plenum, 1985.

Dukelow, W.R.; Ariga, S. Laparoscopic techniques for biomedical research. JOURNAL OF MEDICAL PRIMATOLOGY 5:82–99, 1976.

Dukelow, W.R.; Brüggemann, S. Characteristics of the menstrual cycle in nonhuman primates. II. Ovulation and optimal mating times in macaques. JOURNAL OF MEDICAL PRIMATOLOGY 8:79–87, 1979.

Dukelow, W.R.; Harrison, R.M.; Rawson, J.M.R.; Johnson, M.P. Natural and artificial control of ovulation in nonhuman primates. MEDICAL PRIMATOLOGY 1:232–236, 1972.

Dukelow, W.R.; Jewett, D.A.; Rawson, J.M.R. Follicular development and ovulation in Macaca fascicularis, Saimiri sciureus, and Galago senegalensis. AMERICAN JOURNAL OF PHYSICAL ANTHROPOLOGY 38:207–208, 1973.

Dukelow, W.R.; Theodoran, C.G.; Howe-Baughman, J.; Magee, W.T. Ovulatory patterns in the squirrel monkey (Saimiri sciureus). ANIMAL REPRODUCTION SCIENCE 4:55–63, 1981.

Ehara, Y.; Ryan, K.J.; Yen, S.S.C. Insensitivity of synthetic LRF in LH-release of the rhesus monkey. CONTRACEPTION 6:465–478, 1972.

Espey, L.L. Ovarian contractility and its relationship to ovulation: A review. BIOLOGY OF REPRODUCTION 19:540–551, 1978.

Espey, L.L. Ovulation as an inflamatory reaction—a hypothesis. BIOLOGY OF REPRODUCTION 22:73–106, 1980.

Fujimoto, S.; Pahlavan, N.; Dukelow, W.R. Chromosome abnormalities in rabbit implantation blastocysts induced by superovulation. JOURNAL OF REPRODUCTION AND FERTILITY 38:97–103, 1974.

Gaddum-Rosse, P.; Blandau, R.J.; Thiersch, J.B. Ciliary activity in the human and Macaca nemestrina oviduct. AMERICAN JOURNAL OF ANATOMY 138:269–275, 1973.

Gosselin, R.E.; Fuller, G.B.; Coy, D.H.; Schally, A.V.; Hobson, W.C. Inhibition of gonadotropin release in chimpanzees by the LH-RH antagonist (D-Phe^2, D-Trp^3, D-Phe^6)-LH-RH (40480). PROCEDURES FOR THE SOCIETY OF EXPERIMENTAL BIOLOGY AND MEDICINE 161:21–24, 1979.

Graham, C.E. Menstrual cycle of the great apes. Pp. 1–43 in REPRODUCTIVE BIOLOGY OF THE GREAT APES. C.E. Graham, ed. New York, Academic Press, 1981.

Graham, C.E.; Gould, K.G.; Collins, D.C.; Preedy, J.R.K. Regulation of gonadotropin release by luteinizing hormone–releasing hormone and estrogen in chimpanzees. ENDOCRINOLOGY 105:269–275, 1979.

Graham, C.E.; Keeling, M.; Chapman, C.; Cummins, L.B.; Haynie, J. Methods of endoscopy in the chimpanzee: Relations of ovarian anatomy, endometrial histology and sexual swelling. AMERICAN JOURNAL OF PHYSICAL ANTHROPOLOGY 38:211–216, 1973.

Harrison, R.M.; Dukelow, W.R. Megestrol acetate: Its effect on the inhibition of ovulation in squirrel monkeys, Saimiri sciureus. JOURNAL OF REPRODUCTION AND FERTILITY 25:99–101, 1971.

Harrison, R.M.; Dukelow, W.R. Seasonal adaption of laboratory-maintained squirrel monkeys (Saimiri sciureus). JOURNAL OF MEDICAL PRIMATOLOGY 2:277–283, 1973.

Harrison, R.M.; Dukelow, W.R. Morphological changes in Saimiri sciureus ovarian follicles as detected by laparoscopy. PRIMATES 15:305–309, 1974.

Harrison, R.M.; Rawson, J.M.R.; Dukelow, W.R. Megestrol acetate. II. Effects on ovulation in nonhuman primates as determined by laparoscopy. FERTILITY AND STERILITY 25:51–56, 1974.

Hartman, C. Pelvic (rectal) palpation of the female

monkey with special reference to the ascertainment of ovulation time. AMERICAN JOURNAL OF OBSTETRICS AND GYNECOLOGY 26:600–608, 1933.

Hearn, J.P. The common marmoset (*Callithrix jacchus*). Pp. 183–215 in REPRODUCTION IN NEW WORLD PRIMATES. J.P. Hearn, ed. Lancaster, U.K., MTP Press, 1983.

Hertig, A.T.; Barton, B.R.; Mackey, J.J. The female genital tract of the owl monkey (*Aotus trivirgatus*) with special reference to the ovary. LABORATORY ANIMAL SCIENCE 26:1041–1067, 1976.

Hobson, W.; Fuller, G.B. LH-RH induced gonadotropin release in chimpanzees. BIOLOGY OF REPRODUCTION 17:294–297, 1977.

Hodgen, G.D. The dominant ovarian follicle. FERTILITY AND STERILITY 38:281–300, 1982.

Jarosz, S.J.; Kuehl, T.J.; Dukelow, W.R. Vaginal cytology, induced ovulation and gestation in the squirrel monkey. BIOLOGY OF REPRODUCTION 16:97–103, 1977.

Jewett, D.A.; Dukelow, W.R. Serial observations of follicular morphology near ovulation in *Macaca fascicularis*. JOURNAL OF REPRODUCTION AND FERTILITY 31:287–290, 1972.

Jewett, D.A.; Dukelow, W.R. Follicular observation and laparoscopic aspiration techniques in *Macaca fascicularis*. JOURNAL OF MEDICAL PRIMATOLOGY 2:108–113, 1973.

Katzberg, A.A.; Hendrickx, A.G. Gonadotropin-induced anomalies of the zona pellucida of the baboon ovum. SCIENCE 151:1225–1226, 1966.

Katzberg, A.A.; Hendrickx, A.G. HMG-HCG induced morphological changes in the maturation of the baboon, *Papio anubis*. Pp. 129–143 in USE OF NONHUMAN PRIMATES IN DRUG EVALUATION. H. Vagtborg, ed. Austin, University of Texas Press, 1968.

Kirton, K.T.; Niswender, G.D.; Midgley, A.R.; Jaffe, R.B.; Forbes, A.D. Serum luteinizing hormone and progesterone concentration during the menstrual cycle of the rhesus monkey. JOURNAL OF CLINICAL ENDOCRINOLOGY 30:105–110, 1970.

Kling, O.R.; Westfahl, P.K. Steroid changes during the menstrual cycle of the baboon (*Papio cynocephalus*) and human. BIOLOGY OF REPRODUCTION 18:392–400, 1978.

Knobil, E. On the regulation of the primate corpus luteum. BIOLOGY OF REPRODUCTION 8:246–258, 1973.

Knobil, E.; Morse, A.; Greep, R.O. The effects of beef and monkey pituitary growth hormone on the costochondral junction in the hypophysectomized rhesus monkey. ANATOMICAL RECORD 124:320–324, 1956.

Koering, M.J. Cyclic changes in ovarian morphology during the menstrual cycle in *Macaca mulatta*. AMERICAN JOURNAL OF ANATOMY 126:73–101, 1969.

Koyama, T. Mechanisms of LH release with synthetic LH-RH. FOLIA ENDOCRINOLOGICA JAPAN 52:881–897, 1976.

Kraemer, D.C.; Hendrickx, A.G.; Kriewaldt, F.H. Experience with nonrethindrone mestranal, human gonadotropins (HMG + HCG) and clomiphene citrate in baboons. Pp. 118–128 in USE OF NONHUMAN PRIMATES IN DRUG EVALUATION. H. Vagtborg, ed. Austin, University of Texas Press, 1968.

Kuehl, T.J.; Dukelow, W.R. Ovulation induction during the anovulatory season in *Saimiri sciureus*. JOURNAL OF MEDICAL PRIMATOLOGY 4:23–31, 1975.

Kuehl, T.J.; Dukelow, W.R. The effect of a synthetic polypeptide, threonyl-prolyl-arginyl-lysine, on ovulation in the squirrel monkey (*Saimiri sciureus*). BIOLOGY OF REPRODUCTION 21:545–556, 1979.

Lipner, H. Mechanisms of mammalian ovulation. In HANDBOOK OF PHYSIOLOGY, Sec. 7. R.O. Greep; E.B. Astwood, eds. Washington, Physiology Society, 1974.

Mastroianni, L.; Suzuki, S.; Manabe, Y.; Watson F. Further observations on the influence of the intrauterine device on ovum and sperm distribution in the monkey. AMERICAN JOURNAL OF OBSTETRICS AND GYNECOLOGY 99:649–653, 1967.

McArthur, J.W. An animal model for the induction of ovulation by means of gonadotropin treatment. Pp. 77–83 in GONADOTROPIN IN FEMALE FERTILITY. E. Rosenbert, ed. International Congress Series No. 266. Amsterdam, Excerpta Medica, 1973.

Nadler, R.D. Sexual cyclicity in captive lowland gorillas. SCIENCE 189:813–814, 1975.

Nadler, R.D.; Graham, C.E.; Collins, D.C.; Gould, K.G. Plasma gonadotropins, prolactin, gonadal steroids and genital swelling during the menstrual cycle of lowland gorillas. ENDOCRINOLOGY 105:290–296, 1979.

Nagle, C.A.; Denari, J.H.; Quiroga, S.; Riarte, A.; Merlo, A.; Germino, N.I.; Gomes-Argana F.; Rosner, J.A. The plasma pattern of ovarian steroids during the menstrual cycle in capuchin monkeys (*Cebus apella*). BIOLOGY OF REPRODUCTION 21:979–983, 1979.

Nagle, C.A.; Riarte, A.; Quiroga, S.; Azorero, R.M.; Carril, M.; DeNari, J.H.; Rosner, J.M. Temporal relationship between hormonal profile in the capuchin monkey (*Cebus apella*). BIOLOGY OF REPRODUCTION 23:629–635, 1980.

Neill, J.D.; Johansson, E.D.B.; Knobil, E. Levels of progesterone in peripheral plasma during the menstrual cycle in the rhesus monkey. ENDOCRINOLOGY 81:1161–1164, 1967.

Nigi, H. Laparoscopic observations of ovaries before

and after ovulation in the Japanese monkey (*Macaca fuscata*). PRIMATES 18:243–259, 1977A.

Nigi, H. Laparoscopic observations of follicular rupture in the Japanese macaque (*Macaca fuscata*). JOURNAL OF REPRODUCTION AND FERTILITY 50:387–388, 1977b.

Nigi, H. Histological ovarian changes in *Macaca fuscata* before and after ovulation. JAPANESE JOURNAL OF VETERINARY SCIENCE 40:297–307, 1978.

Norman, R.L.; Spies, H.G. Effect of luteinizing hormone–releasing hormone on the pituitary gonadal axis in fetal and infant rhesus monkeys. ENDOCRINOLOGY 105:655–659, 1979.

Okamura, H.; Takenzka, A.; Yajima, Y.; Nishimura, T. Ovulatory changes in the wall at the apex of the human graafian follicle. JOURNAL OF REPRODUCTION AND FERTILITY 58:153–155, 1980.

Parr, E.L. Rupture of ovarian follicles at ovulation. JOURNAL OF REPRODUCTION AND FERTILITY SUPPLEMENT: 22:1–22, 1975.

Rawson, J.M.R.; Dukelow, W.R. Observation of ovulation in *Macaca fascicularis*. JOURNAL OF REPRODUCTION AND FERTILITY 34:187–190, 1973.

Rawson, J.M.R.; Dukelow, W.R. Effects of intrafollicular administration of gonadotropins in two species of nonhuman primates using laparoscopy. JOURNAL OF MEDICAL PRIMATOLOGY 7:223–227, 1978.

Riesen, J.W.; Meyer, R.K.; Wolf, R.C. The effect of season on occurrence of ovulation in the rhesus monkey. BIOLOGY OF REPRODUCTION 5:111–114, 1971.

Rondell, P. Biophysical aspects of ovulation. BIOLOGY OF REPRODUCTION SUPPLEMENT 2:64–89, 1970.

Roussel, J.D.; Clewe, T.H.; Austin, C.R. Use of human postmenopausal gonadotropophin (Pergonal) for promoting ovarian follicular and oocyte development in monkeys. Pp. 162–171 in USE OF NONHUMAN PRIMATES IN DRUG EVALUATION. H. Vagtborg, ed. Austin, University of Texas Press, 1968.

Schoonmaker, J.N.; Bergman, K.S.; Steiner, R.A.; Karsch, F.J. Estradiol-induced luteal regression in the rhesus monkey: Evidence for an extraovarian site of action. ENDOCRINOLOGY 110:1708–1715, 1982.

Shah, R.W.; Sheth, A.R.; Godgil, B.A.; Swamy, X.R. Effect of LH/FSH-RH on circulating serum gonadotropins in the bonnet monkey. INDIAN JOURNAL OF EXPERIMENTAL BIOLOGY 14:171–174, 1976.

Shaikh, A.A.; Celaya, C.L.; Gomez, I.; Shaikh, S.A. Temporal relationship of hormonal peaks to ovulation and sex skin deturgescence in the baboon. PRIMATES 23:444–452, 1982.

Simpson, M.R.; van Wagenen, G. Induction of ovulation with human urinary gonadotrophins in the monkey. FERTILITY AND STERILITY 13:140–152, 1962.

Spies, H.G.; Niswender, G.D. Effect of progesterone and estradiol on LH release and ovulation in rhesus monkeys. ENDOCRINOLOGY 90:257–261, 1972.

Stevens, V.C.; Sparks, S.J.; Powell, J.E. Levels of estrogens, progesterones and luteinizing hormone during the menstrual cycle of the baboon. ENDOCRINOLOGY 87:658–666, 1970.

Travis, J.C.; Holmes, W.N. Some physiological and behavioural changes associated with oestrus and pregnancy in the squirrel monkey (*Saimiri sciureus*). JOURNAL OF ZOOLOGY (LONDON) 174:41–66, 1974.

van Wagenen, G. Induction of ovulation in *Macaca mulatta*. FERTILITY AND STERILITY 19:15–29, 1968.

Wan, L.S.; Balin, H. Induction of ovulation in rhesus monkeys: A comparative study. FERTILITY AND STERILITY 20:111–126, 1969.

Weick, R.F.; Dierschke, D.J.; Karsch, F.J.; Butler, W.R.; Hotchkiss, J.; Knobil, E. Periovulatory time courses of circulating gonadotropic and ovarian hormones in the rhesus monkey. ENDOCRINOLOGY 93:1140–1147, 1973.

Westfahl, P.K.; Kling, O.R. Relationship of estradiol to luteal function in the cycling baboon. ENDOCRINOLOGY 110:64–69, 1982.

Wildt, D.E.; Doyle, L.L.; Stone, S.C.; Harrison, R.M. Correlation of perineal swelling with serum ovarian hormone levels, vaginal cytology and ovarian follicular development during the baboon reproductive cycle. PRIMATES 18:261–270, 1977.

Wilks, J.W.; Marciniak, R.D.; Hildebrand, D.L.; Hodgen, G.D. Periovulatory endocrine events in the stumptailed monkey (*Macaca arctoides*). ENDOCRINOLOGY 107:237–244, 1980.

Williams, R.F.; Hodgen, G.D. Disparate effects of human chorionic gonadotropin during the late follicular phase in monkeys: Normal ovulation, follicular atresia, ovarian acyclicity, and hypersecretion of follicle stimulating hormone. FERTILITY AND STERILITY 36:64–68, 1980.

Yen, S.S.C.; Rebar, R.; Vandenburg, G.; Naftolin, F.; Ehara, Y.; Engblom, E.; Ryan, K.T.; Guillemin, R.; Benirschke, K. Synthetic luteinizing hormone-releasing factor: A potent stimulator of hormone release in man. JOURNAL OF CLINICAL ENDOCRINOLOGY 42:432–442, 1972.

Zeleznik, A.J.; Schuler, H.M.; Reichart, L.E. Gonadotropin-binding sites in the rhesus monkey ovary: Role of the vasculature in the selective distribution of human chorionic gonadotropin to the preovulatory follicle. ENDOCRINOLOGY 109:356–362, 1981.

Sperm Capacitation and Fertilization

W. Richard Dukelow and Yutaka Yorozu

Endocrine Research Center, Michigan State University, East Lansing, Michigan 48824

INTRODUCTION

The study of sperm capacitation, ovum fertilization, and the early preimplantation stages of development is critical in determining the exact developmental biology of mammalian species. Traditionally such studies have been carried out by mating the female of the species at a time estimated to be that of ovulation (timed-mating studies), and then at varying times subsequent to that mating, efforts are made to recover the fertilized embryo and assess its rate of development and normality. Such studies in primates have traditionally been confounded by several factors. For one, the time of ovulation has traditionally been difficult to control and predict in all primates, both human and nonhuman. Secondly, the cost of the animals and the difficulty of recovering oviductal and uterine embryos has resulted in very low numbers of actual observations of the embryos produced.

With the announcement in 1969 [Edwards et al, 1969] of the first successful in vitro fertilization in the human, a new era of developmental biology began. A few years later similar studies were completed with nonhuman primates [Johnson et al, 1972; Cline et al, 1972]. In 1978 the birth of baby Louise Brown by in vitro fertilization and embryo transfer [Steptoe and Edwards, 1978] occurred. In 1983 the first birth of a nonhuman primate infant by in vitro fertilization was reported by Kuehl et al [1985]. All of these events have led to increased interest in the early development of the nonhuman primate. Despite the rapid advances in recent years, a long history of classical descriptive studies has provided the groundwork for current studies. The major advances as well as the deficiencies of these early studies leading to successful in vitro

fertilization have been described by Blandau [1980]. The value of such studies in gaining a better understanding of the early fertilization and development procedures has been emphasized by Brackett [1979]. Not of insignificant interest is the fact that the possibilities for chromosomal or developmental abnormalities, or for teratogenic effects, are exerted most strongly between the period from fertilization to immediately after implantation, emphasizing the need for continuing research.

SPERM CAPACITATION

For over 60 years scientists attempted to mix spermatozoa and oocytes in a test tube and to bring about what we now term in vitro fertilization. No repeatable nor confirmed procedures were ever developed for this technique. In 1951 the joint discovery by Drs. C.R. Austin and M.C. Chang of the phenomenon we now call capacitation revolutionized approaches to in vitro fertilization research. The discovery that the sperm must incubate for a period of time (normally in the female reproductive tract) before they achieve the capacity to fertilize was a revolutionary event. The long delay in the discovery of this basic physiological phenomenon is probably attributed to the very short time requirement for capacitation compared with other physiological aspects of fertilization and development. Indeed, in most common laboratory species the time required for capacitation ranges from 1 to 15 hours. Once capacitation was discovered in 1951 it was a relatively simple step to achieve in vitro fertilization (first done with rabbits) and ultimately transfer those embryos to produce a live birth. From working with other species we know that capacitation generally requires an

Comparative Primate Biology, Volume 3: Reproduction and Development, pages 277–289

estrous state of the animal, that it is species-specific, and that it results in various metabolic changes in the sperm which enable it to penetrate the egg. Basically these include an increase in oxygen uptake, a change in membrane permeability, and activation of various enzymes involved in sperm penetration [Dukelow and Williams, 1983]. A second phase of the capacitation phenomenon (originally included as a part of it but now viewed as a separate event) is the acrosome reaction, whereby a vesiculation occurs between the plasma membrane and the outer acrosomal membrane of the sperm head providing for release of sperm enzymes and activation of the egg penetration process. Unfortunately, in studies with nonhuman primate sperm and eggs, it is not yet possible to separate the capacitation and acrosome reaction events. So for the purpose of this review the term "capacitation" is used to include both the initial activation and the acrosome reaction.

Historical Proof of Capacitation By Timed-Mating Techniques

The classical method of demonstrating a need for capacitation in any species is to naturally mate the animal at a timed interval after ovulation is known to have occurred. Then, by recovering the eggs at varying times and studying the temporal stages of development, one can determine if a period of delay was experienced before the sperm penetrated the egg. Such approaches are necessarily crude but have traditionally given preliminary evidence for capacitation. In 1933 Hartman demonstrated that the rhesus monkey ovulates on approximately day 13 of the menstrual cycle, and van Wagenen [1945] showed that the optimal time for mating in the rhesus monkey was on days 11 and 12, suggesting that a period of delay was required. In timed-mating studies, Marston and Kelly [1968] reported that the rhesus monkey required a 3- to 4-hour period of time for capacitation in vivo, and this value corresponds to the 5- to 7-hour value reported for humans [Soupart and Morgenstern, 1973; Soupart and Strong, 1974]. It also corresponds with the value of 2 to 5 hours for in vitro capacitation of squirrel monkey sperm utilized for in vitro fertilization [Kuehl and Dukelow, 1982].

Indirect Measures of Primate Sperm Capacitation

While the ideal and finite test of sperm capacitation rests with its ability to penetrate a homologous oocyte, such tests are difficult to run with nonhuman primates because of the difficulty of obtaining adequate numbers of eggs for the individual tests themselves. In vitro fertilization procedures (to be discussed later in this chapter) offer increased hope for such assays. A variety of indirect methods of assessing sperm capacitation have evolved, primarily based on the usual characteristics possessed by capacitated sperm but not by freshly ejaculated sperm. These include an increased oxygen uptake, the presence of decapacitation factor in primate seminal plasma, and the ability to remove a tetracycline coating from the surface of the sperm after incubation in a foreign uterine environment. All of these procedures have been utilized with rhesus sperm [Dukelow and Chernoff, 1969], and all yielded positive results relative to an indication of a requirement for sperm capacitation in this species. The decapacitation factor was definitely present in rhesus seminal plasma, and a variety of laboratory species (mouse, rat, hamster, and rabbit) had the ability to remove tetracycline coating from both rhesus and human sperm. Rhesus sperm incubated for 12 hours in hamster uteri consumed oxygen at a level nearly equal to freshly ejaculated sperm, which was in contrast to a 93% reduction in oxygen consumption of control sperm stored for 12 hours at 3°C.

In recent years the zona-free hamster egg (with the zona pellucida removed by trypsin treatment) has been used as a test system to observe penetration of the ovum. This technique, developed by Yanagimachi et al [1976], has been ascribed to be a measure of capacitation and the acrosome reaction, and human sperm [Yanagimachi et al, 1976] and squirrel monkey sperm [Burke, 1979] will penetrate the zona-free egg. Kreitmann and Hodgen [1980] found limited usefulness of this test with the rhesus monkey. This is a useful screening test for assessing fertilizability of sperm. However, there is some question if this is a true measure of capacitation. In 1967 Bedford and Shalkovsky indicated a role of sperm capacitation in penetrating the cumulus layer of cells, and the acrosome reaction has been implicated in the penetration of the zona pellucida. One can reason that if these layers are removed from the hamster oocyte prior to exposure of the sperm, one may be bypassing the capacitation process.

For the above reasons all indirect measures of capacitation must be considered temporary, and the finite demonstration of capacitation requires the penetration of an egg of a species homologous to the sperm. A more complete discussion of capacitation and its role in the fertilization of eggs has been published by Dukelow and Williams [1983].

Sperm Enzymes

In the past 15 years a great deal of scientific effort has been expended to determine the enzyme components of the acrosome resting on the head of the sperm beneath the plasma membrane. During capacitation and the acrosome reaction various enzymes are released or activated, and it is postulated that these enzymes play a role in allowing sperm to penetrate the outer vestments of the egg (cumulus cells, corona radiata, and zona pellucida) to bring the sperm into contact with the vitelline membrane and allowing it to penetrate the egg cytoplasm. This is related not only to the basic scientific phenomena but also the fact that control of these enzymes would effectively allow contraceptive means to be applied.

Basically there are three enzymes that have been suggested to play a major role in penetration [McRorie and Williams, 1974]. The first enzyme released from the sperm head is hyaluronidase, and this occurs at the time of the acrosome reaction. About 50% of the hyaluronidase is free within the acrosomal head (the remainder being bound to the inner acrosomal membrane). This was the first sperm enzyme discovered, and its action is to disperse or dissolve the hyaluronic acid matrix that binds the cumulus cells. Following release of the hyaluronidase, an esterase termed the corona-penetrating enzyme allows passage of the sperm through the corona radiata layer. The sperm then lies in close apposition to the zona pellucida, and a third enzyme, called acrosin, allows penetration of the zona pellucida. The latter two enzymes are believed to be bound to the inner acrosomal membrane of the sperm, and other enzyme systems have been proposed for the activation of these various enzyme structures. Comparative studies of the acrosomal enzymes of the rhesus monkey and human sperm [Stambaugh and Buckley, 1970] have been carried out, and acrosin has been isolated from these sperm. Acrosin inhibitors to rhesus monkey sperm have been identified in the oviductal fluid [Stambaugh et al, 1974] of this species. In a wide variety of laboratory species naturally occurring inhibitors to several of the sperm penetration enzymes have been isolated, suggesting a delicate control mechanism to activate or inactivate these enzymes. The presence of acrosin appears to be universal in a great many species, and

much more emphasis has been placed on this enzyme from human sperm than other primates [Tobias and Schumacher, 1976; Anderson et al, 1981a,b]. Lysosomal hydrolases isolated from sperm acrosomes and seminal plasma were studied in nine chimpanzee semen samples by Srivastava et al [1981]. β-N-Acetylhexosaminidase and hyaluronidase showed the highest specific activity in the acrosomal extracts. Other enzymes isolated included arylsulfatase, β-glucuronidase, and α-L-fucosidase. Seminal plasma also showed high activity of acid and alkaline phosphatases and low specific activity of β-galactosidase. A great deal of additional work will have to be carried out before the exact function of each of these enzymes in the reproductive process (if any) can be shown, and in addition there is a need for comparative studies between primate species.

FERTILIZATION

Fertilization can be defined as all events leading to the actual fusion (syngamy) of the male and female pronucleus within the egg cytoplasm, or it can be defined as the actual penetration process. In this review we have already discussed sperm maturation, capacitation. and the acrosome reaction, all of which are required before penetration of the egg cytoplasm itself. After the sperm head attaches to the vitelline membrane, it is engulfed by an outpocketing of the membrane, and the sperm head, midpiece, and tail are drawn into the cytoplasm where the latter two structures are rapidly dismantled and the sperm head moves toward the center of the ooplasm for fusion with the female pronucleus. These events have been extensively studied in laboratory species, but few studies have been carried out with nonhuman primates. In a recent review of studies in the squirrel monkey, Dukelow et al [1983] reported that condensation and swelling of the sperm occurred 6 hours after insemination and the pronucleate stage at 10 hours after insemination. In the rhesus monkey following in vitro fertilization, Bavister et al [1983] found sperm tail remnants 18–24 hours after fertilization in only two of 13 fertilized oocytes. In one of these, three sperm were present in the vitellus, each showing a swelling of the sperm nucleus, the initial stage of nuclear decondensation. The author suggests that these sperm could have penetrated the oocyte shortly before fixation or could have penetrated soon after insemination and failed for some reason to have progressed beyond the stage of nuclear decondensation. Thus the 18 to 24 hour value for the rhesus may not be comparable to the 10 hours reported for the squirrel monkey. Since both of these studies involve in vitro–fertilized oocytes, further discussion will be deferred until a later section of this chapter.

Timed Mating and In Vivo Fertilization

As with most laboratory and domestic species, initial studies on capacitation, fertilization, and gestation length have normally involved mating the animal at a time interval related to a known time of ovulation. Allowing for sperm capacitation time, the exact time of fertilization can then be determined. Difficulties with this procedure have generally reflected the inability of investigators with human or nonhuman primates to accurately predict or induce the time of ovulation (see chapter by Dukelow, Fan, and Sacco, this volume). Nevertheless, some of the earliest studies of in vivo–fertilized primate ova derived from investigators attempting to predict the time of ovulation and making the recovery of the oocytes relative to that time.

Lewis and Hartman [1941] reported the development of 12 rhesus monkey eggs recovered at various stages from one to 16 cells and cultured in vitro to study further development. These were largely anecdotal studies in which the time of ovulation was estimated using a variety of observational techniques and with natural mating. Generally speaking, ovulation has been assumed to occur at midcycle or slightly before. This necessitated the prediction of ovulation on the length of the previous cycle, which has been shown in the cynomolgus macaque to not be particularly accurate [Yoshida et al, 1982]. In a retrospective study of the stump-tailed macaque (*M. arctoides*) whereby the day of ovulation was based on timed matings (exposure to the male for 20 min or less) resulting in pregnancy, Brüggemann and Dukelow [1980] reported that the highest conception rate occurred after matings on day 11 of the cycle, and using this technique 16.3% of the matings resulted in pregnancy. Similarly, Jewett and Dukelow [1971] utilized laparoscopy in the cynomolgus macaque combined with 20-minute mating periods to produce four pregnancies in 80 attempts. Dukelow and Brüggemann [1979] summarized the pregnancies that occurred in colonies of stump-tailed and cynomolgus macaques over a 10-year period with 20-minute female exposure to males once each

cycle. Successful pregnancies were calculated on the basis of the day of breeding compared to the previous cycle length (DB/CL ratio), and additional pregnancies were available from a limited number of rhesus monkey matings as well. Maximum conception occurred at a DB/CL ratio from 0.40 to 0.41 with a range of DB/CL ratios for successful mating from 0.39 to 0.44. There were no significant differences between the three species involved. In similar studies in the pig-tailed macaque (*N. nemestrina*) but where the male and female were left together for 48 hours, Blakley et al [1981] found that the optimum time for mating based on a DB/CL ratio was 0.46, a value comparable to those found for other macaque species. In a similar calculation with the only seven known timed matings in chimpanzees (with data graciously provided by Dr. David Martin of the Yerkes Regional Primate Research Center), a DB/CL ration of 0.58 was noted.

Others have used variation in timed matings including the continuous housing of males with females but with daily observation of vaginal lavage for the presence of sperm. This procedure was used by Stolzenberg et al [1979] in the squirrel monkey to assess pregnancy rate for single matings in a large colony and to assess gestation length. Similarly, the time of detumescence has been used as an indicator of ovulation [Blakley et al, 1981] in the pig-tailed macaque and in baboons. While such techniques are useful in breeding programs and to crudely estimate gestation length, they are of less value to fix precisely the time of fertilization as required in capacitation-fertilization studies. Such techniques primarily represent indirect estimates of ovulation time and suffer from normal biological variation between animals.

By the use of timed-mating procedures followed by surgical or nonsurgical recovery of embryos at various times relative to estimated time of fertilization, the state of development of the primate embryo can be compared. Such in vivo–developed embryos can also be compared to those developed by in vitro culture following in vitro fertilization. Table 1 presents a comparison of such values for several primate species including man. An examination of this table indicates the present state of the art of such studies with nonhuman primates. First it is evident that a degree of study has been carried out on different aged embryos from several different species, and secondly it is obvious that such developmental times are comparable between

TABLE 1. Comparative Rates of Primate Preimplantation Development

Species type of culture	Two polar bodies	Two-cell	Four-cell	Eight-cell	Sixteen-cell	Morula	Blastocyst
Squirrel monkey							
In vivo fert, in vivo culture[a]							96
In vitro fert, in vitro culture[b]	6–22	22–40	46–52	52–72			
Rhesus macaque							
In vitro fert, in vitro culture[c]		24–36	36–48	48–72	72–96		
In vitro fert, in vitro culture[d]		26	38	54	87		
Cynomolgus macaque							
In vivo fert, in vitro culture[e]		24	48	48–72			
Baboon							
In vivo fert, in vivo culture[f,g]	24		48	48–72	96–120	120–148	96–144
In vitro fert, in vitro culture[h]	6–12	24		72*			
Human							
In vivo fert, in vivo culture[i,j,k]		30		72	96	96–120	120
In vitro fert, in vitro culture[l]	12	38	38–46	51–62	85	111–135	123–147

*Xenogenously fertilized.
[a]Ariga and Dukelow, 1977b; [b]Kuehl and Dukelow, 1979; [c]Lewis and Hartman, 1941; [d]Bavister et al, 1983; [e]Kreitman et al, 1982; [f]Kraemer and Hendrickx, 1971; [g]Pope et al, 1982; [h]Kuehl, personal communication; [i]Hertig et al, 1954; [j]Croxatto et al, 1972; [k]Avendano et al, 1975; [l]Edwards and Steptoe, 1975.

species and with human embryos. On the negative side it is evident that there are still gaps in our knowledge and that a great many more species and a great many more embryos should be studied, especially control embryos produced by natural mating. Another concern is the large number of values that are divisible by 24, indicating that the embryos are being examined only on a once-a-day basis. While this normally has resulted from a desire not to disturb the embryos, it does indicate variation in the timing of the embryonic development that should be made more precise. In the squirrel monkey [Dukelow et al, 1983] first, second, and third cleavages occur after in vitro fertilization at 16, 46–52, and 52–72 hours after insemination, respectively. Using laparoscopic recovery techniques [Dukelow and Ariga, 1976; Ariga and Dukelow, 1977a] two squirrel monkey blastocysts were recovered following ovulation induction and natural mating. One 5-day

preimplantation blastocyst had an estimated fertilization age of 93–109 hours and was just beginning expansion with no evident zona pellucida. The second blastocyst was recovered 126 hours after human chorionic gonadotropin (hCG) administration and was estimated to be a 5-day blastocyst. Expansion had not begun, but there was no evidence of the zona pellucida being present [Ariga and Dukelow, 1977b]. The status of ovulation induction and embryo transfer in the nonhuman primate has been summarized by Kraemer et al [1979]. Kraemer earlier recovered a baboon embryo 5 days after natural ovulation and mating, and this early morula embryo was transferred to a recipient baboon to yield the first surgically transferred nonhuman primate offspring [Kraemer et al, 1976]. Pope et al [1980] used a nonsurgical method of recovering uterine embryos from the baboon. They recovered 21 eggs from flushes during 44 mated cycles on 21 animals and, of these,

14 (67%) were fertilized. The recovered embryos ranged from four-cell to expanding blastocyst. These workers also cultured embryos recovered nonsurgically from the baboon, and 12 of 35 developed to the expanded blastocyst stage and hatched from the zona pellucida. Hatching occurred after 4–7 days in culture following recovery at the eight-cell to morula stage. Most blastocysts underwent further expansion and attached to the culture dish within the 5 days after hatching [Pope et al, 1982]. These workers subsequently transferred a four-cell embryo from one baboon to a recipient which resulted in the first birth of a nonhuman primate from nonsurgical transfer [Pope et al, 1983].

In the rhesus monkey a successful surgical flushing technique for collection of uterine embryos has been described by Hirst et al [1976]. These workers recovered nine embryos from 22 flushes performed between days 17 and 19 of the menstrual cycle. The embryos comprised both zonal and hatched blastocyst and one 22-cell morula. The ultrastructural features of two cleavage stage embryos, two blastocysts with zona pellucida, and two hatched blastocysts from this recovery procedure have been described by Hirst et al [1978]. Batta and Channing [1979] successfully recovered preimplantation rhesus monkey morulae and blastocysts from the rhesus by a surgical uterine flushing procedure and subsequently measured progesterone synthesis from these embryos. The morulae and blastocyst resulted in a 196% and 905% stimulation of progesterone secretion by granulosa cells with which they were cocultured for 7–9 days.

Other aspects relating to embryo transfer and successful establishment of pregnancies in nonhuman primates will be discussed subsequently in this chapter. Two other techniques should be mentioned relative to fertilization of nonhuman primate eggs even though they represent artificial techniques that would be utilized in research situations or, in the case of humans, to correct causes of infertility. The xenogenous fertilization of squirrel monkey eggs by squirrel monkey sperm in a foreign uterine environment (the pseudo-pregnant rabbit oviduct) has been reported by DeMayo et al [1980]. This technique resulted in a 37% rate of fertilization for the squirrel monkey. Although the procedure may appear to be unusual, the use of the pseudo-pregnant rabbit oviduct for the culture of embryos from domestic and laboratory animals has a long and illustrious history, dating back to 1951. In fact the xenogenous fertilization of a variety of laboratory and domestic species has been provided [Hirst et al, 1981]. Furthermore, squirrel monkey oocytes have been successfully frozen, thawed, and xenogenously fertilized [DeMayo et al, 1983].

Kreitmann and Hodgen [1980] reported the successful transfer of ova aspirated from the preovulatory follicle of rhesus and cynomolgus monkeys and injected into the oviduct 1 to 2 cm above the uterotubal junction. These animals were mated the day prior to and the day after the transfer and pregnancy resulted in five of 31 attempts (16.1%). These studies illustrate that surgical procedures can be utilized with resultant pregnancies as a possible aid to human infertility problems.

Sperm Penetration of the Ovum

Reference has been made to the engulfment of the sperm head by the vitelline membrane and movement of the sperm within the periphery of the egg. The mechanism of fertilization in laboratory and domestic animals has been reviewed by Yanagimachi [1981] and provides a good picture of the overall process which appears to be uniform throughout the animal kingdom. Unfortunately, few such studies have been carried out in nonhuman primates.

Once a sperm enters the egg cytoplasm the nuclear membrane surrounding the sperm head nucleus disappears and decondensation of the nucleus begins. In the squirrel monkey this event takes place about 6 hours after initial sperm penetration [Dukelow et al, 1983]. After decondensation occurs, a new nuclear envelope appears around the decondensed chromatin and this is termed the male pronucleus. During decondensation there is a loss of basic proteins, rich in arginine (from the sperm nucleus). DNA synthesis occurs in both the male and female pronuclei in a synchronous manner. As the two pronuclei approach each other the nuclear membranes disappear and the chromosomes from the sperm and the eggs then mix for the first meiotic division.

The egg must be mature for decondensation of the sperm nuclei to occur. When sperm are injected into the cytoplasm of immature eggs, no decondensation occurs. There is thus some evidence for specific factors within the egg cytoplasm that are necessary for nuclear decondensation; this phenomenon is referred to as cytoplasmic maturation. Yanagimachi and Usui [1972] and Usui and Yanagimachi [1976] reported the presence of a substance in the hamster egg that they termed the "sperm nucleus decondensing factor (SNDF)." Little is known of this substance, but it obviously plays an important role in the final fertilization process. No work on this phenomenon has been carried out in nonhuman or human primates.

The movement of the pronuclei to the center of the cytoplasm appears to involve microtubules and actin of sperm origin which join the actin and microtubule structures of the egg to participate in the migration.

Puromycin inhibits the migration of pronuclei in the rabbit egg, and actinomycin D blocks the breakdown of nuclear membrances [Longo, 1978]. Therefore the migration of the pronuclei and their syngamy seems to require synthesis of proteins, and these are an aid within the egg cytoplasm after sperm penetration has been achieved.

In Vitro Fertilization and Embryo Transfer

This section of review will be divided into three general areas: success with in vitro fertilization, embryo transfer, and biochemical and cytogenetic studies carried out on embryos produced by in vitro fertilization. The subject of in vitro fertilization and embryo transfer in nonhuman primates has recently been reviewed [Dukelow, 1983a,b].

In vitro fertilization has been achieved in five nonhuman primate species: the squirrel monkey, the marmoset, the baboon, the rhesus macaque, and the cynomolgus macaque. The first successful report was by Dr. D.C. Kraemer at the International Congress of Animal Reproduction and Artificial Insemination in Munich in 1972 (personal communication). Unfortunately, this work was not published. Kraemer did report the possible fertilization of four baboon eggs in vitro, and a fifth egg exposed to sperm developed to a six-cell stage which, on staining, clearly demonstrated nuclei in each blastomere. In 1972 two reports appeared [Johnson et al, 1972; Cline et al, 1972] announcing in vitro fertilization of the squirrel monkey oocyte. The first full publication of the latter studies appeared in 1973 [Gould et al, 1973]. In this report 22 mature oocytes were recovered and 11 of these showed sperm in the perivitelline space, extrusion of the second polar body, or pronuclear formation. Six of the 11 cells cleaved to two-cell stage. Expanded reports of in vitro fertilization in the squirrel monkey from the former laboratory (that of the author) appeared in early 1975 [Kuehl and Dukelow, 1975b] with 32 of 79 oocytes fertilized in vitro. This number was expanded to 58 of 175

(33.1%) in a subsequent publication [Dukelow and Kuehl, 1979]. In vitro fertilization studies in the squirrel monkey had the advantage of a rich background of techniques for ovulation induction and semen collection in the squirrel monkey [Bennett, 1967a,b]. Multiple and controlled ovulation can be induced in the squirrel monkey by administration of a regimen of 4 days of follicle-stimulating hormone (FSH) followed by an intermuscular injection of human chorionic gonadotropin (hCG) with ovulation occurring 8–16 hours later [Dukelow, 1970, 1973]. Since the squirrel monkey is a seasonal breeder [Harrison and Dukelow, 1973], during the nonbreeding season the amount of FSH must be extended to 5 days [Kuehl and Dukelow, 1975a]. This regimen has been demonstrated to allow mating, ovulation, and pregnancy during the nonbreeding season with in vivo fertilization [Jarosz et al, 1977]. Laparoscopic techniques are also available for collection of follicular oocytes from the squirrel monkey [Dukelow and Ariga, 1976] and for semen collection by electroejaculation [Kuehl and Dukelow, 1974]. Using these procedures in trials conducted over a 5-year period, 745 oocytes were aspirated from 2,168 follicles. Of these oocytes 137 (18.4%) were atretic. Of the remaining 608 oocytes, 38% matured to the metaphase II stage and 78 of these were fertilized in vitro (33.5%). Of five media tested, the most successful consisted of TC-199 with 20% agamma newborn calf serum with 72 μg/ml of pyruvate and added antibiotics and heparin. Fertility differences between males were observed and quantitated using in vitro fertilization. There was no difference in maturation rates between eggs recovered by laparotomy or laparoscopy. Additionally it was found that oocytes induced to maturation from a variety of different-sized follicles could be successfully fertilized in vitro. The poorest results occurred with oocytes of 1 ml or less but included many oocytes undergoing atresia. The oocyte classification system of Soupart and Morgenstern [1973] was adopted for classifying the oocytes, and this was correlated with the in vitro fertilization rates. From these studies the temporal events of early preimplantation development was ascertained as recently reviewed by Dukelow et al [1983]. In subsequent studies the effect of varying quantities of cumulus cells on squirrel monkey oocyte in vitro fertilization were quantitated [Chan et al, 1982]. If no cumulus cells were present maturation was reduced in the oocytes but even as little as one-quarter of the oocyte covered with cumulus cells resulted in satisfactory maturation (about 70%) and in vitro fertilization. It was also found that if oocytes were collected 15–16 hours after hCG administration and allowed to incubate for an additional 21 hours prior to sperm addition (ie, fertilization at about 37 hours after hCG), a higher level of fertilization was achieved. This temporal delay is in accord with the normal time of oocyte maturation in the human. Furthermore, if 1 μm of dibutyryl cAMP was added to the culture media, an increase in in vitro fertilization rate from 60% to 90% was observed. This effect was believed to be the result of stimulation of sperm capacitation, the acrosome reaction, and whiplash motility required for penetration of the egg. The effect appeared to be exerted on the sperm only, and had no effects on the egg itself. Similarly, dbcAMP had no effect on subsequent cleavage of the fertilized oocyte. Varying levels of lactate and pyruvate have been added to the in vitro fertilization culture media as energy sources. Pyruvate at a level of 1.05 mm significantly increased the rate of in vitro fertilization of squirrel monkey oocytes [Chan and Dukelow, 1982] reported successful in in vitro fertilization in the marmoset.

Kreitman et al [1982] found positive signs of fertilization for 22 cynomolgus monkey oocytes after incubation with homologous sperm with some development up to the morula stage. Bavister et al [1983] utilized a pregnant mare serum (PMS) regimen for 12 days beginning on day 3–5 of the cycle in the rhesus monkey. Follicles were aspirated laparoscopically about 30 hours after hCG. In five experiments 13 out of 30 (43%) oocytes showed signs of fertilization with development to the eight-cell stage or further. The times of cleavage were comparable to earlier reports by Lewis and Hartman [1941] on in vivo–fertilized rhesus oocytes but were somewhat faster than the cleavage rates reported by Kreitman and Hodgen [1981]. Kuehl [1983] reported successful in vitro fertilization of baboon oocytes recovered from ovaries recovered surgically. Additionally, Kuehl and colleagues were the first to report a live birth resulting from in vitro fertilization and embryo transfer [Clayton and Kuehl, 1984; Kuehl et al, 1985].

While the transfer of in vitro–fertilized eggs in humans has become common, success has been more difficult with the nonhuman primates, reflecting the delay in progress with in vitro fertilization and, in many cases, the smaller size of the animal involved. Embryo transfer in the nonhuman primate has been reviewed by Kraemer et al [1979]. Thirteen attempts to transfer squirrel monkey in vitro–fertilized eggs from one- to the four-cell stage with the eggs being placed in the oviduct were not successful [Kuehl and Dukelow, 1979]. In view of the modern practice of transferring human four- to eight-cell eggs directly to the uterus, this approach may have been more successful than attempting to replace the oocytes within the oviduct. Studies of such transfer with many of the New World primates will be difficult owing to the high stress and natural abortion rate of the animals. The first successful transfer (surgical) was by Kraemer et al [1976]. A 5-day-old baboon embryo was transferred to a naturally synchronized but nonmated baboon and 174 days later an infant was delivered by cesarean section. This represented one successful transfer out of ten attempts.

In the rhesus monkey a simple surgical flushing technique was developed by Hurst et al [1976]. From 22 flushes nine embryos and two unfertilized ova were recovered. Using a similar technique Marston et al [1977] recovered fertilized eggs from the rhesus monkey and transferred these to the opposite oviduct or the uterus of the donor animal within 30 minutes of recovery. Of eight transfers to the oviduct eight resulted in pregnancy. Additionally they transferred one five-cell egg and two seven- to eight-cell eggs to the uterus without a resultant pregnancy. Subsequently however, two six-cell embryos were transferred to the uterus and resulted in pregnancy (Marston, personal communication). It was these experiments that led other English workers, using human in vitro–fertilized eggs, to attempt the transfer of the early developmental stage eggs directly to the uterus, and this subsequently led to the first successful in vitro fertilization and transfer of human eggs.

As with domestic animal species and humans, the completion of a successful nonsurgical recovery and transfer is crucial for eventual success of these techniques. Pope et al [1980] reported the successful recovery of uterine embryos from the baboon. To accomplish this they utilized an Isaacs endometrial cell sampler modified for continuous flush and recovery. Initially 37 eggs were recovered from 80 flushes on 33 baboons, and as of the date of this writing over 500 blastocysts have been recovered by this technique. The procedure was subsequently used to recover a four-cell embryo which was transferred to a recipient female baboon and resulted in the birth of the first non-surgical, in vivo–fertilized nonhuman primate [Pope et al, 1983].

The remaining major event in this series of pioneering efforts was to collect oocytes, fertilize them in vitro, and nonsurgically transfer the embryos to create a pregnancy. This event was accomplished on July 25, 1983, exactly 5 years to the day from the birth of the first human in vitro-fertilized, nonsurgically transferred offspring, by Kuehl et al [1985] in San Antonio, Texas. This 975-gm female baboon was delivered after a normal gestation length from a primagravida baboon. Earlier this female had received four embryos that had been collected from follicles from the ovary of a female that was autopsied. After 24 hours of culture at 37°C to achieve maturation, sperm were collected by electroejaculation and incubated in culture medium for 15 minutes. An aliquot of this sperm suspension was added to 1 ml of culture media containing mature ova. At 24 hours 19 of 22 mature ova were fertilized and, of these, three zygotes at the two pronucleus stage and one at the two-cell stage were transferred into the oviduct of the recipient. Sonography was utilized to study development throughout the pregnancy.

Once embryos have been produced from nonhuman primates in any number, it is possible to study normal embryonic development of these embryos by a number of different means. These include the morphological stage of development relative to time, the chromosomal normality of the embryo, and the metabolic or biochemical normality of the embryo. Reference has already been made in Table 1 to the normal development that occurs with nonhuman primate embryos produced by in vitro fertilization or by in vivo fertilization and cultured in vivo.

One of the problems in determining chromosomal normality of multicelled eggs is the tendency for the mixing of chromosomes following disruption of the blastomere membranes due to the fixing process. Kamiguchi et al [1976] developed a technique for the chromosomal studies of Chinese hamster oocytes that was subsequently modified [Mizoguchi and Dukelow, 1981] for chromosomal studies on squirrel monkey oocytes before and after in vitro fertilization. Utilizing this technique, Asakawa and Dukelow [1982] and Asakawa et al [1982] studied the normality of chromosomal number in oocytes recovered from follicles of the squirrel monkey after ovulation induction and of

embryos of the same species following in vitro fertilization. By the metaphase II stage from 7.4% to 14% abnormalities were observed, a value comparable to that found in other laboratory species. In similar trials carried out with squirrel monkey oocytes exposed to in vitro fertilization conditions, a total of 877 oocytes were recovered and of these 330 were suitable for chromosomal analysis. Again, the incidence of abnormality was approximately 9–16% with the common abnormalities being missing or extra chromosomes. These levels are comparable with those of other species that have been studied for in vitro fertilization including humans. Interestingly, using the chromosomal technique, the incidence of triploidy of in vitro fertilized squirrel monkey oocytes was 16.7%. Triploidy is commonly encountered with in vitro fertilization in all laboratory species. In humans, Edwards [1973] found no evidence of triploid embryos after in vitro fertilization. However, Lopata et al [1978] observed three or more pronuclei in the ooplasm of some in vitro fertilized human embryos.

Little research has focused on the biochemistry of in vitro–fertilized primate ova. The work of Hutz et al [1983a] was designed to examine alterations in protein synthesis, uptake of steroid hormones, oxygen consumption, and overall viability of squirrel monkey embryos produced by this method. Incorporation of $[^3H-]$ leucine as an indicator of protein synthesis declined with oocyte maturation in vitro and remained constant after in vitro fertilization as assessed by audoradiography. There was a nonsignificant elevation at first cleavage. Uptake of estradiol and progesterone increased after in vitro fertilization in these oocytes, but there were no further changes in uptake of either steroid at first cleavage. Uridine incorporation and uptake, as a measure of RNA synthesis, decreased in oocytes recovered from squirrel monkeys 36 hours after hCG administration compared to oocytes recovered at 16 hours [Dukelow et al, 1983]. There was an approximate doubling of uridine incorporation after fertilization, with a further increase as development progressed beyond the first cleavage division. This is in accord with other studies on early embryonic stages of development in the mouse. Uridine incorporation has also been studied on a comparative basis for nonfertilized oocytes in squirrel monkeys and humans [Hutz et al, 1983b]. There was a significant decline in both the uptake and incorporation of uridine in squirrel monkey oocytes 36 hours after hCG administration (as mentioned above), and similarly RNA synthesis diminished in human oocytes collected 35 hours after hCG compared to 12 hours after hCG. These studies provide emphasis for the use of an increased interval between hCG administration and follicular aspiration in order to recover mature oocytes for in vitro fertilization studies.

Gonadotropin production by baboon embryos has been studied in vitro by Pope et al [1982]. Embryos recovered from the baboon at the six-cell to blastocyst stage were cultured in vitro, and radioimmunoassay for chorionic gonadotropin by a double antibody precipitation technique was utilized. All 12 embryos secreted gonadotropin in vitro, with measurable quantities detectable at or following attachment of the hatched blastocyst to the culture vessel. Production peaked 7–12 days after hatching from the zona pellucida and continued for up to 27 days longer.

CONCLUSION

Sperm capacitation and fertilization have been studied for over 50 years in nonhuman primates, but it has only been in the past 15 years that extensive studies on sizable numbers of embryos have been carried out. The number of species that have been utilized is small and the majority of the findings come from studies in the squirrel monkey, the baboon, the rhesus, and the cynomolgus macaque. The capacitation and fertilization processes appear to be similar to these reported in other animals including humans, but it is only with the advent of in vitro fertilization procedures (since 1972) that more extensive studies can be carried out. In reports from five different species, in vitro fertilization and in vitro development of in vivo-fertilized nonhuman primate embryos are comparable in temporal development to those encountered with humans.

In studies with the squirrel monkey, no chromosomal changes as a result of in vitro fertilization have occurred that would suggest any concern on the normality of the offspring produced and, indeed, biochemical and metabolic normality of the embryos also appears normal when compared with similar studies in laboratory animals.

The recent success (in 1983) of the births of the first nonsurgically transferred, in vivo-fertilized embryo and the first in vitro-fertilized embryo, both baboons, are encouraging in that they provide the groundwork for future substantive progress.

It is anticipated that in the near future we will see more standardization of culture conditions so that results from different laboratories can be compared. There are several areas of concern in this field including the high incidence of triploidy in in vitro-fertilized eggs and problems with in vitro nuclear and cytological maturation of the oocyte. The development of refined methods of culture and the application of egg- and embryo-freezing techniques to the research will help immeasurably in solving these problems.

REFERENCES

Anderson, R.A.; Oswald, C.; Zaneveld, L.J.D. Inhibition of human acrosin by monosaccharides and related compounds: Structure-activity relationships. JOURNAL OF MEDICAL CHEMISTRY 24:1288–1291, 1981a

Anderson, R.A.; Beyler, S.A.; Mack, S.R.; Zaneveld, L.J.D. Characterization of a high-molecular-weight form of human acrosin. BIOCHEMISTRY JOURNAL 199:307–316, 1981b.

Ariga, S.; Dukelow, W.R. Non-surgical (laparoscopic) uterine flushing and egg recovery techniques in the squirrel monkey (Saimiri sciureus). PRIMATES 18:453–457, 1977a.

Ariga, S.; Dukelow, W.R. Recovery of preimplantation blastocysts in the squirrel monkey by a laparoscopic technique. FERTILITY AND STERILITY 28:577–580, 1977b.

Asakawa, T.; Dukelow, W.R. Chromosomal analyses after in vitro fertilization of squirrel monkey (Saimiri sciureus) oocytes. BIOLOGY OF REPRODUCTION 26:579–583, 1982.

Asakawa, T.; Chan, P.J.; Dukelow, W.R. Time sequence of in vitro and chromosomal normality in metaphase I and metaphase II of the squirrel monkey (Saimiri sciureus) oocyte. BIOLOGY OF REPRODUCTION 27:118–124, 1982.

Avendano, S.; Croxatto, H.D.; Pereda, J.; Croxatto, H.B. A seven-cell human egg recovered from the oviduct. FERTILITY AND STERILITY 26:1167–1172, 1975.

Batta, S.K.; Channing, C.P. Preimplantation rhesus monkey blastocyst: Secretion of substance capable of stimulating progesterone secretion by granulosa cell cultures. LIFE SCIENCES 25:2057–2063, 1979.

Bavister, B.D.; Boatman, D.C.; Leibfried, L.; Loose, M.; Vernon, M.W. Fertilization and cleavage of rhesus monkey oocytes in vitro. BIOLOGY OF REPRODUCTION 28:983–999, 1983.

Bedford, J.M.; Shalkovsky, S. Species specificity of sperm capacitation in the rabbit. JOURNAL OF REPRODUCTION AND FERTILITY 13:361–364, 1967.

Bennett, J.P. The induction of ovulation in the squirrel

monkey (*Saimiri sciureus*) with pregnant mares serum (PMS) and human chorionic gonadotropin (HCG). JOURNAL OF REPRODUCTION AND FERTILITY 13:357–459, 1967a.

Bennett, J.P. Artificial insemination of the squirrel monkey. JOURNAL OF ENDOCRINOLOGY 13:473–474, 1967b.

Blakley, G.B.; Beamer, T.W.; Dukelow, W.R. Characteristics of the menstrual cycle in nonhuman primates. IV. Timed mating in *Macaca nemestrina*. LABORATORY ANIMALS 15:351–353, 1981.

Blandau, R.J. In vitro fertilization and embryo transfer. FERTILITY AND STERILITY 33:3–11, 1980.

Brackett, B.G. In vitro fertilization and its assessment with embryo culture. Pp. 171–193 in ANIMAL REPRODUCTION (BARC Symposium No. 3). H. Hawk, ed. Montclair, NJ, Allanheld and Osmun, 1979.

Brüggemann, S.; Dukelow, W.R. Characteristics of the menstrual cycle in nonhuman primates. III. Timed mating in *Macaca arctoides*. JOURNAL OF MEDICAL PRIMATOLOGY 9:213–221, 1980.

Burke, D.B. In vitro sperm-ovum interaction utilizing golden hamster and squirrel monkey spermatozoa with hamster zona-free ova. M.S. Thesis, Endocrine Research Unit, Michigan State University, East Lansing, 57 pp., 1979.

Chan, P.J.; Dukelow, W.R. Effects of lactate and pyruvate on it vitro fertilization of hamster and squirrel monkey oocytes. PROCEEDINGS OF THE 8TH INTERNATIONAL CONGRESS OF PRIMATOLOGY, Atlanta, Georgia August 11–14, 1982.

Chan, P.J.; Hutz, R.J.; Dukelow, W.R. Nonhuman primate in vitro fertilization: Seasonality, cumulus cells, cyclic nucleotides, ribonucleic acid and viability assays. FERTILITY AND STERILITY 38:609–615, 1982.

Clayton, O.; Kuehl, T.J. The first successful in vitro fertilization and embryo transfer in a nonhuman primate. THERIOGENOLOGY 21:228, 1984.

Cline, E.M.; Gould, K.G; Foley, C.W. Regulation of ovulation, recovery of mature ova and fertilization in vitro of mature ova of the squirrel monkey (*Saimiri sciureus*). FEDERATION PROCEEDINGS 31:277, 1972.

Croxatto, H.B.; Diaz, S.; Fuentealga, B.; Croxatto, H.D.; Carrillo, D.; Fabres, C. Studies on the duration of egg transport in the human oviduct. I. The time interval between ovulation and egg recovery from the uterus in normal women. FERTILITY AND STERILITY 23:477–458, 1972.

DeMayo, F.J.; Mizoguchi, H.; Dukelow, W.R. Fertilization of squirrel monkey and hamster ova in the rabbit oviduct (xenogenous fertilization). SCIENCE 208:1468–1469, 1980.

DeMayo, F.J.; Chan, P.J.; Dukelow, W.R. In vitro and xenogenous fertilization of cryopreserved squirrel monkey ova. SCIENCE, 1983 (submitted).

Dukelow, W.R. Induction and timing of single and multiple ovulations in the squirrel monkey (*Saimiri sciureus*). JOURNAL OF REPRODUCTION AND FERTILITY 22:303–309, 1970.

Dukelow, W.R. Human chorionic gonadotropin: Induction of ovulation in the squirrel monkey. SCIENCE 206:234–235, 1979.

Dukelow, W.R. Ovum recovery and embryo transfer in primates. Pp. 155–174 in MAMMALIAN EGG TRANSFER. C.E. Adams, ed. Boca Raton, FL, CRC Press, 1983a.

Dukelow, W.R. The squirrel monkey (*Saimiri sciureus*). Pp. 149–179 in REPRODUCTION IN NEW WORLD PRIMATES. J.P. Hearn, ed. Lancaster, U.K., MTP Press, 1983b.

Dukelow, W.R.; Ariga, S. Laparoscopic techniques for biomedical research. JOURNAL OF MEDICAL PRIMATOLOGY 5:82–99. 1976.

Dukelow, W.R.; Brüggemann, S. Characteristics of the menstrual cycle in nonhuman primates. II. Ovulation and optimal mating times in macaques. JOURNAL OF MEDICAL PRIMATOLOGY 8:79–87, 1979.

Dukelow, W.R.; Chernoff, H.N. Primate sperm survival and capacitation in a foreign uterine environment. AMERICAN JOURNAL OF PHYSIOLOGY 216:682–686. 1969.

Dukelow, W.R.; Kuehl, T.J. In vitro fertilization of nonhuman primates. Pp. 67–80 in LA FECONDATION. Paris, Masson, 1975.

Dukelow, W.R.; Williams, W.L. Capacitation of sperm. In PROGRESS IN INFERTILITY. J. Behrman: R. Kistner, eds. Boston, Little, Brown, 1983.

Dukelow, W.R.; Chan, P.J.; Hutz, R.J.; DeMayo, F.J.; Dooley, V.D.; Rawlins, R.G.; Ridha, M.T. Preimplantation development of the primate embryo after in vitro fertilization. JOURNAL OF EXPERIMENTAL ZOOLOGY 228:215–221, 1983.

Edwards, R.G. Studies on human conception. AMERICAN JOURNAL OF OBSTETRICS AND GYNECOLOGY 1117:589–601, 1973.

Edwards, R.G.; Steptoe, P.C. Physiological aspects of human embryo transfer. Pp. 377–409 in PROGRESS IN INFERTILITY. S.J. Behrman; R.W. Kistner, eds. Boston, Little, Brown 1975.

Edwards, R.G.; Bavister, B.D.; Steptoe, P.C. Early stages of fertilization in vitro of human oocytes matured in vitro. NATURE (LONDON) 221:632–633, 1969.

Gould, K.G.; Cline, E.M.; Williams, W.L. Observations on the induction of ovulation and fertilization in vitro in the squirrel monkey (*Saimiri sciureus*). FERTILITY AND STERILITY 24:260–268, 1973.

Harlow, C.R.; Gems, S.; Hearn, J.P. The prediction and detection of ovulation in the marmoset monkey, *Callithrix jacchus*. P. 7 in PROCEEDINGS OF THE WINTER MEETING OF THE SOCIETY TO STUDY FERTILITY. Cambridge, U.K., 1982.

Harrison, R.M.; Dukelow, W.R. Seasonal adaption of laboratory-maintained squirrel monkeys (*Saimiri sciureus*). JOURNAL OF MEDICAL PRIMATOLOGY 2:277–283, 1973.

Hartman, C. Pelvic (rectal) palpation of the female monkey with special reference to the ascertainment of ovulation time. AMERICAN JOURNAL OF OBSTETRICS AND GYNECOLOGY 26:600–608, 1933.

Hertig, A.T.; Rock, J.; Adams, E.C.; Mulligan, W.J. On the preimplantation stages of the human ovum: A description of four normal and four abnormal specimens ranging from the second to the fifth day of development. CONTRIBUTIONS TO EMBRYOLOGY, CARNEGIE INSTITUTIONS, WASHINGTON 35:199–230, 1954.

Hurst, P.R.; Jefferies, K. Eckstein, P.; Wheeler, A.G. Recovery of uterine embryos in rhesus monkeys. BIOLOGY OF REPRODUCTION 15:429–434, 1976.

Hurst, P.R.; Jefferies, K.; Eckstein, P.; Wheeler, A.G. An ultrastructural study of preimplantation uterine embryos of the rhesus monkey. JOURNAL OF ANATOMY 126:209–220, 1978.

Hutz, R.J.; Chan, P.J.; Dukelow, W.R. Nonhuman primate in vitro fertilization: Biochemical changes associated with embryonic development. FERTILITY AND STERILITY 40:521–524, 1983a.

Hutz, R.J.; Holzman, G.V.; Dukelow, W.R. Synthesis of ribonucleic acid in oocytes collected from squirrel monkeys and humans following chorionic gonadotropin administration. AMERICAN JOURNAL OF PRIMATOLOGY 5:267–270, 1983.

Jarosz, S.J.; Kuehl, T.J.; Dukelow, W.R. Vaginal cytology, induced ovulation and gestation in the squirrel monkey (*Saimiri sciureus*). BIOLOGY OF REPRODUCTION 16:97–103, 1977.

Jewett, D.A.; Dukelow, W.R. Laparoscopy and precise mating techniques to determine gestation length in *Macaca fascicularis*. LABORATORY PRIMATE NEWSLETTER 10:16–17, 1971.

Johnson, M.J.; Harrison, R.M.; Dukelow, W.R. Studies on oviductal fluid and in vitro fertilization in rabbits and nonhuman primates. FEDERATION PROCEEDINGS 31:278, 1972.

Kamiguchi, Y.; Funaki, K.; Mikamo, K. A new technique for chromosome study of murine oocytes. PROCEEDINGS JAPAN ACADEMY 52:316–319, 1976.

Kraemer, D.C.; Hendrickx, A.G. Description of stages I, II, III. Pp. 45–52 in EMBRYOLOGY OF THE BABOON. A.G. Hendrickx, ed. Chicago, University of Chicago Press, 1971.

Kraemer, D.C.; Moore, G.T.; Kramen, M.A. Baboon infant produced by embryo transfer. SCIENCE 192:1246–1247, 1976.

Kraemer, D.C.; Flow, B.L.; Schriver, M.D.; Kinney, G.M.; Pennycock, J.W. Embryo transfer in the nonhuman primate, feline and canine. THERIOGENOLOGY 11:51–62, 1979.

Kreitmann, O.; Hodgen, G.D. Low tubal ovum transfer: An alternate to in vitro fertilization. FERTILITY AND STERILITY 34:375–378, 1980.

Kreitmann, O.; Hodgen, G.D. Retarded cleavage rates of preimplantation monkey embryos in vitro. JOURNAL OF THE AMERICAN MEDICAL ASSOCIATION 246:627–630, 1981.

Kreitmann, O.; Lynch, A.; Nixon, W.E.; Hodgen, G.D. Ovum collection, induced luteal dysfunction, in vitro fertilization, embryo development and low tubal ovum transfer in primates. Pp. 303–324 in IN VITRO FERTILIZATION AND EMBRYO TRANSFER. E.S.E. Hafez; K. Semm, eds. Lancaster, U.K., MTP Press, 1982.

Kuehl, T.J. In vitro and xenogenous fertilization of baboon follicular oocytes. FERTILITY AND STERILITY 39:422, 1983.

Kuehl, T.J.; Dukelow, W.R. A restraint device for electroejaculation of squirrel monkeys (*Saimiri sciureus*). LABORATORY ANIMAL SCIENCE 24:364–366, 1974.

Kuehl, T.J.; Dukelow, W.R. Ovulation induction during the anovulatory season in *Saimiri sciureus*. JOURNAL OF MEDICAL PRIMATOLOGY 4:23–31, 1975a.

Kuehl, T.J.; Dukelow, W.R. Fertilization in vitro of *Saimiri sciureus* follicular oocytes. JOURNAL OF MEDICAL PRIMATOLOGY 4:209–216, 1975b.

Kuehl, T.J.; Dukelow, W.R. Maturation and in vitro fertilization of follicular oocytes of the squirrel monkey (*Saimiri sciureus*). BIOLOGY OF REPRODUCTION 21:545–556, 1979.

Kuehl, T.J.; Dukelow, W.R. Time relations of squirrel monkey (*Saimiri sciureus*) sperm capacitation and ovum maturation in an in vitro fertilization system. JOURNAL OF REPRODUCTION AND FERTILITY 64:135–137, 1982.

Kuehl, T.J.; Clayton, O.; Reyes, P.S. Live birth following in vitro fertilization and embryo transfer in a nonhuman primate. AMERICAN JOURNAL OF PRIMATOLOGY, 1985 (in press).

Lewis, W.H.; Hartman, C.G. Tubal ova of the rhesus monkey. CONTRIBUTIONS TO EMBRYOLOGY (CARNEGIE INSTITUTION, WASHINGTON) 29:(108):9–14, 1941.

Longo, F.J. Effects of puromycin and actinomycin D on fertilized rabbit eggs cultured in vitro. JOURNAL OF EXPERIMENTAL ZOOLOGY 203:223–250, 1978.

Lopata, A.; Brown, J.B.; Leaton, J.F.; McTalbot, J.; Wood, C. In vitro fertilization of preovulatory oocytes and embryo transfer in infertile patients. FERTILITY AND STERILITY 30:27–35, 1978.

Marston, J.H.; Kelly, W.A. Time relationships of spermatozoa penetration into the egg of the rhesus monkey. NATURE (LONDON) 217:1073–1074, 1968.

Marston, J.H.; Penn, R.; Sivelle, P.C. Successful autotransfer of tubal eggs in the rhesus monkey (*Macaca mulatta*). JOURNAL OF REPRODUCTION AND FERTILITY 49:175–176, 1977.

McRorie, R.A.; Williams, W.L. Biochemistry of mammalian fertilization. ANNUAL REVIEWS OF BIOCHEMISTRY 43:777–803, 1974.

Mizoguchi, H.; Dukelow, W.R. Gradual fixation method for chromosomal studies of squirrel monkey oocytes after gonadotropin treatment. JOURNAL OF MEDICAL PRIMATOLOGY 10:180–186, 1981.

Pope, C.E.; Pope, V.Z.; Beck, L.R. Nonsurgical recovery of uterine embryos in the baboon. BIOLOGY OF REPRODUCTION 23:657–662, 1980.

Pope, C.E.; Pope, V.Z.; Beck, L.R. Development of baboon preimplantation embryos to post-implantation stages in vitro. BIOLOGY OF REPRODUCTION 27:915–923, 1982.

Pope, C.E.; Pope V.Z.; Beck L.R. Successful nonsurgical transfer of a nonsurgically recovered four-cell uterine embryo in the baboon. TERATOLOGY 19:144, 1983.

Pope, V.Z.; Pope, C.E.; Beck, L.R. Gonadotropin production by baboon embryos in vitro. Pp. 129–135 in IN VITRO FERTILIZATION AND EMBRYO TRANSFER. E.S.E. Hafez; K. Semm, eds. Lancaster, U.K., MTP Press, 1982.

Soupart, P.; Morganstern, L.L. Human sperm capacitation and in vitro fertilization. FERTILITY AND STERILITY 24:462–478, 1973.

Soupart, P.; Strong, P.A. Ultrastructural observations on human oocytes fertilized in vitro. FERTILITY AND STERILITY 25:11–44, 1974.

Srivastava, P.N.; Farooqui, A.S.; Gould, K.G. Studies on hydrolytic enzymes of chimpanzee semen. BIOLOGY OF REPRODUCTION 25:363–369, 1981.

Stambaugh, R.; Buckley, J. Comparative studies of the acrosomal enzymes of rabbit, rhesus monkey, and human spermatozoa. BIOLOGY OF REPRODUCTION 3:275–282, 1970.

Stambaugh, R.; Seitz, H.M.; Mastroianni, L. Acrosomal proteinase inhibitors in rhesus monkey (*Macaca mulatta*) oviduct fluid. FERTILITY AND STERILITY 25:352–357, 1974.

Steptoe, P.C.; Edwards, R.G. Birth after the reimplantation of a human embryo. LANCET 2:366, 1978.

Stolzenberg, S.J.; Jones, D.C.L.; Kaplan, J.N.; Barth, R.A. Hodgen, G.D.; Madan, S.M. Studies with timed-pregnant squirrel monkeys (*Saimiri sciureus*). JOURNAL OF MEDICAL PRIMATOLOGY 8:29–38, 1979.

Tobias, P.S.; Schumacher, G.F.B. The extraction of acrosin from human spermatozoa. BIOLOGY OF REPRODUCTION 15:187–194, 1976.

Usui, N.; Yanagimachi, R. Behavior of hamster sperm nuclei incorporated into eggs at various stages of maturation, fertilization and early development: The appearance and disappearance of factors involved in sperm chromatin decondensation in egg cytoplasm. JOURNAL OF ULTRASTRUCTURAL RESEARCH 57:276–288, 1976.

van Wagenen, G.W. Mating and pregnancy in the monkey. ANATOMICAL RECORD 91: 304, 1945.

Yanagimachi, R. Mechanisms of fertilization in mammals. Pp. 81–182 in FERTILIZATION AND EMBRYONIC DEVELOPMENT IN VITRO. L. Mastroianni; J.D. Biggers, eds. New York, Plenum, 1981.

Yanagimachi, R.; Usui, N. The appearance and disappearance of factors involved in sperm chromatin decondensation in the hamster egg. JOURNAL OF CELL BIOLOGY 55:293a, 1972.

Yanagimachi, R.; Yanagimachi, H.; Rogers, B.J. The use of zona-free animal ova as a test system for the assessment of the fertilizing capacity of human spermatozoa. BIOLOGY OF REPRODUCTION 15:471–476, 1976.

Yoshida, T.; Nakajima, M.; Hiyaoka, A.; Suzuki, M.T.; Cho, F.; Honjo, S. Menstrual cycle lengths and the estimated time of ovulation in the cynomolgus monkey (*Macaca fascicularis*). JOURNAL OF EXPERIMENTAL ANIMALS 31:165–174, 1982.

Implantation in Nonhuman Primates and in the Human

Allen C. Enders and Sandra Schlafke

Department of Human Anatomy and California Primate Research Center, University of California, School of Medicine, Davis, California 95616

INTRODUCTION

Implantation is the process by which an unattached ("free") blastocyst becomes fixed in position in the uterus, and a series of events leading to a more intimate physiological and morphological relationship between the blastocyst and endometrium is initiated. It is the necessary prerequisite to placentation, and in mammals that develop a hemochorial placenta follows a definite sequence: apposition, adhesion, penetration of uterine luminal epithelium, basal lamina penetration, and tapping of maternal blood vessels. There is generally little question that once adhesion can be demonstrated implantation has begun. In primates, implantation can be considered completed and placentation initiated when the portion of the trophoblast that will form the chorioallantoic placenta has reached its most intimate morphological relationship to the uterus, and formation of definitive structural features of the placenta has begun.

Since implantation involves interaction of the blastocyst and endometrium within the uterus, study of this interaction ordinarily necessitates removal of the uterus from the animal being studied, and consequently termination of its reproductive career. This necessity has severely limited our information on this stage of development in primates.

IMPLANTATION IN PROSIMIANS

Reports in the literature on implantation in lorises, lemurs, and *Tarsius* are based largely on material preserved in the field and embedded and sectioned for light microscopy. Consequently, there is no morphological material prepared for electron microscopy, or even embedded in plastic for light microscopy, nor in any of these species is the precise timing of events of early implantation known. Some stages in implantation have been described using materials collected and sectioned in the early part of this century; even more recent reviews [Hendrickx and Houston, 1971; Luckett, 1974] have leaned heavily on the materials of Gerard [1932] and Hill [1932].

All the prosimians have bicornuate uteri, and a blastocyst that at implantation is expanded, bilaminar and tends to be oriented with the inner cell mass orthomesometrially (although it appears that in *Tarsius* the orientation of the blastocyst may vary a bit).

Lemurs. Implantation in the lemurs was originally described by Hill [1932], and reconsidered by Luckett [1974]. Reng [1977] and Strauss [1978] recently described new material from *Microcebus murinus*. At the adhesion stage of implantation in *Microcebus*, the blastocyst fills the uterine lumen; the inner cell mass is oriented orthomesometrially and is no longer covered by trophoblast. The trophoblast of the abembryonic pole of the blastocyst is columnar, and forms an absorption plaque. This is a region of tall cells, much like the paraplacental trophoblast of carnivores, that appears to be involved in uptake of material from the uterine lumen. As the adhesion stage continues, the peripheral trophoblast forms pockets around the openings of uterine glands. After the trophoblast becomes lined by mesoderm, each pocket is termed a chorionic vesicle. The rest of the trophoblast maintains close apposition to the uterine luminal epithelium in a typical epitheliochorial relationship.

The area of the absorption plaque undergoes a

transition and, according to Strauss, trophoblast invades the mucosa to the extent that a syndesmochorial relationship is formed; that is, the trophoblast intermingles with the endometrial stroma. He therefore suggests that at this time the plaque be called the nidation plaque. The rest of the trophoblast is in an epitheliochorial relationship to the uterine surface, a situation that persists to term.

Lorises. The unusual mechanism of implantation in *Galago senegalensis* has been described by Butler [1964, 1967]. At the start of the adhesion stage, the orientation of the blastocyst is orthomesometrial, similar to that in *Microcebus.* When the blastocyst is about 0.5 mm in diameter, an abembryonic attachment plaque forms. Although this is in the same location as the absorption plaque in lemurs, it is composed of large ("giant") trophoblast cells with large, apparently polyploid nuclei. The uterine luminal epithelium disappears in the area of the attachment plaque, so that the abembryonic trophoblast cells appear to be apposed to the basal lamina of the epithelium. The attachment plaque occupies about one-fourth to one-half of the circumference of the blastocyst at its maximum development; it then begins to recede, and the uterine luminal epithelium reforms. The trophoblast is closely applied to the uterine luminal epithelium except at the openings of some of the uterine glands, where it is deflected into cup-shaped structures, the chorionic vesicles. The placenta is consequently a diffuse epitheliochorial structure. The dwarf galago *(G. demidovi)* has an unusual type of implantation in that, unlike other galagos and lemurs, the blastocyst does not fill the uterine lumen when it first attaches to the orthomesometrial aspect of the endometrial surface. Furthermore, annular endometrial folds around the paraembryonic end of the blastocyst grow over the blastocyst, making it temporarily secondarily interstitial [Hill, 1938; Luckett, 1974]. However, further growth results in return of the blastocyst to the lumen and central superficial implantation similar to other galagos. Consequently, the mature placenta is once more epitheliochorial.

The general pattern of orientation, exposed inner cell mass, and antimesometrial absorption plaque is present throughout the lorises and lemurs. Only in *G. senegalensis* has a transitory trophoblast giant cell layer been described, and only in *Microcebus* has stromal invasion been reported. The secondarily interstitial condition found in *G. demidovi* is

usually considered the result of the unusual uterine folds rather than trophoblast invasive activity.

Tarsius. Implantation in *Tarsius* has been described by Hubrecht [1908], Hill [1932], and Luckett [1974]. It shows many intermediate characteristics between other prosimians and anthropoids. By the time of implantation, the blastocyst loses the covering of polar trophoblast over the inner cell mass, as in lorises and lemurs. The inner cell mass is oriented either orthomesometrially or nearly antimesometrially. Subsequently there is a paraembryonic trophoblastic invasion of the mesometrial uterine mucosa. This association occurs at an early stage, when the blastocyst is still small and has not expanded to fill the uterine lumen as it does in most lorises and lemurs at the adhesion stage. The invasion of the mesometrial mucosa leads to the formation of a placental disk in this position.

Unlike lorises and lemurs, in which the endoderm is temporarily associated with the trophoblast at early implantation, the precocious formation of an exocelom in *Tarsius* separates the extraembryonic endoderm from the trophoblast and precludes the presence of a transitory choriovitelline placenta. The trophoblast in the mesometrial area eventually develops a hemochorial relationship to the uterus in the placental disk. During the early invasion of the endometrium, a mass of cells accumulates between the trophoblast adjacent to the blastocyst cavity and the hypertrophied ends of the occluded uterine glands. This cluster of cells has been interpreted as cytotrophoblast by Hill, and as glandular epithelium by Luckett. Considering the way in which the cytotrophoblast proliferates during implantation in the rhesus monkey [Enders et al, 1983a], such a source for this growth of cells seems reasonable. However, preparations that allow more basis for identification of these cells will be necessary before the origin of this cellular pad can be clarified.

IMPLANTATION IN NEW WORLD PRIMATES

The morphology of the events of early implantation in New World primates is essentially unknown. Scattered individual observations are little more informative than when described by Hill [1932], and much of the material was reexamined in more recent context by Luckett [1974]. In contrast to the paucity of morphological data, a great deal of information is now available on the behavior, breeding, and steroid levels in a number of species, including the cebus monkey *(Cebus apella)* [Nagle and Denari, 1982], owl monkey *(Aotus trivirgatus)* [Dixson, 1982], squirrel monkey *(Saimiri sciureus)* [Dukelow, 1982], and marmoset *(Callithrix jacchus)* [Hearn, 1980, 1982]. In the latter two small New World monkeys, studies of in vitro fertilization and cleavage have been carried out.

Preliminary studies from Hearn's laboratory have included the observation that blastocysts cultured in vitro will continue to develop beyond the time and condition of normal implantation [Hearn, 1982]. Timed collections of blastocysts indicate that in this marmoset implantation may not occur until day 10 or 11. The marmoset is also unusual in commonly having twins, and frequently triplets.

Studies with the squirrel monkey suggest that cleavage is relatively rapid; blastocysts were recovered 96–120 hours after fertilization [Ariga and Dukelow, 1977; Dukelow, 1982]. The description by Hill [1932] and the accompanying precise drawings by A.K. Maxwell indicate that in the squirrel monkey, after the initial penetration of the maternal uterine epithelium, the trophoblast is slow in further penetration of the endometrium. Thus chorionic mesoderm formation occurs before any tapping of maternal vessels. With further development the syncytial trophoblast increases in mass surrounding maternal capillaries, and forming a series of labyrinthine spaces into which maternal blood passes from interrupted endometrial vessels.

Wislocki [1929] had access to a small series of howler monkey *(Alouatta* sp.) placentas, the youngest of which was in a presomite stage of embryonic development. This species, which usually has only a single placental disk, has a massive amount of syncytial trophoblast at the early stages. This syncytium appears to partition the blood-filled spaces of the trophoblastic plate into a series of lacunae, suggesting that the initial formation of cytotrophoblast columns plays a less important role in determining placental arrangement in this species than in catarrhine monkeys.

A comparison of late implantation stages of the platyrrhine and catarrhine monkeys indicates that 1) the proportion of syncytial trophoblast to cytotrophoblast is much higher in the platyrrhines when intrasyncytial blood spaces are first forming, 2) some maternal vessels persist within the region occupied by syncytial trophoblast during early pla-

cental formation in the platyrrhines, and 3) this syncytial trophoblast partitions the intratrophoblastic maternal blood spaces into numerous labyrinthine channels.

A series of early implantation stages embedded in plastic would be extremely helpful in determining why the placenta of the platyrrhine monkeys develops in a more labyrinthine fashion than that of many catarrhines.

IMPLANTATION IN OLD WORLD PRIMATES

Preimplantation Stages of Rhesus Monkey, Baboon, and Human

Since Hendrickx and Kraemer [1968] introduced direct flushing of the uterus at laparotomy, a number of variations of this technique have been introduced which have made available cleavage and blastocyst stages of primates. Some of these methods were used principally to determine the rate of tubal transport [eg, Croxatto et al, 1972; Eddy et al, 1975]. Hurst et al [1976, 1978] used a modification of this method to study the fine structure of the rhesus monkey blastocyst, and Panigel et al [1975] made some observations on the ultrastructure of baboon cleavage stages and early blastocysts. More recently Pope et al [1980, 1982] have used a nonsurgical method for flushing embryos from the uterus of the baboon, and have used in vitro culture to obtain further development. The methods of both Hurst and Pope have been used in our laboratory to obtain stages for the study of differentiation of the blastocyst of the rhesus monkey [Enders and Schlafke, 1981, Enders et al, 1982, 1983b] and the baboon.

Rhesus Monkey. Prior to the assumption of a fixed relationship with the uterine luminal epithelium (pragmatically determined by no longer being disrupted by flushing), the blastocyst of the rhesus monkey undergoes a number of changes.

Loss of the zona pellucida. Large zona-free blastocysts have been flushed from the uterus [Hurst et al, 1978; Enders and Schlafke, 1981]. We have flushed both a split distended zona and a blastocyst from the same uterus, and a large zona was obtained from an animal that proved to be pregnant and thus was probably implanted at the time of the flush. Although there is some thinning of the zona pellucida prior to shedding, the thinning appears in proportion to the increase in size of the late blastocyst as compared with the morula (the diameter roughly doubles). Although it is possible that uterine secretions might soften or modify the zona, the zona is probably shed rather than dissolved. No fragments of the zona are found in implantation sites.

Differentiation of endoderm. Continuous differentiation of the blastocyst prior to implantation results in the establishment of an endodermal layer underlying the inner cell mass and extending beyond it. This layer is largely separated from both trophoblast and epiblast by a basal lamina associated with the trophoblast except at the inner cell mass, where it underlies the epiblast. The endoderm lacks a basal lamina and there are occasionally gap junctions between endoderm and epiblast, where the epiblast basal lamina is lacking.

Differentiation of trophoblast. The trophoblast, in addition to having typical apical junctional complexes and an apical vacuolar system, has numerous microvilli. A very large preimplantation blastocyst had a number of long irregular processes from the free surface of trophoblast cells in a paraembryonic region (Fig. 1). Such structures would be well suited to initiating the adhesion to uterine luminal epithelium, and could in this fashion account for the orientation of the blastocyst at the time of implantation.

Preimplantation Embryos of the Baboon. Hendrickx [1971] illustrated a baboon blastocyst that

may be in the process of hatching from its zona pellucida. No zona-free blastocysts of the baboon have been studied by electron microscopy. No syncytium formation has been seen prior to implantation in blastocysts flushed from the uterus. However, Pope et al [1982] found that in vitro-cultured baboon blastocysts apparently form syncytial trophoblast when cultured beyond the time of implantation.

Preimplantation Human Embryos. The oldest preimplantation stage from in vivo fertilization in the human described using electron microscopy is a seven-cell stage [Pereda and Croxatto, 1978]. However, the use of in vitro fertilization is rapidly adding material from this period. In particular, the "hatched" blastocyst described by Mohr and Trounson [1982] demonstrates the basic similarity of the human to that of the rhesus monkey. In addition to evidence of some cell death, this blastocyst illustrates normal development of endoderm. Consequently it seems probable that endoderm in the human (primary endoderm, hypoblast) forms in a similar manner to that of other mammals. No syncytial trophoblast formation was noted in this blastocyst.

No studies of transport of materials across trophoblast, nature of trophoblastic glycocalyx, or lytic potential of primate blastocysts have yet been made. It is becoming increasingly evident that primate blastocysts are "ugly" compared to those of laboratory species insofar as they demonstrate appreciable irregularity in overall shape, numerous cell

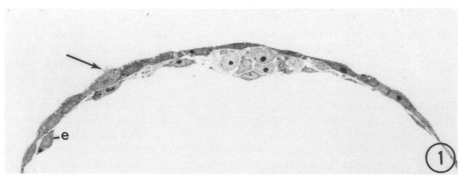

Fig. 1. Blastocyst from a rhesus monkey, recovered on day 8 of pregnancy. A small portion of the inner cell mass appears in the middle. The endodermal cells (e) extend beyond the inner cell mass under the trophoblast. The type of projection seen at the arrow is postulated to participate in adhesion of the blastocyst to the endometrium. ×500.

deaths, and variation in the extent of swelling and collapse. The extent to which the stages can suffer cellular attrition and damage without compromise to the continued viability of the conceptus awaits experimental analysis.

Implantation in the Rhesus Monkey

The exact method of apposition and adhesion of the blastocysts and uterus in the rhesus monkey is not known. Some of the blastocysts that are zona free and have numerous trophoblast protrusions were probably displaced from a location of incipient implantation. In studies in our laboratory we have attempted to fix the uterus by introduction of fixative via the vasculature prior to removal. By such methods it can be determined whether or not the uterine lumen is closed at the time of association of blastocyst and uterus. Although it seems likely that the lumen is largely obliterated at this time, and consequently that apposition is brought about in large part by luminal closure, in our specimens the endometrial fixation with intravascular injection of fixative was not ideal, and it could not be determined whether or not the apposition of the two uterine luminal surfaces is as close as that in laboratory rodents. At any rate closure but not microvillous interdigitation was observed.

Early stages of penentration of uterine epithelium by trophoblast have been described by light and electron microscopy [Wislocki and Streeter, 1938; Heuser and Streeter, 1941; Enders et al, 1983a]. Wislocki and Streeter, in their classical description of implantation in the rhesus monkey, divided the period of early placental development into three stages: the prelacunar stage, the stage of trophoblast lacunae, and the villous stage. It is useful to further subdivide the prelacunar stage into the stage of epithelial penetration and the stage of the trophoblastic plate.

Epithelial Penetration. Several stages in implantation in the rhesus monkey, in which trophoblast has not yet penetrated through the basal lamina of the uterine luminal epithelium, were described by Wislocki and Streeter [1938], and in somewhat more detail but unfortunately more fancifully by Heuser and Streeter [1941]. Wislocki and Streeter showed that trophoblastic processes in the paraembryonic region first associate intimately with the luminal epithelium, and that at the initiation of trophoblastic invasion of the endometrium there is

no noticeable change in the endometrium at the region of implantation. Because of the nature of the preparations (serially sectioned paraffin-embedded material), it was difficult to discern cell boundaries, or even to distinguish in all instances uterine cells and trophoblast cells.

A perfusion fixed plastic embedded specimen collected on day 9.5 of gestation [Enders et al, 1983a] is particularly informative. Although three small masses of syncytial trophoblast are present, only in one place at the margin of the inner cell mass does trophoblast penetrate between uterine epithelial cells (Fig. 2). In this site, syncytial trophoblast shares junctional complexes with adjacent uterine luminal epithelial cells, surrounds several epithelial cells, and penetrates to but not through the basal lamina of the uterine epithelium (Fig. 3). Although there is at least one dead cell surrounded by syncytial trophoblast, the advanced cytolysis of this cell does not allow determination of its origin. Several uterine cells are appreciably distorted by syncytial trophoblast, and may have been fragmented. It was concluded that the syncytial trophoblast penetrates principally by infiltrating between epithelial cells. The adhesion of the trophoblast to the lateral sides of the luminal epithelial cells serves both to orient the trophoblast invasion and to maintain luminal integrity. The uterine luminal basal lamina is initially resistant to further trophoblastic penetration. The only apparent stromal response at this stage is a great abundance of eosinophilic leukocytes in the area of the implantation site.

Subsequently the implantation site expands rapidly and the uterine endometrium initiates a pronounced response. A marked proliferation of cytotrophoblast occurs on day 10. This proliferation expands the implantation site in the plane of the uterine epithelium (Fig. 4). In addition trophoblast appears to penetrate along any uterine glands with which it is in contact. The result of the cytotrophoblast proliferation is a solid mass of syncytial and cytrophoblast, constituting the trophoblastic plate. The syncytial trophoblast characteristically has multiple lamellar processes at its border with the cytotrophoblast (Fig. 6). At a few areas in the trophoblastic plate some syncytial trophoblast develops thin microvillous-lined clefts in which the syncytium demonstrates marked polarity. This change represents differentiation of lamellar syncytial trophoblast, as opposed to less polarized more massive earlier syncytium in which the nuclei are often largely aggregated.

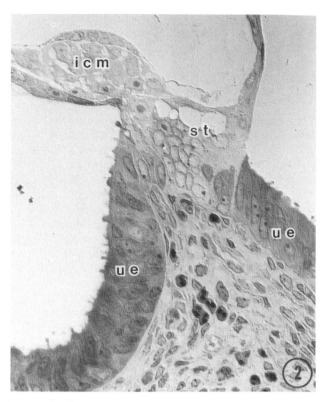

Fig. 2. The inner cell mass (icm) and area of penetration of uterine luminal epithelium (ue) of a day-9.5 implantation site from a rhesus monkey. The mass of pale syncytial trophoblast (st) has penetrated through the epithelium and surrounded several epithelial cells on the right. Trophoblast has not penetrated through the basal lamina of this epithelium. The small dark cells in the stroma are eosinophils. Photographed with Nomarski optics. ×500.

The uterus at day 10 responds to the blastocyst by 1) the initiation of an epithelial plaque response by the basal cells of the luminal epithelium and the necks of the glands (Fig. 5), 2) a peripheral subepithelial edema, and 3) hyperplasia and beginning hypertrophy of the endothelial cells of maternal vessels (see Fig. 10).

The inner cell mass at this time shows a radiate arrangement of the epiblast with apical junctional complexes directed inward. The smaller cells of this mass are in contact with cytotrophoblast. The larger cells are associated with endodermal layers, from which they are separated by an epiblast basal lamina that reflects back and is continuous with that of the trophoblast. In addition to the thin layer of primary endoderm a few isolated cells are interposed between the endoderm and the basal lamina of the trophoblast. The abembryonic trophoblast has not yet attached to the luminal epithelium of the opposite surface, but usually elicits a subadjacent epithelial plaque reaction.

By days 10–11, trophoblast reaches maternal vessels. Since trophoblast can be found constituting a portion of the wall of such vessels, neither the basal lamina nor the endothelium of these vessels can be considered a restraint to trophoblastic invasion. As a result of vascular penetration, maternal blood enters the region of the trophoblastic plate, and particularly tends to be present in lacunae that are expanded on the embryonic side of the trophoblastic plate (Fig. 8). Such lacunae are lined by syncytial trophoblast with numerous microvilli of the type previously seen only in prelacunar clefts (Fig. 7). These lacunae rapidly increase in number and

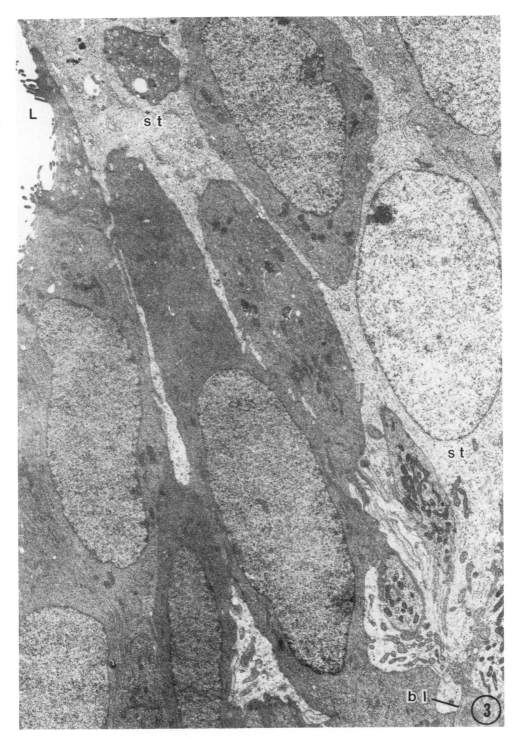

Fig. 3. Implantation site from day 9.5 of pregnancy in the rhesus monkey. The pale syncytial trophoblast (st) has partially surrounded several uterine epithelial cells in the process of penetrating from the lumen (L) to the basal lamina (bl). ×7,100.

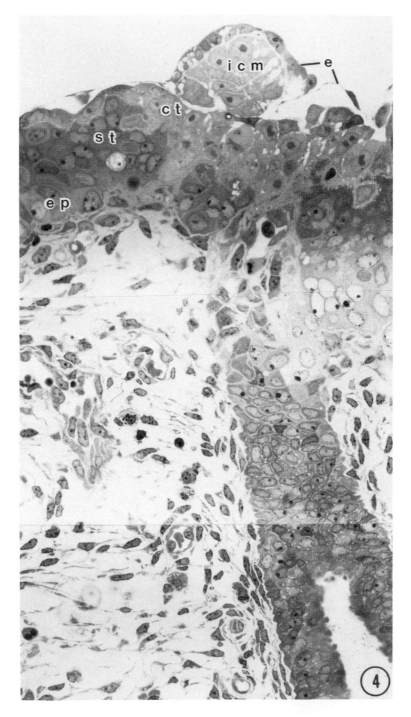

Fig. 4. Day-10.0 implantation site, rhesus monkey, showing the inner cell mass (icm), underlain by the trophoblastic plate, then uterine stroma and a gland. At this stage a combination of cytotrophoblast (ct) and syncytial trophoblast (st) forms the trophoblastic plate. A few epithelial plaque cells (ep) can be seen at the left. Endoderm (e). ×700.

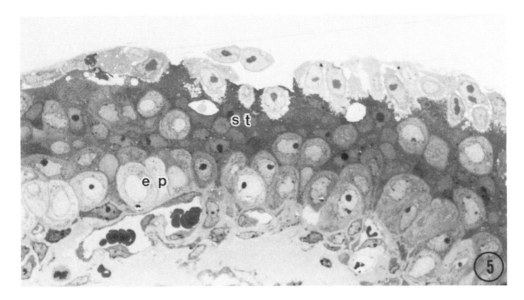

Fig. 5. Margin of the implantation site seen in Figure 4. The epithelial plaque cells (ep) form a complete layer of rounded cells underlying the dark syncytial trophoblast (st). The syncytial trophoblast is intimately associated with the plaque cells and has a more imbricated border with the overlying pale cytotrophoblast cells, which form an incomplete layer. Note the subepithelial capillaries. ×780.

extent, and in the process the implantation site tends to become more superficial (Fig. 9). Attachment of abembryonic trophoblast to the opposite uterine surface initiates formation of the secondary placenta. At this stage there is a distinct amnion, but no indication of a secondary yolk sac.

After lacunae are well organized, the cytotrophoblast forms a series of columns that are interposed between lacunae and expanded at the maternal fetal interface (Fig. 9). By 13–14 days mesoderm is forming at the fetal surface of these cell columns, converting them from primary to secondary villi. It should be noted that secondary villi are present for some time in that although blood vessels form in the mesodermal villi, blood cells do not enter these vessels until they become confluent with those in the splanchnopleure and the fetal heart initiates circulation to the villi.

During the previllous and early villous stages, the epithelial plaque cells not only hypertrophy but also accumulate glycogen. Peripheral to the plaque, a pronounced subepithelial edema occurs. Thus implantation sites at this stage can be readily seen

by a pink central spot (due to blood in the lacunae), surrounded by a pale gelatinous-appearing endometrium (due to the subepithelial edema). The maternal blood vessels under the forming placenta and in the area of the plaque, and in the secondary plaque formed on the other surface of the uterus, undergo varying degrees of endothelial hypertrophy in addition to hyperplasia (Fig. 10) [Enders and Hendrickx, 1980].

The epithelial plaque reaction and endothelial response can be induced by trauma in an endometrium of a nonpregnant animal with appropriate hormonal support[Dallenbach-Hellweg et al, 1966; Denker and Enders, unpublished results]. A minor decidual reaction is also initiated in the stromal cells of the endometrium toward the close of this period.

The secondary yolk sac develops from the mass of endodermal cells underlying the embryonic shield. Luckett [1978] has suggested that the secondary yolk sac forms from a folding of the primary yolk sac. The presence of a complex epithelial mass at this time under the embryonic plate sug-

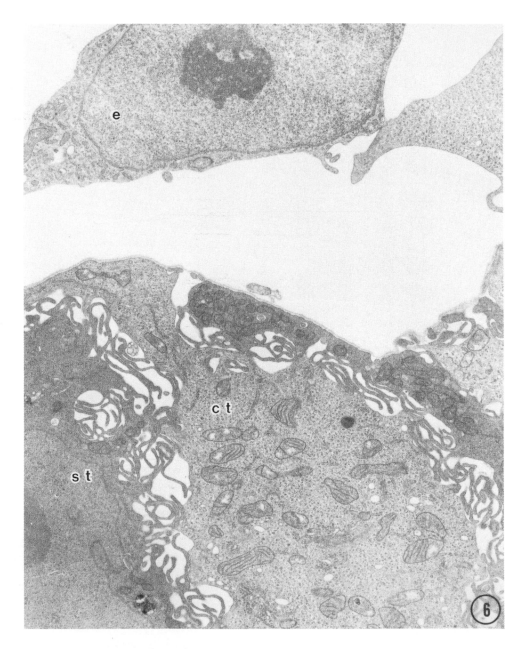

Fig. 6. Electron micrograph of a portion of an implantation site on day 10.0, rhesus monkey. Note that there is no basal lamina on the endoderm (e), but a pronounced basal lamina adjacent to the trophoblast. The lamellar folds of the syncytial trophoblast (st) produce an imbricated border with the cytotrophoblast (ct). ×10,500.

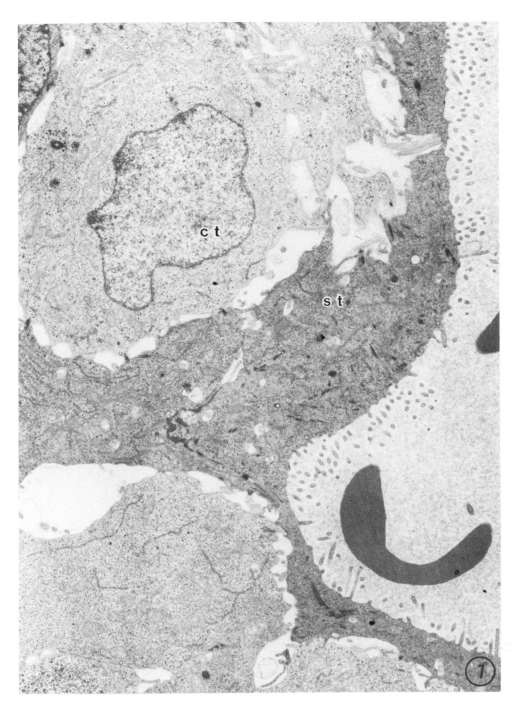

Fig. 7. Cellular trophoblast (ct) and syncytial trophoblast (st) from an implantation site on day 10.5, rhesus monkey. The character of the syncytium has changed; note especially the many microvilli bordering the blood-filled lacuna. ×7,900.

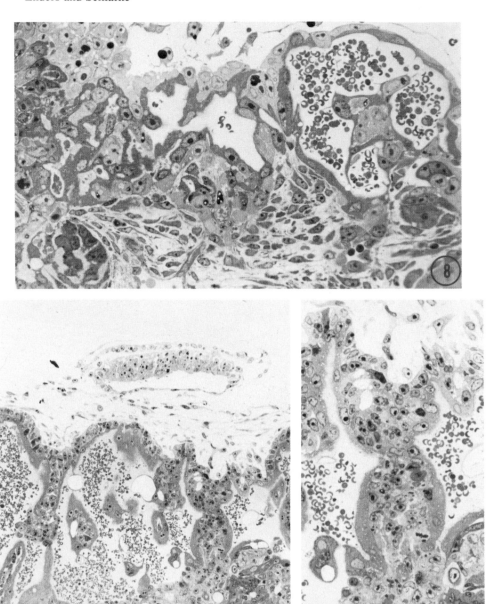

Fig. 8. Trophoblastic lacuna of a placenta of a day-10.5 implantation site, rhesus monkey. Note the expansion of these lacunae, especially directly under the developing chorionic plate. ×320. [From Enders et al, 1983a.]

Fig. 9. Implantation site from a rhesus monkey on day 15.0. a) The embryo has both a well-formed amnion and a secondary yolk sac. b) Higher-magnification micrograph of a primary villus extending to the forming basal plate. There has been extensive expansion of the lacunae, and primary villi have formed. The lacunar expansion apparently permits superficial growth of the placenta. a, ×140; b, ×300.

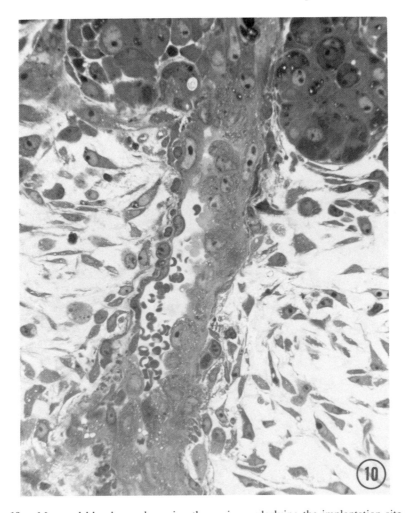

Fig. 10. Maternal blood vessel nearing the region underlying the implantation site on day 13 of gestation, rhesus monkey. The endothelial cells on the left side of the vessel are relatively normal, whereas the endothelial cells on the right side are hypertrophied and contain a number of small lipid droplets. The dark cells above are glycogen-containing epithelial plaque cells. ×450.

gests that the secondary yolk sac might arise from proliferation of visceral ("embryonic") endoderm.

Although it is clear that mesoderm does not form from cytotrophoblast, it is not clear whether or not some of the early mesodermal cells are derived from the endoderm (endodermal reticulum of Luckett [1978]). Cells detached from the endoderm are present, but their fate is not certain.

Implantation in the Baboon

Hendrickx and Houston [in Hendrickx, 1971] have described the histology of implantation stages in the baboon. Their earliest implanting blastocyst was adherent to uterine epithelium in several places near the inner cell mass. The contact with uterine epithelium appears to be initiated by syncytial trophoblast. In the subsequent stage, described but illustrated only by a drawing [Houston, 1971], trophoblast has formed a trophoblastic plate similar to that in the rhesus monkey. Although a uterine epithelial plaque reaction is not described, they mention that the uterine stroma is edematous and that trophoblast attains its greatest depth of penetration in the necks of the uterine glands. The

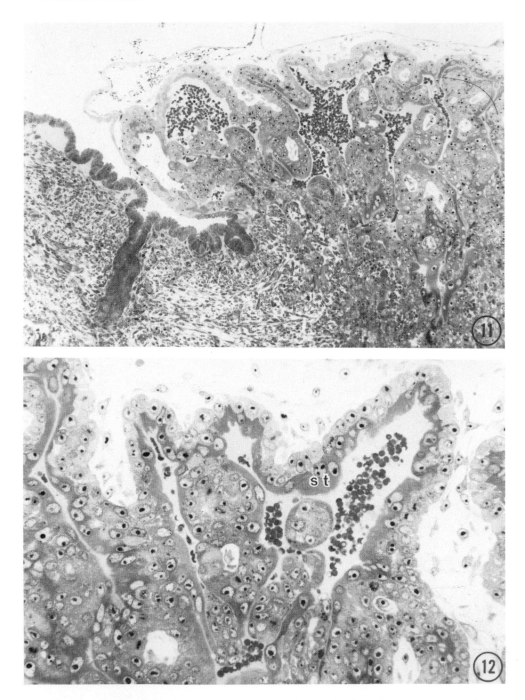

Fig. 11.   Section through the margin of a day-11 baboon implantation site. The lacunae filled with maternal blood mushroom above the level of the uterine luminal epithelium. (Materials collected by Dr. Ross Tarara.) ×110.

Fig. 12.   Higher magnification showing lacunae from the placenta illustrated in Figure 11. At this stage secondary villi (with mesodermal cores) are forming. Note that the lacunae are now lined by a uniform layer of syncytial trophoblast (st). ×280.

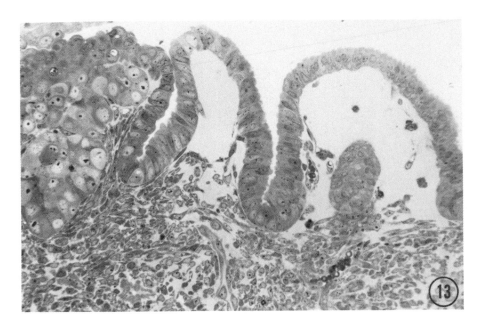

Fig. 13. Margin of the implantation site of a day-12 baboon. The pronounced subepithelial edema is characteristic of implantation stages in both baboon and the rhesus monkey. On the left is a cluster of epithelial plaque cells; the epithelial plaque is less extensive and more variable in the baboon than in the rhesus monkey. ×270.

specimen from this early stage (5) was reported to be in poor condition.

They described the subsequent formation of blood-filled lacunae within the trophoblast plate, and eventual formation of cytotrophoblastic columns. At this stage the placenta tends to lift off the surface of the endometrium and becomes somewhat mushroom-shaped (Figs. 11, 12).

We have recently examined a series of plastic embedded specimens of stages 5–7 [Tarara et al, in preparation]. Of particular interest in these stages is the variable presence of an epithelial plaque reaction restricted to the epithelium immediately adjacent to the implantation site (Fig. 13), a feature not previously reported in the baboon [Ramsey et al, 1976]. A pronounced endothelial hypertrophy and hyperplasia, and a peripheral subepithelial edema so characteristic of both the baboon and the rhesus monkey are also prominent (Fig. 13). The early formation of trophoblastic lacunae in this species is remarkable, and appears to lead to the transient partial eversion of the forming placenta.

Implantation in Other Cercopithicids

For none of the other Old World primates is there a comprehensive series of implantation stages. Individual observations of early villus stages, like those of Burton [1980] on the langur *(Presbytis)*, suggest that the stage of large trophoblast lacunae filled with maternal blood is the common late previllous condition.

Implantation in the Chimpanzee and Human

Because of behavioral, endocrine, and phylogenetic considerations, the chimpanzee is considered closely related to the human with regard to its reproduction. The endometrium shows a pseudodecidual ("predecidual") response during the normal cycle, and an elevated estradiol level at midluteal phase [Graham, 1976]. The often-stated similarity of implantation in the chimpanzee and human rests on the observation of a single implantation site. This site, described first by Elder et al [1938] and later by Heuser [1940], is a late previllous stage. Although the decidua capsularis is not complete, the blastocyst is largely interstitial.

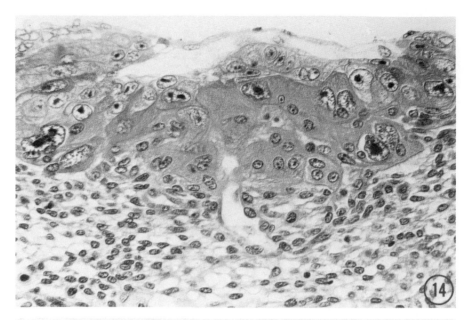

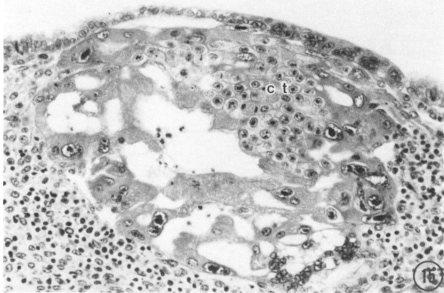

Fig. 14. Micrograph of a portion of a stage 5a human implantation site. This stage corresponds to the trophoblastic plate stage in the rhesus monkey. Note the large polyploid nuclei in the syncytial trophoblast and the irregularity of the border between trophoblast and uterine stroma. (Photographed with Nomarski optics; embryo 8020, Carnegie collection). ×440.

Fig. 15. A stage-5b human implantation site (Carnegie 8171). This stage corresponds to the early lacunar stage in the rhesus monkey and baboon. Note the irregular nature of the intrasyncytial lacunae, and the mass of proliferating cytotrophoblast (ct). ×335.

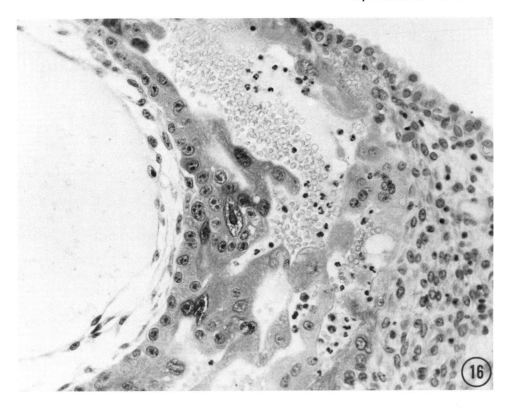

Fig. 16. Stage-5c human implantation site (Carnegie 7700). The lacunae are broadly anastomotic and have expanded, and most of the syncytial trophoblast is now lamellar. This is the last previllous stage. ×350.

Peripheral intrasyncytial lacunae are numerous, and cytotrophoblast has begun to proliferate.

The series of studies that constitute our information on implantation in the human were summarized by Hertig et al [1956], and more recently by O'Rahilly [1973]. The earliest of these specimens (designated stage 5a) is thought to be approximately 2 days after implantation (Fig. 14). The conceptus is already beneath the uterine luminal epithelium, which partially covers it. The trophoblast consists of a series of syncytial masses with large apparently polyploid nuclei, and a few irregular clumps of cytotrophoblast. Clustered at the periphery of the syncytial masses are small nuclei; these were not described by the original authors, and their origin is currently in doubt. They appear similar in size to the nuclei of uterine epithelial cells, and could be phagocytized or fused cells, but their cytoplasm cannot be discerned in these

preparations [see discussion in Falck Larsen, 1980]. There is no inflammatory response surrounding these earliest implantation sites. This stage corresponds to the trophoblastic plate stage of the rhesus monkey.

Stage 5b shows progressive spread of trophoblast within the endometrium (Fig. 15). A number of lacunae have developed within the trophoblast plate. The syncytial masses surround occasional vessels, especially at the periphery of the site. However, within the syncytial mass open lacunae are present. These lacunae tend to be labyrinthine and are smaller than those in the rhesus and baboon, but are larger than capillaries. Surrounding the conceptus the endometrium now shows a pronounced leucocytic infiltration. However, there is still no decidual response.

At stage 5c, a marked transition occurs (Fig. 16). Syncytial trophoblast thins and there are fewer polyploid nuclei. Cytotrophoblast forms a complete, well-defined layer on the embryonic side of the syncytium, with few clusters and as yet no primary villi. It should be noted that this stage (9–11 days, ca 1 mm diameter conceptus), like the previous ones, generally protrudes from the endometrial surface, but the inner cell mass per se is deep within the site and lacunae have extended well toward the abembryonic pole. At the margins of the lacunae confluence between maternal blood vessels and lacunae can be observed. Knoth and Falck Larsen [1972] reported that in their valuable 11-day specimen the trophoblast intruded into maternal vessels, between endothelial cells.

Unfortunately the timing of human implantation stages is based on menstrual data, and no early stages timed by LH or E peaks are available. Nevertheless it appears to take approximately 5–6 days for development from initial attachment (which has not been observed) to a 1-mm late previllous stage. Accounting for elevation from uterine surface, the conceptus penetrates less than half a millimeter into the endometrium.

Consequently, although implantation in the human is interstitial, the invasion of the endometrium and establishment of blood-filled lacunae appear to be appreciably slower than in the rhesus monkey and baboon. A major difference between the human blastocyst and that of the rhesus and baboon would appear to be the rapidity with which the latter two tap maternal blood. Their trophoblast does not seem to surround maternal vessels at any stage, and large lacunae form rapidly, and subsequently growth is more superficial. The human blastocyst, being confined to or within the endometrium, develops less rapidly in the early stages but apparently implants earlier.

SUMMARY AND FUTURE RESEARCH NEEDS

As can be seen from the preceding brief summarization of the morphological events in implantation in primates, our information is surprisingly fragmentary. Even in the rhesus monkey, implantation has been only partially described. Comparative material has nearly been ignored in recent decades, and information on the actual events of trophoblast-uterine interaction has rarely been sought. The recent surge of studies of in vitro fertilization should permit studies of development of the blastocyst, and some experimental studies on potential properties of trophoblast in vitro. Should methods of reintroduction of the blastocyst into the uterus reach a success level of close to

50% in nonhuman primates, many more studies of implantation would become possible, and in vivo as well as in vitro experimental exploration of process of implantation could be initiated.

What factors promote the following: syncytium formation by the trophoblast, adherence of trophoblast to uterine epithelium, intrusion of trophoblastic processes between epithelial cells, penetration of the basal lamina, conversion of the originally invasive trophoblast into lamellar trophoblast, and formation of the lacunae? Such questions should remain in our minds as we continue to explore the events of implantation in primates.

ACKNOWLEDGMENTS

This research has been supported by grant HD 10342 from the National Institute of Child Health and Human Development, and by NIH grant RR00169.

We also acknowledge Dr. Andrew G. Hendrickx, Dr. S. Prahalada, Dr. David L. Hess, Dr. Ross Tarara, Pamela E. Binkerd, Carolyn Booher, and Katherine Lantz for valuble assistance with collection of the preimplantation and implantation stages from the rhesus monkey and baboon.

REFERENCES

Ariga, S.; Dukelow, W.R. Recovery of preimplantation blastocysts in the squirrel monkey by a laparoscopic technique. FERTILITY AND STERILITY 28:577–580, 1977.

Burton, G.J. Early placentation in the dusky leaf monkey (Presbytis obscura). PLACENTA 1:187–195, 1980.

Butler, H. The reproductive biology of a strepsirhine (Galago senegalensis senegalensis) INTERNATIONAL REVIEW OF GENERAL AND EXPERIMENTAL ZOOLOGY 1:241–296, 1964.

Butler, H. The giant cell trophoblast of the Senegal galago (Galago senegalensis senegalensis) and its bearing on the evolution of the primate placenta. JOURNAL OF ZOOLOGY 152:195–207, 1967.

Croxatto, H.B.; Funtealba, B.; Diaz, S.; Dastene, L.; Tatum, H.J. A simple nonsurgical technique to obtain unimplanted eggs from human uteri. AMERICAN JOURNAL OF OBSTETRICS AND GYNECOLOGY 112:662–671, 1972.

Dallenbach-Hellweg, G.; Dawson, A.B.; Hisaw, F.L. The effect of relaxin on the endometrium of monkeys. Histological and histochemical studies. AMERICAN JOURNAL OF ANATOMY 119:61–78, 1966.

Dixson, A.F. The owl monkey (Aotus trivirgatus). Pp. 69–113 in REPRODUCTION IN NEW WORLD

PRIMATES. J.B. Hearn, ed. Boston, MTP Press, 1982.

Dukelow, W.R. The squirrel monkey *(Saimiri sciureus)*. Pp. 149–179 in REPRODUCTION IN NEW WORLD PRIMATES. J.B. Hearn, ed. Boston, MTP Press, 1982.

Eddy, C.A.; Garcia, R.G.; Kraemer, D.C. Detailed time course of ovum transport in the rhesus monkey *(Macaca mulatta)*. BIOLOGY OF REPRODUCTION 13:363–369, 1975.

Elder, J.H.; Hartman, C.G.; Heuser, C.H. A ten and one-half day chimpanzee embryo, "Yerkes A." JOURNAL OF THE AMERICAN MEDICAL ASSOCIATION 111:1156–1159, 1938.

Enders, A.C.; Hendrickx, A.G. Morphological basis of implantation in the rhesus monkey. PROGRESS IN REPRODUCTIVE BIOLOGY 7:270–283, 1980.

Enders, A.C.; Schlafke, S. Differentiation of the blastocyst of the rhesus monkey. AMERICAN JOURNAL OF ANATOMY 162:1–21, 1981.

Enders, A.C.; Hendrickx, A.G.; Binkerd, P.E. Abnormal development of blastocysts and blastomeres in the rhesus monkey. BIOLOGY OF REPRODUCTION 26:353–366, 1982.

Enders, A.C.; Hendrickx, A.G.; Schlafke, S. Implantation in the rhesus monkey: Initial penetration of endometrium. AMERICAN JOURNAL OF ANATOMY 167:275–298, 1983a.

Enders, A.C.; Hess, D.L.; Hendrickx, A.G. Pregnancy detection and preimplantation development in the rhesus monkey. PROCEEDINGS, INDO-U.S. SYMPOSIUM ON OVUM IMPLANTATION (Indian Council of Medical Research), 1983b.

Falck Larsen, J. Human implantation and clinical aspects. PROGRESS IN REPRODUCTIVE BIOLOGY 7:284–296, 1980.

Gerard, P. Etudes sur l'ovogenese et l'ontogenese chez les lemuriens du genre *Galago*. ARCHIVES DE BIOLOGIE 43:93–151, 1932.

Graham, C.E. The chimpanzee: A unique model for human reproduction. Pp. 29–38 in THE LABORATORY ANIMAL IN THE STUDY OF REPRODUCTION. T. Antikatzides; S. Erichsen; A. Spiegel, eds. Stuttgart, Fischer Verlag, 1976.

Hearn, J.P. Endocrinology and timing of implantation in the marmoset monkey, *Callithrix jacchus.* PROGRESS IN REPRODUCTIVE BIOLOGY 7:262–269, 1980.

Hearn, J.P. The common marmoset *(Callithrix jacchus)*. Pp. 181–215 in REPRODUCTION IN NEW WORLD PRIMATES. J.B. Hearn, ed. Boston, MTP Press, 1982.

Hendrickx, A.G. EMBRYOLOGY OF THE BABOON. Chicago, University of Chicago Press, 1971.

Hendrickx, A.G.; Houston, M.L. Prenatal and postnatal development. Pp. 334–381 in COMPARATIVE REPRODUCTION OF NONHUMAN PRIMATES. E.S.E. Hafez, ed. Springfield, IL, Thomas, 1971.

Hendrickx, A.G.; Kraemer, D.C. Preimplantation

stages of baboon embryos *(Papio* sp.*)*. ANATOMICAL RECORD 162:11–120, 1968.

Hertig, A.T.; Rock, J.; Adams, E.C. A description of 34 human ova within the first 17 days of development. AMERICAN JOURNAL OF ANATOMY 98:435–494, 1956.

Heuser, C.H. The chimpanzee ovum in the early stages of implantation (10-1/2 days). JOURNAL OF MORPHOLOGY 66:155–174, 1940.

Heuser, C.H.; Streeter, G.L. Development of the macaque embryo. CONTRIBUTIONS TO EMBRYOLOGY, CARNEGIE INSTITUTION 29:15–55, 1941.

Hill, J.P. The developmental history of the primates. PHILOSOPHICAL TRANSACTIONS OF THE ROYAL SOCIETY, B 221:45–178, 1932.

Hill, J.P. Implantation of the blastocyst in *Galago demidoffi*. BIO-MORPHOSIS 1:333, 1938.

Houston, M.L. The placenta. Pp. 153–172 in THE EMBRYOLOGY OF THE BABOON. A.G. Hendrickx, ed. Chicago, University of Chicago Press, 1971.

Hubrecht, A.A.W. Early ontogenetic phenomena in mammals and their bearing on our interpretation of the phylogeny of the vertebrates. QUARTERLY JOURNAL OF MICROSCOPICAL SCIENCE 53:1–181, 1908.

Hurst, P.R.; Jefferies, K.; Eckstein, P.; Wheeler, A.G. Recovery of uterine embryos in rhesus monkeys. BIOLOGY OF REPRODUCTION 15:429–434, 1976.

Hurst, P.R.; Jeffries, K.; Eckstein, P.; Wheeler, A.G. An ultrastructural study of preimplantation uterine embryos of the rhesus monkey. JOURNAL OF ANATOMY 126:209–220, 1978.

Knoth, M.; Falck Larsen, J. Ultrastructure of a human implantation site. ACTA OBSTETRICA GYNECOLOGICA SCANDINAVIA 51:385–393, 1972.

Luckett, W.P. Comparative development and evolution of the placenta in primates. CONTRIBUTIONS TO PRIMATOLOGY 3:142–234, 1974.

Luckett, W.P. Origin and differentiation of the yolk sac and extraembryonic mesoderm in presomite human and rhesus monkey embryos. AMERICAN JOURNAL OF ANATOMY 152:59–98, 1978.

Mohr, L.R.; Trounson, A.O. Comparative ultrastructure of the hatched human, mouse and bovine blastocysts. JOURNAL OF REPRODUCTION AND FERTILITY 66:499–504, 1982.

Nagle, C.A.; Denari, J.H. The cebus monkey *(Cebus apella)*. Pp. 39–67 in REPRODUCTION IN NEW WORLD PRIMATES. J.B. Hearn, ed. Boston, MTP Press, 1982.

O'Rahilly, R. Developmental stages in human embryos. Part A: Embryos of the first three weeks (stages 1 to 9). CARNEGIE INSTITUTION OF WASHINGTON 631:1–167, 1973.

Panigel, M.; Kraemer, D.C.; Kalter, S.S.; Smith, G.C.; Heberling, R.L. Ultrastructure of cleavage stages

310   Enders and Schlafke

and preimplantation embryos of the baboon. ANATOMY AND EMBRYOLOGY 147:45–62, 1975.

Pereda, J.; Croxatto, H.B. Ultrastructure of a seven-cell human embryo. BIOLOGY OF REPRODUCTION 18:481–489, 1978.

Pope, C.E.; Pope, V.Z.; Beck, L.R. Nonsurgical recovery of uterine embryos in the baboon. BIOLOGY OF REPRODUCTION 23:657–662, 1980.

Pope, C.E.; Pope, V.Z.; Beck, L.R. Development of baboon preimplantation embryos to postimplantation stages in vitro. BIOLOGY OF REPRODUCTION 27:915–923, 1982.

Ramsey, E.M.; Houston, M.L.; Harris, J.W.S. Interactions of the trophoblast and maternal tissues in three closely related primate species. AMERICAN JOURNAL OF OBSTETRICS AND GYNECOLOGY 124:647–652, 1976.

Reng, R. Die Placenta von Microcebus murinus. ZEITSCHRIFT FÜR SAEUGETIER 42:201–214, 1977.

Strauss, F. The ovoimplantation of *Microcebus murinus* Miller (Primates, Lemuroidea, Strepsirhini). AMERICAN JOURNAL OF ANATOMY 152:99–110, 1978.

Tarara, R.; Enders, A.C.; Hendrickx, A.G. Implantation in the baboon. (In preparation).

Wislocki, G.B. On the placentation of primates, with a consideration of the phylogeny of the placenta. CONTRIBUTIONS TO EMBRYOLOGY, CARNEGIE INSTITUTION 20:51–80, 1929.

Wislocki, G.B.; Streeter, G.L. On the placentation of the macaque *(Macaca mulatta)*, from the time of implantation until the formation of the definitive placenta. CONTRIBUTIONS TO EMBRYOLOGY, CARNEGIE INSTITUTION 27:1–66, 1938.

Morphology of the Placenta and Fetal Membranes

Barry F. King

Department of Human Anatomy, University of California School of Medicine, Davis, California 95616

INTRODUCTION

The placenta is the most important organ during the period of intrauterine development. From the time of its establishment at implantation until the time of parturition, the placenta carries out a complex array of physiological activities. These functional activities include gaseous exchange, absorption of metabolites vital for embryonic growth and development, and removal of waste products from the fetus. The placenta is also an active synthetic organ; perhaps best known among its synthetic products are its diverse endocrine products.

The morphological diversity of the placenta in different species appears to be as complex as its many functional activities. Many of the general placental relationships among mammals have been previously reviewed by Mossman [1937, 1967, 1974], Amoroso [1952], Wimsatt [1962], and King [1982b]. Several books devoted to general comparative placentation have also appeared [Steven, 1975; Ramsey, 1982]. Reviews of placentation of primates include those of Wislocki [1929], Hill [1932], Starck [1956], Luckett [1974, 1976], and Benirschke and Miller [1982]. In this review, emphasis will be placed upon electron-microscopic analysis of placental structure and, where possible, the relationship of this structure to the various functions of the placenta.

THE PLACENTA AND FETAL MEMBRANES
General Overview

Mossman [1937] defined the placenta as "an apposition or fusion of the fetal membranes to the uterine mucosa for physiological exchange." The extraembryonic fetal membranes consist of the chorion, allantois, amnion, and yolk sac. Of these, the chorion and allantois are the most important in the formation of the definitive placentas of primates. The true chorion consists of an outer layer of trophoblast associated with a layer of avascular fetal mesoderm. It is the trophoblast that makes contact with the uterine epithelium and becomes the dominant fetal component of the placenta.

The mode of formation and eventual size of the allantoic sac vary among primates, but in all cases it consists of an endodermal lining associated with a highly vascularized mesoderm. The vessels that vascularize the primitive true chorion are derived from this mesoderm, and establish the *chorioallantoic* placenta. The chorioallantoic placenta is so characteristic of Eutherian mammals, especially primates, that it is often referred to as "the" placenta.

The amnion provides the embryo with an aqueous environment that prevents desiccation as well as being a milieu in which embryonic tissues can develop symmetrically and free from distortion by pressures from the surrounding structures [Mossman, 1937].

The yolk sac, comprising extraembryonic endoderm and mesoderm, develops differently in various primates [Luckett, 1974]. In some prosimians, a portion of the chorion is vascularized by vessels from the wall of the yolk sac forming a transient choriovitelline placenta. In higher primates, precocious development of the extraembryonic mesoderm and exocoelom separates the yolk sac from the chorion prior to the development of blood vessels in the yolk sac mesoderm and no choriovitelline placenta is present. The vascular yolk sac of higher primates may play a role in embryonic nutrition by absorption of substances from the exocoelom [Luckett, 1974, King and Wilson, 1983].

Comparative Primate Biology, Volume 3: Reproduction and Development, pages 311–331
© 1986 Alan R. Liss, Inc.

Classification of Placentas

Classification by Shape. Chorioallantoic placentas can be classified in a number of ways [Ramsey, 1982]. One method is by examining the distribution of outgrowths of the chorion (chorionic villi) over the surface of the gestation sac. On this basis four categories are recognized: diffuse, discoid, cotyledonary, and zonary. Of these only the diffuse and discoid have been described in primates. In the diffuse placenta, chorionic villi are distributed more or less uniformly over the chorionic surface. Examples of this type of placenta are the pig and bush baby (*Galago*). A discoidal placenta is one in which the chorionic villi are limited to a round or oval disk-shaped area. Discoidal placentas are characteristic of higher primates and may occur singly (monodiscoidal) as in the human, chimpanzee, and baboon, or as two separate disks (bidiscoidal) as in many other primates. In a cotyledonary (or multiplex) type, characteristic of ruminants, the villi occur in groups over the sac. In a zonary type of placenta the villi occur in a band or girdle; this type is characteristic of many carnivores.

Classification by Internal Structure. Within the chorioallantoic placenta several types of internal structure can be recognized: villous, labyrinthine, and pseudolabyrinthine (or trabecular). In the villous type, fetal vessels travel in an arborizing maze of fingerlike projections. In the labyrinthine type, fetal blood travels in a system of anastomosing channels. A pseudolabyrinthine or trabecular type results from syncytiotrophoblastic connections between otherwise separate villi. For a more extensive discussion see Wynn [1964] and Ramsey [1982]. All of these types are found in primates.

Classification by Composition of the Interhemal Membrane. The layer separating the fetal and maternal blood is known as the placental barrier, the placental membrane, or preferably the interhemal membrane [King and Mossman, 1974]. The composition of the interhemal membrane is another way of classifying chorioallantoic placentas [Grosser, 1927].

As a general rule, the different classes result from a reduction in the number of maternal layers whereas the fetal component remains intact. In an *epitheliochorial* placenta, the uterine epithelium is in intimate contact with the chorion and there is no reduction in the number of maternal layers. A *syndesmochorial* placenta is one in which the maternal epithelium has been lost, resulting in the chorion's becoming apposed to the endometrial connective tissue. An *endotheliochorial* placenta arises when the loss of maternal epithelium and connective tissue results in the apposition of the maternal capillary endothelium to the chorion. When the maternal capillary wall is lost as well, maternal blood bathes the trophoblast directly, establishing a *hemochorial* arrangement. Electron microscopy subsequently revealed that in the latter type there may be one, two, or three layers of trophoblast present, leading to the classification of placentas as hemomonochorial, hemodichorial, and hemotrichorial, respectively [Enders, 1965a].

The "Grosser system" has been criticized because of its failure to take into account considerable histological variation within the same placenta and because of the implication that the number of layers was of major importance in determining physiological transfer between mother and fetus. It has also been criticized for its failure to take into account various accessory placental structures although, as Wimsatt [1962] pointed out, Grosser never intended his classification to apply to those structures. This classification scheme has retained its usefulness, but must be interpreted cautiously with regard to its physiological implications.

General Functions of the Placenta

Nutritional Support of the Embryo. Two general types of material (embryotroph) support the growth and development of the embryo. The first general category is hemotroph, which is direct exchange of materials between maternal and fetal capillaries across the interposed layers of the placenta. The second type, histotroph, is a product of the uterine endometrium and involves absorption of uterine secretions ("uterine milk") or of materials derived from breakdown of tissues or extravasation of blood. Placentas in different species transfer materials between mother and fetus by a variety of mechanisms including passive diffusion, facilitated diffusion, active transport, and pinocytosis. Structural specializations in primate placentas relating to some of these transport activities will be noted in the subsequent sections.

Paraplacental Structures

In many animals, including primates, accessory or paraplacental organs may function to provide nutrients to the fetus. In some cases, these structures play a role in histotrophic nutrition and in other cases are involved in exchange between the mother and various fetal compartments. In primates, one major example of paraplacental organs is the chorionic vesicles of the strepsirhines. Cho rionic vesicles are specialized invaginations of the chorion that develop opposite the mouths of uterine glands. These will be described in detail in the section on strepsirhine placenta. The other major example of a paraplacental organ is the chorioamnionic relationship observed in higher primates. In this case, the expansion of a nonvillous part of the chorion results in its apposition or fusion with the uterine decidua (decidua parietalis). Also, the expansion of the amnion may result in its eventual apposition or fusion with both the nonvillous and the villous chorion. Thus, the potential exists for transfer of substances from maternal compartments (eg, decidua parietalis) across the smooth chorion and amnion into amniotic fluid. From there the fetus may absorb materials either as a result of swallowing amniotic fluid or as a consequence of uptake across the fetal epidermis. The apposition of the amnion to the fetal surface of the placental disk allows for exchange between maternal blood in the intervillous space and amniotic fluid. These relationships will be described in more detail in subsequent sections.

PLACENTATION IN STREPSIRHINI

Introduction

The placentas of lower primates differ considerably from those of higher forms. Most strepsirhine placentas thus far described have a diffuse epitheliochorial type of placenta, in which relatively simple villi cover most of the chorionic surface and interdigitate with crypts or folds in the endometrium. Ramsey's [1982] statement that "all prosimians have labyrinthine placentas" is clearly erroneous. In addition, specialized absorptive areas, the *chorionic vesicles*, have been described in a number of species.

Chorioallantoic Placenta

Light-Microscopic Studies. One of the earliest descriptions of placentation in strepsirhines was that of Turner [1876, 1878], who examined gravid uteri of *Propithecus*, *Lemur* and *Indris*. Although short on histological detail, it was clear that Turner appreciated the diffuse, villous nature of the placenta in these species and the similarities with the placenta of the pig. Hubrecht [1894] examined the placenta in *Nycticebus* and noted the chorionic villi which were relatively simple in early gestation and became increasingly folded in later stages. The villi fitted into crypts in the uterine wall lined by a persistent uterine epithelium. He also noted certain nonvillous areas of the chorion, notably at the cervical end.

Strahl [1899] studied placentation in *Galago* and was one of the first to describe the placenta in much histological detail. He observed short cylindrical villi situated in crypts lined by a persistent uterine epithelium. He also noted a depression at the tip of each villus containing a greenish substance. Jenkinson [1916] described irregular, branched, leaflike villi in *Lepilemur*; the villi were covered by columnar trophoblastic cells that were quite vacuolated. Otherwise the placenta was similar to that described above. Subsequent studies by Hill and Burne [1922] *(Chiromys)*, Hill et al [1928] *(Loris)*, and Hill [1932] *(Loris, Nycticebus)* established a basically similar placental structure in other strepsirhines. Detailed accounts of placental development and histology in *Galago* can be found in Gerard [1932] and Butler and Adam [1964]. Butler and Adam [1964] also made a number of histochemical observations of the placenta in *Galago*.

There are two exceptions to the general finding of an epitheliochorial type of placenta in strepsirhines. Gerard [1932] described an endotheliochorial condition early in development in one region of the placenta of *Galago demidovii* [see also Luckett, 1974, and Enders, this volume]. Also, Reng [1977] reported that the central part of the placenta in *Microcebus murinus* becomes invasive and establishes a syndesmochorial relationship, whereas the remainder of the placenta remains epitheliochorial. Benirschke and Miller [1982] have reported the structure of mature chorionic villi in several species of *Lemur*. They illustrated the branched nature of the villi, the abundant connective tissue in the villous core, and the frequently attenuated nature of the trophoblastic epithelium.

Electron-Microscopic Observations. Electron-microscopic studies of strepsirhine placentas are limited in number and completeness. Butler and Adam [1964] described, but did not illustrate, some electron-microscopic observations of the chorioallantoic placenta in *Galago senegalensis*. Dempsey [1969] presented a single illustration from a placenta of *G. senegalensis*, and Panigel [1970] illustrated the zone of interdigitation of fetal and maternal microvilli in *G. demodovii*. Benirschke and Miller [1982] collected several *Lemur variegatus* placentas for electron-microscopic examination; unfortunately preservation was not sufficient to maintain the integrity of the trophoblast. We have recently analyzed a series of specimens of *G. crassicaudatus* at both the light- and electron-microscopic levels [King, 1984]. The descriptions that follow are based on that series of specimens mainly from the last half of gestation.

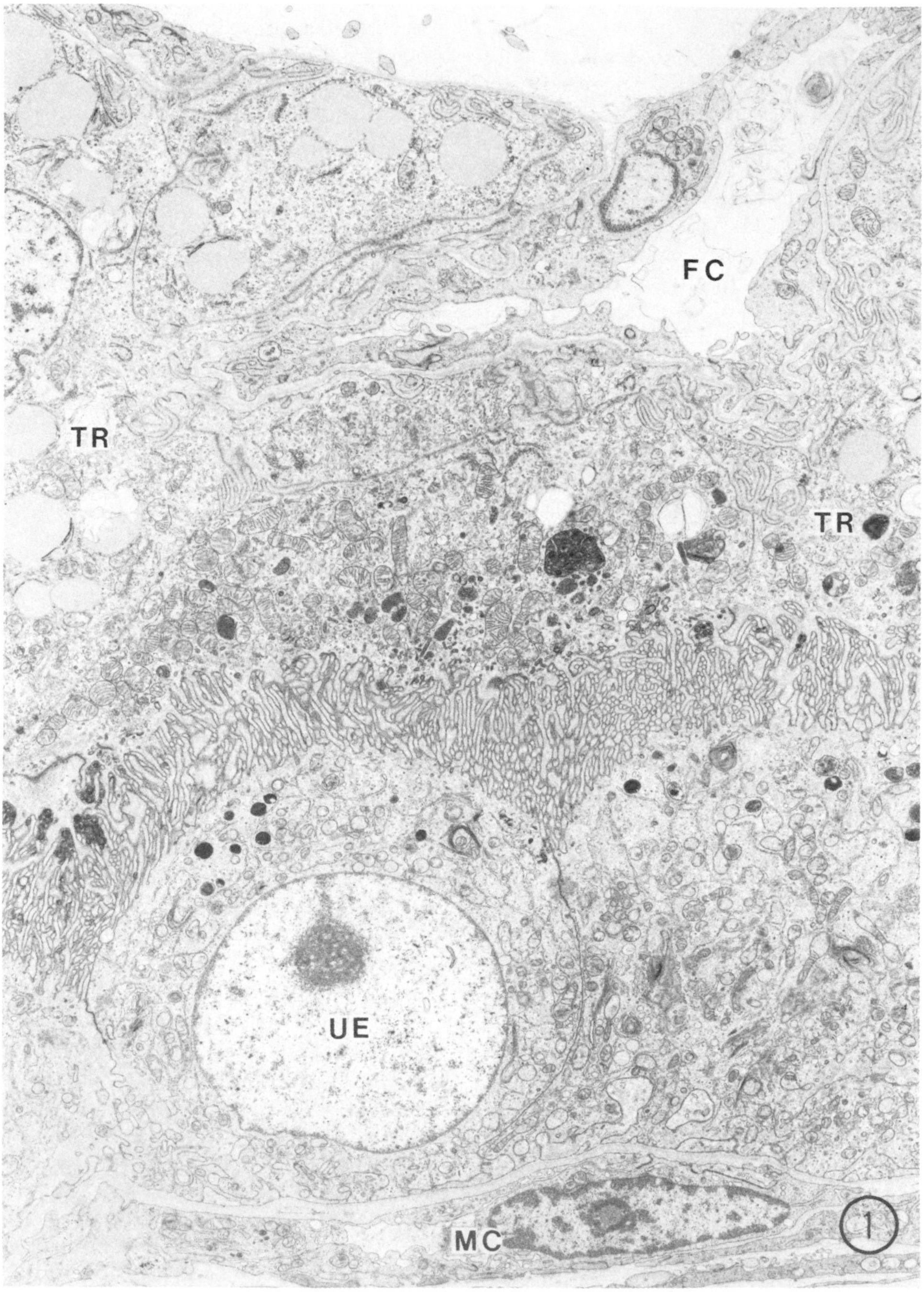

Fig.1. Low-magnification electron micrograph of interhemal membrane of *Galago* placenta illustrating its epitheliochorial structure. Trophoblastic cells (TR) interdigitate with uterine epithelial cells (UE). Fetal capillaries (FC) indent the trophoblast cells; maternal capillaries (MC) indent the uterine epithelial cells. Dense granules occur in the apices of both the trophoblast and uterine epithelial cells. 105 days of gestation. ×570.

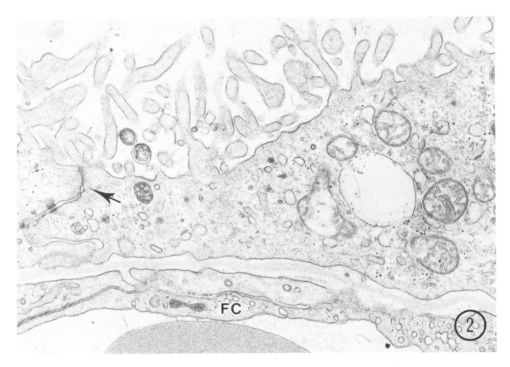

Fig. 2. Higher magnification of the trophoblastic epithelium of *Galago* later in gestation, showing junction between two trophoblastic cells (arrow) and the continuous endothelium of the fetal capillary (FC). The microvilli of the attenuated trophoblastic layer would normally interdigitate with processes of uterine cells, but in this case the uterine tissue is absent. 120 days of gestation. ×26,500.

Figure 1 illustrates the general relationships of the components of the interhemal membrane at 105 days of gestation. The close interdigitation of the chorionic villi with the folds of endometrium is evident. Trophoblastic epithelial cells are cuboidal to columnar in shape except where fetal capillaries indent the basal surface of the trophoblast. Maternal epithelial cells are cuboidal and are indented by the uterine capillaries. At the electron-microscopic level, a close interdigitation of microvilli from the trophoblastic epithelium and uterine epithelium is observed. The trophoblastic cells have small dense vacuoles in their apical cytoplasm and abundant lipid droplets in the basal cytoplasm. Near term, the trophoblastic epithelium becomes quite attenuated as the fetal capillaries progressively indent this layer (Fig. 2). The fetal capillaries appear to be of the continous type throughout gestation (Figs. 1, 2).

The uterine epithelial cells have smooth endoplasmic reticulum and a well-developed Golgi apparatus. Electron-dense granules are abundant in the apical cytoplasm (Fig. 1). Maternal capillaries are generally of the continuous type, but occasional fenestrae have been observed.

In chorionic fossae or in the pits at the villous tips, the trophoblastic epithelial cells are usually columnar throughout the latter half of gestation and have numerous basal lipid droplets and many electron-dense granules in the apical cytoplasm [King, 1984].

Chorionic Vesicles

Light-Microscopic Studies. Specially modified absorptive areas known as chorionic vesicles are found opposite the mouths of uterine glands. Chorionic vesicles with villous projections were described by Hubrecht [1894] in *Nycticebus*. Strahl [1899] noted chorionic vesicles in *Galago*. As in *Nycticebus*, the vesicles contained branched vascularized villi. He also described the wall of the vesicle as having a layer of smooth muscle cells, an observation recently confirmed [King, 1984]. The chorionic vesicles of *Galago* were also described by Gerard [1932] and Butler and Adam [1964]. Hill [1932] described similar chorionic vesicles in *Loris*; Hill and Burne [1922] described less complex chorionic vesicles in *Chiromys*. Butler and Adam [1964] also studied the chorionic vesicles of *Galago* by histochemical methods.

Electron-Microscopical Studies. King [1984] recently described the fine structure of the chorionic vesicles in *Galago crassicaudatus*. Each vesicle has a narrow opening; the more dilated portions have projecting villi. Transmission electron micrographs of the trophoblastic cells lining the vesicle show columnar cells with many microvilli. There are deep recesses between the cells, but the cells are eventually joined by tight junctions (Fig. 3). The apical surfaces of the cells contain invaginations, including coated pits, suggesting endocytosis of vesicular content. The basolateral membranes of the trophoblastic cells are often highly folded. A capillary bed is located in the underlying mesoderm, and the wall of the chorionic vesicle contains a conspicuous layer of smooth muscle (Fig. 3).

Other Fetal Membranes

Little is known of the structure of other fetal membranes in strepsirhines. The allantois is large and lobulated [Hill and Burne, 1922; Hill et al, 1928; Hill, 1932]. Jenkinson [1916] noted the allantoic epithelium in *Lepilemur* was "very flat and covered by a cuticular layer." On the other hand, Benirschke and Miller [1982] described a prominent allantoic epithelium in several species of *Lemur*. The amnion appears to be delicate, with a flattened epithelium in strepsirhines.

Functional Considerations

Chorioallantoic Placenta. There is little direct evidence relating to transport or synthetic functions of the placenta in strepsirhines. Based on morphological evidence, the chorioallantoic placenta appears to be involved in both hemotrophic and histotrophic nutrition of the fetus. Exchange of substances between maternal and fetal blood is enhanced in later gestation by the marked thinning of the interhemal membrane brought about by the indentation of the trophoblast by fetal capillaries. This situation is similar to that observed in nonprimate epitheliochorial placentas such as the pig [Friess et al, 1980]. Endocytosis (pinocytosis) of material from the narrow space between the maternal and fetal microvilli may represent a form of histotrophic

nutrition similar to the situation observed in the interareolar portion of the epitheliochorial placenta of the pig [Dantzer et al, 1981]. The uterine epithelium, with its well-developed Golgi apparatus, areas of smooth endoplasmic reticulum, and apical granules, may be involved in the synthesis and secretion of materials that are absorbed by the trophoblast. It would be interesting to know something about lipid metabolism in these species, not only because of the appearance of the uterine epithelium, but also because of the abundant lipid droplets stored in the trophoblastic epithelium. The placenta of at least one strepsirhine produces a chorionic gonadotropin [Hobson and Wide, 1981].

The pits at the tips of the chorionic villi as well as indentations elsewhere on the villi appear to be involved mainly in phagocytosis or pinocytosis of material from the uterine lumen (histotroph).

Chorionic Vesicles. The chorionic vesicles appear to be specialized for uptake of the secretions of the uterine glands. Although no direct physiological evidence is yet available to support this hypothesis, the ultrastructure of the vesicle wall has substantial similarities to the structure of the areolae of the pig [King, 1984]. The trophoblastic cells appear actively endocytic and are undoubtedly important in the nutrition of the fetus. On the basis of histochemical studies [Butler and Adam, 1964] and the similarities to pig areolae [Friess et al, 1981], it appears likely that the chorionic vesicle in *Galago* may have an especially important role in transfer of iron to the fetus [King, 1984].

PLACENTATION IN HAPLORHINI

In contrast to the diffuse epitheliochorial placenta characteristic of most strepsirhines, a discoidal, hemochorial placenta is present in haplorhines.

Placentation in Tarsiiformes

Development and Structure of the Placenta. Early placental development in *Tarsius* is characterized by the formation of a thickened tissue mass. The origin of this mass is uncertain, but Luckett [1974] favors the interpretation that it is modified uterine glandular epithelium rather than trophoblast. Somewhat later in development this nodular mass is invaded and replaced by multinucleated trophoblastic giant cells which gradually form a meshwork of syncytial trophoblast. Mesodermal villi extend into this region and lacunar spaces form in

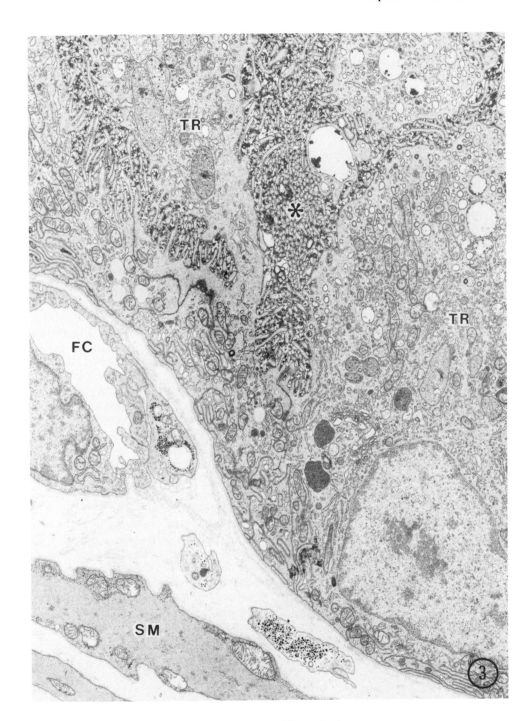

Fig. 3. Low magnification of part of a chorionic vesicle from *Galago* showing columnar trophoblastic (TR) cells and electron-dense material in lumen (*). The epithelial cells contain many absorptive vesicles. The wall of the chorionic vesicle contains capillaries (FC) and a layer of smooth muscle (SM). 100 days of gestation. ×12,200.

the syncytial masses [Hill, 1932]. As gestation advances, the vascularized mesodermal villi, surrounded by syncytial trophoblast, branch and elongate. The definitive placenta consists of a single lobule with a narrow attachment to the uterus. One artery enters the center of the lobule and branches into a system of fibrin-lined channels [Gruenwald, 1973]. Maternal blood circulates in the irregular lacunae lined by syncytium. Multiple veins at the edge of the attachment area collect blood from the lacunae. The definitive placenta is classified, therefore, as discoidal, labyrinthine, and hemochorial.

Other Fetal Membranes. In *Tarsius* the allantoic vesicle is small and rudimentary in distinct contrast to the situation in the strepsirhines. Hill [1932] noted that the yolk sac of *Tarsius* was modified. He observed that it was well vascularized and that the mesothelial covering of the yolk sac was hypertrophied into columnar cells with a distinctly granular cytoplasm.

Functional Considerations. Little is known regarding the function of the placenta or fetal membranes in *Tarsius*. Hill [1932] noted the considerable alterations that occurred in the maternal glandular tissue associated with the placenta and suggested that the degenerating maternal tissue constituted an important source of embryotroph (histotroph) available for the nutrition of the embryo prior to the complete establishment of the placental circulation. In relation to this, he considered the hypertrophied mesothelium of the yolk sac to be an adaptation "the object of which is to facilitate the absorption of the abundant embryotrophic material present in the exocoelom. . ." He regarded the yolk sac in *Tarsius* as playing an important role in embryonic nutrition at least during the early part of gestation.

Virtually nothing is known of chorioallantoic placental function in *Tarsius*. Exchange of nutrients between maternal and fetal blood is presumably initiated at about the 9–10 somite stage with the appearance of fetal blood in the mesodermal villi [Luckett, 1974].

Placentation in Platyrrhini

Placental Structure

Light-microscopic studies. The chorioallantoic placenta of platyrrhine primates is discoidal (often bidiscoidal) and hemochorial [Wislocki, 1929; Hill, 1932; Mossman, 1937]. Features associated with early placentation in platyrrhines include a broad

attachment of the trophoblast to the endometrium, and the proliferation of uterine epithelial cells to form an "epithelial plaque" [Hill, 1932]. Another characteristic feature of the platyrrhine placenta is the envelopment of intact maternal arterial blood vessels by the growing syncytiotrophoblast [Hill, 1932]. These "intraplacental maternal capillaries" [Hill, 1932] are not destroyed but persist until late stages. The endothelium of these vessels hypertrophies and walls become thickened or hyalinized. These arterial vessels penetrate the centers of the placental lobules and approach the fetal surface of the placenta [Hill, 1932; Gruenwald, 1972, 1973]. At this point the endothelial lining ends and maternal blood empties into spaces lined by syncytiotrophoblast. Blood then flows toward the basal surface of the disk and drains into veins [Gruenwald, 1972].

The branching and anastomosing pattern of the chorionic villi initially forms a trabecular meshwork with a core of mesoderm covered by syncytiotrophoblast. The definitive chorioallantoic of most platyrrhines is therefore classified as trabecular, labyrinthine, or pseudolabyrinthine. This type of organization has been described in *Alouatta* [Wislocki, 1929], *Ateles* [Wislocki, 1930], *Saguinus* [Wislocki, 1932b, 1939, 1943; Benirschke and Miller, 1982], *Cebus* [Hill, 1932; Benirschke and Miller, 1982], and *Saimiri* [Hill, 1932; Amoroso, 1952; Wynn, 1964; Benirschke and Miller, 1982]. In late stages of gestation, syncytiotrophoblastic "bridges" between adjacent trabeculae become reduced, resulting in an increased number of free villi [Hill, 1932; Amoroso, 1952; Wynn, 1964; Luckett, 1974]. Thus, quite late in gestation certain areas of the platyrrhine placenta may approach the villous organization observed in catarrhines [Hill, 1932]. In platyrrhine monkeys there are no anchoring villi but a profusion of small trabecular attachments to the decidua basalis.

Electron-microscopic studies. There have been very few electron-microscopic studies of platyrrhine placentas. Jollie [1973] and Wynn et al [1975] have described the interhemal membrane in *Saguinus*. Jollie [1973] reported that at early stages the placenta is hemodichorial with a complete layer of cytotrophoblast underlying the syncytiotrophoblastic covering of the trabeculae. With the reduction in cytotrophoblast, the interhemal membrane becomes hemomonochorial. He also reported that the trabecular cores contained very little connective tissue and were composed mainly of the allantoic blood vessels. The capillary endothelium was of the continuous (nonfenestrated) type. The surface of the syncytiotrophoblast facing the maternal blood had abundant microvilli and coated pits. Wynn et al [1975] confirmed these findings. Both laboratories noted that the fine structure of the marmoset interhemal membrane was strikingly similar to that of higher primates.

Other Fetal Membranes. Information on other fetal membranes in platyrrhines is fragmentary. The paraplacental (membranous) chorion in *Ateles* is fused with the endometrium late in gestation [Wislocki, 1930]. The amnion of the marmoset has been described as flattened and associated with a narrow mesodermal layer [Wislocki, 1932b]. Wynn et al [1975] examined the amnion of the marmoset by electron microscopy. They noted the cuboidal shape of the amniotic epithelial cells and the tortous intercellular channels in the epithelium. In these respects the amnion appeared similar to that described in higher primates. The yolk sac of the marmoset remains fairly large and its wall is thrown into folds [Wislocki, 1932b]. The cells are described as swollen, cuboidal, and having a cytoplasm filled with small droplets or granules. An unusually prominent allantois has been reported by *Ateles* [Benirschke and Miller, 1982].

Functional Considerations. As described above, the arrangement of the blood vessels in the placenta indicates that maternal blood enters the placenta in arterial channels that branch near the fetal surface. Blood then enters trophoblast-lined intertrabecular spaces and drains via veins at the base of the placenta. This arrangement is quite similar to that observed in many nonprimate labyrinthine placentas [Mossman, 1964; King and Mossman, 1974]. It is possible that a countercurrent circulation exists in these species.

An interesting feature of the placenta of many platyrrhines is the presence of hematopoietic foci in the mesoderm of the placental trabeculae. This was first described by Hill [1932] and later in several other platyrrhines by Wislocki [1943]. Jollie et al [1975] examined hemopoiesis in the marmoset at the electron-microscopic level. They reported cells of the erythroid line at all stages of gestation, but granulopoiesis was not observed. Megakaryocytes and macrophages also are present [Wislocki, 1943; Jollie et al, 1975]. The placenta of *Saguinus* has also been reported to transport

exogenous proteins from mother to fetus [Jollie, 1972]. The uptake appears to involve vesicular transport and in that sense the mechanism appears to be similar to that in higher primates including the human [King, 1982c]. Uptake of nutrients across the microvillous border of the syncytiotrophoblast would appear to be the basis of hemotrophic nutrition in platyrrhines. In early gestation it has been suggested that the breakdown of the thickened uterine epithelium constitutes an important source of histotrophic material available to the embryo [Hill, 1932]. The placentas of a number of platyrrhines apparently produce chorionic gonadotropins [see Hobson and Wide, 1981, for references]. The precise site of the hormone production within the placenta is not yet known.

Placentation in Catarrhini

Cercopithecoidea Placental Structure. Fragmentary observations on the placentas of several cercopithecines are available, but detailed observations throughout gestation are known only for *Macaca* and *Papio*. Thus, discussion here will emphasize placentation in these two genera.

Light-microscopic studies. The placenta of the rhesus monkey is usually bidiscoid, but single disks have been reported in about 20% of the pregnancies of several colonies [Martin and Ramsey, 1970; Chez et al, 1972]. The two disks are usually located on the anterior and posterior walls of the uterus. The umbilical cord inserts near the center of the primary disk. The two disks are interconnected by one or more sets of interplacental blood vessels that course in the membranous chorion [Martin and Ramsey, 1970]. The arrangement of the vessels on the chorionic plate resembles that of human placentas. The rhesus monkey placenta contains proportionally more stem villi than the human placenta, but the stem villi are smaller and less complexly branched in the monkey.

Branches of one or more stem villi give rise to discrete placental structures, known as cotyledons, that correspond to the lobulations visible on the maternal surface of the delivered placenta [Martin and Ramsey, 1970]. The maternal spiral or uteroplacental arteries have straight terminal segments and enter the intervillous space by single orifices in the center of the cotyledons [Arts and Lohman, 1974; Ramsey and Donner, 1980]. The blood pressure in the decidual part of the spiral arteries, when the uterus is relaxed, is fairly low [Moll et al,

1974]. The cells lining the arteries may be of fetal (trophoblastic) origin [Beck and Beck, 1967]. Careful injection corrosion cast studies by Arts and Lohman [1974] and others have shown the villi in the monkey to be distributed rather evenly, there being no villus-free space in the center of the cotyledon. The circulation of blood in the rhesus monkey placenta has been extensively studied by a variety of methods. A full discussion of the findings is beyond the scope of this review, but a thorough account of most of the findings can be found in Ramsey and Donner [1980]. There is general agreement that maternal blood enters via the spiral artery into the center of the cotyledon, and is propelled in a fountainlike manner toward the chorionic plate. Blood flows past the villous tree toward the periphery of the cotyledon and then back toward the basal plate where it exits via uteroplacental veins.

The earliest stages of placental development in the rhesus monkey (*Macaca mulatta*) have been described by Wislocki and Streeter [1938] and Enders (this volume). The initial stage in the formation of placental villi is the conversion of reticulated plates or trabeculae of syncytial trophoblast into chorionic villi as a result of proliferation and growth of cytotrophoblastic cell columns. This occurs at about 15–17 days of gestation [Wislocki and Streeter, 1938]. The villi continue to grow in length, attain a vascularized mesodermal core, and become more complexly branched from then until 35 days of gestation. At this point, the placenta was considered to have reached its definitive situation. Autoradiographic evidence has demonstrated that cytotrophoblast gives rise to syncytiotrophoblast [Midgley et al, 1963]. Considerable histological and histochemical details of the rhesus monkey placenta can be found in the monograph of Wislocki and Bennett [1943].

Growth of the rhesus monkey placenta has been studied by several groups. Van Wagenen et al [1965] tabulated changes in placental weight, area, and volume in rhesus monkeys between 30 days of gestation and term. Placental weight (including both disks and fetal membranes) increased in a linear fashion. The ratio of placental:fetal weight changed from 10:1 at the earliest ages to 1:4 near term. Kerr et al [1974] reported that the rhesus monkey placenta continued to increase in weight throughout gestation. Kerr et al [1974] and Novy et al [1981] placed the maximum rate of placental and fetal growth between 125 and 150 days of gestation. The

placenta reached its maximum weight at about 145 days of gestation. Hill [1975] and Novy et al [1981] both noted a linear increase in placental DNA content during gestation. Novy et al [1981] also made the interesting observation that during early gestation (day 80–90) ligation of the interplacental vessels bridging between the primary and secondary disks resulted in atrophy of the secondary disk, and an increase in the weight and DNA content of the primary disk. Fetal weight was normal. Myers et al [1971] reported that similar ligations at day 100 of gestation resulted in reduced fetal weight.

A very complete series of baboon *(Papio)* placentas has been studied by Houston [1969a,b, 1971], who has reviewed the sparse early literature on placentation in this genus. The baboon has a superficial type of implantation and chorionic villi develop only in the area of original attachment to the uterine mucosa. As a result, a single placental disk is formed with a membranous (smooth) chorion peripheral to the disk. Villus formation begins at about 13–18 days of gestation with the outgrowth of solid cytotrophoblastic columns into the syncytiotrophoblast; subsequently, mesodermal cores appear. From about days 18–25 the villi undergo considerable branching and fetal capillaries appear. This stage is followed by the "period of the definitive embryonic placenta" during which further differentiation of these structural components occurs. This stage is complete by about day 35. The chorionic villi are initially covered by a double layer of trophoblast: syncytiotrophoblast on the exterior next to maternal blood and an internal cytotrophoblastic layer. During the fetal period of gestation (45–175 days) the cytotrophoblast gradually disappears and there is an accumulation of fibrin and fibrinoid in the basal plate and anchoring villi. Further details on the development and distribution of blood vessels in the baboon placenta can be found in Houston and Hendrickx [1968].

Information on other cercopiths is fragmentary. Burton [1980] described several early placentas of langurs (*Presbytis obscura*) and reviews earlier literature on placentation in colobins. The placenta is bidiscoidal and of the villous hemochorial type, and these early stages have many similarities to the early rhesus monkey placentas. Karim and Vashishta [1981] examined the placental circulatory patterns and villus structure in *Presbytis entellus*. Benirschke and Miller [1982] have described general characteristics of the placentas of *Pygathrix, Presbytis, Colobus, Nasalis, Erythrocebus,*

Cercopithecus, Macaca silensis, Cynopithecus, and *Mandrillus.* The gross morphology of the placentas was nearly identical and almost always bidiscoidal. They all appeared to be of the villous hemochorial type. Further details on placentation in the proboscis monkey (*Nasalis larvatus*) can be found in Soma and Benirschke [1977].

Electron-microscopic studies. The development of placental villi and cell columns in the rhesus monkey has recently been studied by King and Mais [1982]. These authors noted a number of discrete stages of morphogenesis of the villi between 19 days of gestation and term. The earliest stages of villus formation appeared similar to that described by Wislocki and Streeter [1938] resulting in thick, relatively unbranched villi. The next phase of development was the longitudinal splitting of the villi and cell columns to form groups of parallel branches (Fig. 4). These branches had a common insertion into the basal plate. This was followed by a stage characterized by the outgrowth of large-diameter side branches. At about 40 days of gestation numerous small syncytial sprouts made their appearance. Continued proliferation of villi at later stages of gestation resulted in a decreased diameter of the villi and an increasing complexity of the course of the fetal capillaries in terminal villi.

Pierce et al [1964] conducted one of the earliest ultrastructural studies of nonhuman primate placental villi. They examined specimens of rhesus monkeys at 19, 130, and 160 days of gestation and noted the progressive diminution of the cytotrophoblast and the thinning of the trophoblast layer in later gestation. They also documented the apparent fusion of cytotrophoblast with syncytium. The brush border and highly differentiated cytoplasm of syncytiotrophoblast was in distinct contrast to that of the cytotrophoblast. A wider sample of placental stages (50–150 days) in rhesus monkeys was studied by Luckett [1970]. He noted the abundant apical vacuoles in syncytiotrophoblast at 50–100 days of gestation and suggested these may be secretory vesicles. Lipid droplets were abundant in syncytium at 50 days of gestation, but not later. Otherwise the syncytiotrophoblast cytoplasm during these ages was characterized by abundant granular endoplasmic reticulum and a well-developed Golgi apparatus. A micrograph illustrating syncytiotrophoblast and cytotrophoblast in a rhesus monkey villus in early gestation is shown in Figure 5. The villous cores contained vacuolated macrophages (Hofbauer cells) and capillaries of the con-

tinuous (nonfenestrated) type. Panigel [1970] briefly described similar ultrastructural findings in *Macaca mulatta, Macaca fascicularis,* and *Erythrocebus patas.*

Houston [1971] and Wynn et al [1971] examined the fine structure of baboon placental villi. Both groups showed the structural similarity of baboon placental villi to those of the human. The syncytium thinned as gestation advanced. The surface of the syncytium in contact with maternal blood has a well-developed microvillous border and numerous pinocytotic vesicles. Like the rhesus monkey, the syncytiotrophoblast cytoplasm was characterized by abundant granular endoplasmic reticulum and a well-developed Golgi apparatus. Other ultrastructural features of the baboon placenta are very similar to that described for rhesus monkey and human. An electron micrograph of a portion of a baboon placental villus is shown in Figure 6.

Other Fetal Membranes. The fetal membranes of cercopithecines have received relatively little attention. King [1980] carried out a fine-structural study of developing rhesus monkey amnion from 26–72 and 145–170 days of gestation. He noted that early in gestation, the amniotic epithelial cells were flattened, had few microvilli, and contained abundant glycogen stores. Later in gestation the cells were cuboidal and had numerous microvilli and moderate numbers of lipid droplets. The intercellular pathway appeared to be important in the movement of large molecules across the amniotic epithelium. An unusual extracellular layer of microfibrils forms beneath the amniotic epithelium at about 70 days of gestation. More limited observations of a rhesus monkey amnion [Wynn and French, 1968] and baboon amnion [Wynn et al, 1971] showed similar results. The structure of the rhesus monkey and baboon amnion appears similar in virtually all respects to human amnion.

Developmental changes in the chorion laeve (smooth or membranous chorion) of the rhesus monkey have been studied by King [1981]. Early in gestation (19–60 days), before the chorionic epithelium fuses with the parietal decidua, the trophoblastic cells are columnar or cuboidal in shape and have numerous vesicles and vacuoles in their apical cytoplasm.

The apical surfaces of the cells have microvilli and coated pits and vesicles. Later in gestation the amnion fuses with the chorion, and amniochorion "fuses" with the parietal decidua. By term, the

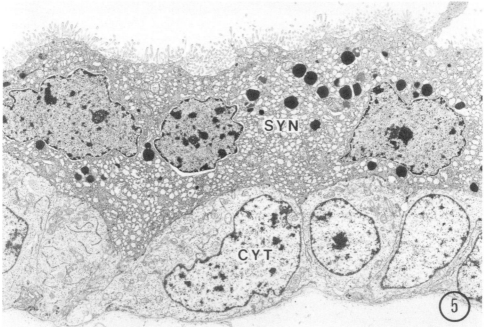

Fig. 4. Low-magnification scanning electron micrograph of rhesus monkey placenta at 34 days of gestation. Note the stem villi (SV) emerging from the chorionic plate (CP). Free villus side branches occur in the midregion of the placenta, whereas the villi and cell columns undergo longitudinal splitting nearer the basal plate (bottom). ×30.

Fig. 5. Low-magnification electron micrograph of rhesus monkey placental villus at 25 days of gestation. Intervillous space containing maternal blood is at the top. The syncytiotrophoblast (SYN) has a brush border; its cytoplasm is rich in cisternae of granular endoplasmic reticulum and dark-staining lipid droplets. Beneath the syncytium is a layer of lighter-staining cytotrophoblast (CYT). ×3,300.

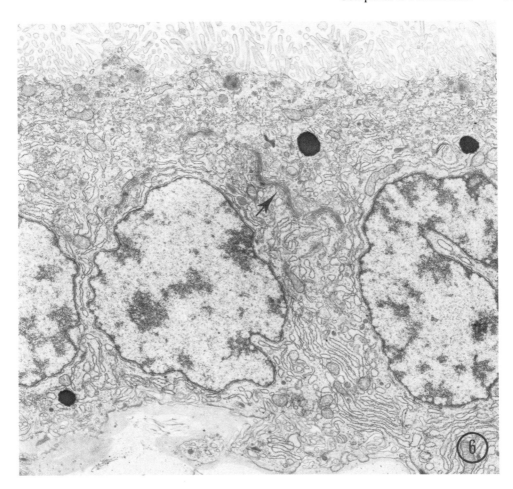

Fig. 6. Electron micrograph of part of a baboon placental villus showing brush border of syncytium adjacent to intervillous space (top). The cytoplasm has well-developed granular endoplasmic reticulum and Golgi apparatus (arrow). ×5,300.

relationship of the fetal membranes to the maternal decidua is very similar to that seen in the human. The membranous chorion in the baboon appears to undergo similar changes, at least at the light-microscopic level [Houston, 1971].

The early yolk sac of the rhesus monkey appears to undergo a series of the developmental changes very similar to that of the human [Luckett, 1978]. The primary yolk sac reaches its peak development during day 12 in both rhesus monkey and human, and the secondary yolk sac becomes segregated from the primary yolk sac at 12–14 days of gestation. The secondary yolk sac is a unique and characteristic feature of all anthropoid primates and it will become the definitive yolk sac of the older embryo [Luckett, 1978]. The secondary yolk sac goes through a transient period of growth and ex-

pansion before involuting. A recent study of the fine structure and cytochemistry of rhesus monkey yolk sac between 25 and 66 days of gestation has shown many developmental parallels with characteristics of early human yolk sac [King and Wilson, 1983]. Endodermal cells of the yolk sac were characterized by abundant granular endoplasmic reticulum, well-developed Golgi apparatus, and moderate numbers of microperoxisomes and lysosomes. Later in development these cells acquire granules with a heterogeneous content that may contain iron compounds. The mesothelial covering of the yolk was composed of flattened cells with long microvilli, and had limited acid phosphatase activity.

Functional Considerations

Placenta. There are few studies of cercopithecine placentas that have correlated structure with specific functions. The placentas of the rhesus monkey and baboon synthesize a chorionic gonadotropin and a chorionic somatomammotropin [Josimovich et al, 1973; Walsh et al, 1977; Novy et al, 1981]. There is a significant relationship between placental weight and circulating chorionic somatomammotropin concentrations [Novy et al, 1981]. Presumably the syncytiotrophoblast of the villi is the major source of these hormones. The well-developed granular endoplasmic reticulum and Golgi apparatus are probably related to their synthesis. The placenta is also involved in steroid synthesis [Ainsworth et al, 1969]. For a further discussion of possible steroid synthesis in monkey placenta see Luckett [1970]. The placenta of the rhesus monkey transfers IgG and some albumin to the fetus [Bangham, 1960]. The cellular pathways involved in this transfer are unknown, but the trophoblastic surface bordering maternal blood has numerous coated pits which may be involved in receptor-mediated endocytosis of macromolecules similar to that observed in the human placenta [King, 1982c]. The pattern of transferrin localization in baboon placenta is similar to that observed in the human [King, 1976; Galbraith et al, 1980].

Other fetal membranes. Ultrastructural studies of rhesus monkey smooth chorion (chorion laeve) [King, 1981] and amnion [King, 1980] indicate that both the cellular trophoblast and the amniotic epithelial cells remain metabolically active throughout gestation. There is little direct evidence, however, as to the nature of the metabolic pathways in these tissues. Permeability studies of rhesus monkey amnion, chorion, and fused amniochorion have been carried out in vitro [Battaglia et al, 1964, 1968]. In most cases, permeability characteristics were comparable to those observed for human smooth chorion. The permeability of rhesus monkey amniotic epithelium to a low-molecular-weight protein (peroxidase) is similar to that reported in human amnion [King, 1980]. Ultrastructural and cytochemical studies of developing rhesus monkey yolk sac [King and Wilson, 1983] suggest a possible role for serum protein synthesis by endodermal cells. Mesothelial cells were active in absorption and may have a role in uptake of substances from the exocoelom during early development. In this regard, rhesus monkey yolk sac has many similarities to human yolk sac.

Hominoidea

Placental Structure. Placental structure in many hominoids has been examined and, except for mi-nor variations, all authors agree that later placental development and structure are remarkably similar to that of the human. Thus, the placenta in hominoids is discoidal, villous, and hemochorial in structure. No attempt will be made here to review the extensive literature on the morphology and function of the human placenta. However, a very brief introduction to some of the literature will be presented, particularly when there are similarities between the human and nonhuman primates.

Light-microscopic studies. Strahl [1903] found the placenta of the orang-utan and gibbon to be similar to that of the human. A minor difference noted was the more slender and delicate chorionic villi in these species, an observation confirmed in a single orang-utan placenta examined by Graham-Jones and Hill [1962]. The suggestion by the latter authors that the syncytiotrophoblast is lost in the mature placenta is not supported by the observations of Benirschke and Miller [1982] and seems unlikely. Wislocki [1932a] examined a gorilla placenta and noted its similarity to that of the human. He found the chorionic villi in the gorilla to be slightly larger and more cellular than in human placentas of equivalent ages. Subsequent studies of the gorilla placenta [Ludwig, 1961a,b] noted the presence of many more epithelial plates than in the human, as well as the presence of syncytial bridges between villi. A marginal insertion of the umbilical cord appears to be common. Histochemically, the gorilla placenta also appears similar to that of the human [Ludwig, 1961b].

Appreciable detail regarding placentation in the chimpanzee *(Pan)* can be found in Ludwig and Baur [1971]. Wislocki [1933] was one of the earliest authors to study the chimpanzee placenta. He noted its overall similarity to that of the human. One difference between the chimp placenta and those of other hominoids is the more pronounced fibrin deposits in the former [Wislocki, 1933; Ludwig and Baur, 1971]. Ludwig and Baur [1971] carried out morphometric measurements on the placentas of a number of hominoids. The total surface area of the villi in the chimp placenta was found to be 5.4–6.2 m^2. Their morphometric results for other placentas, including the human, showed a great similarity among the hominoids.

Reviewing the vast literature on the light-microscopic structure of the human placenta is beyond the scope of this chapter. Readers are referred to the book by Boyd and Hamilton [1970] for a thorough treatment of virtually all studies up to that time. Only selected aspects of the structure of the human placenta will be dealt with here, mostly in

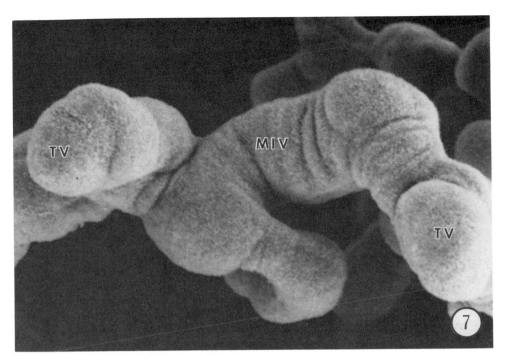

Fig. 7.   Scanning electron micrograph of mature intermediate villus (MIV) and terminal villi (TV) of a term human placenta. ×900.

comparison to other catarrhines. Development of placental villi in the human appears to be similar in many respects to that described earlier for rhesus monkeys, although comparison is made difficult by the lack of closely staged human material. Hamilton and Boyd [1960] studied a number of early human specimens. It is apparent from their illustrations that the arrangement of human villi is much less orderly than that observed in the rhesus monkey [King and Mais, 1982] or baboon [Houston, 1969a,b]. Boyd and Hamilton [1970] suggested that second-and third-order villi in the human placenta originated by longitudinal splitting of preexisting villi or cytotrophoblastic cell columns, not to free outgrowths. This may occur by a process similar to that observed in early rhesus monkey placentas [King and Mais, 1982]. Kaufmann et al, [1979] have proposed a modification of the traditional classification of human placental villi. Stem villi were characterized not only by their large diameter, but also the presence of a fibrous connective tissue and fetal vessels with a distinct tunica media. These authors introduced the concept of intermediate villi. Immature intermediate villi were 60–200 μm in diameter and were characterized by a reticular stroma and numerous macrophages (Hofbauer cells). Mature intermediate villi were smaller in

diameter with a loose stroma poor in cells. The function of the intermediate villi is supposedly to act as a site of proliferation for new terminal villi and to provide a supportive "backbone" for terminal villi. Terminal villi are about 30–80 μm in diameter and contain dilated sinusoidal fetal capillaries. A scanning electron micrograph of human placental villi is shown in Figure 7. Corresponding morphometric values for the different categories of villi can be found in Sen et al [1979]. Other morphometric studies of human placenta include Aherne and Dunhill [1966], Laga et al [1973], and Teasdale [1980].

A number of studies have established different zones of villi within the human placenta, in either a vertical or horizontal plane [Alvarez et al, 1970; Teasdale, 1978]. Histochemical and biochemical variations in placental lobules have also been reported. According to Schuhmann [1982] the centers of the circulatory units are areas of growth and regeneration, whereas the lobule periphery is the main area for placental transfer and metabolism. This sort of detail regarding zonal variations within the placenta is generally lacking for nonhuman primates.

The placental circulation has been discussed by many authors, and readers are referred to Ramsey and Donner [1980] for details. There are many similarities between the circulatory pathways in the human and rhesus monkey. One difference appears to be the finding by at least some authors that some uteroplacental arteries open at the periphery of lobules in the human whereas the arteries invariably enter at the center of the lobules in rhesus monkeys.

Electron-microscopic studies. Early electron-microscopic studies of human placenta established the basic cytological characteristics of syncytial and cytotrophoblast [Wislocki and Dempsey, 1955; Rhodin and Terzakis, 1962; Terzakis, 1963; Lister, 1963a,b, 1964; Martin and Spicer, 1973]. The ultrastructural characteristics of the trophoblast are very similar to those of rhesus monkey and baboon placenta. Cytological pathways involved in protein and glycoprotein synthesis by human trophoblast have been studied [Nelson et al, 1978a,b]. Enders [1965b] studied the formation of syncytium from cytotrophoblast. A number of ultrastructural studies have focused on more restricted areas of the placenta. Enders [1968] has examined the structure of cells and extracellular material in the anchoring villi of human placenta. Enders and King [1970], Vacek [1970], and Castellucci et al [1980] have examined the fine structure of placental macrophages (Hofbauer cells) present in the villous core. Cytological characteristics of other components of the villous core have also been examined in some detail [Kaufmann et al, 1977; Castellucci et al, 1982].

The ultrastructure of fetal placental capillaries have also been studied [Becker and Siefert, 1963; Dempsey, 1972; Nikolov and Schiebler, 1973; Martinek et al, 1975; Heinrich et al, 1976; Bartels et al, 1978]. Intercellular junctions between the different cell types have been examined by thin section and freeze-fracture methods [Metz et al, 1979; Metz and Weihe, 1980]. Morphometric analysis of changes in major trophoblastic cell organelles during pregnancy has also been studied [Tedde and Kujawa, 1978]. For the most part, similarly detailed analyses of these features in nonhuman primates are lacking.

Other Fetal Membranes. There is scant information available on the amnion, membranous chorion, and yolk sac in nonhuman hominoids. The voluminous literature on these human fetal membranes suggests that there are fundamental similarities between human and cercopithecoid fetal membranes. Early light-microscopic studies of the amnion and chorion have been summarized by Bourne [1962]. Hoyes [1975] has reviewed light- and electron-microscopic studies and development of the amnion. More recent electron-microscopic observations of surface specializations and intercellular junctions in human amnion can be found in King [1982a] and Bartels and Wang [1983]. The amniotic epithelium of the human has many similarities to that of the baboon [Wynn et al, 1971] and the rhesus monkey [King, 1980]. Electron-microscopic studies of the human chorion laeve at term have established that the trophoblast in this region remains cellular. The cells appear to be joined by desmosomes and occasional gap junctions; wide intercellular spaces are common [Petry, 1963; Anderson and McKay, 1966; Thliveris and Speroff, 1977; Bartels and Wang, 1983]. The chorion laeve at term is quite similar in structure to that of the rhesus monkey [King, 1981]. Additional references to the permeability of the human chorion laeve can be found in King [1981].

The development of the yolk sac of the human has been studied in some detail [Luckett, 1978]. Its formation shows many similarities to that observed in the rhesus monkey. The fine structure of the human yolk sac has also been studied. The earliest human specimen examined ultrastructurally appears to be one at 39 days of age [Gonzales-Crussi and Roth, 1976]. Hemopoietic tissue in several yolk sacs at 4–5 weeks of age was examined by Fukuda [1973]. The most detailed studies of human yolk sacs are limited to specimens principally between 8 and 10 weeks of gestation [Hesseldahl and Larsen, 1969, 1971; Hoyes, 1969]. Although closely staged human material has not been available, those examined have many similarities to the yolk sac of the rhesus monkey [King and Wilson, 1983]. Further references on the function of the yolk sac can be found in King and Wilson [1983].

CONCLUSIONS
General Principles

The chorioallantoic placentas of the strepsirhines are, with a few exceptions, of the diffuse epitheliochorial type. As such, they resemble certain nonprimate placentas much more than the placentas of higher primates. The paraplacental structures in strepsirhines, such as the chorionic vesicles, resemble areolae in nonprimate species.

The chorioallantoic placenta of *Tarsius* more closely resembles placentas of higher primates in that the placenta is discoidal and hemochorial, but differs in having a labyrinthine rather than a villous architecture. Chorioallantoic placentas of most cercopiths and hominoids are quite similar and are villous, hemochorial, and discoidal (sometimes bidiscoidal). Thus, as models for human placental and fetal membrane structure, development, and physiology, the placentas of the macaques and baboon are to be recommended and are the only practical choices in terms of availability.

Research Needs

Electron-microscopic studies of strepsirhine and platyrrhine placentas would be useful additions to our understanding of placental characteristics in these primates. Electron-microscopic studies of placental and fetal membrane development in rhesus monkeys and baboons indicates these species have much in common with the human placenta throughout most of gestation. Combined cytological and physiological studies of placentation in these species continue to offer the best possibility for advancing our knowledge of human pregnancy.

ACKNOWLEDGMENTS

The author's original work reported herein was supported by National Institutes of Health grants HD 11658 and RR 00169. The author thanks Grete Fry and John Mais for their technical assistance, and Clarrise Northern for her careful typing of the manuscript. Special thanks are due Dr. A.G. Hendrickx and the staff of the Perinatal Biology Unit of the California Primate Research Center for their assistance in obtaining tissue from nonhuman primates.

REFERENCES

Aherne, W.; Dunhill, M.S. Morphometry of the human placenta. BRITISH MEDICAL BULLETIN 22:5–8, 1966.

Ainsworth, L.; Daenen, M.; Ryan, K.J. Steroid hormone transformations by endocrine organs from pregnant mammals. IV. Biosynthesis and metabolism of estrogens and progesterone by primate placental preparations in vitro. ENDOCRINOLOGY 84:1421–1429, 1969.

Alvarez, H.; Benedetti, W.L.; Morel, R.L.; Scavarelli, M. Trophoblast development gradient and its relationship to placental hemodynamics. AMERICAN JOURNAL OF OBSTETRICS AND GYNECOLOGY 106:416–420, 1970.

Amoroso, E.C. Placentation. Pp. 127–331 in MARSHALL'S PHYSIOLOGY OF REPRODUCTION, 3rd Ed., Vol. 2. London, Longmans Green, 1952.

Anderson, W.A.; McKay, D.G. Electron microscope study of the trophoblast in normal and toxemic placentas. AMERICAN JOURNAL OF OBSTETRICS AND GYNECOLOGY. 95:1134–1148, 1966.

Arts, N.F.T.; Lohman, A.H.M. An injection-corrosion study of the fetal and maternal vascular systems in the placenta of the rhesus monkey. EUROPEAN JOURNAL OF OBSTETRICS GYNECOLOGY AND REPRODUCTIVE BIOLOGY 4:133–141, 1974.

Bangham, D.R. The transmission of homologous serum proteins to the foetus and to the amniotic fluid in the rhesus monkey. JOURNAL OF PHYSIOLOGY 153:265–286, 1960.

Bartels, H.; Wang, T. Intercellular junctions in the human fetal membranes. A freeze-fracture study. ANATOMY AND EMBRYOLOGY 166:103–120, 1983.

Bartels, H.; Dec, W.; Cieciura, L.; Krajewski, J. Ultrastructure of capillaries in villi of human placenta. FOLIA MORPHOLOGIA 37:315–320, 1978.

Battaglia, F.C.; Behrman, R.E.; Meschia, G.; Seeds, A.E.; Bruns, P.D. Clearance of inert molecules, Na, and Cl ion across the primate placenta. AMERICAN JOURNAL OF OBSTETRICS AND GYNECOLOGY 102:1135–1143, 1968.

Battaglia, F.C.; Bruns, P.D.; Behrman, R.E.; Seeds, A.E.; Hellegers, A.E. Comparison of permeability of different layers of the primate placenta to D-arabinose and urea. AMERICAN JOURNAL OF PHYSIOLOGY 207:500–502, 1964.

Beck, A.J.; Beck, F. The origin of intra-arterial cells in the pregnant uterus of the macaque (*Macaca mulatta*). ANATOMICAL RECORD 158:111–113, 1967.

Becker, V.; Siefert, K. Die Ultrastruktur der Kapillarwand in der menschlichen Placenta zur Zeit der Schwangerschaftsmitte. ZEITSCHRIFT FÜR ZELLFORSCHUNG 65:380–396, 1963.

Benirschke, K.; Miller, C.J. Anatomical and functional differences in the placenta of primates. BIOLOGY OF REPRODUCTION 26:29–53, 1982.

Bourne, G.L. THE HUMAN AMNION AND CHORION. London, Lloyd-Luke, 1962.

Boyd, J.D.; Hamilton, W.J. THE HUMAN PLACENTA. Cambridge, England, W. Heffer & Sons, 1970.

Burton, G.J. Early placentation in the dusky leaf monkey (*Presbytis obscura*). PLACENTA 1:187–195, 1980.

Butler, H.; Adam, K.R. The structure of the allantoic placenta of the Senegal bush baby (*Galago senega-*

lensis senegalensis). FOLIA PRIMATOLOGICA 2:22–49, 1964.

Castellucci, M.; Kaufmann, P. A three-dimensional study of the normal human placental villous core: II. Stromal architecture. PLACENTA 3:269–286, 1982.

Castellucci, M.; Zaccheo, D.; Pescetto, G. A three-dimensional study of the normal placental villous core. I. The Hofbauer cells. CELL AND TISSUE RESEARCH 210:235–247, 1980.

Chez, R.A.; Schlesselman, J.J.; Salazar, H.; Fox, R. Single placentas in the rhesus monkey. JOURNAL OF MEDICAL PRIMATOLOGY 1:230–240, 1972.

Dantzer, F.; Bjorkman, N.; Hasselager, E. An electron microscopic study of histiotrophe in the interareolar part of the porcine placenta. PLACENTA 2:19–28, 1981.

Dempsey, E.W. Comparative aspects of the placentae of certain African mammals. JOURNAL OF REPRODUCTION AND FERTILITY, SUPPLEMENT 6:189–192, 1969.

Dempsey, E.W. The development of capillaries in the villi of early human placentas. AMERICAN JOURNAL OF ANATOMY 134:221–238, 1972.

Enders, A.C. A comparative study of the fine structure of the trophoblast in several hemochorial placentas. AMERICAN JOURNAL OF ANATOMY 116:29–68, 1965a.

Enders, A.C. Formation of syncytium from cytotrophoblast in the human placenta. OBSTETRICS AND GYNECOLOGY 25:378–386, 1965b.

Enders, A.C. Fine structure of anchoring villi of the human placenta. AMERICAN JOURNAL OF ANATOMY 122:419–452, 1968.

Enders, A.C.; King, B.F. The cytology of Hofbauer cells. ANATOMICAL RECORD 167:231–252, 1970.

Friess, A.E.; Sinowatz, F.; Skolek-Winnisch, R.; Trautner, W. The placenta of the pig. I. Fine structural changes of the placental barrier during pregnancy. ANATOMY AND EMBRYOLOGY 158:179–191, 1980.

Friess, A.E.; Sinowatz, F.; Skolek-Winnisch, R.; Trautner, W. The placenta of the pig. II. The ultrastructure of the areolae. ANATOMY AND EMBRYOLOGY 163:43–53, 1981.

Fukuda, T. Fetal hemopoiesis. I. Electron microscopic studies on human yolk sac hemopoiesis. VIRCHOWS ARCHIV, B. CELL PATHOLOGY 14:197–213, 1973.

Galbraith, G.M.P.; Galbraith, R.M.; Faulk, W.P. Immunological studies of transferrin and transferrin receptors of human placental trophoblast. PLACENTA 1:33–46, 1980.

Gerard, P. Etudes sur l'ovogenèse et l'ontogenèse chez les Lemuriens du genre *Galago*. ARCHIVES DE BIOLOGIE (PARIS) 43:93–151, 1932.

Gonzales-Crussi, F.; Roth, L.M. The human yolk sac and yolk sac carcinoma. An ultrastructural study. HUMAN PATHOLOGY 7:675–691, 1976.

Graham-Jones, O.; Hill, W.C.O. Pregnancy and parturition in a Bornean orang. PROCEEDINGS OF THE ZOOLOGICAL SOCIETY OF LONDON 139:503–510, 1962.

Grosser, O. FRÜHENTWICKLUNG, EIHAUTBILDUNG UND PLACENTATION DES MENSCHEN UND DER SAUGETIERE. München, Bergmann, 1927.

Gruenwald, P. Expansion of placental site and maternal blood supply of primate placentas. ANATOMICAL RECORD 173:189–204, 1972.

Gruenwald, P. Lobular structure of hemochorial primate placentas and its relation to maternal vessels. AMERICAN JOURNAL OF ANATOMY 136:133–152, 1973.

Hamilton, W.J.; Boyd, J.D. Development of the human placenta in the first three months of gestation. JOURNAL OF ANATOMY 94:297–328, 1960.

Heinrich, D.; Metz, J.; Raviola, E.; Forssmann, W.G. Ultrastructure of perfusion-fixed fetal capillaries in the human placenta. CELL AND TISSUE RESEARCH 172:157–170, 1976.

Hesseldahl, H.; Larsen, J.F. Ultrastructure of human yolk sac: Endoderm, mesenchyme, tubules and mesothelium. AMERICAN JOURNAL OF ANATOMY 126:315–336, 1969.

Hesseldahl, H.; Larsen, J.F. Hemopoiesis and blood vessels in human yolk sac. An electron microscopic study. ACTA ANATOMICA 78:274–294, 1971.

Hill, D.E. Cellular growth of the rhesus monkey placenta. Pp. 283–288 in FETAL AND POSTNATAL CELLULAR GROWTH. D.B. Cheek, ed. New York, Wiley, 1975.

Hill, J.P. The developmental history of primates. PHILOSOPHICAL TRANSACTIONS OF THE ROYAL SOCIETY OF LONDON, Series B 221:45–178, 1932.

Hill, J.P.; Burne, R.H. The foetal membranes and placentation of *Chiromys madagascariensis*. PROCEEDINGS OF THE ZOOLOGICAL SOCIETY OF LONDON 2:1145–1170, 1922.

Hill, J.P.; Ince, F.E.; Subba Rau, A. The development of the fetal membranes in *Loris*, with special reference to the mode of vascularisation of the chorion in the Lemuroidea and its phylogenetic significance. PROCEEDINGS OF THE ZOOLOGICAL SOCIETY OF LONDON 2:699–716, 1928.

Hobson, B.M.; Wide, L. The similarity of chorionic gonadotropins and its subunits in term placentas from man, apes, Old and New World monkeys and a prosimian. FOLIA PRIMATOLOGICA 35:51–64, 1981.

Houston, M.L. The villous period of placentogenesis in the baboon (*Papio* sp.) AMERICAN JOURNAL OF ANATOMY 126:1–16, 1969a.

Houston, M.L. The development of the baboon (*Papio* sp.) placenta during the fetal period of gestation. AMERICAN JOURNAL OF ANATOMY 126:17-30, 1969b.

Houston, M.L. Placenta. Pp. 153-172 in EMBRYOLOGY OF THE BABOON. A.G. Hendrickx, ed. Chicago, University of Chicago Press, 1971.

Houston, M.L.; Hendrickx, A.G. Observations on the vasculature of the baboon placenta (*Papio* sp.) with special reference to the transverse communicating artery. FOLIA PRIMATOLOGICA 9:68-77, 1968.

Hoyes, A.D. The human foetal yolk sac: An ultrastructural study of four specimens. ZEITSCHRIFT FÜR ZELLFORSCHUNG 99:469-490, 1969.

Hoyes, A.D. Structure and function of the amnion. Pp. 1-38 in OBSTETRICS AND GYNECOLOGY ANNUAL, Vol. 4. R.M. Wynn, ed. New York, Appleton-Century-Crofts, 1975.

Hubrecht, A.A.W. *Spolia Nemoris.* QUARTERLY JOURNAL OF MICROSCOPICAL SCIENCE 36:77-125, 1894.

Jenkinson, J.W. The placenta of the lemur. QUARTERLY JOURNAL OF MICROSCOPICAL SCIENCE 61:171-184, 1916.

Jollie, W.P. Ultrastructural observations on protein transport in the placenta of the marmoset, *Saguinus oedipus.* MEDICAL PRIMATOLOGY 1972, Part I, pp. 271-287, 1972.

Jollie, W.P. Fine structural changes in the placental membrane of the marmoset with increasing gestational age. ANATOMICAL RECORD 176:307-320, 1973.

Jollie, W.P.; Haar, J.L.; Craig, S.S. Fine structural observations on hemopoiesis in the chorioallantoic placenta of the marmoset. AMERICAN JOURNAL OF ANATOMY 144:9-38, 1975.

Josimovitch, J.B.; Levitt, M.J.; Stevens, V.C. Comparison of baboon and human placental lactogens. ENDOCRINOLOGY 93:242-244, 1973.

Karim, K.B.; Vasishta, U.G. Some observations on the foetal vascularization of the full-term placenta of the Indian langur *Presbytis entellus.* PROCEEDINGS OF THE NATIONAL ACADEMY OF SCIENCE, INDIA 51:205-211, 1981.

Kaufmann, P.; Stark, J.; Stegner, H.E. The villous stroma of the human placenta. I. The ultrastructure of fixed connective tissue cells. CELL AND TISSUE RESEARCH 177:105-121, 1977.

Kaufmann, P.; Sen, D.K.; Schweikhart, G. Classification of human placental villi. I. Histology. CELL AND TISSUE RESEARCH 200:409-423, 1979.

Kerr, G.R.; Allen, J.R.; Scheffler, G.; Couture, J. Fetal and postnatal growth of rhesus monkeys (*M. mulatta*). JOURNAL OF MEDICAL PRIMATOLOGY 3:221-235, 1974.

King, B.F. Localization of transferrin on the surface of the human placenta by electron microscopic immunocytochemistry. ANATOMICAL RECORD 186:151-160,1976.

King, B.F. Developmental changes in the fine structure of rhesus monkey amnion. AMERICAN JOURNAL OF ANATOMY 157:285-307, 1980.

King, B.F. Developmental changes in the fine structure of the chorion laeve (smooth chorion) of the rhesus monkey placenta. ANATOMICAL RECORD 200:163-175, 1981.

King, B.F. Cell surface specializations in human amniotic epithelium: An electron microscopic and freeze-fracture study. ANATOMICAL RECORD 203:73-82, 1982a.

King, B.F. Comparative anatomy of the placental barrier. BIBLIOTHECA ANATOMICA No. 22, pp. 13-28. Basel, Karger, 1982b.

King, B.F. Absorption of peroxidase-conjugated immunoglobulin G by human placenta: An in vitro study. PLACENTA 3:395-406, 1982c.

King, B.F. The fine structure of the placenta and chorionic vesicles of the bush baby, *Galago crassicaudata.* AMERICAN JOURNAL OF ANATOMY, 169:101-116, 1984.

King, B.F.; Mais, J.J. Developmental changes in the rhesus monkey placental villi and cell columns: Scanning electron microscopy. ANATOMY AND EMBRYOLOGY 165:361-376, 1982.

King, B.F.; Mossman, H.W. The fetal membranes and unusual giant cell placenta of the jerboa (*Jaculus*) and jumping mouse (*Zapus*). AMERICAN JOURNAL OF ANATOMY 140:405-432, 1974.

King, B.F.; Wilson, J.M. A fine structural and cytochemical study of the rhesus monkey yolk sac: Endoderm and mesothelium. ANATOMICAL RECORD 205:143-158, 1983.

Laga, E.M.; Driscoll, S.G.; Munro, H.N. Quantitative studies of human placenta. I. Morphometry. BIOLOGY OF THE NEONATE 23:231-259, 1973.

Lister, U.M. Ultrastructure of the human mature placenta. 1. The maternal surface. JOURNAL OF OBSTETRICS AND GYNAECOLOGY OF THE BRITISH COMMONWEALTH 70:373-386, 1963a.

Lister, U.M. Ultrastructure of the human mature placenta. 2. The foetal surface. JOURNAL OF OBSTETRICS AND GYNAECOLOGY OF THE BRITISH COMMONWEALTH 70:766-776, 1963b.

Lister, U.M. Ultrastructure of the early human placenta. JOURNAL OF OBSTETRICS AND GYNAECOLOGY OF THE BRITISH COMMONWEALTH. 71:21-32, 1964.

Luckett, W.P. The fine structure of the placental villi of the rhesus monkey (*Macaca mulatta*). ANATOMICAL RECORD 167:141-164, 1970.

Luckett, W.P. Comparative development and evolution of the placenta in primates. Pp. 142-234 in REPRODUCTIVE BIOLOGY OF THE PRIMATES. W.P. Luckett, ed. Basel, Karger, 1974.

Luckett, W.P. Cladistic relationships among primate higher categories: Evidence of the fetal membranes and placenta. FOLIA PRIMATOLOGICA 25:245–276, 1976.

Luckett, W.P. Origin and differentiation of the yolk sac and extraembryonic mesoderm in presomite human and rhesus monkey embryos. AMERICAN JOURNAL OF ANATOMY 152:59–98, 1978.

Ludwig, K.S. Beitrag zum Bau der Gorilla-Placenta. ACTA ANATOMICA 45:110–123, 1961a.

Ludwig, K.S. Ein weiterer Beitrag zum Bau der Gorilla-Placenta. ACTA ANATOMICA 46:304–310, 1961b.

Ludwig, K.S.; Baur, R. The chimpanzee placenta. Pp. 349–372 in THE CHIMPANZEE, Vol. 4. G. Bourne, ed. Basel, Karger, 1971.

Martin, B.J.; Spicer, S.S. Ultrastructural features of cellular maturation and aging in human trophoblast. JOURNAL OF ULTRASTRUCTURE RESEARCH 43:133–149, 1973.

Martin, C.B. Jr.; Ramsey, E.M. Gross anatomy of the placenta of rhesus monkeys. OBSTETRICS AND GYNECOLOGY 36:167–177, 1970.

Martinek, J.J.; Gallagher, M.L.; Essig, G.F. An electron microscopic study of fetal capillary basal laminas of normal human term placentas. AMERICAN JOURNAL OF OBSTETRICS AND GYNECOLOGY 121:17–24, 1975.

Metz, J.; Weihe, E. Intercellular junctions in the full term human placenta. II. Cytotrophoblast cells, intravillous stroma cells and blood vessels. ANATOMY AND EMBRYOLOGY 158:167–178, 1980.

Metz, J.; Weihe, E.; Heinrich, D. Intercellular junctions within the human full term placenta: I. Syncytiotrophoblastic layer. ANATOMY AND EMBRYOLOGY 158:41–50, 1979.

Midgley, A.R. Jr.; Pierce, G.B. Jr.; Deneau, G.A.; Gosling, J.R.G. Morphogenesis of syncytiotrophoblast in vivo; an autoradiographic demonstration. SCIENCE 141:349–350, 1963.

Moll, W.; Kunzel, W.; Stolte, L.A.M.; Kleinhout, J.; De Jong, P.A.; Veth, A.F.L. The blood pressure in the decidual part of the uteroplacental arteries (spinal arteries) of the rhesus monkey. PFLÜGERS ARCHIV. EUROPEAN JOURNAL OF PHYSIOLOGY 346:291–297, 1974.

Molteni, R.A.; Stys, S.J.; Battaglia, F.C. Relationship of fetal and placental weight in human beings: Fetal/placental weight ratios at various gestational ages and birth weight distributions. JOURNAL OF REPRODUCTIVE MEDICINE 21:327–334, 1978.

Mossman, H.W. Comparative morphogenesis of the fetal membranes and accessory uterine structures. CONTRIBUTIONS TO EMBRYOLOGY OF THE CARNEGIE INSTITUTE 26:129–246, 1937.

Mossman, H.W. The principal interchange vessels of the chorioallantoic placenta of mammals. Pp. 771–786 in ORGANOGENESIS. R. L. DeHaan; H. Ursprung, eds. New York, Holt, Rhinehart and Winston, 1964.

Mossman, H.W. Comparative biology of the placenta and fetal membranes. Pp. 13–97 in FETAL HOMEOSTASIS, Vol. 2. R.M. Wynn, ed. New York, New York Academy of Sciences, 1967.

Mossman, H.W. Structural changes in vertebrate fetal membranes associated with the adoption of viviparity. OBSTETRICS AND GYNECOLOGY ANNUAL 3:7–32, 1974.

Myers, R.E.; Hill, D.E.; Holt, A.B., Scott, R.E.; Mellits, E.D.; Cheek, D.B. Fetal growth retardation produced by experimental placental insufficiency in the rhesus monkey. I. Body weight, organ size. BIOLOGY OF THE NEONATE 18:379–394, 1971.

Nelson, D.M.; Enders, A.C.; King, B.F. Cytological events involved in protein synthesis in cellular and syncytial trophoblast of the human placenta. An electron microscope autoradiographic study of (^{3}H)leucine incorporation. JOURNAL OF CELL BIOLOGY 76:400–417, 1978a.

Nelson, D.M.; Enders, A.C.; King, B.F. Cytological events involved in glycoprotein synthesis in cellular and syncytial trophoblast of human placenta. An electron microscope autoradiographic study of (^{3}H)galactose incorporation. JOURNAL OF CELL BIOLOGY 76:418–429, 1978b.

Nikolov, S.; Schiebler, T.H. Über das fetale Gefasssystem der reifen menschlichen placenta. ZEITSCHRIFT FÜR ZELLFORSCHUNG 139:333–350, 1973.

Novy, M.J.; Aubert, M.L.; Kaplan, S.L.; Grumbach, M.M. Regulation of placental growth and chorionic somatomammotropin in the rhesus monkey: Effects of protein deprivation, fetal anencephaly, and placental vessel ligation. AMERICAN JOURNAL OF OBSTETRICS AND GYNECOLOGY 140:552–562, 1981.

Panigel, M. The electron microscopy of the placental villi in nonhuman primates Galago demodovii, Erythrocebus patas, Macaca fascicularis, Macaca mulatta and Papio cynocephalus. MEDICAL PRIMATOLOGY Part I, pp. 536–552, 1970.

Petry, G. Die Morphologie der ausserhalb der Placenta bestehenden feto-maternen Kontakte. ARCHIV FÜR GYNAKOLOGIE 198:74–81, 1963.

Ramsey, E.M. THE PLACENTA: HUMAN AND ANIMAL. New York, Praeger, 1982.

Ramsey, E.M.; Donner, M.W. PLACENTAL VASCULATURE AND CIRCULATION. Stuttgart, Georg Thieme, 1980.

Reng, R. Die Placenta von Microcebus murinus Miller. ZEITSCHRIFT FÜR SAUGETIERKUNDE 42:201–214, 1977.

Rhodin, J.A.C.; Terzakis, J. The ultrastructure of the human full term placenta. JOURNAL OF ULTRASTRUCTURE RESEARCH 6:88–106, 1962.

Schuhmann, R.A. Histochemical and electron microscopic studies of maternofetal circulatory unit of mature human placentas. OBSTETRICS AND GYNECOLOGY ANNUAL 11:1–30, 1982.

Sen, D.K.; Kaufmann, P.; Schweikhart, G. Classification of human placental villi. II Morphometry. CELL AND TISSUE RESEARCH 200:425–434, 1979.

Soma, H.; Benirschke, K. Observations on the fetus and placenta of a proboscis monkey (*Nasalis larvatus*). PRIMATES 18:277–284, 1977.

Starck, D. Primitiventwicklung und Plazentation der Primaten. Pp. 723–886 in PRIMATOLOGICA, Vol. I. H. Hofer; A.H. Schultz; D. Starck, eds. Basel, Karger, 1956.

Steven, D.H. COMPARATIVE PLACENTATION: ESSAYS IN STRUCTURE AND FUNCTION. New York, Academic Press, 1975.

Strahl, H. Der Uterus gravidus von *Galago agisymbanus*. ABHANDLUNGEN DER SENCKEN-BERGISCHEN NATURFORSCHENDER GES-CHICHTE 25:155–199, 1899.

Strahl, H. Primaten-Placenten. Pp. 417–491 in SELEN-KAS STUDIEN ÜBER ENTWICKLUNGS-GES-CHICHTE DER TIERE, Part 12. Wiesbaden, C.W. Kreidels Verlag, 1903.

Teasdale, F. Functional significance of the zonal morphologic differences in the normal human placenta. A morphometric study. AMERICAN JOURNAL OF OBSTETRICS AND GYNECOLOGY 130:773–781, 1978.

Teasdale, F. Gestational changes in the functional structure of the human placenta in relation to fetal growth. A morphometric study. AMERICAN JOURNAL OF OBSTETRICS AND GYNECOLOGY 137:560–568, 1980.

Tedde, G.; Kujawa, M. Morphometric study of the syncytiotrophoblast of the normal human placenta from the early stages of pregnancy to the term. JOURNAL OF SUBMICROSCOPIC CYTOLOGY 10:65–70, 1978.

Terzakis, J. The ultrastructure of the normal human first trimester placenta. JOURNAL OF ULTRA-STRUCTURE RESEARCH 9:268–284, 1963.

Thliveris, J.A.; Speroff, L. Ultrastructure of the placental villi, chorion laeve, and decidua parietalis in normal and hypertensive pregnant women. AMER-ICAN JOURNAL OF OBSTETRICS AND GYNE-COLOGY 129:492–498, 1977.

Turner, W. On the placentation of the lemurs. PHILO-SOPHICAL TRANSACTIONS OF THE ROYAL SOCIETY LONDON 166:569–587, 1876.

Turner, W. The placentation of lemurs. JOURNAL OF ANATOMY AND PHYSIOLOGY 12:147–153, 1898.

Vacek, Z. Derivation and ultrastructure of the stromal cells of the human chorionic villus. FOLIA MOR-PHOLOGICA (PRAHA) 18:1–13, 1970.

van Wagenen, G.; Catchpole, H.R.; Negri, J.; Butzko, D. Growth of the fetus and placenta of the monkey (*Macaca mulatta*). AMERICAN JOURNAL OF PHYSICAL ANTHROPOLOGY 23:23–34, 1965.

Walsh, S.W.; Wolf, R.C.; Meyer, R.K.; Aubert, M.L.; Friesen, H.G. Chorionic gonadotropin, chorionic somatomammotropin, and prolactin in the uterine vien and peripheral plasma of pregnant rhesus mon-

keys. ENDOCRINOLOGY 100:851–855, 1977.

Wimsatt, W.A. Some aspects of the comparative anatomy of the mammalian placenta. AMERICAN JOURNAL OF OBSTETRICS AND GYNECOL-OGY 84:1568–1594, 1962.

Wislocki, G.B. On the placentation of primates with a consideration of the phylogeny of the placenta. CONTRIBUTIONS TO EMBRYOLOGY OF THE CARNEGIE INSTITUTE 20:51–80, 1929.

Wislocki, G.B. On a series of placental stages of a platyrrhine monkey (*Ateles geoffroyi*) with some remarks upon age, sex and breeding period in the platyrrhines. CONTRIBUTIONS TO EMBRYOL-OGY OF THE CARNEGIE INSTITUTE 22:173–192, 1930.

Wislocki, G.B. On the female reproductive tract of the gorilla, with a comparison of that of other primates. CONTRIBUTIONS TO EMBRYOLOGY OF THE CARNEGIE INSTITUTE 23:163–204, 1932a.

Wislocki, G.B. Placentation in the marmoset (*Oedipomidas geoffroyi*). with remarks on twinning in monkeys. ANATOMICAL RECORD 52:381–399, 1932b.

Wislocki, G.B. Gravid reproductive tract and placenta of the chimpanzee. AMERICAN JOURNAL OF PHYSICAL ANTHROPOLOGY 18:81–92, 1933.

Wislocki, G.B. Observations of twinning in marmosets. AMERICAN JOURNAL OF ANATOMY 64:449–483, 1939.

Wislocki, G.B. Hemopoiesis in the chorionic villi of the placenta of platyrrhine monkeys. ANATOMI-CAL RECORD 85:349–363, 1943.

Wislocki, G.B.; Bennett, H.S. The histology and cytology of the human and monkey placenta, with special reference to the trophoblast. AMERCIAN JOUR-NAL OF ANATOMY 73:335–449, 1943.

Wislocki, G.B.; Dempsey, E.W. Electron microscopy of the human placenta. ANATOMICAL RECORD 123:133–168, 1955.

Wislocki, G.B.; Streeter, G.L. On the placentation of the macaque (*Macaca mulatta*) from the time of implantation until the formation of the definitive placenta. CONTRIBUTIONS TO EMBRYOLOGY OF THE CARNEGIE INSTITUTE 27:1–66, 1938.

Wynn, R.M. Comparative morphogenesis and vascular relationships of the villous hemochorial placenta. AMERICAN JOURNAL OF OBSTETRICS AND GYNECOLOGY 90:758–768, 1964.

Wynn, R.M.; French, G.L. Comparative ultrastructure of the mammalian amnion. OBSTETRICS AND GYNECOLOGY 31:759–774, 1968.

Wynn, R.M.; Panigel, M.; MacLennan, A.H. Fine structure of the placenta and fetal membranes of the baboon. AMERICAN JOURNAL OF OBSTET-RICS AND GYNECOLOGY 109:638–648, 1971.

Wynn, R.M.; Richards, S.C.; Harris, J.A. Electron microscopy of the placenta and related structures of the marmoset. AMERICAN JOURNAL OF OB-STETRICS AND GYNECOLOGY 122:60–69, 1975.

Teratology and Embryogenesis

Andrew G. Hendrickx and Srinivasa Prahalada

California Primate Research Center, University of California, Davis, California 95616

INTRODUCTION AND OVERVIEW

Reports on embryonic development of primates have appeared in the biological literature for at least a century. These earlier studies focused exclusively on developmental anatomy; it was not until the past 30 years that correlations were made between specific embryological events and reproductive events (ie, menstruation, mating, ovulation) to establish a developmental timetable [Hendrickx, 1971c]. Most of the studies on embryogenesis of primates that were done in the past 15 years have been presented as developmental stages [O'Rahilly, 1963; Hendrickx, 1971a].

The embryonic development of primates, thus far studied, is characterized by considerable diversity and well-recognized phylogenetic patterns. Tupaiidae, Lemuridae, and Lorisidae show similarities to lower mammals, and Tarsiidae representing an intermediate step between the prosimians and Callitrichidae and Cebidae. Cercopithecidae and members of the anthropoid family exhibit the greatest similarities to man. In this chapter emphasis will be placed on the comparative aspects of embryogenesis.

With regard to experimental teratology, the need for animal models with similar developmental timetables exists in at least three areas: 1) screening substances which may, by different routes, be transferred from the mother to the embryo, and which have a high probability of being prescribed or result in embryonic exposure in the pregnant human; 2) studying specific spontaneous or experimentally induced malformations that also occur in humans in order to gain insight into their etiology and pathogenesis; and 3) studying teratogenic mechanisms. The need for further studies in teratology resides in the fact that two-thirds of the reported congenital malformations are of unknown etiology, and efforts to elucidate the causes, pathogenesis, and mechanisms are of great importance. The causative agents that have been studied experimentally are presented in this chapter.

EMBRYOLOGY
Bilaminar Embryonic Disk

Lorisidae. Differentiation of the inner cell mass has been described in one or two embryos of unknown age of several different species [Hubrecht and Keibel, 1907; Hill, 1932; Butler, 1964, 1972]. In *Loris* [Hill, 1932] and *Nycticebus* [Hubrecht and Keibel, 1907] embryos, differentiation of the inner cell mass begins during the preimplantation period and the blastocyst is still covered by the zona pellucida. The inner cell mass is formed into a flattened circular mass, the epiblast, which is clearly distinguishable from the covering trophoblast. The epiblast, comprised of columnar cells, expands and a distinct endodermal layer, the hypoblast, forms on the ventral surface. The endoderm expands and lines the inner surface of the trophoblast. The blastocysts of *Loris* and *Nycticebus* expand rapidly. The blastocysts of these species measure between 2.0 and 3.0 mm in diameter and fill the lumen of the uterine horn. The degree of contact between the trophoblast and uterine epithelium is difficult to ascertain because of shrinkage and other artifacts. This marked increase in blastocyst size is representative of a central type of implantation. The rapid expansion of the blastocyst serves two purposes: 1) to fix the blastocyst in place within the uterine lumen, and 2) to provide a large yolk sac cavity for the storage of nutrients [Hill, 1932].

Tarsiidae. The only data available on Tarsiidae prenatal development is that provided by Hubrecht [1896a,b, 1902] and Hubrecht and Keibel [1907] from specimens obtained in the field with unknown gestational ages. The epiblast differentiates in a similar manner to Lorisidae. Formation of the endoderm has been described as proceeding in two different ways. Hubrecht [1902] described the endoderm as arising from the inner cell mass by the process of delamination, and never lining the inner surface of the trophoblast. Hill's [1932] interpretation of these specimens was that it formed as a layer, not a solid mass, and that the endodermal cells formed a vesicle which spread along the inner surface of the trophoblast, as in Lorisidae. Tarsiidae also retain the central type of implantation, differing from Lorisidae by attaching to the uterus when the blastocyst is much smaller, less than 0.3 mm in diameter. The extraembryonic mesoderm and coelom are established before the blastocyst is 0.5 mm in diameter.

Callitrichidae and Cebidae. Hill [1932] referred to five presomite embryos representing these two families: an early blastocyst of *Cebus macrocephalus* (*C. apella*), a late blastocyst and a presomite embryo of *Chrysothrix (Saimiri) sciureus*, and twin blastocyts of *Hapale (Callithrix) jacchus*. Goss et al [1968] list two squirrel monkey embryos of 23 and 24 days respectively that may represent the bilaminar disk stage of development. Little additional information is provided in either of these two publications, so our knowledge of early differentiation of Callitrichidae and Cebidae is very limited.

Cercopithecidae. The embryos of two genera of this family, *Macaca* and *Papio*, have been studied extensively, and along with the specimens of *Nasalis, Presbytis, Colobus*, and *Cercopithecus* comprise the material that is known to be available for study [Hill, 1932; Heuser and Streeter, 1941; Hendrickx and Sawyer, 1975, 1978a,b]. Developmental staging, according to the criteria established by Streeter [1942], has been done for *Cercopithecus, Macaca* and *Papio*. In *Macaca* and *Papio* differentiation of the inner cell begins before implantation; the endoderm is evident by about day 7. The cells of the epiblast are distinguishable from the amnion by day 10 or 11. During the first few days after implantation the epiblast consists of irregularly arranged cubiodal cells which become pseudostratified columnar. The epiblast expands in

size prior to appearance of the primitive streak. Cells of the hypoblast remain loosely organized until formation of the prochordal plate on about day 16. Bilaminar disk formation is somewhat later in *Cercopithecus*, appearing as late as day 24 of gestation [Hendrickx and Sawyer, 1978a].

Hylobatidae and Pongidae. Only a few early implantation stages of *Pan* are available for study; otherwise the early development of these two families are unrepresented.

Hominidae. Numerous papers describing one or two human embryos have appeared during the past several decades; the following references are among those representative of early *Homo sapiens* development: Hertig and Rock [1941, 1945, 1949], Heuser et al [1945, 1956], Noback et al [1968]. O'Rahilly [1975] has provided the first account of developmental stages for the first 2 weeks of human development.

Trilaminar Embryonic Disk

Overview. With the formation of the primitive streak, mesodermal layer, and the notochord, the bilaminar embryonic disk is converted into the trilaminar embryonic disk. The appearance of these structures signifies the onset of cellular differentiation and the further cellular differentiation into organ systems.

Lorisidae. The primitive streak first appears in *Loris* embryos about 0.5 mm long. It extends cranially about 0.2 mm from the caudal portion of the embryonic disk. Mesoderm extends to the outer borders of the embryonic disk, but not beyond it, and mesodermal cells are associated with the developing prochordal plate [Hill, 1932]. At 0.7 mm in length a distinct primitive knot (node of Hensen) and primitive pit are present. The primitive streak is elongated and the notochordal process remains short. The lateral and cranial extension of the mesoderm is confined within the embryonic disk and extends caudally from the margin of the primitive streak along the trophoblast. Hill [1932] suggested that the origin of the extraembryonic mesoderm was from a backward proliferation of the primitive streak, and that the extraembryonic and embryonic mesoderm form almost simultaneously. Hubrecht and Keibel [1907] stated that the extraembryonic mesoderm formed directly from the endoderm and that blood cells and blood vessels proliferated directly from a peripheral zone of the endoderm, although Hill [1932] was unable to verify these findings.

Tarsiidae. Mesoderm forms relatively early, in contrast to *Loris*, appearing in *Tarsius* embryos measuring 0.15 mm in diameter. The extraembryonic mesoderm forms as an outward extension of the ectoderm before there is a trace of the primitive streak. It is not known whether the mesoderm arises as a localized proliferation from the caudal-median margin of the ectoderm [Hubrecht and Keibel, 1907; Hill, 1932] or as a more diffuse proliferation. In slightly larger specimens the extraembryonic mesoderm extends from the extreme caudal margin of the ectoderm, at its junction with the trophoblast. Although Hubrecht [1902] may have mislabeled it, the ectoderm at the junction with the extraembryonic mesoderm probably represents the primitive streak. The primitive streak is evident in *Tarsius* specimens 0.2 mm in diameter, extending cranially from the caudal region of the embryonic disk.

Callitrichidae and Cebidae. The extraembryonic mesoderm is reported to arise before the primitive streak develops in both *Hapale* (*Callithrix*) and *Cebus* embryos [Hill, 1932]. Goss et al [1968] obtained several embryos of approximately 24–27 days of age which may represent the trilaminar disk stage of development, but no details are provided.

Cercopithecidae and Hominidae. The caudal portion of the primitive streak of *Macaca mulatta* embryos develops precociously, between days 12 and 14, and only extraembryonic mesoderm is derived from it [Luckett, 1971]. Luckett postulates that the caudal portion of the primitive streak is the primary source of the extraembryonic mesoderm with an additional contribution from the trophoblast. A similar precocity of primitive streak formation may occur in lower forms such as *Tarsius* and others; however, additional studies are necessary to confirm this.

In the rhesus monkey and baboon the primitive streak is apparent as an area of proliferation along the craniocaudal axis in the caudal region of the ectodermal plate in 16- and 17-day-old embryos. Throughout its length there are localized areas of disorganized cells until the last segment is laid down. The primitive streak gives rise to embryonic

mesoderm along its craniolateral margins and endodermal cells ventrally. The mesodermal cells accumulate in their craniolateral movement, forming the primitive knot, and subsequently initiate the development of the notochord. The primitive pit forms slightly later as an elevation brought about by the increased proliferation of cells. The endodermal cells contribute to the formation of the gut endoderm.

The notochord appears by day 19 in both rhesus monkeys and baboons as a short column of cells extending from the primitive streak to the prochordal plate [Gilbert and Heuser, 1954; Heuser and Streeter, 1941; Hendrickx, 1971a]. This rodlike structure remains closely apposed to the endoderm and to the neural plate ectoderm at its cranial end. The notochordal canal is a canal which extends from the amniotic cavity dorsally and the vitelline (yolk) cavity ventrally. It appears shortly after the notochord is formed and extends throughout its length by the time the somites appear. The prochordal plate, which marks the location of the buccopharyngeal membrane, also appears early and remains as a distinct landmark until somite formation is under way.

Trilaminar disk formation follows a very similar pattern in *Cercopithecus aethiops* but occurs later in development. The primitive streak is present by day 26 of development compared to days 16–17 for *Macaca mulatta* and *Papio cynocephalus*.

Hominidae. The appearance and origin of extraembryonic mesoderm in *Homo sapiens* embryos follow very similar developmental patterns [Florian, 1933] to those of *Macaca mulatta*. The other characteristics of trilaminar disk formation, referenced above, are similar if not identical to those observed in Cercopithecidae [Hertig and Rock, 1941, 1945, 1949; Heuser et al, 1945; Hertig et al, 1956; Noback et al, 1968].

Organogenesis

Few complete studies have been reported on the development of organ systems in nonhuman primates although numerous reports on this subject are available for humans. Hubrecht and Keibel's [1907] classical study of *Tarsius* and *Nycticebus normentafeln* is one of the few studies of the lower forms. Reports by Hill [1932], Hubrecht [1896a,b, 1902], Mossman [1937], Butler [1964, 1972, 1983], and Müller and O'Rahilly [1980] are also concerned with the early development of Lemuri-

TABLE 1. Summary of the Early Development of the Eye in Primates

Features	Developmental stages						
	Microcebus murinus	*Galago spp.*	*Callithrix jacchus*	*Erythrocebus patas*	*Macaca mulatta*	*Papio spp.*	*Homo sapiens*
Optic primordia first appear.	10				10	10	10
Optic evaginations arise; lateral wall of evagination is at first in contact with surface ectoderm; caudal limiting sulci develop.	11	11	11			11	11
Rostral neuropore closing or closed; optic vesicles form and contribute crest cells to their own mesenchymal sheaths; rostral or ventral sulci develop.	11		11			11	11
Lens and retinal disks appear and are in contact; wall of optic vesicle develops a medial as well as caudal wall.	12		13		13	13	13
Retinal and lens disks begin to invaginate; marginal zone appears in retinal disk; optic vesicle and brain lined by terminal bar net; lens and retinal disks make contact through their basement membranes; a terminal bar net appears to line external surface of lens disk.	13		13		13	13	13
Retinal disk invaginates to form optic cup; retinal fissure begins to form; lens disk invaginates to form a pit and nuclei and cell remnants are extruded into its cavity.	14	14	14	14	14	14	14
First indication of retinal pigmentation (retinal fissure extends into optic stalk); lens pit is closed; lens vesicle is completely invaginated but remains in contact with surface ectoderm; lens fibers appear in the form of elongated cells.	15		15	15[a]		15	15

Description						
Lips of retinal fissure begin to fuse; a nucleus-free zone presents near cavity of the lens vesicle; pigment granules extend almost to optic stalk.	16	16	16	15	16	16
Retinal pigmentation appears near optic stalk (lips of retinal fissure are fused).	17	17	17[b]	17		
Lens cavity is reduced to a slit; lenticular nuclei form a nuclear bow; internal neuroblastic layer forms adjacent to optic disk; lens vesicle no longer in contact with surface ectoderm.	18	18	18	18		
Future cornea is composed of anterior epithelium and an underlying layer of flattened mesenchyme; scleral condensation forms at the margins of the cup.	19	19	19	19	19	19
Pupillary membrane begins to form; lens cavity either closed or closing.	19	20	21[c]	21	19	
Cornea now composed of anterior epithelium, substantia propria, and mesothelium; scleral condensation extends to the equator; internal neuroblastic layer more extensive; optic nerve fibers reach diencephalon; lens sutures appear.	21	21	21	21		
Substantia propria increased in thickness, composed of 9–12 rows of cells; mesothelium and scleral condensation form a continuous band around eye; paraxial fibers of lens concave toward axis; cavity of optic stalk obliterated.	22	23	23	23	23	

[a] Lens separated from surface ectoderm.
[b] Lens vesicle no longer in contact with surface ectoderm.
[c] Pupillary membrane not found in stage 21 embryos, the last stage for which embryos were available [Phillips, 1976].

TABLE 2. Differences in Neurological Development of Rhesus Monkey, Baboon, and Human Embryos (Stages 8–16)

Development event	Embryonic stage		
	Baboon	Rhesus monkey	Human
Otic disk formation	10	10	9
Adenohypophyseal pouch	11–12	11–12	10
Trigeminal primordium	12–13	12–13	14
Motor root, trigeminal	14	14	15
Lens pore closure	14	15	14
Neurohypophyseal evagination	15	15	16
Internal sulcus (hippocampus)	Later than 16	Later than 16	15

From Davignon et al [1980].

dae, Lorisidae, Tarsiidae, Callitrichidae, and Cebidae. Even though there is a relatively large gap in our knowledge of embryonic development between Lemuridae and Cercopithecidae, primates generally follow the mammalian plan of embryonic development. Accurate comparisons of the various forms are difficult to make because of the great differences in time over which the studies were done, the condition and preparation of the specimens, and the objectives of the studies. Developmental staging of primate embryos patterned after Streeter's "Developmental Horizons of Human Embryos" [1942, 1945, 1948, 1951], Heuser and Corner [1957], and O'Rahilly [1963, 1966, 1975] have made it more feasible to show similarities and differences among the species. The embryos of at least six species—Galago spp., Callithrix jacchus, P. cynocephalus, M. mulatta, C. aethiops, and E. patas—have been staged according to the criteria provided by the studies done on human embryos [Hendrickx, 1971a; Butler, 1972; Hendrickx and Sawyer, 1975, 1978a,b; Phillips, 1976; Gribnau and Geijsberts, 1981; Binkerd et al, 1983]. Developmental staging of the nervous system of selected embryos has also been reported for Microcebus murinus, Alouatta seniculus, Cebus apella, Cebus albifrons, and M. mulatta [Müller and O'Rahilly, 1980] and for a larger series of M. mulatta and P. cynocephalus [Davignon et al, 1980].

The early development of the eye for seven species of primates is presented in Table 1. The temporal sequence of major developmental features are generally similar for all species studied, as one would expect. There are, however, deviations in the general pattern. Major features of eye development in Microcebus murinus are delayed

by one developmental stage for four of the 13 features studied in this species [Popko, 1978]. Developmental features of the eye appeared more consistently in the other species, although critical stages were missing for the three species: Galago spp. Callithrix jacchus, and Erythrocebus patas. It is evident that there is a great similarity between M. mulatta, Papio spp., and H. sapiens. Although the mode and sequence of organ formation are similar in these species, the embryonic age during which the specific developmental events occur is variable. This variation has been observed in the morphogenesis of the brain and its derivatives [Davignon et al, 1980]. An example of this variation is the closure of the lens pore, regarded as a reliable criterion for differentiating stage 14 embryos from stage 15 embryos. Lens pore closure in M. mulatta appears to lag behind other normally developing structures within the nervous system which are characteristic of stage 15 baboon or human embryos (Table 2). Closure occurs in stage 15 M. mulatta embryos compared to closure in stage 14 for Papio spp. [Hendrickx, 1971a] and H. sapiens [Streeter, 1948; O'Rahilly, 1966]. In contrast, the elongation of the endolymphatic diverticulum in M. mulatta is similar to that in H. sapiens and far more rapid than in Papio spp. Other major differences in neurological development are shown in Table 2.

TERATOLOGY
Spontaneous Developmental Abnormalities in Nonhuman Primates

Overview. The incidence of developmental abnormalities in primate colonies is not well studied compared to that of other laboratory animals and

TABLE 3. Spontaneous Malformations in Nonhuman Primates at the CPRC (1969–1982)

Family	Genus/species	No. of necropsies	Type of malformation (No. animals)
Cebidae	*Callicebus moloch*	65	Patent ductus arteriosus (1)
	Saimiri sciureus	142	Clubfoot (left hind foot) (1)
			Female pseudohermaphrodite (1)
Callitrichidae	*Saguinus nigricollis*	187	Congenital diaphragmatic hernia (2)
Cercopithecidae	*Cercocebus fulliginosus*	56	Patent ductus arteriosus (1)
	Macaca fascicularis	297	Atrial and ventricular septal defect; intersex; adrenal cortical hypoplasia (1)
			Adrenal cortical hypoplasia (2)
			Microhemartomas-liver (1)
	Macaca mulatta	1,698	Syndactyly, hindlimb, bilateral 2nd and 3rd digit (1)
			Hydrocephalus; inguinal hernia (1)
			Hydrocephalus (1)
			Atrial septal defect (1)
			Severe coarctation of aorta; aortic stenosis (1)
			Developmental arteriovenous fistula—R arm [Rosenberg et al, 1983] (1)
			Renal agenesis—unilateral left (1)
			Renal hypoplasia—unilateral right (1)
			Severe hydronephrosis and aplasia of ureter—unilateral, left (1)
			Wolffian duct remnant—vagina (1)
			Hypoplasia, mammary teat (1)
			Ectopia—adrenocortical, right kidney cortex (1)
			Adrenal aplasia (bilateral) (1)
			Adrenal gland hypoplasia (2)
			Ectopic adrenal nodule (1)
			Pancreatic hypoplasia (1)
	Macaca radiata	452	Hydrocephalus—lateral ventricles bilateral (1)
			Patent ductus arteriosus (1)
			Renal aplasia—unilateral, left (1)
			Renal cortical cysts—multiple, congenital (1)
			Polycystic kidney—bilateral (1)
			Adrenal hypoplasia (1)
	Macaca speciosa	134	Hypoplasia—adrenal gland (2)
	Papio cynocephalus	61	Clubfoot; ventricular septal defect (1)

TABLE 4. Summary of Spontaneous Malformations Reported in Nonhuman Primates

Family	Genus/species	Malformations (No.)	References
Lemuridae	*Cheirogaleus major crossleyi*	Congenital cystic kidney (1)	Hill, 1964
	Lemur catta	Renal hypoplasia	Scott and Lamb, 1925
	Lemur variegatus	Pectus excavatum	Benirschke, 1980
		Marked musculoskeletal anomaly (4), cleft palate (1), exencephaly (3), hypoplasia of lung (1), renal anomaly (1), two-chambered heart (1), aplasia of left lung (1). Represents 4 cases with multiple anomaly	Benirschke et al, 1981
	Microcebus coquereli	Congenital cystic kidney (1)	Scott and Lamb, 1925
Callitrichidae	*Callithrix jacchus*	Cleft palate (1)	Kraus and Garrett, 1968
	Leontopithecus rosalia	Familial diaphragmatic hernia (11)	Bush et al, 1980; Montali et al, 1980; Randolph et al, 1981
	Mico argentatus melanurus	Unilateral renal agenesis (1)	Hill, 1964
	Saguinus nigricollis	Syndactyly (1)	Hetherington et al, 1975
		Anomalous origin of right subclavian artery (1)	Martin et al, 1979
Cebidae	*Alouatta caraya*	Partial renal aplasia—unilateral (1)	Maruffo and Cramer, 1967
	Ateles geoffroyi	Bregmatic fontanelle bones (30), partial congenital anodontia (2)	Smith et al, 1977
	Alouatta palliata	Plagiocephaly (10), partial congenital anodontia (5)	
	Cebus capucinus	Bregmatic fontanelle bones (2)	
	Cebus albifrons	Ectopic splenic nodules in the pancreas (1)	Lau, 1973
	Saimiri sciureus	Congenital fusion and ectopy of the kidneys (1), congenital cortical cystic kidneys (1)	Maruffo and Cramer, 1967
		Cleft lip and palate (4)	Baker et al, 1977
		Multiple vertebral anomalies (1)	Harris et al, 1979
		Diaphragmatic hernia (1), right renal aplasia with A-V shunt (1) cleft lip/palate (1), supernumerary left kidney (1), skeletal dysplasia and corkscrew tail (1), remnant ultimobroncheal gland (1)	Stills and Bullock, 1981
		Congenital rickets (1)	Anver et al, 1973
Cercopithecidae	*Cercopithecus ascanius*	Atrial septal defect (1)	Finlayson, 1965
	Cercopithecus talapoin	Muellerian duct remnant in a male (1)	Adams and Bond, 1977
		Double aortic arch (1)	Still et al, 1979
	Erythrocebus patas	Accessory adrenal cortical tissue—mesovarium (26)	Conaway, 1969
	Macaca arctoides	Anencephaly (1)	Christie, 1969
		Microcephaly (1)	Anver et al, 1973
		Thoracolumbar scoliosis (1)	

TABLE 4. Summary of Spontaneous Malformations Reported in Nonhuman Primates *(Continued)*

Family	Genus/species	Malformations (No.)	References
	Macaca fuscata	Congenital limb anomalies (16)	Homma, 1980
		Congenital anomalies-forelimb (8), hindlimb (2), both limbs (5)	Iwamoto, 1967
		Congenital anomalies—both limbs (1)	Iwamoto and Hirai, 1970
		Split hand and foot anomaly (1)	Irani et al, 1963
		Atrial septal defect (1)	McNalty, 1973
	Macaca fascicularis	Anencephaly (1)	Price and Gilles, 1971
		Anencephaly (1)	Anver et al, 1973
		Microcephaly (1)	
		Porencephaly (1)	Myers et al, 1973
		Persistant cloaca (1)	Lewis et al, 1978
	Macaca mulatta	Split hand and foot anomaly (1)	Pearson, 1931
		Anomalies of eye and musculoskeletal system (1)	Koford et al, 1966
		Right forelimb reduction defect with arthrogryposis (1)	Koford et al, 1966
		Split hand and foot anomaly (2)	Morris and Kerr, 1971
		Cleft lip and palate (1)	Swindler and Merrill, 1971
		Syndactyly—hands and feet (1)	Primack et al, 1972
		Coloboma (1)	Schmidt, 1971
		Persistent pupillary membrane (1)	Kirk, 1972
		Patent ductus arteriosus (1)	Freigang and Knobil, 1967
		Ventricular septal defect (2), patent ductus arteriosis (1), pulmonic stenosis (1)	Krilova and Yakovlera, 1972
		Arteriovenous malformation—retina (1)	Horiuchi et al, 1976
		Anomalies of internal genitalia (1)	Koford et al, 1966
		True hermaphroditism (1)	Sullivan and Drobeck, 1966
		Double ureter—right side (1)	Kaur et al, 1968
		Idiopathic renal ectasia—bilateral (1)	
		Unilateral cystic kidney (1)	
		Ovarian dysgenesis, X–O anomaly (1)	Weiss et al, 1973
		Hypospadia—male (1)	Harrison, 1976
		Renal aplasia and hypoplasia (3)	Wadsworth and Squires, 1980
		Infantile polycystic kidney (1)	Baskin et al, 1981
		Accessory gallbladder	Tittler, 1945
		Gallbladder anomaly (1)	Kirkman, 1946
		Diverticulosis of the gallbladder	Rosenquist and Silverman, 1978
	Macaca nemestrina	Physical and mental retardation—trisomy X (3)	Ruppenthal et al, 1983
		Congenital polycystic kidney (1)	Maruffo and Cramer, 1967
	Mandrillus leucophaeus	Lobster-claw deformity—feet (1)	Hill, 1962

(continued)

TABLE 4. Summary of Spontaneous Malformations Reported in Nonhuman Primates *(Continued)*

Family	Genus/species	Malformations (No.)	References
	Mandrillus sphinx	Partial albinism (1)	Hill and Sabater Pi, 1970
		Cheiloschisis (1)	
	Macaca niger	Spina bifida occulta	Meier et al, 1978
	Papio sp.	Craniofacial deformity (1)	Pruzansky, 1975
		Unilateral renal aplasia (1)	Kim and Kalter, 1972
		Congenital diaphragmatic hernia (1)	Hendrickx and Gasser, 1967
	Papio anubis	Male pseudohermaphroditism (1)	Wadsworth et al, 1978
		Unilateral renal aplasia (1)	McCraw et al, 1973
	Papio cynocephalus	Supernumerary nipple (1)	Buss and Hammer, 1971
	Papio doguera	Coloboma (2)	Schmidt, 1971
	Papio hamadryas	Arnold-Chiari malformation (1)	Cameron and Hill, 1955
		Patent ductus arteriosus, aortic hypoplasia, aortic and pulmonary valvular deformities (1)	Krilova and Yakovlera, 1972
		Ventricular septal defect, overriding aorta, aortic and pulmonic stenosis (1)	
		Ventricular septal defect, mitral and tricuspid valvular deformities, left ventricular hypoplasia (1)	
	Papio sphinx	Hand anomaly (1)	Schultz, 1944
	Papio ursinus	XY gonadal dysgenesis (1)	Bielert et al, 1980
		Retrocaval right ureter (1)	Hesse, 1969
	Pygathrix nemaeus	Pectus excavatum (1)	Sedwick, 1981
Pongidae	*Gorilla gorilla*	Anomaly of the hallux (1)	Hill and Sabater Pi, 1971
		Congenital obstruction, nasolacrimal duct (1)	Nagashima et al, 1974
	Pan satyrus	Interatrial septal defect (1)	Hackel et al, 1953
	Pan troglodytes	Musculoskeletal abnormalities, cardiac anomalies, diaphragmatic hernia—Down's syndrome (1)	McClure, 1972
		Capillary telangiectasis—brain (1)	DiGiacomo et al, 1977
		Coloboma (1)	Schmidt, 1971
		True claw foot (1)	Goldschmidt, 1910
		Monodactyly, right hand (1)	Pearson, 1931
	Pongo pygmaeus	Craniofacial, musculoskeletal and behavior abnormalities; trisomy 22	Andrle et al, 1979
		Left superior vena cava, with partial pulmonary venous drainage into caval system (1)	Chase and DeGaris, 1938
Hylobatidae	*Hylobates* sp.	Hand anomaly—left (1), left and right (1)	Schultz, 1944
	Symphalangus (= Hylobates) syndactylus	Polydactyly (1)	Schultz, 1972

man. Recent reviews [Wilson, 1978; Hendrickx and Binkerd, 1980, 1983; Hendrickx et al, 1983] have summarized the available information on the spontaneous developmental abnormalities reported in various species of nonhuman primates. Because of an increase in the use of nonhuman primates for reproductive and developmental toxicity testing of selected agents, it is necessary to document clearly the spontaneous developmental abnormalities in large primate colonies. This review is confined to a discussion of spontaneous malformation in various species of nonhuman primates reported in the literature and the composite of all malformations documented in pathology reports at the California Primate Research Center (CPRC) between 1969 and 1982.

Spontaneous Malformations at the CPRC, 1969–1982. A total of 3,320 necropsy reports (1969–1982) were reviewed which represented 23 species of nonhuman primates. There were a total of 41 malformations in 36 monkeys of nine species of nonhuman primates belonging to the family Cebidae, Callitrichidae, or Cercopithecidae (Table 3). The nine species represented the majority of animals necropsied (3,092) at the CPRC. Among the various types of malformations observed in monkeys at the CPRC, the cardiovascular system (8/41) and urinary system (6/41) represented the majority of cases. The overall incidence of malformations was 1.08% in our colony, which is higher than the values reported in the literature [Wilson, 1978]; however, the estimated incidence is based on the number of animals necropsied rather than the number of animals born in the colony. Two cases of congenital diaphragmatic hernia in *Saguinus nigricollis* in our colony are interesting to compare with earlier reports in which a larger number of animals with this defect were observed; the defect appears to be inheritable as a simple autosomal-recessive trait [Bush et al, 1980; Randolph et al, 1981].

Spontaneous Malformations Reported in the Literature. Developmental abnormalities in nonhuman primates have been published as single or multiple case reports. The malformations have been reported in four species of Lemuridae and Callitrichidae, six species of Cebidae, 19 species of Cercopithecidae, four species of Pongidae, and one species of Hylobatidae (Table 4). The types of malformations include most of the major organ systems of nonhuman primates. Although the list of malformations reported continues to grow, there is a need to establish the incidence of malformations for individual colonies, as there has been a decrease in the importation of animals and an increase in the breeding of nonhuman primates in colonies for experimental purposes. Monitoring of breeding technique to prevent inbreeding might possibly avoid genetically related abnormal development.

Experimentally Induced Developmental Abnormalities

Among the objectives of experimental teratology are to determine potential adverse effects of drugs, chemicals, and other environmental agents on development prior to widespread human exposure and to recognize and develop animal models for the study of etiology, pathogenesis, and mechanisms. The use of nonhuman primates has been advocated on the basis of their phylogenetic relatedness to man, as reflected by their physiological, anatomical, reproductive, and embryological similarities. The role of the nonhuman primate in experimental teratology has been addressed in previous publications [Poswillo et al, 1972; Hendrickx and Binkerd, 1979, 1980, 1983; Hendrickx et al, 1983].

The purpose of this section is to report the embryotoxic agents that have been studied in the various species of primates; comparison to the human has been done in previous reports [Hendrickx and Binkerd, 1980, 1983]. In this context the term "developmental toxicity" encompasses all adverse effects resulting from exposure to a drug, chemical, or environmental agent during prenatal development.

Manifestations of developmental toxicity include 1) intrauterine death or embryolethality (ie, resorption, abortion, or stillbirth), 2) malformations, 3) growth retardation, and 4) functional deficit. Teratogenic effects will be identified by the anatomic region, organ, or organ system affected (Table 5).

Embryotoxicity studies of infectious agents in nonhuman primates are limited to a few viruses; in addition, except for one study in *Saimiri sciureus*, the studies have been conducted in only two species belonging to the family Cercopithecidae (Table 5). Among the viruses tested in nonhuman primates, the rubella and cytomegaloviruses are known human teratogens, and the mumps and influenza viruses are suspected to be teratogenic in humans; however, the role of the other three vi-

TABLE 5. Summary of Experimental Embryotoxicity Studies in Nonhuman Primates

Family	Genus/species	Agent	Effects	References
Lorisidae	*G. crassicaudatus*	Thalidomide	No teratogenicity, growth retardation at high doses	Wilson, 1971; Butler, 1977, 1978; Newman and Hendrickx, 1983
Callitrichidae	*C. jacchus*	Thalidomide	Limb reduction and otomandibular defects	Poswillo et al, 1972
		Antineoplastic drugs	Embryolethality	Siddall, 1978
		Testosterone	No embryotoxicity	Phillips, 1975
		Vitamin A	Cataracts, heart defects	Phillips, 1975
		Vitamin A and B methasone		
		X-ray	Intrauterine death; head, limb, and orofacial defects	Poswillo et al, 1972
		Hyperthermia	Limb and facial deformities, growth retardation, intrauterine death	Poswillo et al, 1974
		Blighted potatoes	Mild cranial osseous defects, behavioral abnormalities	Poswillo et al, 1972, 1973; Phillips, 1975
Cebidae	*Cebus apella*	DES	Genital lesions	Johnson et al, 1981
	S. sciureus	Tritated H_2O	Depletion of primary oocytes	Jones et al, 1980
		Cytomegalovirus	Visual acuity defects, learning and cognitive impairment, neuromuscular retardation	Ordy et al, 1981
Cercopithecidae	*Saguinus labiatus*	Blighted potatoes	No embryotoxicity	Allen et al, 1977
	C. aethiops	Thalidomide	Limb reduction; craniofacial, internal and external ear defects	Hendrickx and Sawyer, 1978b
	E. patas	Ethylnitrosourea	Brain lesions	Rice et al, 1979
	M. arctoides (speciosa)	Thalidomide	Limb reduction, head defects	Grauwiler and Brüggemann, 1972; Brüggemann and Grauwiler, 1975
		Methyl mercury	Ataxia	Reynolds and Pittsin, 1975
		Fungicides (Captan, Folpet, Difolatan)	No embryotoxicity	Vondruska et al, 1971

Species	Agent	Effect	References
M. fascicularis	Anticonvulsants	Embryolethality at high doses only	Poswillo, 1972
	Antibiotics	No embryotoxicity	Allen et al, 1982
	Thalidomide	Limb reduction defects, hydrocephaly facial hemangioma, anotia	Delahunt and Lassen, 1964; Hendrickx, 1971b, 1973
	Progestin (Depo-provera)	Female pseudohermaphroditism, male hypospadia	Prahalada and Hendrickx, 1982
M. fuscata	Thalidomide	Limb reduction defects	Tanimura, 1971
M. mulatta	Adrenocortical steroids	Craniofacial, brain, visceral, and lymphoid defects; embryo-lethality, growth retardation	Hendrickx et al, 1975, 1977, 1980b
	Oral contraceptive (Norlestrin)	Embryolethal at high dose, no teratogenicity, no functional deficits	Prahalada and Hendrickx, 1983; Golub et al, 1983
	Androgenic hormones	Pseudohermaphroditism in females, cryptorchidism in males	van Wagenen and Hamilton, 1943; Wells and van Wagenen, 1949; Wharton and Scott, 1964; Goy, 1974
	DES	Genital defects in male and female, abortions	Wadsworth and Heywood, 1978; Hendrickx et al, 1979; Thompson et al, 1981
	Antihistamines	No embryotoxicity	Wilson et al, 1971a; Courtney and Valerio, 1968
	Retinoic acid (vitamin A)	Craniofacial, appendicular skeletal, and visceral malformations	Hendrickx et al, 1977, 1980a
	Colcemide	No embryotoxicity	Morris et al, 1967
	Acetazolamide	Embryolethal, growth retardation, no teratogenicity	Scott et al, 1981
	Anticonvulsants	No, or low, levels of embryotoxicity	Wilson, 1974; Esaki et al, 1975
	Anorexic drugs	No embryotoxicity	Courtney and Valerio, 1968
	Oral hypoglycemics	Low levels of embryolethality and minor anomalies	Wilson, 1974

(continued)

TABLE 5. Summary of Experimental Embryotoxicity Studies in Nonhuman Primates *(Continued)*

Family	Genus/species	Agent	Effects	References
Cercopithecidae	*M. mulatta*	Antineoplastic drugs	Appendicular and axial skeletal defects, anotia, kidney agenesis, intrauterine death	Delahunt, 1966; Morris et al, 1967; Courtney and Valerio, 1968; van Wagenen et al, 1970; Wilson, 1971a; McClure et al, 1979
		Thalidomide	Musculoskeletal abnormalities (primarily limb defects), visceral defects, and embryolethality	Wilson and Gavan, 1967; Barrow et al, 1969; Wilson, 1973; Wilson et al, 1977; Theisen et al, 1979
		Thalidomide analogue	No embryotoxicity	Scott et al, 1980
		Antidepressants	No embryotoxicity, no behavioral changes	Gralla and McJehnny, 1972; Wilson, 1974; Hendrickx, 1975
		Tranquilizers	No embryotoxicity, cleft palates	Szabo et al, 1975
		Antibiotics	No embryotoxicity, no abnormalities	Jackson et al, 1975
		Aspirin	Embryolethal and teratogenic in high doses	Wilson, 1971b
		LSD	No embryotoxicity	Wilson et al, 1977; Kato et al, 1970
		Quinine	No embryotoxicity	Tanimura, 1971
		Herbicides (2,4,5-T)	No embryotoxicity	Dougherty et al, 1975
		Fungicides (Captan, Folpet, Difolatan)	No embryotoxicity	Vondruska et al, 1971
		Sodium cyclamate	No embryotoxicity	Wilson, 1971a
		PCBs	No embryotoxicity postnatal toxicity	Allen and Barsotti, 1976
		Low-protein diet	Embryolethal	Kohrs et al, 1976
		X-ray	Head, CNS defects	Rugh et al, 1966
		Blighted potatoes	Behavior defects, no embryotoxicity, internal hydrocephalus	Allen et al, 1977; Poswillo et al, 1972, 1973
		Influenza virus	Hydrocephalus	London et al, 1975
			No malformations	Moreland et al, 1979b
		Mumps virus	Intrauterine death	Moreland et al, 1979b
			Hydrocephalus	London et al, 1979

Species	Agent	Effect	Reference
	Rubella virus	High level of embryolethality; low level of malformations	Delahunt and Rieser, 1967
	Venezuelan equine encephalitis virus	No malformations	Sever et al, 1966
	Western equine encephalitis virus	Microcephaly, hydrocephalus, cataracts, and porencephaly	London et al, 1977
		Intrauterine death and hydrocephalus	Moreland et al, 1979a,b
		Microcephaly and hydrocephalus	London et al, 1982
M. nemestrina	Retinoic acid	Craniofacial defects, ectrodactyly, muscular joint contractures	Fantel et al, 1977; Newell-Morris, 1980; Yip et al, 1980
M. radiata	Alcohol	Facial defects, neurologic and developmental deficiencies	Clarren and Bowden, 1982
	Adrenocortical steroids	Craniofacial and brain defects	Hendrickx et al, 1975, 1977, 1980b
	Thalidomide	Limb reduction and visceral defects	Hendrickx, 1971b; Hendrickx and Newman, 1973; Newman and Hendrickx, 1981
	Imipramine	No embryotoxicity	Hendrickx, 1975
	Hyperthermia	Skeletal and brain defects, intrauterine death	Hendrickx et al, 1979
	X-ray	Ovarian damage	Andersen et al, 1977; Hendrickx et al, 1977
Papio sp.	Thalidomide	Limb reduction defects, spina bifida	Hendrickx et al, 1966, 1971b
	Thalidomide analogue	No embryotoxicity	Hendrickx and Helm, 1980
	Adrenocortical hormones	Craniofacial and brain malformations	Silverman et al, 1977; Hendrickx et al, 1980b
	Progestin (Depo-provera)	No embryotoxicity	Prahalada and Hendrickx, 1983
	DL III (antifertility agent)	No teratogenicity, embryolethality	Galliani et al, 1982
	Lathyrogens	Cleft palate, skeletal defects, intrauterine death	Steffek and Hendrickx, 1972
Papio cynocephalus	Rubella virus	High level of embryolethality	Hendrickx, 1966
	Lymphocytic choriomeningitis virus	No embryotoxicity	Ackermann et al, 1979
	Mumps virus	Growth retardation	St. Geme and Van Pelt, 1974

ruses (Venezuelan and Western equine encephalitis viruses and lymphocytic choriomeningitis virus) in causing teratogenesis in humans is less clear.

Anomalies of the Placenta

Overview. The purpose of this section is to describe spontaneous placental abnormalities observed in our colony of rhesus and bonnet macaques and baboons, and placental anomalies associated with teratology studies carried out in our laboratory. Inasmuch as very little information is available for other families, this section will be restricted to Cercopithecidae and Hominidae. In spite of its crucial role in supporting fetal life, the role of placental pathology in fetal abnormalities and fetal death in nonhuman primates has received little attention until recent years [Myers, 1971; Hendrickx and Binkerd, 1980].

Spontaneous Placental Anomalies. Several variations in placental morphology that differentially affect normal fetal development have been reported in humans and several species of nonhuman primates. Some of these can be considered benign abnormalities, such as placental shape abnormalities and anomalous membrane and cord insertions. Several circulatory and umbilical cord abnormalities that may affect fetal growth have also been described. Other variations that have been reported in nonhuman primates clearly pose a threat to fetal, and sometimes maternal, viability. Among these are placentitis, abruptio placentae, placenta previa, and ectopic pregnancy.

Among the nonpathological abnormalities of placental shape is the occurrence of single or fused placentas in species that normally exhibit bidiscoid placentation. The estimated 18–22% incidence of single placentas in *Macaca mulatta* [Myers, 1971; Chez et al, 1972] compares closely with the 20% incidence observed in our colony of rhesus macaques. The 33% incidence of monodiscoid placentas reported in *Macaca fascicularis* [Fujiwara et al, 1978] is also supported by observations made in our lab, which indicate that 20% of these placentas are monodiscoid and an additional 10% are partially fused. Currently there is no information to suggest a correlation between single placentation and adverse pregnancy outcome in macaque species.

Abnormal insertions of the extraembryonic membranes in both human and nonhuman primates are evidenced in circummarginate placentas (Fig.

1A,B) in which the membranes are inserted upon the fetal surface inward from the margin, and in circumvallate placentas in which the membranes are folded back on the fetal surface and inserted inward far inside the margin of the placenta. These types of extrachorial placentas have been associated with antenatal hemorrhage and subsequent jeopardy of the fetus in humans by some investigators [Scott, 1960], although others claim they have no significance [Woodling et al, 1976]. The estimated 15% incidence of extrachorial placentation in rhesus monkeys [Myers, 1971] compares closely with the 18% level reported in humans [Scott, 1960]. It has been noted that circumvallate and circummarginate placentas appear with a particularly high frequency among the single-disk placentas in this species [Harbert et al, 1970; Myers, 1971]. Placenta extrachorialis has also been diagnosed in two of 56 placentas (3.6%) associated with normal fetal development in *Macaca arctoides* [Johnson et al, 1978]. There is a 56% incidence (n = 66) of extrachorial placentas among our *Papio* spp. colony population which normally exhibits monodiscoid placentation, and a 39% frequency (n = 75) in our *M. mulatta* colony.

Another variation in the nonhuman primate placenta that is also observed in humans is an anomalous insertion of the umbilical cord. The variations in the normal central location of the cord include eccentric, semivelamentous, and velamentous insertions (Fig. 2A,B). In cases of velamentous insertion, in which the cord inserts into the placental membranes rather than on the placental disk, the vessels are susceptible to rupture during labor and delivery in humans [Woodling et al, 1976]. Although eccentric umbilical cords are commonly seen in our colony of *P. cynocephalus* and *M. mulatta* (estimated incidence is 50%), velamentous or semivelamentous cord insertions are rarely observed.

Several types of placental circulatory anomalies have also been observed in nonhuman primates and man. One of the most common and significant types is umbilical cord anomalies, which will be covered in the following section on teratology. Another circulatory disturbance of the placenta is infarction, in which necrosis of a maternal cotyledon is caused by occlusion of the uteroplacental (spiral) artery that supplies it. Some studies in humans indicate that owing to the large functional reserve of the placenta, the reduction in the amount of placental tissue available for nutrition of the fetus

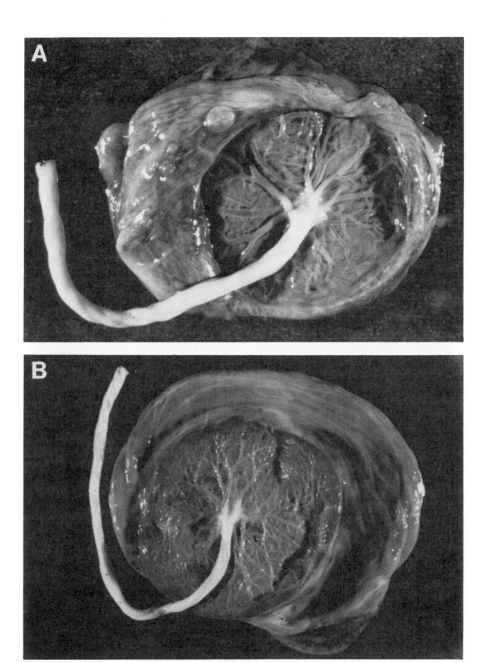

Fig. 1. Extrachorial placentation. A) Circummarginate baboon placenta exhibiting characteristic cuplike appearance around placental margin. B) Normal marginal baboon placenta.

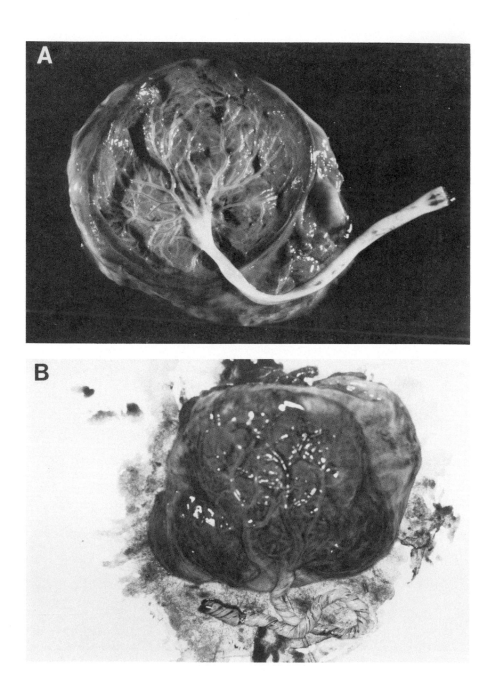

Fig. 2. Abnormal umbilical cord insertions. A) Eccentric. B) Semivelamentous.

due to infarction is rarely of clinical significance [Woodling et al, 1976]. However, a relationship between extensive placental infarction and low birth weight in humans has also been noted [Fox, 1967].

Although an increased level of infarctions has been observed in cases of intrauterine death in our colony, whether placental pathology is the primary or secondary event is difficult to determine. Information regarding the role of placental necrosis in maldevelopment of the fetus in nonhuman primates is limited to reports of perinatal mortality attributable primarily to maternal disease or adverse uterine conditions that disturb placental circulation. One report of spontaneous placental infarction associated with a stillborn fetus with no gross anomalies has been reported in *Erythrocebus patas*. The combination of an extensive level of macroscopic infarcts (60–70% of placenta), intervillous thrombi, excessive fibrinoid, and alterations in decidual vessels suggested a diagnosis of pregnancy complicated by preeclampsia [Gille et al, 1977].

Hertig and colleagues [1971] suggested that viral infections in a group of wild-caught *M. mulatta* may have caused degenerative changes in placental vascularity leading to a high level of intrauterine fetal death. In all abortions and stillbirths in which the placentas were available for study there was evidence of extensive thrombosis of large vessels in the basal plate, leading to massive infarction of the chorion.

Other disturbances in placental morphology and function that may be associated with a potentially adverse outcome for the nonhuman primate fetus or mother include placentitis, abruptio placentae, placenta previa, and ectopic pregnancy. Ascending genital infections leading to placentitis and subsequent fetal anoxia have been attributed to group D streptococci and B-hemolytic, coagulase-positive *Staphylococcus aureus* in a variety of nonhuman primate species [Andrews, 1974]. Additionally, listeric septicemia accompanied by acute fibrinopurulent placentitis and extensive placental necrosis has been diagnosed in a stillborn Celebese black ape, *Macaca niger* [McClure and Strozier, 1975]. Morphologic studies of human placentas also indicate a high percentage of ascending infections from midtrimester spontaneous abortions that resulted in circulatory anomalies and inflammation of the placenta [Ornoy et al, 1976].

Abruptio placentae is characterized by a premature separation of the placenta from the endometrial surface. In humans the incidence of perinatal deaths related to abruptio placentae has been estimated as 3.96 per 1,000 births [Naeye et al, 1977]. Of seven cases of abruptio placentae noted in *M. mulatta* (0.6% incidence), two were associated with fetal brain damage and two with intrauterine death [Myers, 1971]. Four cases of premature placental separation have been reported in our *M. mulatta* breeding colony. Vaginal bleeding occurred near term, and the infants were delivered surgically in all four cases. Two of the infants were viable, one was dead in utero, and the fourth died a few hours after delivery from respiratory difficulties associated with prematurity.

Placenta previa is characterized by partial or complete placental localization over the cervical outlet and may be associated with a high risk of bleeding and ascending infection. The 0.5% incidence of placenta previa among 1,200 rhesus monkey placentas [Myers, 1971] approximates the reported incidence for the human population [Benirschke and Driscoll, 1967].

Another condition involving abnormal placental development leading to fetal demise that is common in human pathology but has been rarely reported in nonhuman primates is extrauterine pregnancy. Three cases of ectopic pregnancy have been reported out of 1,892 pregnancies (0.15% incidence) from green marmosets, baboons, and macaques [Lapin and Yakovleva, 1960], although no pathologic details were given. Two additional cases of abdominal pregnancies have been reported in rhesus monkeys [Myers, 1971]. An oviductal pregnancy in *M. mulatta* has recently been observed in our laboratory [Jerome and Hendrickx, 1982]. Grossly, it was identified as a 1-cm diameter dark red nodule in the left uterine tube. On histological section the nodule comprised placenta with recognizable secondary villi but no identifiable embryonic tissue in the exocoelom.

Teratology Studies. Irregularities in normal placental morphology have become of increasing concern in teratology studies in the determination of mode of action of an environmental agent on the conceptus. However, due to the difficulties inherent in associating spontaneous placental abnormalities with adverse fetal development in an unambiguous way, very little information has been reported on this topic.

The most common abnormality of the placenta that we have seen in our teratology studies is single umbilical artery. In humans this condition occurs

TABLE 6. Incidence of Single Umbilical Artery in Teratology Studies

Species	Experiment	Incidence
Rhesus monkeys	Triamcinolone acetonide	4.5% (1/22)
Baboons	Thalidomide	4.0% (1/25)
Bonnet monkeys	Thalidomide	17.2% (5/29)
Bonnet monkeys	Hyperthermia	50.0% (2/4)
Rhesus monkeys	Control	0.2% (2/1200)[a]
Baboons	Control	4.6% (3/65)
Bonnet monkeys	Control	0% (0/13)

[a]Myers [1971].

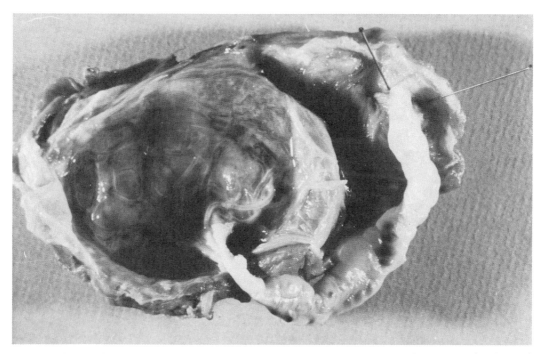

Fig. 3. Monodiscoid, circumvallate placenta from a growth-retarded, stillborn bonnet monkey fetus exhibiting minor anomalies following in utero heat exposure. Fetal death was attributed to a compressed umbilical cord related to placenta previa. Approximately 40% of the maternal surface of the placenta was macroscopically infarcted, and small intervillous thrombi were present throughout.

in less than 1% of single births and in 4–14% of twin births [Benirschke et al, 1964; Woodling et al, 1976]. A positive relationship between the occurrence of single umbilical artery and human fetal malformations has been made, but no specific malformation syndrome has been associated with the defect [Benirschke and Bourne, 1960].

Absence of an umbilical artery (Table 6) as well as limb malformations and minor visceral defects were observed following exposure to thalidomide during early pregnancy in bonnet monkeys and baboons [Hendrickx, 1971b; Hendrickx and Newman, 1973].

In addition to a high incidence (50%) of single umbilical artery following in utero exposure of bonnet monkeys to hyperthermia (Table 6), a marked level of intervillous thrombi and infarctions was observed in the four placentas available for

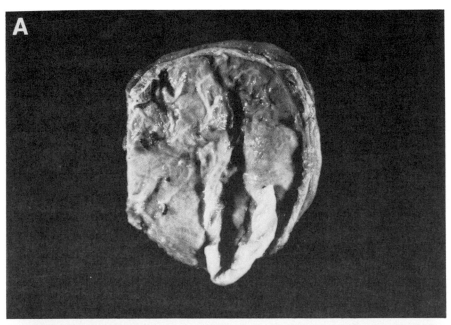

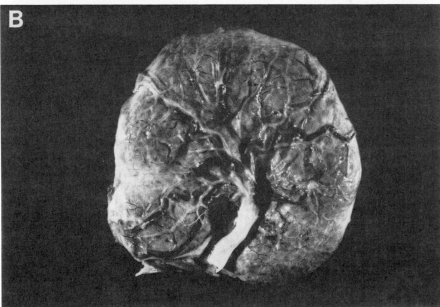

Fig. 4. A) Primary placental lobe from a dead in utero term *M. mulatta* fetus with multiple malformations. The twisted umbilical cord had a single umbilical artery, and large areas of infarctions covered the primary lobe, which was necrotic and smaller in size than the secondary lobe. Triamcinolone acetonide (10 mg/kg) was administered on days 21, 23, and 25 of gestation. B) Normal term placenta.

examination [Hendrickx et al, 1979] (Fig. 3). In each of these cases, placental pathology was associated with fetal death or malformations. Although the number of cases is insufficient to draw firm conclusions, it is possible that hyperthermia interfered with normal embryonic development in these cases by exerting a direct effect on the placenta.

Experiments involving exposure of *M. mulatta* to triamcinolone acetonide, a synthetic corticosteroid, during organogenesis resulted in a higher incidence of placental anomalies in the treated cases than in colony controls. These included absence of an umbilical artery (Table 6) in addition to variable degrees of placental infarctions and hemorrhages (Fig. 4). However, it is difficult to attribute these variations in normal placental morphology to the teratogenic regimen since a wide range of spontaneous circulatory and structural anomalies were also observed in placentas from untreated pregnancies.

CONCLUSIONS

Principles

Reports on embryogenesis and on spontaneous and experimentally induced malformations in Lemuridae, Callitrichidae, and Cebidae are limited. Observations in these species have suggested that the possible adverse effects of inbreeding may result in the occurrence of spontaneous malformations which are genetically related. The reports on the types of spontaneous malformations in Pongidae and Hylobatidae are too limited to make any definitive comparisons with man.

Trends

Fewer species of primates are being studied in biomedical research now than were studied 20 years ago. This is due to the availability of fewer species and to the selection of species with the most background data and recognition as relevant models for man. With this approach interesting biological events may not be observed in those species that have not been identified as animal models for human disease.

Conversely, a few species should be identified and developed to animal models to conduct 1) screening tests for potentially harmful agents in the pregnant human, 2) in utero diagnosis and treatment (ie, surgical) of birth defects (ie, hydrocephaly, hydronephrosis), and 3) correlative studies on teratogenicity and pharmacokinetics of

selected compounds. This approach would provide results which can be readily extrapolated to man and would also conserve species and animals by reducing duplication.

Research Needs

1. Comparative development of organ systems (ie, reproductive, nervous) of different families in the prenatal and perinatal periods.

2. Comparative teratogenicity of specific embryotoxins in representative species of different families. Embryotoxins which give equivocal results in laboratory animals would be of high priority.

3. Comparative embryo and fetal pharmacokinetics of embryotoxins in representative species of different families. Correlation of the teratogenicity and pharmacokinetics of test agents would provide data most readily extrapolated to man.

4. Further studies of spontaneous and experimentally induced malformations as potential models for human disease (ie, neural tube, urogenital, cariovascular defects).

5. Establish developmental stages of species that are being utilized, in some instances without appropriate normative data.

ACKNOWLEDGMENTS

This research was supported by NIH grant RR00169-21.

REFERENCES

Ackermann, R.; Kalter, S.S.; Heberling, R.L.; Mc-Cullough, B.; Eichberg, J.; Rodriguez, A.R. Fetal infection of the baboon (*Papio cynocephalus*) with lymphocytic choriomeningitis virus. ARCHIVES OF VIROLOGY 60:311–323, 1979.

Adams, M.R.; Bond, M.G. A Müllerian duct remnant in an aged male talapoin monkey. JOURNAL OF MEDICAL PRIMATOLOGY 6:5–12, 1977.

Allen, D.G.; Clark, R.; Palmer, A.K.; Heywood, R. An embryotoxicity study in *Macaca fascicularis* with cefotetan disodium (a cephamycin antibiotic). TOXICOLOGY LETTERS 11:43–47, 1982.

Allen, J.R.; Barsotti, D.A. The effects of transplacental and mammary movement of PCBs on infant rhesus monkeys. TOXICOLOGY 6:331–340, 1976.

Allen, J.R.; Marlar, R.J.; Chesney, C.F.; Helgeson, J.P.; Kelman, A.; Weckel, K.G.; Traisman, E.; White, J.W. Jr. Teratogenicity studies on late blighted potatoes in nonhuman primates (*Macaca mulatta* and *Saguinus labiatus*). TERATOLOGY 15:17–24, 1977.

Anderson, A.C.; Hendrickx, A.G.; Momeni, M.H. Fractionated x-radiation damage to developing ovaries in the bonnet monkey (*Macaca radiata*). RADIATION RESEARCH 71:398–405, 1977.

Andrews, E.J. Pulmonary pathology in stillborn nonhuman primates. JOURNAL OF THE AMERICAN VETERINARY MEDICAL ASSOCIATION 164:715–718.

Andrle, M.; Fiedler, W.; Rett, A.; Ambros, P.; Schweizer, D. A case of trisomy 22 in *Pongo pygmaeus*. CYTOGENETICS AND CELL GENETICS 24:1–6, 1979.

Anver, M.R.; Hunt, R.D.; Price, R.A. Simian neonatology. II. Neonatal pathology. VETERINARY PATHOLOGY 10:16–36, 1973.

Baker, C.A.; Hendrickx, A.G.; Cooper, R.W. Spontaneous malformations in squirrel monkey (*Saimiri sciureus*) fetuses with emphasis on cleft lip and palate. JOURNAL OF MEDICAL PRIMATOLOGY 6:13–22, 1977.

Barrow, M.V.; Steffek, A.J.; King, C.T.G. Thalidomide syndrome in rhesus monkeys (*Macaca mulatta*). FOLIA PRIMATOLOGICA 10:195–203, 1969.

Baskin, G.B.; Roberts, J.A.; McAfee, R.D. Infantile polycystic renal disease in a rhesus monkey (*Macaca mulatta*). LABORATORY ANIMAL SCIENCE 31:181–183, 1981.

Benirschke, K. Pectus exavatum in ruffed lemurs (*Lemur [varecia] variegatus*). Pp. 169–172 in SONDERCHUCK AUS VERHANDLUNGSBERICHT DES XXII INTERNATIOLEN SYMPOSIUMS UBER DIE ERKRANKUNGEN DER ZOOTIERE. Arnheim, 1980.

Benirschke, K.; Bourne, G.L. The incidence and prognostic implication of congenital absence of one umbilical artery. AMERICAN JOURNAL OF OBSTETRICS AND GYNECOLOGY 79:251–254, 1960.

Benirschke, K.; Driscoll, S.G. THE PATHOLOGY OF THE HUMAN PLACENTA. New York, Springer-Verlag, 1967.

Benirschke, K.; Kumamoto, A.T.; Bogart, M.H. Congenital anomalies in *Lemur variegatus*. JOURNAL OF MEDICAL PRIMATOLOGY 10:38–45, 1981.

Benirschke, K.; Sullivan, M.M.; Marin-Padilla, M. Size and number of umbilical vessels. OBSTETRICS AND GYNECOLOGY 24:819–834, 1964.

Bielert, C.; Bernstein, R.; Simon, G.B.; Van der Walt, L.A. XY gonadal dysgenesis in a chacma baboon. INTERNATIONAL JOURNAL OF PRIMATOLOGY 1:3–13, 1980.

Binkerd, P.E.; Hendrickx, A.G.; Rice, J.M.; Palmer, A.E. Embryonic development in *Erythrocebus patas*. AMERICAN JOURNAL OF PRIMATOLOGY 6:15–29, 1984.

Brüggemann, S.; Grauwiler, J. The possibilities of using *Macaca arctoides* in teratological experiments. LABORATORY ANIMAL HANDBOOK 6:339–345, 1975.

Bush, M.; Montali, R.J.; Kleiman, D.G.; Randolph, J.; Abramowitz, M.D.; Evans, R.F. Diagnosis and repair of familial diaphragmatic defects in golden lion tamarins. JOURNAL OF THE AMERICAN VETERINARY MEDICAL ASSOCIATION 177:858–862, 1980.

Buss, D.H.; Hamner, J.E. Supernumerary nipples in the baboon (*Papio cynocephalus*). FOLIA PRIMATOLOGICA 16:153–158, 1971.

Butler, H. The reproductive biology of a strepsirhine (*Galago senagelensis senagelensis*). INTERNATIONAL REVIEW OF GENERAL EXPERIMENTAL ZOOLOGY 1:241–296, 1964.

Butler, H. The chronology of embryogeneis in the lesser galago: A preliminary account. FOLIA PRIMATOLOGICA 18:368–378, 1972.

Butler, H. The effect of thalidomide on a prosimian: The greater galago (*Galago crassicaudatus*). JOURNAL OF MEDICAL PRIMATOLOGY 6:319–324, 1977.

Butler, H. The effect of thalidomide on the greater galago (*Galago crassicaudatus*). Pp. 189–190 in RECENT ADVANCES IN PRIMATOLOGY, Vol. 3: EVOLUTION. D.J. Chivers; K.A. Joysey, eds. London, Academic Press, 1978.

Butler, H. The embryology of the lesser galago (*Galago senegalensis*). CONTRIBUTIONS TO PRIMATOLOGY 19:1–156, 1983.

Cameron, A.H.; Hill, W.C.O. The Arnold-Chiari malformation in a sacred baboon (*Papio hamadryas*). THE JOURNAL OF PATHOLOGY AND BACTERIOLOGY 70:552–554, 1955.

Chase, R.F.; DeGaris, C.F. Anomalies of venae cavae superiores in an orang. AMERICAN JOURNAL OF PHYSICAL ANTHROPOLOGY 24:61–65, 1938.

Chez, R.A.; Schlesselman, J.J.; Salazar, H.; Fox, R. Single placentas in the rhesus monkey. JOURNAL OF MEDICAL PRIMATOLOGY 1:230–240, 1972.

Christie, R.J. An occurrence of monozygotic twinning and anencephaly in *Macaca arctoides*. LABORATORY ANIMAL CARE 19:531–532, 1969.

Clarren, S.K.; Bowden, D.M. Fetal alcohol syndrome: A new primate model for binge drinking and its relevance to human ethanol teratogenesis. JOURNAL OF PEDIATRICS 101(5):819–824, 1982.

Conway, C.H. Adrenal cortical rests of the ovarian hilus of the patas monkey. FOLIA PRIMATOLOGICA 11:175–180, 1969.

Courtney, K.D.; Varerio, D.A. Teratology in the *Macaca mulatta*. TERATOLOGY 1:163–172, 1968.

Davignon, R.W.; Parker, R.M.; Hendrickx, A.G. Staging of the early embryonic brain in the baboon (*Papio cynocephalus*) and rhesus monkey (*Macaca mulatta*). ANATOMY AND EMBRYOLOGY 159:317–334, 1980.

Delahunt, C.S. Prepared discussion. Pp. 118–120 in PROCEEDINGS OF THE CONFERENCE OF NONHUMAN PRIMATE TOXICOLOGY. (Food and Drug Administration). C.O. Miller, ed. Washington, D.C., U.S. Government Printing Office, 1966.

Delahunt, C.S.; Lassen, L.J. Thalidomide syndrome in monkeys. SCIENCE 146:1300–1301, 1964.

Delahunt, C.S.; Rieser, N. Rubella-induced embryopathies in monkeys. AMERICAN JOURNAL OF OBSTETRICS AND GYNECOLOGY 99:580–588, 1967.

DiGiacomo, R.F.; Heffner, R.R.; Sulima, M.P.; Gibbs, C.J.; Gajdusek, D.C.; Lemmon, W.B. Capillary telangiectasis of the brain in a chimpanzee. JOURNAL OF PATHOLOGY 123:93–95, 1977.

Dougherty, W.J.; Herbst, M.; Coulston, F. The nonteratogenicity of 2,4,5-trichlorophenoxyacetic acid in the rhesus monkey (*Macaca mulatta*). BULLETIN OF ENVIRONMENTAL CONTAMINATION AND TOXICOLOGY 13:477–482, 1975.

Esaki, K.; Tanioka, Y.; Ogata, T.; Koizumi, H. Effect of sodium dipropylacetate (Dpa) on rhesus monkeys fetuses. CIEA PRECLINICAL REPORTS, JITCHUKEN ZENRINSHO KENKYUHO 1:157–163, 1975.

Fantel, A.G.; Shepard, T.H.; Newell-Morris, L.L.; Moffett, B.C. Teratogenic effects of retinoic acid in pigtail monkeys (*Macaca nemestrina*). I. General features. TERATOLOGY 15:65–72, 1977.

Finlayson, R. Spontaneous arterial disease in exotic animals. JOURNAL OF ZOOLOGY 147:239–343, 1965.

Florian, J. The early development of man, with special references to the development of the mesoderm and the cloacal membrane. JOURNAL OF ANATOMY 67:263–276, 1933.

Fox, H. The significance of placental infarction in perinatal morbidity and mortality. BIOLOGIA NEONATORUM 11:87–105, 1967.

Freigang, B.; Knobil, E. Patent ductus arteriosus with pulmonary hypertension and arteritis in a rhesus monkey. YALE JOURNAL OF BIOLOGY AND MEDICINE 40:239–242, 1967.

Fujiwara, T.; Suzaki, Y.; Honjo, S. Weight and size of the placenta in cynomolgus monkeys (*Macaca fascicularis*). JAPANESE JOURNAL OF MEDICAL SCIENCE AND BIOLOGY 31:365–369, 1978.

Galliani, G.; Assandri, A.; Lerner, L.J.; Omodei-Sale, A.; Lancini, G.; Nock, P.E.; Grant, A.M. DL 111, A new non-hormonal antifertility agent: Contragestational and kinetic profile in baboons. CONTRACEPTION 26(2):165–179, 1982.

Gilbert, C.; Heuser, C.H. Studies in the development of the baboon (*Papio ursinus*). A description of two presomite and two late somite stage embryos. CARNEGIE CONTRIBUTIONS TO EMBRYOLOGY 35:11–54, 1954.

Gille, J.H.; Moore, D.G.; Sedgwick, C.J. Placental infarction: A sign of preeclampsia in a patas monkey (*Erythrocebus patas*). LABORATORY ANIMAL SCIENCE 27:119–121, 1977.

Goldschmidt, W. Uber einen fall von spaltfussbildung bei anthropopitheus troglodytes. ANATOMISCHER ANZEIGER 37:246–249, 1910.

Golub, M.S.; Hayes, L.; Prahalada, S.; Hendrickx, A.G. Behavioral tests in monkey infants exposed embryonically to an oral contraceptive. NEUROBEHAVIORAL TOXICOLOGY AND TERATOLOGY 5:301–304, 1983.

Goss, M.; Popejoy L.T. II; Fusiler, J.L.; Smith, T.M. Observations on the relationship between embryological development, time of conception, and gestation. Pp. 171–191 in THE SQUIRREL MONKEY. L.A. Rosenblum; R.W. Cooper, eds. New York, Academic Press, 1968.

Goy, R.W. Hormonally induced pseudohermaphroditism and behavior. EXCERPTA MEDICA, INTERNATIONAL CONGRESS SERIES 310:155–164, 1974.

Gralla, E.J.; McJehnny, H.M. Studies in pregnant rats, rabbits and monkeys with lithium carbonate. TOXICOLOGY AND APPLIED PHARMACOLOGY 21:428–433, 1972.

Graüwiler, J.; Brüggemann, S. Two years' experience with *Macaca arctoides* as an experimental animal for teratologic drug testing. Pp. 250–258 in MEDICAL PRIMATOLOGY (Part 3). E.I. Goldsmith; J. Moor-Jankowski, eds. Basel, Karger, 1972.

Gribnau, A.A.M.; Geijsberts, L.G.M. Developmental stages in the rhesus monkey (*Macaca mulatta*). ADVANCES IN ANATOMY, EMBRYOLOGY, AND CELL BIOLOGY 68:1–84, 1981.

Hackel, D.B.; Kinney, T.D.; Wendt, W. Pathologic lesions in captive wild animals. LABORATORY INVESTIGATION 2:154–163, 1953.

Harbert, G.M. Jr.; Martin, C.B. Jr.; Ramsey, E.M. Extrachorial (circumvallate) placentas in rhesus monkeys. AMERICAN JOURNAL OF OBSTETRICS AND GYNECOLOGY 108:98–104, 1970.

Harris, R.L.; Bond, M.G.; Bullock, B.C. Atresia ani and multiple vertebral anomalies in a squirrel monkey (*Saimiri sciureus*). VETERINARY PATHOLOGY 16:730–733, 1979.

Harrison, R.M. Hypospadias in a male rhesus monkey. JOURNAL OF MEDICAL PRIMATOLOGY 5:60–63, 1976.

Hendrickx, A.G. Teratogenicity findings in a baboon colony. Pp. 120–123 in PROCEEDINGS OF THE CONFERENCE ON NON-HUMAN PRIMATE

TOXICOLOGY (Food and Drug Administration). C.O. Miller, ed. Washington, D.C., U.S. Government Printing Office, 1966.

Hendrickx, A.G. EMBRYOLOGY OF THE BABOON. Chicago, University of Chicago Press, 1971a.

Hendrickx, A.G. Teratogenicity of thalidomide in the baboon (Papio cynocephalus), bonnet monkey (Macaca radiata), and cynomolgus monkey (Macaca irus). Pp. 230–237 in PROCEEDINGS OF THE THIRD INTERNATIONAL CONGRESS ON PRIMATOLOGY, ZURICH, Vol. 2. Basel, Karger, 1971b.

Hendrickx, A.G. Early development of the embryo in non-human primates and man. ACTA ENDOCRINOLOGY, KBH 166 (Supplement):103:130, 1971c.

Hendrickx, A.G. The sensitive period and malformation syndrome produced by thalidomide in the crab-eating monkey (Macaca fascicularis). JOURNAL OF MEDICAL PRIMATOLOGY 2:267–276, 1973.

Hendrickx, A.G. Teratologic evaluation of imipramine hydrochloride in bonnet (Macaca radiata) and rhesus monkeys (Macaca mulatta). TERATOLOGY 11:219–222, 1975.

Hendrickx, A.G.; Binkerd, P.E. Primate teratology: Selection of species and future use. Pp. 1–23 in ADVANCES IN THE STUDY OF BIRTH DEFECTS. Vol. 2, TERATOLOGICAL TESTING. T.V.N. Persaud, ed. Lancaster, England, MTP Press, 1979.

Hendrickx, A.G.; Binkerd, P.E. Fetal deaths in nonhuman primates. Pp. 45–69 in EMBRYONIC AND FETAL DEATH. I.H. Porter; E.B. Hook, eds. New York, Academic Press, 1980.

Hendrickx, A.G.; Binkerd, P.E. Teratology and birth defects. Pp. 131–158 in NONHUMAN PRIMATE MODELS FOR HUMAN DISEASES. W.R. Dukelow, ed. Boca Raton, FL, CRC Press, 1983.

Hendrickx, A.G.; Binkerd, P.E.; Rowland, J.M. Developmental toxicity and nonhuman primates: Interspecies comparisons. Pp. 149–180 in ISSUES AND REVIEWS IN TERATOLOGY, Vol. 1. H. Kalter, ed. New York, Plenum, 1983.

Hendrickx, A.G.; Gasser, R.F. A description of a diaphragmatic hernia in a sixteen week baboon fetus (Papio sp.). FOLIA PRIMATOLOGICA 7:66–74, 1967.

Hendrickx, A.G.; Helm, F.-C. Nonteratogenicity of a structural analog of thalidomide in pregnant baboons (Papio cynocephalus). TERATOLOGY 22:179–182, 1980.

Hendrickx, A.G.; Houston, M.L. Prenatal and postnatal development. Pp. 334–381 in COMPARATIVE REPRODUCTION OF NON-HUMAN PRIMATES. E.S.E. Hafez, ed. Springfield, IL, Thomas, 1971.

Hendrickx, A.G.; Newman, L. Appendicular skeletal and visceral malformations induced by thalidomide in bonnet monkeys. TERATOLOGY 7:151–160, 1973.

Hendrickx, A.G.; Sawyer, R.H. Embryology of the rhesus monkey. Pp. 141–169 in THE RHESUS MONKEY. Vol. II, MANAGEMENT, REPRODUCTION, AND PATHOLOGY. G. Bourne, ed. New York, Academic Press, 1975.

Hendrickx, A.G.; Sawyer, R.H. Developmental staging and thalidomide teratogenicity in the green monkey (Cercopithecus aethiops). TERATOLOGY 18:393–403, 1978a.

Hendrickx, A.G.; Sawyer, R.H. Embryology of the rhesus monkey. Pp. 141–169 in THE RHESUS MONKEY. G. Bourne, ed. New York, Academic Press, 1978b.

Hendrickx, A.G.; Axelrod, L.R.; Clayburn, L.D. "Thalidomide" syndrome in baboons. NATURE (LONDON) 210:958–959, 1966.

Hendrickx, A.G.; Silverman, S.; Pellegrini, M.; Steffek, A.J. Teratological and radiocephalometric analysis of craniofacial malformations induced with retinoic acid in rhesus monkeys (Macaca mulatta). TERATOLOGY 22:13–22, 1980a.

Hendrickx, A.G.; Stone, G.W.; Henrickson, R.V.; Matayoshi, K. Teratogenic effects of hyperthermia in the bonnet monkey (Macaca radiata). TERATOLOGY 19:177–182, 1979.

Hendrickx, A.G.; Benirschke, K.; Thompson, R.S.; Ahern, J.K.; Lucas, W.E.; Oi, R.H. The effects of prenatal diethylstilbestrol (DES) exposure on the genitalia of pubertal Macaca mulatta. I. Female offspring. JOURNAL OF REPRODUCTIVE MEDICINE 22:233–240, 1979.

Hendrickx, A.G.; Pellegrini, M.; Tarara, R.; Parker, R.; Silverman, S.; Steffek, A.J. Craniofacial and central nervous system malformations induced by triamcinolone acetonide in nonhuman primates. I. General teratogenicity. TERATOLOGY 22:103–114, 1980b.

Hendrickx, A.G.; Sawyer, R.H.; Terrell, T.G.; Osburn, B.I.; Henrickson, R.V.; Steffek, A.J. Teratogenic effects of triamcinolone on the skeletal and lymphoid systems in nonhuman primates. FEDERATION PROCEEDINGS 34:1661–1665, 1975.

Hendrickx, A.G.; Terrell, T.G.; Andersen, A.C.; Osburn, B.I.; Sawyer, R.H.; Steffek, A.J. Induction of abnormal intra-uterine development with triamcinolone, vitamin A, and x-irradiation in non-human primates. Pp. 149–169 in USE OF NON-HUMAN PRIMATES IN BIOMEDICAL RESEARCH. M.R.N. Prasad; T.C. Anand Kumar, eds. New Delhi, Indian National Science Academy, 1977.

Hertig, A.T.; Rock, J. Two human ova of the pre-villous stage, having an ovulation age of about eleven and twelve days respectively. CARNEGIE CON-

TRIBUTIONS TO EMBRYOLOGY 29:127–156, 1941.

Hertig, A.T.; Rock, J. Two human ova of the previllous stage, having a developmental age of about 7 and 9 days respectively. CARNEGIE CONTRIBUTIONS TO EMBRYOLOGY 31:65–84, 1945.

Hertig, A.T.; Rock, J. Two human ova of the previllous stage, having a developmental age of about 8 and 9 days respectively. CARNEGIE CONTRIBUTIONS TO EMBRYOLOGY 33:169–186, 1949.

Hertig, A.T.; King, N.W.; MacKey, J. Spontaneous abortion in wild-caught rhesus monkeys, *Macaca mulatta*. LABORATORY ANIMAL SCIENCE 21:510–519, 1971.

Hertig, A.T.; Rock, J.; Adams, E.C. A description of 34 human ova within the first 17 days of development. AMERICAN JOURNAL OF ANATOMY 98:435–493, 1956.

Hesse, V.E. Retrocaval ureter. SOUTH AFRICAN MEDICAL JOURNAL 43:561–564, 1969.

Hetherington, C.M.; Cooper, J.E.; Dawson, P. A case of syndactyly in the white-lipped tamarin (*Saguinus nigricollis*). FOLIA PRIMATOLOGICA 24:24–28, 1975.

Heuser, C.H.; Corner, G.W. Developmental horizons in human embryos. Description of age group X, 4 to 12 somites. CARNEGIE CONTRIBUTIONS TO EMBRYOLOGY 36:29–39, 1957.

Heuser, C.H.; Streeter, G.L. Development of the macaque embryo. CARNEGIE CONTRIBUTIONS TO EMBRYOLOGY 29:15–56, 1941.

Heuser, C.H.; Rock, J.; Hertig, A.T. Two human embryos showing early stages of definitive yolk sac. CARNEGIE CONTRIBUTIONS TO EMBRYOLOGY 31:85–99, 1945.

Hill, J.P. The developmental history of the primates. PHILOSOPHICAL TRANSACTIONS OF THE ROYAL SOCIETY OF LONDON. Series B: BIOLOGICAL SCIENCES. 221:45, 1932.

Hill, W.C.O. Lobster-claw deformity in a drill (*Mandrillus leucophaeus f. cur*). BIBLIOTHECA PRIMATOLOGICA 1:239–251, 1962.

Hill, W.C.O. Congenital abnormalities of the urinary tract in primates. FOLIA PRIMATOLOGICA 2:111–118, 1964.

Hill, W.C.O.; Sabater Pi, J. Notes on two anomalies in mandrills (*Mandrillus sphinx* Linn.). FOLIA PRIMATOLOGICA 12:290–295, 1970.

Hill, W.C.O.; Sabater Pi, J. Anomaly of the hallux in a lowland gorilla (*Gorilla gorilla gorilla*). FOLIA PRIMATOLOGICA 14:252–255, 1971.

Homma, T. Sequential pattern of limb anomalies in Japanese monkeys on Awajishima Island. PRIMATES 21(1):20–30, 1980.

Horiuchi, T.; Gass, D.M.; David, N.J. Arteriovenous malformation in the retina of a monkey. AMERICAN JOURNAL OF OPHTHALMOLOGY 82:896–904, 1976.

Hubrecht, A.A.W. Die keimblase von *Tarsius*, ein hilfsmittel zur schärferen definition gewisser säugetierordnungen. Pp. 147–178 in FESTSCHRIFT FÜR C. GEGENBAUR II. Leipzig, Engelmann, 1896a.

Hubrecht, A.A.W. Over de kiemblaas van mensch en aap en hare beteekenis voor de phylogenie der primaten. VERSL. GEWONE VERGAD. AKAD. AMSTERDAM 5:23–25, 1896b.

Hubrecht, A.A.W. Furchung und keimblattbildung bei *Tarsius spectrum*. VERH. K. AKAD., AMSTERDAM 2:1–113, 1902.

Hubrecht, A.A.W.; Keibel, F. Normentafeln zur entwicklungsgeschichte des koboldmaki (*Tarsius spectrum*) und des plumplori (*Nycticebus tardigradus*). NORMENTAF. WIRBELT. 7:1–76, 1907.

Irani, J.; Tokuda, K.; Furuya, Y.; Kano, K.; Shin, Y. The social construction of normal troops of Japanese monkeys in Takasakiyama. PRIMATES 4:2–42, 1963.

Iwamoto, M. Morphological observations on the congenital malformation of limbs in the Japanese monkey. PRIMATES 8:247–270, 1967.

Iwamoto, M.; Hirai, M. Case report on a Japanese monkey with congenital malformation of the limbs. PRIMATES 11:395–398, 1970.

Jackson, B.A.; Rodwell, D.E.; Kanegis, L.A.; Noble, J.F. Effect of maternally administered minocycline on embryonic and fetal development in the rhesus monkey (*Macaca mulatta*). TOXICOLOGY AND APPLIED PHARMACOLOGY 33:156, 1975.

Jerome, C.P.; Hendrickx, A.G. A tubal pregnancy in a rhesus monkey (*Macaca mulatta*). VETERINARY PATHOLOGY 19:239–245, 1982.

Johnson, W.D.; Hughes, H.C.; Lang, C.M.; Stenger, V.G. Placenta extrachorialis in the stumptailed macaque (*Macaca arctoides*). LABORATORY ANIMAL SCIENCE 28:81–84, 1978.

Johnson, L.D.; Palmer, A.E.; King, N.W.; Hertig, A.T. Vaginal adenosis in *Cebus apella* monkeys exposed to DES in utero. OBSTETRICS AND GYNECOLOGY 57:629–635, 1981.

Jones, D.C.L.; Krebs, J.S.; Sasmore, D.P.; Mitoma, C. Evaluation of neonatal squirrel monkeys receiving tritiated water throughout gestation. RADIATION RESEARCH 83:592–606, 1980.

Kato, T.; Jarvik, L.F.; Roizin, L.; Moralishvili, E. Chromosome studies in pregnant rhesus macaque given LSD-25. DISORDERS OF THE NERVOUS SYSTEM 31:245–250, 1970.

Kaur, J.; Chakravarti, R.N.; Clugh, K.S.; Chhuttani, P.N. Spontaneously occurring renal diseases in wild rhesus monkeys. JOURNAL OF PATHOLOGY AND BACTERIOLOGY 95:31–36, 1968.

Kim, C.S.; Kalter, S.S. Unilateral renal aplasia in an African baboon (*Papio* sp.) FOLIA PRIMATOLOGICA 17:157–159, 1972.

Kirk, J.H. Persistent pupillary membrane: Developmental review and an occurrence in *Macaca mu-*

latta. LABORATORY ANIMAL SCIENCE 22:122–125, 1972.

Kirkman, H. A simian, deeply cleft, bilobed gallbladder with a "Phrygian cap." ANATOMICAL RECORD 95:423–447, 1946.

Koford, C.B.; Farber, P.A.; Windle, W.F. Twins and teratisms in rhesus monkeys. FOLIA PRIMATOLOGICA 4:221–226, 1966.

Kohrs, M.B.; Harper, A.E.; Kerr, G.R. Effects of a low-protein diet during pregnancy of the rhesus monkey. I. Reproductive efficiency. AMERICAN JOURNAL OF CLINICAL NUTRITION 29:136–145, 1976.

Kraus, B.S.; Garrett, W.S. Cleft palate in a marmoset—report of a case. CLEFT PALATE JOURNAL 5:340–345, 1968.

Krilova, R.I.; Yakovleva, L.A. The pattern and abnormality rate of monkeys of the Sukhumi colony. ACTA ENDOCRINOLOGICA (Supplement 166):309–321, 1972.

Lapin, B.A.; Yakovleva, L.A. COMPARATIVE PATHOLOGY IN MONKEYS. Springfield, IL, Thomas, 1960.

Lau, D.T.L. Ectopic splenic nodules in the pancreas of a capuchin monkey (*Cebus albifrons*). JOURNAL OF MEDICAL PRIMATOLOGY 2:67–70, 1973.

Lewis, R.W.; Palazzo, M.C.; Kim, J.C.S. Persistent cloaca in a cynomolgus monkey (*Macaca fascicularis*). JOURNAL OF MEDICAL PRIMATOLOGY 7:237–241, 1978.

London, W.T.; Fuccillo, D.A.; Sever, J.L.; Kent, S.G. Influenza virus as a teratogen in rhesus monkeys. NATURE (LONDON) 255:483–484, 1975.

London, W.T.; Levitt, N.H.; Kent, S.G.; Wong, V.G.; Sever, J.L. Congenital cerebral and ocular malformations induced in rhesus monkeys by Venezuelan equine encephalitis virus. TERATOLOGY 16:285–296, 1977.

London, W.T.; Kent, S.G.; Palmer, A.E.; Fuccillo, D.A.; Houff, S.A.; Saini, N.; Sever, J.L. Induction of congenital hydrocephalus with mumps virus in rhesus monkeys. JOURNAL OF INFECTIOUS DISEASES 139:324–328, 1979.

London, W.T.; Levitt, N.H.; Altshuler, G.; Curfman, B.L.; Kent, S.G.; Palmer, A.E.; Sever, J.L.; Houff, S.A. Teratological effects of western equine encephalitis virus on the fetal nervous system of *Macaca mulatta.* TERATOLOGY 25:71–79, 1982.

Luckett, W.P. The origin of extraembryonic mesoderm in the early human and rhesus monkey embryos. ANATOMICAL RECORD 169:369–370, 1971.

Martin, J.E.; Gerrity, L.W.; Stein, F.J. Anomalous origin of the right subclavian artery in a marmoset (*Callithrix jacchus*). JOURNAL OF MEDICAL PRIMATOLOGY 8:305–307, 1979.

Maruffo, C.A.; Cramer, D.L. Congenital renal malformations in monkeys. FOLIA PRIMATOLOGICA 5:305–311, 1967.

McClure, H.M. Features of Down's-like syndrome in a chimpanzee. AMERICAN JOURNAL OF PATHOLOGY 67:413–416, 1972.

McClure, H.M.; Strozier, L.M. Perinatal listeric septicemia in a Celebese black ape. JOURNAL OF THE AMERICAN VETERINARY MEDICAL ASSOCIATION 167:637–638, 1975.

McClure, H.M.; Wilk, A.L.; Horigan, E.A.; Pratt, R.M. Induction of craniofacial malformations in rhesus monkeys (*Macaca mulatta*) with cyclophosphamide. CLEFT PALATE JOURNAL 16:248, 1979.

McCraw, A.P.; Rotheram, K.; Sim, A.K.; Warwick, M.H. Unilateral renal aplasia in the baboon. JOURNAL OF MEDICAL PRIMATOLOGY 2:249–251, 1973.

McNulty, W.P. Spontaneous cardiopulmonary disease in nonhuman primates: Potential models. Pp. 829–839 in RESEARCH ANIMALS IN MEDICINE. L.T. Harmison, ed. Washington, D.C., U.S. Government Printing Office, 1973.

Meier, J.E.; Boyce, W.L.; Silverman, N.R. Spina bifida occulta in a Celebes crested macaque. JOURNAL OF THE AMERICAN VETERINARY MEDICAL ASSOCIATION 173:1236–1238, 1978.

Montali, R.J.; Bush, M.; Kleiman, D.; Evans, R. Familial diaphragmatic defects in golden lion tamarins. Pp. 169–172 in SONDERCHUCK AUS VERHANDLUNGSBERICHT DES XXII INTERNATIONALEN SYMPOSIUMS UBER DIE ERKRANKUNGEN DER ZOOTIERE. Arnheim, 1980.

Moreland, A.F.; Schimpff, R.D.; Gaskin, J.M. Fetal mortality and malformations associated with experimental infections of western equine encephalomyelitis vaccine virus in rhesus monkeys (*Macaca mulatta*). TERATOLOGY 20:65–74, 1979a.

Moreland, A.F.; Gaskin, J.M.; Schimpff, R.D.; Woodard, J.C.; Olson, G.A. Effects of influenza, mumps, and western equine encephalitis viruses on fetal rhesus monkeys (*Macaca mulatta*). TERATOLOGY 20:53–64, 1979b.

Morris, J.M.; van Wagenen, G.; Hurteau, G.D.; Johnston; Carlsen, R.A. Compounds interfering with ovum implantation and development. FERTILITY AND STERILITY 18:7–17, 1967.

Morris, L.N.; Kerr, B.A. Split hand and foot anomaly in *Macaca mulatta* —a report of two cases. AMERICAN JOURNAL OF ANATOMY 130:481–494, 1971.

Mossman, H.W. Comparative morphogenesis of the fetal membranes and accessory uterine structures. CARNEGIE CONTRIBUTIONS TO EMBRYOLOGY 26:129–246, 1937.

Müller, F.; O'Rahilly, R. The early development of the nervous system in staged insectivore and primate embryos. JOURNAL OF COMPARATIVE NEUROLOGY 193:741–751, 1980.

Myers, R.E. The pathology of the rhesus monkey placenta. SYMPOSIUM ON THE USE OF NON-HUMAN PRIMATES FOR RESEARCH ON PROBLEMS OF HUMAN REPRODUCTION. Sukhumi, USSR, 1971.

Myers, R.E.; Velerio, M.G.; Martin, D.P.; Nelson, K.B. Perinatal brain damage: Porencephaly in a cynomolgus monkey. BIOLOGY OF THE NEONATE 22:253–273, 1973.

Naeye, R.L.; Harkness, W.L.; Utts, J. Abruptio placentae and perinatal death: A prospective study. AMERICAN JOURNAL OF OBSTETRICS AND GYNECOLOGY 128:740–746, 1977.

Nagashima, K.; Takizaka, A.; Yasui, K.; Nishiyama, M.; Ikai, A.; Hasegawa, T. Congenital obstruction of the nasolacrimal duct in a lowland gorilla. JOURNAL OF ZOO ANIMAL MEDICINE 5(3):9–16, 1974.

Newell-Morris, L.; Sirianni, J.E.; Shepard, T.H.; Fantel, A.G.; Moffett, B.C. Teratogenic effects of retinoic acid in pigtail monkeys (Macaca nemestrina). II. Craniofacial features. TERATOLOGY 22:87–101, 1980.

Newman, L.M.; Hendrickx, A.G. Fetal ear malformations induced by maternal ingestion of thalidomide in the bonnet monkey (Macaca radiata). TERATOLOGY 23:351–364, 1981.

Noback, C.R.; Paff, G.H.; Poppiti, R.J. A bilaminar human ovum. ACTA ANATOMICA 69:485–496, 1968.

O'Rahilly, R. The early development of the otic vesicle in staged human embryos. JOURNAL OF EMBRYOLOGY AND EXPERIMENTAL MORPHOLOGY 11:741–755, 1963.

O'Rahilly, R. The early development of the eye in staged human embryos. CARNEGIE CONTRIBUTIONS TO EMBRYOLOGY 38:1–42, 1966.

O'Rahilly, R. The prenatal development of the human eye. EXPERIMENTAL EYE RESEARCH 21(2):93–112, 1975.

Ordy, J.M.; Rangan, S.R.S.; Wolf, R.H.; Knight, C.; Dunlap, W.P. Congenital cytomegalovirus effects on postnatal neurological development of squirrel monkey (Saimiri sciureus) offspring. EXPERIMENTAL NEUROLOGY 74:728–747, 1981.

Ornoy, A.; Crone, K.; Altshuler, G. Pathological features of the placenta in fetal death. ARCHIVES OF PATHOLOGY AND LABORATORY MEDICINE 100:367–371, 1976.

Pearson, K. On the existence of the digital deformity—so-called "lobster-claw" in the apes. ANNALS OF EUGENICS 4:339–340, 1931.

Phillips, I.R. Macaque and marmoset monkey as animal models for the study of birth defects. LABORATORY ANIMAL HANDBOOK 6:293, 1975.

Phillips, I.R. The embryology of the common marmoset (Callithrix jacchus). ADVANCES IN ANATOMY, EMBRYOLOGY, AND CELL BIOLOGY 52(5):1–47, 1976.

Popko, J.S. The early development of the eye in the lesser mouse lemur (Microcebus murinus). M.S. Thesis, University of California, Davis, 1978.

Poswillo, D.E. Tridione and paradioine as suspected teratogens. ANNALS OF THE ROYAL COLLEGE OF SURGEONS OF ENGLAND 50:367–370, 1972.

Poswillo, D.E.; Hamilton, W.J.; Sopher, D. The marmoset as an animal model for teratological research. NATURE (LONDON) 239:460–462, 1972.

Poswillo, D.E.; Sopher, D.; Mitchell, S.J. Experimental induction of foetal malformation with 'blighted' potato: A preliminary report. NATURE (LONDON) 239:462, 1972.

Poswillo, D.; Nunnerly, H.; Sopher, D.; Keith, J. Hyperthermia as a teratogenic agent. ANNALS OF THE ROYAL COLLEGE OF SURGEONS OF ENGLAND 55:171–174, 1974.

Poswillo, D.E.; Sopher, D.; Mitchell, S.J.; Coxon, D.T.; Curtis, R.F.; Price, K.R. Investigation into the teratogenic potential of imperfect potatoes. TERATOLOGY 8:339–347, 1973.

Prahalada, S.; Hendrickx, A.G. Teratogenicity of medroxyprogesterone acetate (MPA) in cynomolgus monkeys. TERATOLOGY 25:67–68a, 1982.

Prahalada, S.; Hendrickx, A.G. Effect of medroxyprogesterone acetate (MPA) on the fetal development in baboons. TERATOLOGY 27:69–70A, 1983.

Prahalada, S.; Hendrickx, A.G. Embryotoxicity of Norlestrin, a combined synthetic oral contraceptive, in rhesus macaques (Macaca mulatta). TERATOLOGY 27:215–222, 1983.

Price, R.A.; Gilles, F.H. Telencephalic remnants in simian and human anencephaly. ARCHIVES OF PATHOLOGY 91:529–536, 1971.

Primack, A.; Young, D.; Homan, E. Syndactyly in a rhesus monkey: A case report. TERATOLOGY 5:137–142, 1972.

Pruzansky, S. Anomalies of face and brain. BIRTH DEFECTS: ORIGINAL ARTICLE SERIES 11(7):183–204, 1975.

Randolph, J.; Bush, M.; Abramowitz, M.; Kleiman, D.; Montali, R.J. Surgical correction of familial diaphragmatic hernia of Morgagni in the golden lion tamarin. JOURNAL OF PEDIATRIC SURGERY 16:396–401, 1981.

Reynolds, W.A.; Pitkin, R.M. Methylmercury toxicity in utero in the macaque. JOURNAL OF MEDICAL PRIMATOLOGY 4:372, 1975 (abstract).

Rice, J.M.; Sly, D.L.; Palmer, A.E.; London, W.T. Transplacental effects of ethylnitrosourea in a nonhuman primate (Erythrocebus patas). NATIONAL CANCER INSTITUTE MONOGRAPHS 51:185–192, 1979.

Rosenberg, D.P.; Link, D.P.; Prahalada, S. Arteriovenous malformation in a rhesus monkey (Macaca mulatta). LABORATORY ANIMAL SCIENCE 33:183–186, 1983.

Rosenquist, C.J.; Silverman, S. Diverticulosis of the

gallbladder in a rhesus monkey. JOURNAL OF THE AMERICAN VETERINARY RADIOLOGY SOCIETY 19:38–40, 1978.

Rugh, R.; Duhamel, L; Skaredoff, L.; Somogyi, C. Gross sequelae of fetal x-irradiation of the monkey *Macaca mulatta*. ATOMPRAXIS 12:519–524, 1966.

Ruppenthal, G.C.; Caffery, S.A.; Goodlin, B.L.; Sackett, G.P.; Vigfusson, N.V.; Peterson, V.G. Pigtailed macaques (*Macaca nemestrina*) with trisomy X manifest physical and mental retardation. AMERICAN JOURNAL OF MENTAL DEFICIENCY 87:471–476, 1983.

Schmidt, R.E. Colobomas in non-human primates. FOLIA PRIMATOLOGICA 14:256–268, 1971.

Schultz, A.H. Age changes and variability in gibbons. A morphological study on a population sample of a man-like ape. AMERICAN JOURNAL OF PHYSICAL ANTHROPOLOGY 2:1–129, 1944.

Schultz, A.H. Polydactylism in a siamang. FOLIA PRIMATOLOGICA 17:241–247, 1972.

Scott, H.H.; Lamb, H. Congenital malformations of the kidney. PROCEEDINGS OF THE ZOOLOGICAL SOCIETY OF LONDON 2:1259–1270, 1925.

Scott, J.S. Placenta extrachorialis (placenta marginata and placenta circumvallata). JOURNAL OF OBSTETRICS AND GYNAECOLOGY OF THE BRITISH EMPIRE 67:904–918, 1960.

Scott, W.J.; Wilson, J.G.; Helm, F.-C. A metabolite of a structural analog of thalidomide lacks teratogenic effect in pregnant rhesus monkeys. TERATOLOGY 22:183–185, 1980.

Scott, W.J.; Hirsch, K.S.; DeSesso, J.M.; Wilson, J.G. Comparative studies on acetazolamide teratogenesis in pregnant rats, rabbits, and rhesus monkeys. TERATOLOGY 24:37–42, 1981.

Sedgwick, C.J. Pectus excavatum in a douc langur (*Pygathrix nemaeus*): One reason for managing genetic variation in zoo animal breeding programs. JOURNAL OF ZOO ANIMAL MEDICINE 12:124–127, 1981.

Sever, J.L.; Meier, G.W.; Windle, W.F.; Schiff, G.M.; Monif, G.R.; Fabiyi, A. Experimental rubella in pregnant rhesus monkeys. JOURNAL OF INFECTIOUS DISEASES 116:21–26, 1966.

Siddall, R.A. Use of marmosets (*Callithrix jacchus*) in teratological and toxicological research. PRIMATES MEDICINE 10:215–224, 1978.

Silverman, S.; Merten, D.F.; Anderson, J.H.; Hendrickx, A.G. Radiographic diagnosis of choanal atresia induced prenatally with triamcinolone in the baboon (*Papio cynocephalus*). JOURNAL OF MEDICAL PRIMATOLOGY 6:284–297, 1977.

Smith, J.D.; Genoways, H.H.; Jones, J.K. Jr. Cranial and dental anomalies in three species of platyrrhine monkeys from Nicaragua. FOLIA PRIMATOLOGICA 28:1–42, 1977.

St. Geme, J.W. Jr.; Van Pelt, L.F. Fetal and postnatal growth retardation association with gestational

mumps virus infection of the rhesus monkey. LABORATORY ANIMAL SCIENCE 24:895–899, 1974.

Steffek, A.J.; Hendrickx, A.G. Lathyrogen-induced malformations in baboons: A preliminary report. TERATOLOGY 5:171–180, 1972.

Stills, H.F. Jr.; Bullock, B.C. Congenital defects of squirrel monkeys (*Saimiri sciureus*). VETERINARY PATHOLOGY 18:29–36, 1981.

Stills, H.F. Jr.; Bond, M.G.; Bullock, B.C. *Double aortic arch* in a talapoin monkey (*Miopithecus talapin*). VETERINARY PATHOLOGY 16:266–267, 1979.

Streeter, G.L. Developmental horizons of human embryos: Description of age group XI, 13–20 somites, and age group XII, 21–29, somites. CARNEGIE CONTRIBUTIONS TO EMBRYOLOGY 30:211–246, 1942.

Streeter, G.L. Developmental horizons in human embryos: Description of age group XIII, embryos about 4 or 5 millimeters long, and age group XIV, period of indentation of the lens vesicle. CARNEGIE CONTRIBUTIONS TO EMBRYOLOGY 31:27–64, 1945.

Streeter, G.L. Developmental horizons in human embryos: Description of age groups XV, XVI, XVII, and XVIII, being the third issue of a survey of the Carnegie Collection. CARNEGIE CONTRIBUTIONS TO EMBRYOLOGY 32:135–204, 1948.

Streeter, G.L. Developmental horizons in human embryos: Description of age groups XIX, XX, XXII, and XXIII, being the fifth issue of a survey of the Carnegie Collection. CARNEGIE CONTRIBUTIONS TO EMBRYOLOGY 34:165–196, 1951.

Sullivan, D.J.; Drobeck, H.P. True hermaphrodism in a rhesus monkey. FOLIA PRIMATOLOGICA 4:309–317, 1966.

Swindler, D.R.; Merrill, O.M. Spontaneous cleft lip and palate in a living nonhuman primate, *Macaca mulatta*. AMERICAN JOURNAL OF PHYSICAL ANTHROPOLOGY 34:435–440, 1971.

Szabo, K.T.; DiFebbo, M.E.; Kang, Y.J.; Palmer, A.K.; Brent, R.L. Comparative embryotoxicity and teratogenicity of various tranquilizing agents in mice, rats, rabbits, and rhesus monkeys. TOXICOLOGY AND APPLIED PHARMACOLOGY 33:124, 1975 (abstract).

Tanimura, T. Effects on macaque embryos of drugs reported or suspected to be teratogenic to humans. ACTA ENDOCRINOLOGICA (Supplementum) 166:293–308, 1971.

Theisen, C.T.; Bodin, J.D.; Svoboda, J.A.; Pettinelli, M.W. Unusual muscle abnormalities associated with thalidomide treatment in a rhesus monkey: A case report. TERATOLOGY 19:313–320, 1979.

Thompson, R.S.; Hess, D.L.; Binkerd, P.E.; Hendrickx, A.G. The effects of prenatal diethylstilbestrol (DES) exposure on the genitalia of pubertal

Macaca mulatta. II. Male offspring. JOURNAL OF REPRODUCTIVE MEDICINE 26:309–316, 1981.

Tittler, I.A. Two cases of accessory gallbladder in the rhesus monkey (*Macaca mulatta*). ANATOMICAL RECORD 91:257–260, 1945.

van Wagenen, G.; DeConti, R.C.; Handschumacher, R.E.; Wade, M.E. Abortifacient and teratogenic effects of triacetyl-6-azauridine in the monkey. AMERICAN JOURNAL OF OBSTETRICS AND GYNECOLOGY 108(2):272–281, 1970.

van Wagenen, G.; Hamilton, J.B. The experimental production of pseudohermaphroditism in the monkey. Pp. 583–607 in ESSAYS IN BIOLOGY. Berkeley, University of California Press, 1943.

Vondruska, J.F.; Francher, O.E.; Calandra, J.C. An investigation into the teratogenic potential of captan, folpet, and difolatan in nonhuman primates. TOXICOLOGY AND APPLIED PHARMACOLOGY 18:619–624, 1971.

Wadsworth, P.F.; Heywood, R. The effect of prenatal exposure of rhesus monkeys (*Macaca mulatta*) to diethylstilbestrol. TOXICOLOGY LETTERS 2:115–118, 1978.

Wadsworth, P.F.; Squires, P.F. Renal aplasia and hypoplasia in the rhesus monkey (*Macaca mulatta*). LABORATORY ANIMALS 14:1–2, 1980.

Wadsworth, P.F.; Allen, D.G.; Prentice, D.E. Pseudohermaphroditism in a baboon (*Papio anubis*). TOXICOLOGY LETTERS 1:261–266, 1978.

Weiss, G.; Weick, R.F.; Knobil, E.; Wolman, S.R.; Gorstein, F. An X–O anomaly and ovarian dysgenesis in a rhesus monkey. FOLIA PRIMATOLOGICA 19:24–27, 1973.

Wells, L.J.; van Wagenen, G. Observations on the reproductive organs of monkeys with induced female pseudohermaphroditism. ANATOMICAL RECORD 103:587, 1949.

Wharton, L.R. Jr.; Scott, R.B. Experimental production of genital lesions with norethindrone. AMERICAN JOURNAL OF OBSTETRICS AND GYNECOLOGY 89(6):701–715, 1964.

Wilson, J.G. Abnormalities of intrauterine development in non-human primates. ACTA ENDOCRINOLOGICA, KBH 166 (Supplement):261–292, 1971a.

Wilson, J.G. Use of rhesus monkeys in teratological studies. FEDERATION PROCEEDINGS 30:104–109, 1971b.

Wilson, J.G. An animal model of human disease: Thalidomide embryopathy in primates. COMPARATIVE PATHOLOGY BULLETIN 5:3–4, 1973.

Wilson, J.G. Teratologic causation in man and its evaluation in nonhuman primates. Pp. 191–203 in BIRTH DEFECTS. A.G. Motulsky; W. Lenz, eds. Amsterdam, Excerpta Medica, 1974.

Wilson, J.G. Developmental abnormalities: Nonhuman primates. Pp. 1911–1946 in PATHOLOGY OF LABORATORY ANIMALS, Vol. II. K. Benirschke; F.M. Garner; T.C. Jones, eds. New York, Springer-Verlag, 1978.

Wilson, J.G.; Gavan, J.A. Congenital malformation in nonhuman primates: Spontaneous and experimentally induced. ANATOMICAL RECORD 158:99–109, 1967.

Wilson, J.G.; Scott, W.J.; Ritter, E.J. Digital abnormalities in monkeys and rats. BIRTH DEFECTS: ORIGINAL ARTICLE SERIES 13:203–220, 1977.

Woodling, B.A.; Puffer, H.W.; Anderson, G. Jr.; Warner, N.E. Gross examination of the placenta. CLINICAL OBSTETRICS AND GYNECOLOGY 19:21–44, 1976.

Yip, J.E.; Kokich, V.G.; Shepard, T.H. The effect of high doses of retinoic acid on prenatal craniofacial development in *Macaca nemestrina*. TERATOLOGY 21(1):29–38, 1980.

Growth

Kenneth R. Brizzee and William P. Dunlap

Delta Regional Primate Research Center, Tulane University, Covington, Louisiana 70433, and Department of Psychology, Tulane University, New Orleans, Louisiana 70118

INTRODUCTION

It is well established that growth processes in man, both prenatally and postnatally, are vulnerable to many environmental factors, notably nutritional status, toxins, physical influences (eg, temperature, radiation), and the sociomedical milieu. Although there is a compelling need for more information on growth phenomena in all human systems, ethical as well as practical considerations preclude any research efforts on this problem other than retrospective epidemiological studies or correlative clinicopathological evaluations of human growth phenomena under existing environmental conditions. It is logical, therefore, to seek animal models in which growth processes may be differentially manipulated in well-designed experimental protocols, and from which the data may be extrapolated with a reasonable degree of confidence to man.

Although many structural, physiological, and metabolic differences related to growth processes exist between the human and nonhuman primate, such differences are qualitatively and quantitatively less than between man and nonprimate mammals. The greater similarities between man and nonhuman primates render the latter the most suitable subjects for controlled experimental manipulation of factors that are known or believed to influence growth processes in man. Prior to the 1950s, very little information on normal growth in nonhuman primates of known age was available. Since that time, however, the number of reports on physical growth of nonhuman primates of certain species raised under controlled environmental conditions has increased notably. This accumulation of data, however, has been extremely uneven throughout the taxonomic families of nonhuman primates. Among these groups the rhesus monkey and chimpanzee have received the greatest amount of attention, whereas others such as the lemur, loris, and even the gorilla and orang-utan, have been subjects of very few systematic investigations.

In view of the paucity of information on growth phenomena in most nonhuman primate families, the primary goal of the present chapter is to present available information on the growth process on those forms as completely as possible and at the same time to summarize the voluminous data on species that have been studied most extensively. It is hoped that this chapter may thus constitute a nucleus of information which may serve as baseline data for more comprehesive integrative surveys of the growth process in nonhuman primates. It should also serve as a basis for future experimental studies involving manipulation of various factors influencing growth in the continuing search for guiding principles that will enhance our knowledge of growth processes in various organs and the body as whole.

PHYSICAL GROWTH

Prenatal Period

Duration of Gestation. A list of gestation lengths in various nonhuman primate genera and species was published by Ardito [1976], together with a list of references from which the data were obtained. This list is included in the present chapter as Table 1 with the list of references presented according to Ardito's designations. Some discrepancies between authors' reports for some species are evident, and are probably due to difficulties in estimating the precise date of conception. More recent and per-

TABLE 1. Check-list of the Data on the Gestation Length of Primates

	Taxa[a]	Gestation length (days unless otherwise specified)	References (see Ardito [1976])
1.1.1.	*Tupaia* sp.	40–52	145
		41–52	26
1.1.1.1.	*Tupaia glis*	40–52	2,65,149
		41–50	27
		42–46	90
		43–51	117
		45–52	44
		46–50	5
		47	78
1.1.3.1.	*Urogale everetti*	50	144
		50–56	5
		56	166
1.2.1.	*Loris* sp.	160–174	119
		6 months	68
1.2.1.1.	*Loris tardigradus*	5 months	132
		160–166	112
		174	115,120
1.2.2.	*Nycticebus* sp.	193	119
1.2.2.1.	*Nycticebus coucang*	90	5,85
		174	120
		193	112,114,115
1.2.3.	*Arctocebus* sp.	131	119
1.2.3.1.	*Arctocebus calabarensis*	131–136	95,112,114,115
1.2.3.1.	*Perodicticus potto*	170	20
		180–195	29
		193	23
1.3.1.1.	*Galago senegalensis*	4 months	5,19,105,106
		120	140
		120–125	31
		122–125	32
		122–128	51
		136–142	28
		144–146	112,119
1.3.1.2.	*Galago crassicaudatus*	130–135	18,119,126
		130–136	35
1.3.1.3.	*Galago alleni*	180	163
1.3.1.4.	*Galago demidovii*	3 months	21
		108–110	11
		110	164
		129	163
1.4.1.	*Microcebus* sp.	59–62	119
		2 months	78
		60–65	116
1.4.1.1.	*Microcebus murinus*	59–62	13,113,126,127
1.4.2.1.	*Cheirogaleus major*	70	13,127
1.4.5.	*Lemur* sp.	60	85,94
		120–135	119
		146	142
1.4.5.1.	*Lemur catta*	120–135	127
		5 months	98

TABLE 1. Check-list of the Data on the Gestation Length of Primates (*Continued*)

	Taxa[a]	Gestation length (days unless otherwise specified)	References (see Ardito [1976])
1.4.5.3.	*Lemur macaco*	120–135	127
		145	142
		5 months	5
1.4.5.4.	*Lemur fulvus*	4–4½ months	46,71
1.4.6.	*Lepilemur* sp.	120–150	98,119,126
1.4.6.1.	*Lepilemur mustelinus*	120–150	126,127
1.5.1.	*Propithecus* sp.	60	12
		150	119
		5 months	78
1.5.1.2.	*Propithecus verreauxi*	5 months	126,127
1.5.3.	*Indri* sp.	60	12
1.5.3.1.	*Indri indri*	60	33,85
1.7.1.	*Tarsius* sp.	180	119,155
1.7.1.1.	*Tarsius spectrum*	6 months	75
2.1.1.	*Callithrix* sp.	140	119
		140–150	5
2.1.1.3.	*Callithrix jacchus*	117–156	110
		140	55
		140–146	135
		140–150	39,94,100,107,108
		160–173	39
2.1.2.1.	*Cebuella pygmaea*	140–150	25
2.1.3.1.	*Leontideus rosalia*	132–134	131,154
		140	107
2.1.4.3.	*Saguinus fuscicollis*	134–170	170–180
2.1.4.5.	*Saguinus nigricollis*	132–134	165
2.1.4.10.	*Saguinus oedipus*	140–150	56,57,118
2.3.3.1.	*Pithecia pithecia*	101	58
2.3.6.	*Alouatta* sp.	139	94,119
2.3.6.3.	*Alouatta seniculus*	139	85
2.3.7.1.	*Saimiri sciureus*	152–168	104
		158–172	169
		160–170	168
		5½ months	10
		168–172	48
		168–182	119
		24–26 weeks	15,80
		180	137
		6 months	73
2.3.8.	*Cebus* sp.	180	24,70,119
2.3.9.	*Ateles* sp.	139	94,119
2.3.9.1.	*Ateles paniscus*	139	45,85
2.3.11.	*Lagothrix* sp.	139	94
		225	119
2.3.11.1.	*Lagothrix lagothricha*	139	85
		7½ months	167
		250	72
2.2.1.1.	*Callimico goeldii*	4½ months	103
		149–152	102
3.1.1.	*Macaca* sp.	146–186	119

(continued)

TABLE 1. Check-list of the Data on the Gestation Length of Primates (*Continued*)

	Taxa[a]	Gestation length (days unless otherwise specified)	References (see Ardito [1976])
3.1.1.2.	*Macaca nigra*	155–175	119
		160–165	82
3.1.1.3.	*Macaca sylvana*	210	17,124
3.1.1.4.	*Macaca arctoides*	168–183	153
		170–184	54
		181.5 (mean)	109
		207	92
3.1.1.6.	*Macaca sinica*	180	74
3.1.1.7.	*Macaca radiata*	153–169	62,63
3.1.1.8.	*Macaca cyclopis*	163 (mean)	1,181
3.1.1.9.	*Macaca mulatta*	135–171	41
		135–185	54
		146–180	5,62
		156–177	66
		158–173	88
		159–169	161
		159–174	61
		160–174	129,156,157
		160–170	162
		160–180	151
		162–175	159
		163–171	130
		163–174	83
		164–168	158
		165 (mean)	128,179
		168 (mean)	91,160
		172	37
3.1.1.10.	*Macaca fuscata*	150–170	64,152
		5–6 months	5
		170	119
		171–180	84
3.1.1.11.	*Macaca nemestrina*	168–170 (mean)	89
		171	174,176
3.1.1.12.	*Macaca fascicularis*	153–179	147,148,182
		160–170	146
		163	1
		163–165	34
		164–165	96
		165	97,109
		167	148
		168	42
		169	133
3.1.2.	*Papio* sp.	154–183	119
		164–186	81
		190	24
3.1.2.1.	*Papio hamadryas*	154–183	177,178
		172 (mean)	78
		172–185	175
3.1.2.2.	*Papio ursinus*	173–193	47
		187 (mean)	78
3.1.2.3.	*Papio anubis*	175	87

TABLE 1. Check-list of the Data on the Gestation Length of Primates (*Continued*)

Taxa[a]	Gestation length (days unless otherwise specified)	References (see Ardito [1976])
3.1.2.4.	*Papio cynocephalus*	189–194	79
3.1.2.6.	*Papio sphinx*	220	94
		245	36,119
		270	6,85
3.1.3.	*Theropithecus*	6 months	77
3.1.3.1.	*Theropithecus gelada*	170	177
3.1.4.	*Cercocebus* sp.	213	94
3.1.4.5.	*Cercocebus albigena*	174	136
		6 months	22
3.1.5.	*Cercopithecus* sp.	180–213	119
		210	177
		213	86–94
3.1.5.1.	*Cercopithecus aethiops*	188	143
		210	36
3.1.5.17.	*Cercopithecus ascanius*	6 months	53
		180	36
		210	4
3.1.5.20.	*Cercopithecus mitis*	140	78
3.1.5.22.	*Cercopithecus talapoin*	28 weeks	76
3.1.6.	*Erythrocebus* sp.	7 months	93
		213	94
3.1.6.1.	*Erythrocebus patas*	170	49
		213	24
3.2.1.	*Presbytis* sp.	168	119
3.2.1.1.	*Presbytis entellus*	169	69
		196	36
3.2.1.10.	*Presbytis obscurus*	150	8
3.2.2.1.	*Pygathrix nemaeus*	180–190	16,101
3.2.5.	*Nasalis* sp.	166	119
3.2.5.1.	*Nasalis larvatus*	166	5,141
3.2.6.1.	*Colobus polykomos*	180–213	60
3.3.1.	*Hybolates* sp.	210	119
3.3.1.1.	*Hylobates lar*	210–217	134
		7½ months	9
3.3.2.1.	*Symphalangus syndactylus*	230–235	67,119
		238	59
3.4.3.1.	*Gorilla gorilla*	251–289	119
		252	24,99,138,139
		255	40,122
		257–259	30,150
3.4.1.1.	*Pongo pygmaeus*	210–270	94,123
		225–275	14
		227–275	33,119
		8–9 months	17
		261	3
		263	50
		275	7
3.4.2.1.	*Pan troglodytes*	210–270	123,171
		214–270	52
		215–238	43
		215–241	121

(continued)

TABLE 1. Check-list of the Data on the Gestation Length of Primates (*Continued*)

	Taxa[a]	Gestation length (days unless otherwise specified)	References (see Ardito [1976])
3.4.2.1.	*Pan troglodytes*	225	119
		227	33
		231	36
		250	78
		34 weeks	172
		270	173
3.4.2.2.	*Pan paniscus*	196–260	125

Reprinted with permission from JOURNAL OF HUMAN EVOLUTION, © 1976 by Academic Press, Inc., London, Ltd. and Ardito [1976].

[a]The code numbers for the species are the ones used in A.B. Chiarelli [1972]: TAXONOMIC ATLAS OF LIVING PRIMATES. London: Academic Press.

haps better controlled data on nine species are available from Cross and Martin [1981].

The relationship between length of gestation and prenatal growth is assumed to be governed by maternal metabolism in placental mammals, which in turn is related to maternal weight [Kihlström, 1972]. Kihlström found gestation duration and maternal weight to be related by the power function, $G = aW^b$, where G is gestation duration, W is maternal adult weight, and a and b are fitted constants. The correlations between log G and log W in 16 species of primates were reported to be 0.8102.

The following is a fit of the above power function to the more complete data in Table 1: $G = 62.3 W^{0.12}$. The parameters differ considerably from those reported by Kihlström's reported value. Although Kihlström's findings do suggest that type of placenta is another important determinant of the relation between gestation and maternal weight, fitting separate functions for primates of specific placental types appears to be of doubtful utility.

Ponderal Growth

Body Weight

Data on changes in fetal weight with age do not appear to be available in the literature on prosimians. In captive-bred squirrel monkey fetuses (subspecies not given) Manocha [1979] reported the mean body weight at 115 days' gestation to be 56.6 gm (n = 2) and at 145 days' gestation to be 65.2 gm (n = 2). In studies at Delta Regional Primate Research Center, the timing of insemination in Bolivian squirrel monkeys was estimated by recording the time of increase of chorionic gonadotropin (Wampole Laboratory, "Biocept-G" kit). In these specimens body weights and dimensional measurements were made at various postfertiliza-

tion intervals. Prenatal body weight data are summarized in Table 2 along with crown-rump length (CRL), head circumference, and various organ weights. Within the age range available, body weight appeared to be approximately a linear function of gestational age; however, since estimating prenatal age from fetal body weight is most often needed, the fitted function in that form is $A = 0.646 W + 91.5$, where A is age from fertilization in days and W is fetal body weight in grams.

Van Wagenen et al [1965] presented data from a fairly large series of rhesus monkey fetuses, as shown in Figure 1 (n = 338). They observed that from about 90–100 days to about 155–160 days (term) the fetal weight curve for *Macaca mulatta* follows a nearly linear course. The overall curve, however, obviously presents a sigmoid configuration as in the growth curve of the human embryo.

The birth weights in this series appeared to be in good agreement with those of Schultz [1937], Jacobson and Windle [1960], and Dawes et al [1960] except for a single deviant 145-day fetus in the last study. The fetal weights recorded by Kerr et al [1969a] are somewhat higher than those of van Wagenen et al [1965], but it appears that the birth weights in the two groups are about equal. From the data on fetal weight changes, presented above, in the squirrel monkey, it is clear that in the latter species the fetal whole body growth rate (approximately 1.6 gm/day) is much lower than in the rhesus monkey (approximately 5.7 gm/day).

Organ Weight

Although there is considerable information on organ weight changes during the gestation period in the rhesus monkey, there are no such data on prosimians and only preliminary data on Bolivian squirrel monkeys. Data from 11 prenatal and perinatal Bolivian squirrel monkeys, as functions of

TABLE 2. Prenatal and Newborn Body, Placenta, and Organ Weight, and Body Measurements of Squirrel Monkeys as Functions of Age From Fertilization as Estimated From Change in Circulating Chorionic Hormone

	Age from fertilization	Body weight	CRL	Head circumference	Spleen	L. kidney	Liver	Thymus	Brain	Placenta
Prenatal										
X̄	114	31.6	10.8	9.2	0.06	0.12	0.78	0.07	4.9	9.6
SD		(5.4)	(1.4)	(0.2)	(0.02)	(0.06)	(0.12)	(0.02)	(1.2)	(0.7)
N		3	3	3	3	3	3	3	3	3
X̄	120	48.9	11.3	10.6	0.04	0.22	1.32	0.11	6.8	12.5
SD		(0.9)	(0.1)	(0.5)	(0.00)	(0.04)	(0.02)	(0.01)	(0.8)	(0.2)
N		2	2	2	2	2	2	2	2	2
X̄	143	78.8	13.0	12.4	0.09	0.26	1.62	0.22	11.4	17.7
SD		(2.0)	(1.5)	(0.8)	(0.04)	(0.06)	(0.23)	(0.07)	(0.5)	(2.3)
N		2	2	2	2	2	2	2	2	2
Day of birth										
X̄	155	97.7	13.2	12.9	0.11	0.29	3.36	0.26	13.6	16.0
SD		(5.1)	(0.9)	(—)	(0.02)	(0.02)	(0.87)	(—)	(0.9)	(—)
N		4	4	1	3	3	3	3	3	1

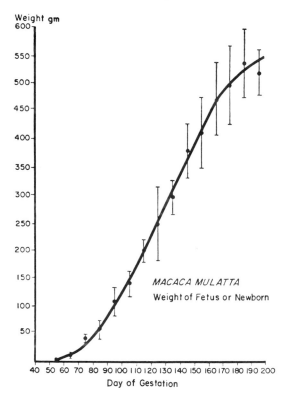

Weight gm

MACACA MULATTA
Weight of Fetus or Newborn

Day of Gestation

Fig. 1. Weight of embryos and fetuses removed at hysterotomy, and of newborn infants (338 animals, day 40 to day 195). Means and standard deviations are shown. The curve was fitted by eye. [From van Wagenen et al, 1965, with permission.]

gestational age, for spleen, left kidney, liver, thymus, brain, and placenta, are presented in Table 2. Using the previous function of age predicted from body weight, additional Bolivian squirrel monkey organ weight data from 22 fetuses are presented in Table 3.

Growth data on organ weights in the rhesus monkey are illustrated in Table 4 [Kerr et al, 1969a]. The growth in fetal organ weight tended to parallel the body weight increase except for lungs and thymus which showed a decrease in weight between 150 and 175 days' gestational age. According to Kerr et al [1969a], the brain, spleen, kidneys, thyroid, and heart constituted about the same proportion of total body weight throughout fetal life. The liver showed a decrease in relative growth rate throughout this period, and a similar decrease was observed in the adrenal glands except for an apparent growth "spurt" between 150 and 175 days. The lungs and thymus also showed a

decrease in relative growth rate in the same time period.

The ratio of placental to body weight showed a rapid decrease during early gestation and midgestation, and the decrease continued at a slower rate during late gestation. Most organs and the total body weight had achieved 9–14% of their adult weight by gestation day 175. The spleen, adrenals, and brain exceded this value, however, being about 20%, 40%, and 65% of their adult weight, respectively. The same authors [Kerr et al, 1969a] found that comparisons of the logarithmic value of the mean organ weight with that of the mean body weight throughout the entire life cycle showed a linear function for the growth of most organs (Fig. 2), but the brain differed in that it showed a postnatal decrease in relative growth rate. As is evident in this figure the lungs and thymus also exhibit a different pattern of growth from most organs. This is due to a relative decrease in weight between 150 and 175 days' gestational age while the adrenals show a marked increase at this time (Table 4).

Dimensional Growth of Fetus

Crown-Rump Length or Sitting Height

No information is available on dimensional growth in fetal prosimians. However, among the New World forms of anthropoids, namely Bolivian squirrel monkeys in our laboratories, crown-rump length (CRL) as a function of gestational age from 114 to 155 days has been recorded as shown in Table 2. The correlation between CRL and body weight in these subjects was r = 0.978. When plotted relative to age, the greatest discrepancy between CRL and body weight functions is during the final 10 days before birth, when the CRL growth decelerates somewhat whereas body weight continues its linear relation to gestational age. A deceleration of CRL with the approach of birth as contrasted to a more linear relation between prenatal weight and age is also typical of the rhesus monkey, as will be seen next.

Data on fetal CRL in the rhesus monkey as presented in the van Wagenen et al [1965] study are shown in Figure 3. The fetal growth curve for this parameter shows a linear increase from 40 to nearly 100 days of gestation, but becomes negatively accelerated from about 100 days on into the early postnatal period. The values appear to be in good agreement with those of Heuser and Streeter [1941] throughout most of the extent of the curve, and the fetal growth curve also is closely

TABLE 3. Prenatal Organ Weights of Bolivian Squirrel Monkeys as Functions of Age From Fertilization Estimated by Linear Interpolation of Mean Body Weight

Estimated age[b]	BW	Thyroid	Kidneys (both)	Liver	Spleen	Adrenal	Lung	Salivary gland	Pancreas	Heart	Thymus	Small intestine
112	24–37 $\overline{X}=31$ N = 4	0.01 —[a]	0.22 (0.11)	0.78 (0.10)	0.05 (0.02)	0.10 —[a]	0.62 —[a]	0.01 —[a]	0.01 —[a]	0.18 —[a]	0.06 (0.03)	0.56 —[a]
124	48–55 $\overline{X}=51$ N = 3	0.05 —[a]	0.42 (0.05)	1.35 (0.6)	0.05 (0.2)	0.22 —[a]	1.64 —[a]	0.08 —[a]	0.04 —[a]	0.30 —[a]	0.13 (0.04)	0.83 —[a]
139	71–76 $\overline{X}=73$ N = 3	0.05 (0.01)	0.57 (0.12)	1.60 (0.16)	0.09 (0.02)	0.23 (0.02)	1.77 (0.13)	0.06 (0.02)	0.04 (0.01)	0.49 (0.02)	0.16 (0.02)	0.96 (0.10)
149	84 – 95 $\overline{X}=89$ N = 6	0.05 (0.02)	0.64 (0.09)	2.06 (0.35)	0.09 (0.02)	0.24 (0.02)	1.90 (0.31)	0.06 (0.03)	0.06 (0.02)	0.54 (0.08)	0.26 (0.05)	0.81 (0.28)
163	102–119 $\overline{X}=110$ N = 6	0.06 (0.03)	0.93 (0.40)	3.30 (0.86)	0.11 (0.03)	0.29 (0.07)	2.10 (0.62)	0.10 (0.03)	0.08 (0.04)	0.61 (0.06)	0.23 (0.06)	1.29 (0.22)

Note: Standard deviations are in parentheses.

[a]Based on one subject only.

[b]Age estimated by linear interpolation from mean body weight.

TABLE 4. The Growth in Weight of Major Organs During Fetal Life of the Rhesus Monkey

Organ	Gestation age (days)					
	50	75	100	125	150	175
Total body wt (gm)	4.003 ± 0.987	43.27 ± 3.49	149.29 ± 9.73	295.30 ± 27.00	467.38 ± 42.76	544.4 ± 101.6
Placenta (gm)	21.23 ± 6.59	59.99 ± 12.23	97.27 ± 14.66	114.82 ± 21.28	165.88 ± 33.82	206.40 ± 49.52
Brain (gm)	—	5.26 ± 0.64	18.36 ± 1.15	41.25 ± 3.57	51.85 ± 3.04	58.00 ± 5.97
Spleen (gm)	0.017	0.068 ± 0.014	0.271 ± 0.071	0.495 ± 0.096	0.739 ± 0.131	0.861 ± 0.265
Thyroid (gm)	—	0.015 ± 0.007	0.054 ± 0.011	0.0966 ± 0.052	0.175 ± 0.060	0.263 ± 0.137
Kidneys (gm)	0.017 ± 0.07	0.225 ± 0.080	1.145 ± 0.155	1.92 ± 0.37	2.37 ± 0.37	2.96 ± 0.67
Adrenals (gm)	0.007 ± 0.003	0.065 ± 0.022	0.138 ± 0.026	0.192 ± 0.026	0.259 ± 0.100	0.649 ± 0.279
Liver (gm)	0.148 ± 0.061	1.80 ± 0.40	5.84 ± 0.69	9.33 ± 1.38	14.81 ± 1.49	15.85 ± 2.84
Heart (gm)	0.025 ± 0.006	0.226 ± 0.048	0.800 ± 0.090	1.72 ± 0.39	2.66 ± 0.35	3.55 ± 1.22
Lungs (gm)	0.097 ± 0.41	1.32 ± 0.20	4.01 ± 0.88	6.48 ± 1.42	9.53 ± 1.27	6.29 ± 0.99
Thymus (gm)	—	0.086 ± 0.035	0.333 ± 0.126	0.829 ± 0.277	1.331 ± 0.432	0.635 ± 0.223

Figures indicate mean weight ± 1 standard deviation.
From Kerr et al [1969a], with permission.

comparable to that for sitting height for both the rhesus monkey and man reported by Schultz [1937] as illustrated in his Figure 1. According to the latter author, on the 83rd day after conception (midgestation) the rhesus fetus has an average sitting height (114 mm) which is more than half its average sitting height at term. The sitting height of human fetuses at midgestation (133 days) is less than half its size at term. The relative gain in length is smaller in the rhesus monkey than in man during the first and last quarters of prenatal life, but it is greater in the former than in the latter during the second and third quarters.

In another comparative study [Tanimura and Tanioka, 1975], it was shown that the mean CRL in the embryonic period in human embryos for a given age is slightly less than that of rhesus embryos (Fig. 4). For a given gestational age up to about 140 days in American human fetuses and 170 days in Japanese human fetuses, rhesus fetuses are taller than human fetuses.

As pointed out by Hendrickx and Houston [1971], the baboon and rhesus monkey fetuses develop at approximately the same rate through about the 11th gestational week. From the 11th week to the end of gestation, the baboon grows at a faster rate so that it is approximately 2 cm longer than the rhesus monkey at birth.

Proportional Growth
Chest and hip proportions. In rhesus monkeys the most significant body proportions according to Schultz [1937] are listed in Tables 5 and 6. These tables correspond to Schultz's Tables 2 and 3, but also include part of Schultz's Table 1 relating to the sex and known or estimated age of the animals studied. The averages of the various specific proportions in a series of selected, normal, fully adult male and female rhesus monkeys are given at the bottom of the tables. The figures presented in these tables represent the percentage value of the numerator in relation to the denominator.

The first proportion as presented by this author is chest girth relative to trunk height which expresses the degree of stoutness of the trunk. In the youngest fetuses the chest circumference is nearly three times as great as the trunk height. The percentage relation between these two measurements

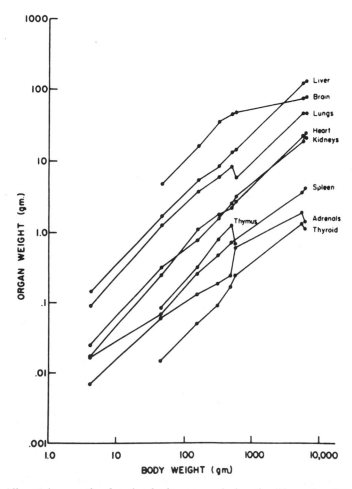

Fig. 2. Allometric growth of major body organs during the life cycle of the rhesus monkey. [From Kerr et al, 1969a, with permission.]

decreases rapidly with advancing fetal growth, but very little during postnatal growth.

Shoulder breadth/trunk height and hip breadth/ trunk height proportions show that the rhesus fetuses become relatively more slender with advancing growth. The percentage value of relative shoulder breadth decreases from 76 to 42 during fetal life and the relative hip breadth from 53 to 36, and most of this latter change occurs at the beginning of fetal growth. Schultz [1937] notes further that in young fetuses shoulder breadth surpasses hip breadth to a greater proportionate extent than in older fetuses and newborn, and in adults the two breadths have become nearly equal in size, with the hip breadth in females surpassing the shoulder breadth.

The proportion between the two chest diameters does not change notably during fetal life, but in the postnatal period chest depth increases slightly more than chest breadth. In the human fetus the chest index is about the same as in the rhesus fetus, but it increases with growth to 118 at birth and to about 130 in adults [Schultz, 1937]. In regard to this proportion the rhesus monkey agrees with other simpler primates, and the human agrees with the anthropoid apes [see Schultz, 1926, Table 6, and Schultz 1933, Tables 8 and 9].

Limb proportions. Information on changing limb proportions is lacking in the literature on prosimians and the New World anthropoids. In rhesus monkeys, as shown in Table 5 [Schultz,

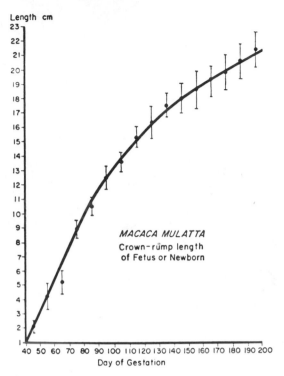

Fig. 3. Crown-rump length of fetuses removed at hysterotomy and of newborn infants (326 animals, day 40 to day 195). Means and standard deviation are shown. Curve fitted by eye. [From van Wagenen et al, 1965, with permission.]

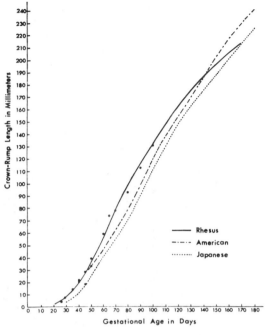

Fig. 4. Comparison of the prenatal growth among rhesus macaque embryos and fetuses, American human fetuses, and Japanese human embryos and fetuses. Fifteen rhesus specimens in the present study are shown as discrete points. [From Tanimura and Tanioka, 1975, with permission.]

1937], the relation in length between the upper and lower extremities decreases in prenatal as well as in postnatal life. As in man the upper limb grows more slowly than the lower limb in the first half of fetal life, but the index remains unaltered in the second half. At the beginning of fetal growth the limb indices of the rhesus monkey and man are nearly alike—eg, 139.6 in the former and 133 in the latter [Schultz, 1937]. However, during subsequent growth this index decreases much more in man than in the rhesus monkey, dropping to 114.2 in adult humans and, as seen in Table 6, to 125 in the rhesus monkey. In his text description Schultz [1937] gives the ultimate intramembral index in man as 83 and in the rhesus monkey as from 111 to 114.

The percentage proportion between leg length and thigh length (crural index) in the rhesus monkey increases during early fetal growth, with the leg growing faster than the thigh. After the age of 117 days of gestation this index doesn't undergo

any further changes. The corresponding proportion of the upper extremity (brachial index) between forearm and upper arm lengths (Table 6) also increases with advanced age, from about 76 in the youngest fetus to 95 at term.

Foot length in the youngest monkey fetus exceeds the leg by 56% of the latter measurement, and the hand length surpasses the forearm by 7%. In a relatively short period, however, these indices drop markedly, but they increase again in later fetal life to about 130 and 90, respectively. In postnatal life both indices drop markedly again. Similar alterations in the relative rates of growth of the middle and distal limb segments are observed in man [see Schultz, 1926, Fig. 3].

The relative length of the thumb was greatest in the youngest of the rhesus fetuses in Schultz's series [1937]. This author notes that relative thumb length undergoes no further significant change in older fetuses. The relative breadth of the hand decreases with advancing growth in all primates

TABLE 5. Body Proportions of Rhesus Monkeys

Sex	Age (days) Known	Age (days) Estimated	Chest circumference/ trunk height	Shoulder breadth/ trunk height	Hip breadth/ trunk height	Chest breadth/ chest depth	Nipple height/ trunk height	Tail length/ sitting height	Total lower-limb length/ trunk height	Total upper-limb length/ trunk height	Total upper-limb length/ total lower limb length	Leg length/ thigh length
?	44	—	282.3	76.5	52.9	98.6	?	27.3	80.0	111.6	139.6	71.4
M	53	—	178.6	50.0	38.3	94.7	72.8	27.3	77.7	109.6	141.2	79.2
M	57	—	160.7	43.8	34.4	95.9	74.4	32.6	80.4	111.0	138.0	81.2
M	66	—	141.8	44.2	34.9	97.2	76.7	40.0	81.3	105.8	130.0	83.4
M	75	—	153.8	46.0	35.4	96.2	77.9	40.0	91.2	113.3	124.5	86.2
F	86	—	149.8	44.1	35.0	96.3	77.5	39.0	89.2	114.0	128.0	83.3
F	100	—	141.0	44.1	36.8	96.4	75.0	37.4	100.0	126.4	126.4	88.2
F	117	—	146.3	54.9	40.2	92.3	74.3	45.8	101.2	134.2	132.5	92.5
M	125	—	154.7	54.7	41.7	92.5	78.5	50.9	101.1	131.0	129.4	91.4
F	—	120	154.1	49.4	40.9	98.6	78.3	55.0	109.0	142.2	130.4	90.7
F	—	125	148.8	48.8	39.5	97.3	78.4	?	108.0	137.8	127.4	90.0
F	120	—	132.6	42.9	36.4	97.4	77.2	46.5	104.3	134.2	128.6	91.5
F	—	132	126.0	42.7	37.5	92.1	76.1	49.1	105.2	132.3	125.7	93.8
M	—	136	130.0	44.3	37.1	97.5	77.3	47.8	103.0	134.0	130.0	91.7
F	—	141	147.5	48.5	39.4	100.0	77.8	54.0	113.1	143.4	126.7	90.7
M	—	142	141.4	45.5	37.4	97.6	76.8	56.0	109.1	138.3	126.8	91.3
F	—	143	141.8	45.9	38.3	92.8	78.6	?	112.2	141.8	126.3	90.6
F	145	—	134.2	46.6	38.1	97.5	80.0	50.8	110.4	139.0	125.7	92.8
M	146	—	131.1	48.1	37.7	96.4	80.1	53.2	109.3	138.6	126.7	93.0
F	146	—	129.6	45.3	36.1	92.7	77.7	55.3	101.8	129.6	127.2	92.4
M	—	150	144.0	48.0	39.2	93.4	78.4	55.0	115.6	147.0	127.0	92.8
F	155	—	129.0	45.8	39.2	93.8	75.7	56.3	114.9	143.4	124.7	94.0
F	—	152	135.9	45.6	39.8	93.4	75.2	57.5	118.5	152.4	128.6	91.5
F	162	—	129.4	43.7	38.4	97.7	79.4	56.3	112.5	136.5	121.4	91.9
M	169	—	131.4	44.4	37.9	91.3	79.1	53.7	114.8	142.5	124.1	90.0
M	170	—	125.0	41.9	36.3	91.5	79.8	59.9	110.5	138.2	125.1	92.3
A			97.4	31.9	32.5	89.2	79.2	45.3	99.5	111.5	111.1	90.6
B			111.2	37.7	34.1	86.8	80.8	47.7	96.6	110.3	114.2	91.3

A = averages of 17 adult females; B = averages of five adult males.
From Schultz [1937], with permission.

TABLE 6. Body Proportions of Rhesus Monkeys (Continued from Table 5)

	Age (days)			Forearm length/ upper arm length	Foot length/ leg length	Hand length/ forearm length	Thumb length/ hand length	Hand breadth/ hand length	Average head diameter/ trunk height	Total face height/ trunk height	Upper face height/ average head diameter	Inner eye breadth/ face breadth	Ear height × breadth/ head length × total head height
Sex	Known	Estimated											
?	44	—		75.7	155.9	107.1	66.7	70.0	103.5	48.2	34.1	40.0	2.2
M	53	—		81.5	121.5	78.7	59.3	55.9	69.4	33.0	34.9	30.0	2.4
M	57	—		75.4	115.2	81.9	58.8	54.4	66.8	31.9	35.0	28.6	2.7
M	66	—		85.7	106.6	86.7	56.1	50.0	55.5	27.9	36.5	25.0	4.6
M	75	—		88.2	113.5	83.4	54.4	46.1	56.1	30.1	37.9	19.7	4.5
F	86	—		86.5	128.8	88.9	57.5	45.0	52.5	28.3	38.1	19.4	5.3
F	100	—		90.6	120.0	86.2	56.0	42.4	51.9	27.9	39.6	21.5	8.7
F	117	—		90.0	135.0	94.4	54.4	44.1	55.2	26.8	39.7	19.1	9.3
M	125	—		90.0	138.5	94.4	58.8	42.7	54.4	27.4	41.5	19.1	11.2
F	—	120		90.5	138.4	100.0	57.9	41.6	55.6	28.9	39.4	21.0	10.8
F	—	125		89.4	133.3	100.0	57.9	40.8	53.7	29.0	40.0	21.9	12.0
F	120	—		92.0	127.8	96.3	53.9	38.5	49.3	26.1	41.9	21.4	10.9
F	—	132		89.1	134.7	97.5	53.7	38.7	47.9	26.0	40.8	19.0	13.5
M	—	136		91.4	136.2	93.0	57.5	40.0	48.7	25.8	42.2	18.6	14.3
F	—	141		92.1	134.6	93.6	54.6	40.9	49.3	28.3	43.0	20.9	15.6
M	—	142		91.8	134.6	95.6	55.8	39.5	49.5	28.3	40.8	20.9	13.6
F	—	143		93.7	137.4	102.2	56.5	38.7	50.9	27.5	41.1	21.1	13.5
F	145	—		92.4	129.8	89.8	56.8	40.9	47.3	26.6	42.3	19.1	17.3
M	146	—		92.4	126.3	91.8	57.8	40.0	46.8	26.4	42.3	20.4	17.8
F	146	—		92.0	136.6	95.7	56.8	38.6	44.3	25.0	41.8	22.6	15.1
M	—	**150**		92.5	138.4	92.0	56.5	39.1	48.0	27.4	40.8	20.4	14.7
F	155	—		93.4	133.3	97.0	59.2	37.7	46.7	25.2	41.0	21.1	15.6
F	—	**152**		94.4	135.0	96.1	53.0	38.0	47.3	28.2	45.1	20.9	18.4
F	162	—		92.7	127.0	92.2	59.6	40.4	46.1	25.9	42.5	19.1	16.6
M	169	—		94.5	133.2	90.4	53.2	40.4	47.8	29.6	46.4	19.5	14.4
M	170	—		95.0	131.0	94.7	52.8	37.0	43.3	28.2	46.5	20.8	14.7
A				94.9	97.7	69.3	57.1	34.0	20.4	19.2	71.3	15.7	14.2
B				99.2	100.7	72.4	54.8	35.1	22.3	21.4	71.3	16.9	16.4

A = averages of **17 adult** females; B = averages of five adult males.
From Schultz [1937], **with permission.**

TABLE 7. Growth in Body Weight

							Age (days)								
	Birth	7	14	21	28	42	56	90	120	150	180	210	240	300	360
Body weight (gm) (n = 27)	472 ± 56	476 ± 60	530 ± 69	570 ± 68	619 ± 73	717 ± 86	816 ± 100	962 ± 106	1,158 ± 137	1,340 ± 150	1,512 ± 154	1,669 ± 182	1,829 ± 208	2,089 ± 242	2,380 ± 330
Rate of growth (gm/kg/day)[a]	—	1.3 ± 5.7	16.3 ± 6.4	11.0 ± 5.7	12.3 ± 5.3	10.4 ± 2.9	9.9 ± 4.4	8.8 ± 1.8	6.8 ± 1.1	5.3 ± 1.0	4.3 ± 1.1	3.5 ± 1.1	3.2 ± 1.1	2.7 ± 1.0	2.0 ± 0.7

All values expressed as mean ± 1 SD.

[a]The rate of growth was calculated separately for each animal; figures represent the mean values ± 1 SD for all animals. Calculations are based on the rate of growth for the previous 7-day period prior to 60 days of age; thereafter for the previous 30-day period. From Kerr et al [1969b], with permission.

TABLE 8. Birth Changes in Kilograms per 6 Months, in Lowland and Mountain Gorillas

Age (yr)	Lowland gorilla			Mountain gorilla		
	♂ Gust	♀ Kora	♂ Kaisi	♂ Kisubi	♀ Pega	♀ Quivu
0.5	—	—	—	—	—	—
1	—	—	—	—	—	—
1.5	—	—	—	—	—	—
2	+ 4.9	—	—	—	—	—
2.5	+ 7.7	—	+ 3.8	+ 3.5	—	—
3	+ 1.0	+ 5.3	+ 3.9	+ 3.4	—	—
3.5	+ 3.0	+ 3.2	+ 5.3	+ 5.4	—	—
4	+ 4.0	+ 3.2	+ 1.2	+ 2.7	—	—
4.5	− 2.0	+ 3.2	+ 5.1	+ 4.8	+ 5.8	—
5	+ 5.4	+ 4.9	+ 6.0	+ 4.7	+ 8.3	—
5.5	+ 6.0	− 1.0	+ 4.0	+ 3.8	+ 6.6	+10.3
6	+ 3.7	+ 1.5	+ 5.3	+ 4.8	+ 2.0	+ 6.3
6.5	+ 1.8	+ 2.1	+ 8.0	+ 6.5	+ 3.6	+ 5.3
7	+ 7.4	+ 0.8	+ 7.5	+ 7.1	+ 5.9	+ 2.4
7.5	+ 7.1	+16.3	+ 6.9	+ 5.2	+ 6.1	+ 7.0
8	+ 8.9	+ 8.0	+11.7	+ 6.7	+ 3.4	+ 7.7
8.5	+ 7.3	+ 2.8	+10.4	+ 8.6	+11.2	− 1.2
9	+11.4	+ 3.8	+14.2	+11.4	+ 8.7	+ 4.3
9.5	+11.8	+ 4.1	+12.0	+13.2	+ 1.6	+ 3.7
10	+ 6.6	+ 0.8	+ 9.8	+ 5.0	− 1.0	+ 1.4
10.5	+ 7.4	+ 4.0	+11.8	+ 7.3	− 1.7	—
11	+11.8	+ 0.5	+ 2.7	+ 2.7	+ 1.4	—
11.5	+ 8.4	+ 5.1	+14.4	+ 4.8	—	—
12	+ 4.0	+ 1.4	+ 6.3	+ 4.2	—	—
12.5	+ 1.5	+ 0.3	+ 7.2	− 0.3	—	—
13	− 0.9	− 0.6	+ 0.8	+ 1.2	—	—
13.5	+ 8.0	+ 0.5	+ 0.6	+ 1.0	—	—
14	+ 0.5	− 0.6	+ 1.3	+ 0.7	—	—
14.5	+ 6.8	− 0.3	—	—	—	—
15	+ 5.3	—	—	—	—	—
15.5	+ 0.4	—	—	—	—	—
16	+ 0.6	—	—	—	—	—
16.5	+ 2.2	—	—	—	—	—
17	+ 1.4	—	—	—	—	—
17.5	+ 0.8	—	—	—	—	—
18	—	—	—	—	—	—

From Gijzen and Tijkens [1971], with permission of the publisher.

[Schultz, 1937]. In Schultz's studies the rhesus hand breadth constituted 70% of the hand length in the youngest fetus, 37% in newborns, and about 35% in adults.

Head Diameter

No information is available in the literature on changing head dimensions in fetal prosimians. In Bolivian squirrel monkeys, head circumference as a function of gestational age is provided in Table 2. Although head circumference shows a nega-

tively accelerated function of gestational age, circumference can be converted to approximate head volume by the formula $V = C^3/(\pi^2)$. Estimated head volume shows a much more linear but slightly decelerating relation to prenatal age, and, as would be expected, correlates highly with brain weight, $r = 0.995$. In rhesus monkeys [Schultz, 1937] the average percentage relationship of the relative head diameter (average head diameter/trunk height) (Table 6) is 43.3 in newborns, 20.4 in adult females, and 22.3 in adult males as compared with

TABLE 9. Birth Weights and Weight Increases of Zoo-Born Orang-utans, *Pongo pygmaeus*

Number, sex, name, and birthplace of orang-utans	Date of birth	Weights in gm							
		First day	3 Months	6 Months	9 Months	12 Months	18 Months	24 Months	36 Months
1. ♂ Henry St. Louis	8/18/63	1,755	4,875			6,580	8,170	10,440	
2. ♂ Marudi Colorado Springs	9/5/64	1,590	3,520	3,400		6,800			
3. ♂ Toni Hamburg	9/10/64	1,600	3,680[a]	4,400[b]	5,070	6,500	7,500	9,300	
4. ♂ Sigli Colorado Springs	9/27/64	1,815	4,100	6,000					
5. ♂ Viko Nuremberg	1/13/65	1,650	4,130	5,860	7,500	9,500	14,500	16,400	19,900
6. ♂ No name Dallas	5/30/65	1,750							
7. ♂ Sandy Columbus	1/21/62	2,015	3,320	5,275		5,620	5,960	6,360	12,430
8. ♂ Noell San Diego	12/25/55	1,420	2,835	4,025	5,220	6,230			
9. ♀ Roberta San Diego	2/5/58	1,710	2,815	4,080	5,274				
10. ♀ Elli Vienna	12/26/59	2,040		5,280					
11. ♀ Ani W. Berlin	6/28/66	1,650	3,000	3,505					
12. ♀ Daisy Dallas	9/10/66	1,650	2,610	2,810	5,190	6,415			
13. ♀ Carmen St. Louis	7/17/66	1,050		4,540	5,900	7,066			
14. ♂ Anak W. Berlin	12/21/65			3,700	5,810	7,200	11,200	17,100	
15. ♂ Samu Detroit	7/9/66		3,490	6,040	8,300	11,500			
16. ♀ Marud Nuremberg	3/17/66			3,500	5,400	6,700	9,100	10,100	

[a]Weight at 94 days.
[b]Weight at 186 days.
From Seitz [1969], with permission.

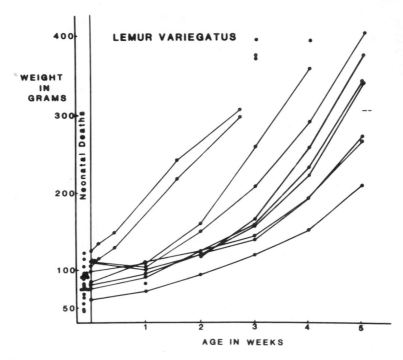

Fig. 5. Weights of 24 perinatal deaths, three neonates, ten hand-raised *Lemur variegatus* newborns, and five young animals. [From Benirschke and Miller, 1981, with permission.]

56.6 in newborns and 31.1 in adult human subjects of both sexes. According to Schultz [1937], the value at birth in percentage of the value in adult life is 214 in the monkey and 182 in man. The reduction in relative head size at the time of birth has, therefore, not gone as far toward its final condition in adult monkeys as in adult human subjects.

Facial Dimensions

The total height of the face in rhesus monkeys in relation to the height of the trunk becomes smaller with advancing prenatal growth. This relative face height decreases during early fetal life from about 48 to 28 (Table 6) and after birth decreases further to about 20. In man the same proportion decreases from 40 to 28 during fetal growth and to 23 during postnatal growth. Thus the total ontogenetic change is smaller in man than in the rhesus, but proceeds in the same direction in both.

The proportion between the facial components of the skull and those that form the brain case is best expressed, according to Schultz [1937], by the percentage relationship between the upper face height and the average head diameter. In the rhesus monkey this index increases steadily (Table 6) during growth before and after birth, demonstrating that the face grows faster than the brain case. This proportion is much smaller in man than in the monkey.

Postnatal Period

Ponderal Growth

Body Weight

Although data on birth weights for lemurs and other prosimians are rather rare, Benirschke and Miller [1981] recently published birth weights for nine ring-tailed lemurs (*Lemur catta*) which died perinatally as ranging between 50 and 70 gm. They concluded on the basis of histologic examination of the renal cortices that weights below 55 gm are indicative of immaturity. In a single animal that was successfully hand-raised, the body weight was approximately 72 gm at 1 week, 92 gm at 2 weeks, 127 gm at 3 weeks, and 170 gm at 4 weeks.

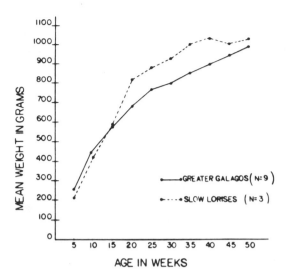

MEAN WEIGHT IN GRAMS

AGE IN WEEKS

●━━●GREATER GALAGOS (N=9)

●----●SLOW LORISES (N= 3)

Fig. 6. Mean weight gain during first fifty weeks of life in twelve mother-reared infants. [From Ehrlich, 1974, with permission.]

In the red-ruffed lemur (*Lemur variegatus ruber*) birth weights of seven animals that died perinatally varied from about 25 to 100 gm. The mean weights of a pair of twins that were successfully hand-raised increased from roughly 150 gm at 1 week to about 280 gm at 2 weeks, 360 gm at 3 weeks, and 370 gm at 4 weeks. Data from a large group of the black-and-white-ruffed lemur (*L. variegatus variegatus*) from the studies of Benirschke and Miller [1981] are shown in Figure 5. This figure shows the weights of 24 animals which died neo-natally and the individual growth curves for ten neonates which survived at least to 5 weeks of age.

In a male potto (*Periodicticus potto*) born in captivity [Grand et al, 1964], body weight increased from approximately 65 to 70 gm at 4 days of age to about 675 gm at 109 days of age. It was evident from their Table 1 that growth progressed at a steady rate in a linear pattern. The authors state that the animal attained a tenfold increase in body weight in 109 days, presumably from birth, although the birth weight is not stated.

Mean birth weights in the greater galago (*Galago crassicaudatus*) (n = 9) and slow loris (*Nycticebus coucang*) (n = 3) were 46.4 and 46.7 gm, respectively [Ehrlich, 1974], despite the fact that the mean length of the gestation period was 187 days in the loris as compared with 128 days in the galago (P < 0.01). The mean weight in grams

during the first 50 weeks of life in these species is illustrated in Figure 6.

In a captive-born, hand-reared specimen of the lesser bush baby (*Galago senegalensis*), body weight increased from about 40 gm a few but unknown number of days after its birth, to 110 gm approximately 100 days later [Ward and Scott, 1970]. In another animal reared by its mother, a weight increase of about the same magnitude occurred over a period of about 70 days.

Gucwinska and Gucwinski [1968] reported the body weight of twin specimens of *G. senegalensis* as 14.3 and 13.0 gm at 2 days of age, 21.9 and 26.4 gm at 7 days, 38.4 and 48.4 gm at 14 days, 41.1 and 51.7 gm at 28 days, 35.1 and 45.1 gm at 31 days, and 62.7 gm at 39 days in a single specimen of a twin pair. In single-born animals they reported a weight of 15.0 gm at 1 day, 25.0 gm at 12 days, 52.5 gm at 22 days, and 63.1 gm at 28 days.

In the family Callitrichidae (marmosets) born in captivity, birth weight has been reported as 34.7 gm in a female newborn (*Callithrix jacchus*) and 41 gm in a newborn of the tamarin (*Saguinus geoffroyi*) [Epple, 1970]. In a male *Callithrix* body weight increased from 70 gm at 38 days to 105 gm at 73 days, 164 gm at 130 days, 266 gm at 253 days, 377 gm at 532 days, and 375 gm at 2¼ years. A female weighed 70 gm at 42 days, 88 gm at 60 days, 137 gm at 119 days, 201 gm at 259 days, 221 gm at 400 days, and 300 gm at 2 years. Thus, although the comparative ages do not compare very closely, it is evident that male weight exceeds and diverges from that of the female after about the 120th postnatal day.

An increase in postnatal body weight in a female Goeldii marmoset (*Callimico goeldii*) from 55 gm at 29 days postnatal age to 265 gm at 125 days of age, 525 gm at 341 days of age, and 570 gm at 497 days of age was reported by Lorenz and Heinemann [1967; their Fig. 6 and Table 1]. Two male animals increased in weight from 100 and 110 gm at 27 and 24 days of age to 315 gm at 116 days and 290 gm at 122 days, respectively. One of these males then increased in weight to 635 gm at 329 days while the other increased to 335 gm at 163 days. From these data it appears that males are considerably heavier than females at comparable age levels, but more data are needed to gain a clear picture of ponderal growth in this species.

Birth weight in both sexes of captive-bred squirrel monkeys of Bolivian and Colombian subspe-

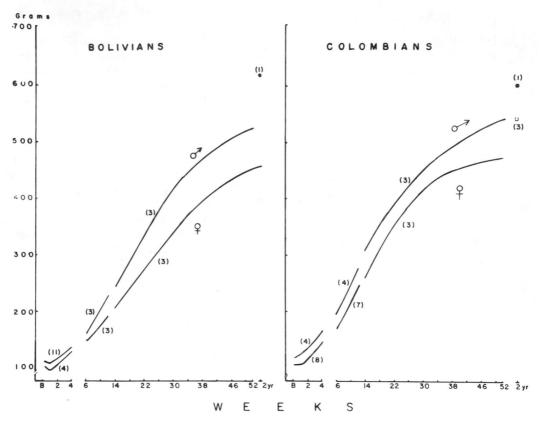

Fig. 7. Mean body weight for squirrel monkeys from the day of birth through 2 years. Number of subjects in group in parentheses. [From Kaack et al, 1979, with permission.]

cies as measured in our laboratory are shown in Figure 7 [Kaack et al, 1979]. In the same figure it can be observed that body weight in both of these subspecies after the first week of life increases more or less at a steady pace until approximately the 30th month. After 20 months the slope of the curves for both sexes in both subspecies decreased, the overall growth curve for the 2-year period following birth being sigmoid. In a later study [Walker et al, 1981], it was shown that Colombian offspring were significantly heavier (P = 0.006) than their Bolivian counterparts across the first 28 postnatal days.

Another study of physical growth and brain development in captive-bred squirrel monkeys (subspecies not given) was conducted by Manocha [1979]. This author reported that the male grows significantly faster in postnatal life, starting from the preweaning stage, than does the female. During prenatal life, male and female fetuses grow at the same rates with regard to body weight and brain weight.

The values for body weight reported by Long and Cooper [1968], Manocha [1979], and Kaplan [1974] for Colombian squirrel monkeys are consistently higher at comparable age levels than the weights observed in our studies. The weights of Peruvian squirrel monkeys were significantly lower (P < 0.01) than the Colombian animals [Kaplan, 1974], and the differences were accentuated as the animals became older. The values presented by Ploog et al [1967] for body weight in squirrel monkeys of unknown subspecies appear to be more comparable to those obtained in our laboratory than the values reported by Long and Cooper [1968] or Kaplan [1974].

In female *Cebus* monkeys (*C. albifrons*) Wilen and Naftolin [1978] reported that the average weight at birth (n = 10) was 226 ± 5.8 gm and at puberty was 1,617 ± 32.45 gm. The average age at puberty was 3.59 ± 0.17 years. The average weight velocity for the ten monkeys included in the study showed the maximum rate of weight gain to occur shortly after birth and to decrease rapidly to its smallest prepubertal increment at 9 months of age (weaning). From 9 months there was a postweaning weight spurt which reached its greatest velocity at an average age of 15 months. Thereafter, the weight velocity decreased to its lowest level.

Fleagle and Samonds [1975] gave the mean birth weight for female *Cebus* monkeys (*C. albifrons*) to be 222.1 ± 9.1 gm (n = 14) and for males at 250.7 ± 18.9 gm (n = 20). At 1 year of age the corresponding values in the same subjects were 1,167.9 ± 104.9 gm in females and 1,388.8 ± 128.7 gm in males. Males are consistently heavier than females at all ages.

In a more recent study of growth, development, and body composition in *Cebus* monkeys (*C. albifrons*) hand-reared from birth and fed semipurified "control" diets, Ausman et al [1982] in their Figures 1 and 2 plot the mean body weight in males (n = 50) as increasing from about 300 gm at birth to about 2,800 gm at 450 weeks of age. The mean adult weight of males from a breeding colony (n = 24) at 500 weeks of age was 3,258 ± 858 gm. In females (n = 35) the mean body weight increased from about 200 gm at birth to nearly 2,000 gm at 400 weeks of age. The mean adult body weight of females from the same breeding colony (n = 43) referred to above was 2,130 ± 564 gm. An exponential equation relating body weight to age (R^2 = 0.999) described the pattern of growth for the first 2 years of life.

In owl monkeys (*Aotus trivirgatus griseimembra*) body weights were shown in six male subjects between 114 and 711 days of age [Dixson et al, 1980, Fig. 4, p. 137). Estimating body weights from that figure, it appears that body weight increased in these subjects from about 400 gm to 900 gm in that time period. The weight range for adult males was given as from 800 gm to 1,080 gm.

For howler monkeys (*Alouatta caraya*) very few anthropometric data are available [Malinow et al, 1966]. Fully mature male howler monkeys weighed from 4.0 to 9.9 kg, and female weights ranged from 4.0 to 6.5 kg [Malinow et al, 1966]. It was not possible in that study to prove that a truly random sample of the field distribution of the animals had been obtained. However, from the data

at hand, it appeared likely that normal adult females were somewhat smaller than males. The animals of both sexes showed about the same amount of tooth wear and eye lens weight, thus suggesting general equality of ages. The data published by Malinow et al [1966] on the howler monkey appear to be generally in accord with the growth patterns of rhesus monkeys, chimpanzees, and humans.

In an analysis of growth in body weight in 13 male and 18 female captive-born patas monkeys (*Erythrocebus patas*) from birth to 6 months of age, as indicated by gain in body weight [Sly et al, 1978], a linear growth rate was reported during the first year of life. The mean birth weight for males was 541 ± 33 gm and females weighed 468 ± 54 gm at birth. The difference in male and female birth weight was statistically significant at the 0.1% level and persisted through the first year. Subjects of both sexes more than doubled their birth weight by 1½ months of age. Average weights at 1 year of age were 3,010 gm for males and 2,590 gm for females.

The average birth weight for captive-born rhesus monkey (*Macaca mulatta*) female offspring (n = 50) was 465 ± 70 gm (range: 325–640 gm) [van Wagenen and Catchpole, 1956]. In the male offspring (n = 37–43) the average body weight at birth was 490 ± 60 gm (range: 390–670 gm). In the early postnatal period in rhesus monkeys, nursing infants usually lost weight during the postnatal period. However, among female offspring most subjects regained their birth weight within the first 2 weeks, and the birth weight doubled in 92 ± 21 days, ranging from 53 to 150 days. Formula-fed animals (n = 32) achieved straight-line growth by the end of the first week and thereafter gained 45 gm weekly. Breast-fed animals (n = 38) reached straight-line growth in the third week after which they showed weekly increments of 35 gm. The time required to double the birth weight was significantly earlier in formula-fed than in breast-fed female offspring.

In male offspring, as in females, birth weights were regained within the first 2 weeks and were doubled at 90 days, ranging from 50 to 140 days. Doubling time had no apparent relationship to birth weight. As in female offspring, the weight curve in formula-fed males (n = 29) became a straight line at the end of the first week and at the end of the third week in nursing subjects (n = 26). In the female offspring (n = 50 to 24) body weight

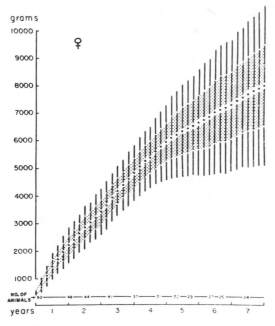

Fig. 8. Body weight of female macaques in relation to chronological age. Included are areas showing one standard deviation of the mean (68.3%) and two standard deviations (95.4%). [From van Wagenen and Catchpole, 1956, with permission.]

increases with chronological age are illustrated in Figure 8 [van Wagenen and Catchpole, 1956]. As illustrated in the figure, the slope of the curve is relatively steep and the variability in weight values increases with age. The variability becomes relatively large after the fifth year, at which time the curve flattens somewhat.

The increment in body weight of female offspring was greatest (140–170 gm/mo) during the first 7 months (Fig. 9) and diminished to 90–100 gm/mo at 1.5–1.83 years [van Wagenen and Catchpole, 1956]. A growth spurt then occurred, reaching 140 gm/mo at 2.33 years. It was observed in this group of animals that the "adolescence" growth spurt at the end of the second year coincided closely with the mean date of menarche.

In male offspring (n = 28 to 6) a notable increase in slope of the composite growth curve was observed at 2.5 years (Fig. 10), but did not plateau through the sixth and seventh years as in the female group [van Wagenen and Catchpole, 1956]. The initial increments are high (170 gm/mo) in the first year but decreased to 100 gm/mo toward the

end of the second year (Fig. 11). In the third year and continuing through the first half of the fourth year a marked growth spurt was observed, attaining a maximum of 220 gm/mo in the latter half of the third year. Following this growth spurt the increments fall to 60–70 gm/mo at 5.5–6 years. The growth spurt surpasses that in the female in extent and duration, and was believed to be due to the anabolic effect of the male sex hormone.

In another well-controlled study by Kerr et al [1969b], 27 newborns were separated from their mothers within 4 hours of birth and placed on a standardized diet at about 8 hours of age. The feedings were carried out at 4-hour intervals and records were kept for the first year of life of daily weight changes. In eight of these animals (3 females and 5 males), changes in length and head circumference were also recorded at 15-day intervals for the first 3 months, and thereafter at monthly intervals.

The growth in body weight for the 27 animals (9 females and 18 males) through a 1-year period is shown in Table 7 [Kerr et al, 1969b]. Since significant differences between the results observed in the sexes were not evident, the data from both sexes were combined. In these studies those infant monkeys that had been weighed at 4-hour intervals during the first week of life lost approximately 10% of their birth weight (50 gm) by 36 hours of age. In close agreement with the findings of van Wagenen and Catchpole [1956], they recovered this weight by the end of the fourth postnatal day. Body weight showed a steady increase during the first year, but the rate of weight gain (gm/kg/day) reached a peak value during the first month and showed a steady decrease thereafter (Table 7).

In another fairly recent study of a group of 19 male and seven female wild-captured *M. mulatta*, total body weight was recorded once each year for 7 years beginning at the end of 2 years [Kirk, 1972]. The age at the inception of the study was estimated from dental examination. Changes in body weight throughout this time period were quite similar to the van Wagenen and Catchpole [1956] data for males and females. It is interesting that the results of the two studies are closely comparable despite the fact that one group was captive-born and the other wild-born.

In the stump-tailed monkey (*M. arctoides*) mean body weight at birth appeared to be approximately 430 gm [estimated from Scheffler and Kerr, 1975,

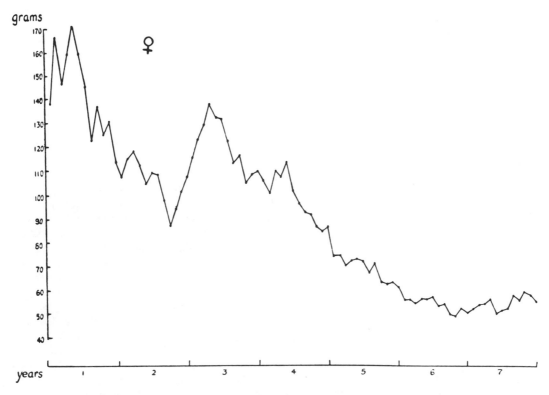

grams

years

Fig. 9. Weight increment curve for female macaques. Numbers of animals as in Figure 8. [From van Wagenen and Catchpole, 1956, with permission.]

Fig. 1]. Body weight in this species at 1 week of age is given as 450 gm by Faucheux et al [1978] and increases steadily during the first year (Fig. 12), with the mean 30-day value for this parameter being significantly greater in males than females (P < 0.005). The differences in rate of physical growth between the sexes, however, were not statistically significant [Scheffler and Kerr, 1975].

Comparing the data of Kerr et al [1969b] on the rhesus monkey with those of Scheffler and Kerr [1975] on the stump-tailed monkey, it is evident that body weight is greater in the stumptails than in the rhesus monkeys. The rate of growth in body weight, however, is very similar in the two species; rhesus monkeys grew 392% and stumptails grew 409% during the first postnatal year.

The data of Faucheux et al [1978] in both zoo-bred (n = 7 females, 3 males) and lab-bred (n = 5 females, 1 male) stumptails also appear to be in general agreement with those of Scheffler and Kerr [1975] in that weight and linear measurements in this species increased rapidly during the first year

of life. Faucheux et al [1978], however, continuing their studies into the pubertal period, observed that growth occurred more slowly until 2.5 years of age. The growth rate increased again during the pubertal period (Fig. 12). This growth spurt was more obvious for body weight than for body dimensions, and more evident in males than in females. Adult weight and linear dimensions began to stabilize around 3.5–4 years of age in both sexes, but weight continued to increase for several years.

Data on birth weight in the pig-tailed monkey (*M. nemestrina*) are not available, but postnatal weight gain in laboratory specimens of this species up to 10 years of age is illustrated by Rosenblum and Smiley [1980] in their Figure 1. These authors noted that sexual dimorphism in weight gain did not become evident until the age of 4 years. Weight gain in males accelerated from about 1 kg/yr to 2 kg/yr at 4 years of age, and this rate was maintained through 8.5 years of age, the adult weight averaging 16.5 kg. In females the weight gain was

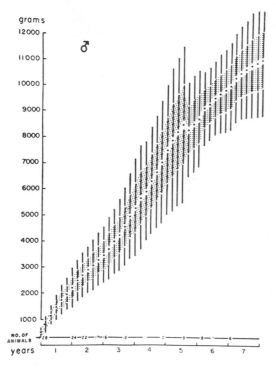

Fig. 10. Body weight of male macaques in relation to chronological age. Means with one (68.3%) and two (95.4%) standard deviations. [From van Wagenen and Catchpole, 1956, with permission.]

approximately 1 kg/yr through the age of 6 years after which the weights became relatively stable, the adult weight averaging 7.0 kg.

Average weights of male and female bonnet macaques (*M. radiata*) are illustrated by Rosenblum and Smiley [1980] in their Figures 2 and 3. The authors show growth curves for normal and obese animals of the same sex together to illustrate the progression of abnormal weight gains as compared to weight gain in normal development. The authors noted that divergence from the normal weight curve became evident at 5.5 years for female obese and at 7 years for male obese animals. In females, the initial weight gain progressed at the rate of 0.5 kg/yr for both normal and obese subjects. At 5.5 years of age, however, the weight stabilized at about 5.0 kg in normal females, but continued to increase at about 1.0 kg/yr in obese subjects. In males, both normal and obese subjects gained weight at a rate of 0.5 kg/yr for the first 3 years. From 3 to 6 years of age, both groups gained

weight at a rate of 1.5 kg/yr. In normal males, weight gain was gradual from 6 to 8 years, and body weight stabilized at an average of about 9.0 kg by 8 years of age. Weight gain in normal animals decelerated after 6 years of age, but obese subjects continued to gain weight at a rate of 1.5 kg/yr over the next 6 years. From these studies, it appears that in bonnet macaques, obesity progresses after the age at which normal animals begin weight maintenance. The incidence of spontaneous obesity in the laboratory-born specimens in this species was about 20%. In pig-tailed monkeys the incidence was less than 2%.

In laboratory-born Japanese macaques (*M. fuscata*) the average body weight at birth of 12 subjects (10 males and 2 females) was 472 ± 62 gm [Ohno et al, 1980]. These workers observed that subjects weighing less than 350 gm at birth could not survive. In their Figure 1 they plot the relative change of body weight as a percent of the body weight in fully mature animals. The values appeared to increase in males from about 8% at 3 months of age to about 32% at 33 months of age. As noted by the authors, the rate of increase of body weight was almost comparable in the male and the female, but the data on body weight showed a little higher value in the males than in the females. These authors also plotted the relative growth curves for male and female wild Japanese macaques from the data of Hazama [1964]. The values for wild-born females were higher throughout the period covered (from about 3 months to 36 months) than for laboratory-born females. In males the values for wild-born subjects were higher than for laboratory-born animals from about 14 months of age to about 36 months.

In crab-eating macaques (*Macaca fascicularis*) the mean birth weight (n = 24) was 338 ± 80 gm with a range of 153–470 gm [Berkson, 1968]. It is evident from these values that birth weight as well as adult weight (mean about 1.15 kg) in this species is substantially less than in the rhesus monkey. Weight increments during the first year of life were plotted by half-month intervals as illustrated in their Figure 1. The animals were divided into five groups separated from their mothers at birth and at 1, 2, 4, and 6 months of age and fed ad lib with monkey bisquits with fruit and vitamin supplements. The weight changes through the first year were substantially the same for all five groups. The mean weight for all five groups increased in a fairly linear pattern from about 0.40 kg at 1 month

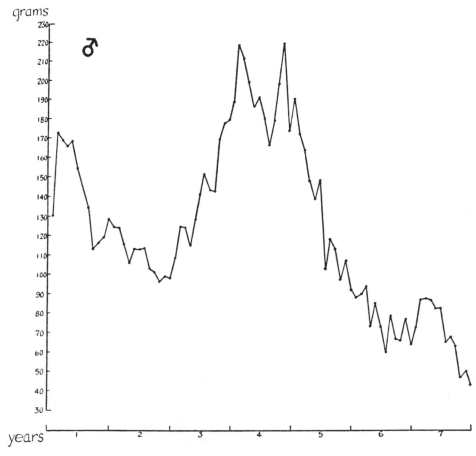

grams

years

Fig. 11. Weight increment curve for male macaques. Numbers of animals as in Figure 10. [From van Wagenen and Catchpole, 1956, with permission.]

postnatal age to about 1.1 kg at 6 months. An analysis of variance for repeated measures showed no significant effect of the time of maternal separation.

In proboscis monkeys (*Nasalis larvatus*) the youngest specimen reported by Schultz [1942] showed a conspicuous and quite fresh umbilical scar and had only a few milk incisors just appearing about the gums. This specimen weighed 0.454 kg. In the adult the average weight in females (n = 15) was 9.873 kg (range: 8.165–11.794 kg) and in males (n = 10) 20.344 kg (range: 14.062–23.587 kg). Schultz noted that this sex difference in size in the proboscis monkey, showing a ratio of roughly 1:2, is equalled among simian primates by only a few forms, such as orang-utan, gorilla, and some baboons. The weight of the newborn in

percent of average weight of adult females was 4.6 in the proboscis monkey. The corresponding figure for other primates as given by Schultz [1941] was 6.7 in macaques, 4.1 in orang-utans, 4.0 in chimpanzees, and 5.5 in man.

Although the baboon (*Papio* sp.) has become a popular research animal in the past few years, there are relatively few data available on the growth in weight of the normal infant baboon under controlled conditions. In one of the available studies, McMahan et al [1976] reported estimated weight percentiles for male (Fig. 13) and female (Fig. 14) laboratory-born baboons (*P. cynocephalus*) from birth to 15 weeks of age. The baboons in this study were heavier than those reported by Vice et al [1966] in which (3 *P. papio* and 7 *P. cynocephalus*) the mean weight gain from

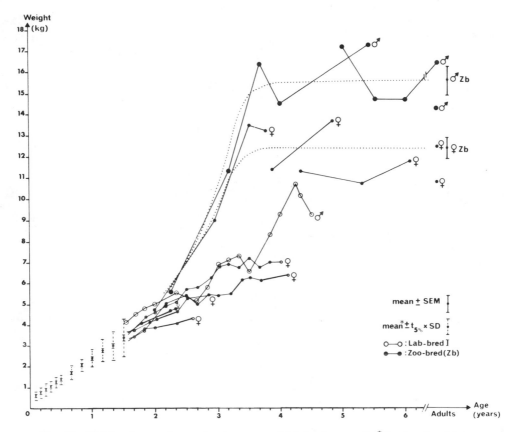

Fig. 12. Weight changes in zoo-bred group and lab-bred group I. *Zoo-bred and lab-bred I males and females pooled together. [From Faucheux et al, 1978, with permission.]

birth to 60 days was 325 gm compared to 534 gm in the McMahan et al [1976] study. In another study [Berchelmann et al, 1971] a group of maternally reared baboons (*P. cynocephalus*) exhibited about the same mean weights at various ages as the animals described by McMahan, although no separation by sex was made.

In laboratory-reared baboons (apparently, *P. papio* and *P. cynocephalus*) [Snow, 1967], sexual dimorphism in weight appeared in the 3-year-olds. However, in free-ranging hamadryas baboons, observed for 5.5 years in Ethiopia [Sigg et al, 1982], such sexual dimorphism in weight did not appear to occur in animals less than 5 years old. In the latter animals no conspicuous changes in the external appearance occurred after 5.6 years of age in females and 6.8 years in males. Males experienced a subadult phase lasting approximately 5 years, in the course of which the mantle developed and body

weight almost doubled. As pointed out by Snow [1967], a female newborn baboon must undergo an approximately 18-fold increase in body weight to attain adult size, and a male must undergo a 30-fold increase. Changes in body weight through the first 7 postnatal years and in the adult are shown in Figure 15 [Sigg et al, 1982].

Postnatal weight changes in three lowland gorillas (*Gorilla g. gorilla*—2 males, 1 female) and three mountain gorillas (*Gorilla g. beringei*—2 females, 1 male) were reported over various postnatal periods. The longest record in this series covered a time span from age 2 years through 17.5 years. The shortest record covered a time span from age 5.5 years through 10 years as shown in Table 8 [Gijzen and Tijskens, 1971].

In a male specimen of a lowland gorilla born at the Frankfurt Zoo, the birth weight was 2,100 gm [Kirchshofer et al, 1967]. This animal's weight decreased to 2,040 gm on the day after birth, but the birth weight was regained by the end of the first week. Subsequent weighings at successive 4-week intervals revealed the following weight levels in grams: 2,100, 2,780, 3,920, 6,730, 7,770, 8,680, 9,720, 11,140, 12,480, 14,060, 15,500, and 16,000. Within the first year the subject had increased his birth weight eight times. A similar male specimen born in the St. Louis Zoo [Kirchshofer et al, 1968] weighed 2,097 gm at 2 days of age, 2,126 gm at 1 week, 2,391 gm at 3 weeks, 2,608 gm at 4 weeks, 2,778 gm at 5 weeks, 3,090 gm at 6 weeks, 3,542 gm at 7 weeks, 4,081 gm at 9 weeks, 4,364 gm at 10 weeks, 4,960 gm at 3 months, 5,924 gm at 4 months, 6,094 gm at 5 months, 6,489 gm at 6 months, and 7,086 gm at 7 months. The weights at approximately equal age levels in the animal at the St. Louis Zoo appear to be appreciably lower than the specimen in the Frankfurt Zoo, but data are too sparse on normal distributions of weights in juveniles to permit an evaluation of the significance of the weight difference.

For practical reasons it has been very difficult for interested investigators to obtain weights of orang-utans (*Pongo* sp.) in the wild state, and the normal rate of weight increase in the juvenile orang-utan in the wild is unknown. Schultz [1941] reported the average weight of the orang-utan at birth as 1.50 kg. For animals in captivity, Brandes [1931] and Portmann [1956] give a mean value of 1,500 gm and a maximum of 2,500 gm. A male baby orang-utan at Dresden Zoo reared by its mother weighed 3,410 gm at the age of 6 months, which was presumed by Brandes [1931] to be double its birth weight. Portmann gave 1,500 gm as the birth weight for this species and 75 kg as the average normal body weight of the adult animal. Seitz [1969], on the other hand, considered 75 kg too high for the normal weight and a birth weight of 1,500 gm to be below the average. The mean body weight and standard deviation at birth in seven male orang-utans calculated from Seitz's data is 1,739.29 ± 148.20 gm. In females Seitz reported a mean birth weight of 1,694.00 ± 223.00 gm. The birth weights and weight increases for 16 zoo-born orang-utans are illustrated in Table 9. A comparison of the postnatal weight increase in a mountain gorilla (Victoria) and an orang-utan (Ursula) is shown in Figure 16 [Gijzen and Tijskens, 1971].

According to Gavan [1953], the end of the growth period in chimpanzees is considered to be the time when the epiphyses of the long bones in the shoulder, elbow, hip, and knee have completed at least one-half of the union with their diaphyses. The average for males was 135 months (range: 132–144 months) and the average for the female was 124 months (range: 120–132 months). These estimates are in fairly close agreement with the value of 11 years as given by Schultz [1940] and that of 11 to 12 years as given by Grether and Yerkes [1940] for age at completion of growth. Schultz [1940] stated that the postnatal growth period in the chimpanzee is 15.7 times longer than the prenatal period, whereas in man it is 27 times longer.

Birth weight in the chimpanzee according to Gavan [1952] was 1.8 kg (n = 42), with no significant sex difference. Birth weight expressed as a percent of the mother's weight at the time of conception averages 4.25% (range: 2.29–5.8%). Schultz [1940] reported 4.00% for chimpanzee and 5.50% for human subjects. According to this worker, the average adult female chimpanzee weighs 40 kg and the male 45 kg. Values of 50 kg in males and 40 kg in females were reported by Grether and Yerkes [1940].

As noted by Gavan [1953], body weight in chimpanzees continues to increase after adulthood is reached. The averages of the maximum weights are 53.4 kg (range: 40.8–64.1) and 40.2 kg (range: 37.7–84.4) in males and females, respectively. No significant sex difference was evident in the ranges reported by this author. Adulthood in primates is the longest part of the life-span, and in chimpanzees lasts at least two-thirds of their total life-span [Gavan, 1953]. The averages of the maximum weights were 53.4 kg and 49.2 kg for males and females, respectively, but the ranges (40.8–64.1 and 37.7–84.4) show no real sex difference. The weight range by chronological age is shown by Gavan [1953] in his Figure 1, in which a gradual increase in variability and the sex overlap in the range are shown.

No sex difference in body weight in the chimpanzee is evident until 30 months of age, but from 30 to 120 months the average female weight is greater than the male. After 120 months the males increase to the average male adult weight of 46.5 kg, whereas the females reached only 41.8 kg by 12 years of age. Grether and Yerkes [1940] re-

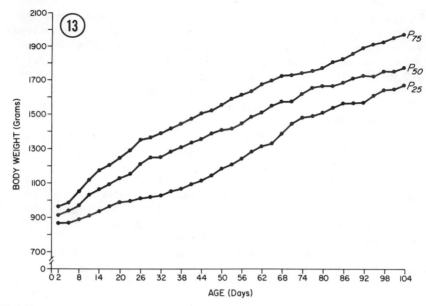

Fig. 13. Estimated weight percentiles of male baboons from birth to 15 weeks. [From McMahan et al, 1976, with permission.]

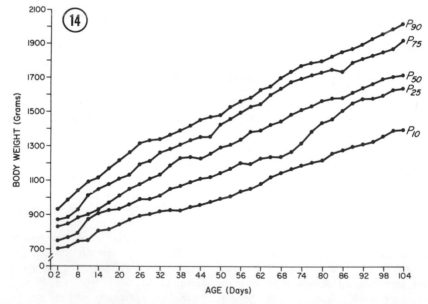

Fig. 14. Estimated weight percentiles of female baboons from birth to 15 weeks. [From McMahan et al, 1976, with permission.]

ported no sex difference in body weight until 7 years of age, at which time the males became heavier and remained so. Gavan [1953] suggested that the differences between his series of chimpanzees and those reported by Grether and Yerkes [1940] may be due to the fact that the latter authors used both feral- and laboratory-born animals, whereas Gavan [1953] restricted his study entirely to the latter group.

A comparison of average weight by chronological age in the chimpanzee and in man is given by Gavan [1953] in his Figure 2. The figure shows that boys are initially and finally heavier than girls, but that during the pubertal period girls surpass them. No such changing relationship between body weights in the sexes is seen in chimpanzees. Although the human child is heavier at birth and in adulthood than the chimpanzee, male chimpanzees are heavier than boys of the same postnatal age from about 4½ to 14 years. Female chimpanzees are heavier than girls from 3½ until 12 years.

Studying the rate of weight growth by means of average annual increments, Gavan [1953] plotted in his Figure 3 the amount of average gain per year against chronological age. The author points out that all four curves are of the form found for primate growth rates, exhibiting a rapid decline after birth, a gradual increase culminating at about puberty, and a final decline to zero as maximum adult weight is attained. Females, both human and chimpanzee, grow faster than males of the same species until about 7 years of age, and chimpanzees grow faster than humans during this period.

Then for about 3 years male chimpanzees grow much faster than the other three groups. At about 10 years of age the chimpanzee curves begin to decline. The male curve drops to zero before the female because of the latter's extended period of weight increase as noted earlier in this discussion. At the same age (10 years) the human growth curves are still rising, and human children then grow faster than chimpanzees.

In human subjects the age of maximum growth is achieved prior to puberty, but the chimpanzee maximums are reached just after puberty. In view of this observation, Gavan [1953] raises the question as to whether there may be a causal relationship between the age of maximum growth and puberty. Plotting annual growth increments against the percent of maximum weight attained at the beginning of the year, Gavan found that in all four curves the maximum increment occurs at approximatly 70% of mature size. This level is attained after puberty in chimpanzees but before puberty in human children.

Organ Weight

A problem encountered throughout various reports on organ weights in primates is whether the data are reported as growth relative to chronological age or whether the data are reported as *allometric* measures—that is, organ weight relative to total body weight. Clearly, the latter data are more easily obtained owing to the difficulty in establishing reasonably accurate determinations of age, particularly among wild-captured primates. However, for purposes of this chapter, we have chosen to concentrate on the data of the former (or rarer) type.

Data on changes in organ weights during postnatal growth are available mainly for macaques. A comprehensive study of organ weights in the rhesus monkey at both prenatal and postnatal stages was conducted by Kerr et al [1969a, 1974]. The data relating to the prenatal period have been described above (Table 4).

In the more recent studies, Kerr et al [1974] recorded body and organ weights in animals of various conceptual and postnatal ages which were obtained from normal pregnancies at the Wisconsin Regional Primate Research Center. The postnatal animals were fed a milk-based diet during the first 6 months of life, and were gradually weaned to a diet of commercial monkey chow with vitamin and fruit supplements. Data on these two

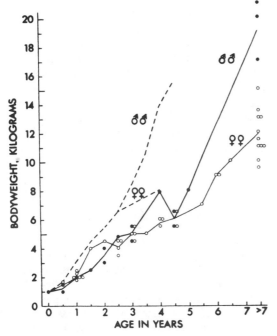

Fig. 15. Increase of body weight dependent on age. Broken line: mean weights (n = 1–10 of baboons reared in the SFRE laboratory, San Antonio; *P. anubis, P. cynocephalus*, and their hybrids); circles: individual weights of hamadryas baboons from this study; white circles are females, black circles are males; solid lines: mean weights of hamadryas baboons. [From Sigg et al, 1982, with permission.]

parameters were combined into the conceptual age levels of 40, 50, 75, 100, 125, 150 (term), and 378 days (7 months postnatal age). Thereafter, data from all animals within a given year of postnatal age were combined into age groups of 1–2, 2–3, 3–4, 4–5, and > 5 years. Comparative data were also obtained on organ weights of 27 male and 15 female adult feral animals estimated to be between 5 and 10 years of age.

As shown by Kerr et al [1974] in their Table 1, animals over 5 years of age were considered mature, since, according to these workers, pubertal changes are generally seen in rhesus monkeys during the second and third years, and reproductive maturity is established by 4–5 years of age.

Kerr et al [1974] note that most organs show continuous growth with increasing age and body weight. However, a few organs show unique patterns of growth. These authors point out that growth in weight of the central nervous system is largely completed by the end of the first year of extrauterine life at a time when most other organs have achieved only 20–50% of their full adult weight. In the adrenals a marked increase in weight occurs during late gestation, concurrently with a transient weight loss of the thymus. Subsequently there is a reduction in growth of the adrenals and an increase in thymus weight during the first 7

months of postnatal life. Body weight and placental weight increase throughout gestation, but their growth rate decreases markedly during the last few weeks of pregnancy.

In a quantitative analysis of growth velocity, Kerr et al [1974] noted that the maximum weight increase per day occurs at different times for different organs. Their data indicate that the maximum rate of growth for body weight and for the placenta and most of the major body organs occurs at between 125 and 150 days of fetal life. In the brain and kidney the maximal rate occurs about 25 days earlier. In the pancreas the maximum rate of growth is seen during late gestation.

From the observations of these workers in this cross-sectional study there is no evidence of an adolescent growth spurt for the body or most of its major organs. However, the testes exhibit a marked increase in weight beginning at 2–3 years of postnatal age which continues until after the age of 5 years. In the ovaries a less marked increase is seen at 3–4 years of life, and there is little additional increase thereafter.

Kerr et al [1974] point out that most organs represent a larger portion of the total body weight in fetal life than they do after birth. This is ascribed, in part at least, to the increased bone, muscle, and adipose tissue mass of postnatal animals. The reverse trend is seen only in the testes and pancreas, in which the relative weight increases during postnatal life. The relative weights of the heart and pituitary were described as being more or less constant at all ages.

Dimensional Growth

Crown-Rump Length (CRL) and Trunk Height

In a potto (*Perodicticus potto*) born in captivity [Grand et al, 1964], total body length increased from about 17 cm at 4 days of age to approximately 47 cm at 109 days of age. From these data and the values on increase in weight presented above, the authors gained the impression that pottos grow and mature precociously. In squirrel monkeys born in our laboratories [Kaack et al., 1979], there was little difference in CRL between Bolivian and Colombian animals or between the sexes within subspecies at earlier postnatal age levels (Fig. 17). At about 14 weeks, however,

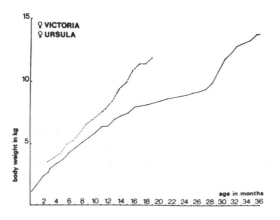

Fig. 16. Graph showing growth in body weight of zoo-born mountain gorilla (*Gorilla gorilla beringei* "Victoria" [dotted line] and orang-utan *Pongo pygmaeus* "Ursula" [solid line]). [From Gijzen and Tijkens, 1971, with permission of publisher.]

differences between sexes began to appear, and a continuous divergence in these parameters was then observed. The Colombian animals were larger at all age levels, and in our later studies [Walker et al, 1981] it was shown that Colombian offspring measured across the first 28 postnatal days had significantly longer CRL than did Bolivian offspring at comparable ages (F [1, 37] = 4.95, P = 0.032).

The monthly increments of CRL in rhesus monkeys [van Wagenen and Catchpole, 1956] were greatest during the first year in both males and females (Figs. 18, 19). The male curve shows a clear and prolonged increase commencing at 2.5 years and continuing into the fourth and fifth years, and exceeds the increment curve for females. In infant rhesus monkeys on a standardized diet (n = 3 females, 5 males [Kerr et al, 1969b]), body length showed appropriate increases, but rates of linear growth decreased steadily until constant values were achieved during the latter part of the first year of life (Table 10). Head circumference showed a similar pattern of dimensional growth in the rhesus monkey.

In *M. arctoides* [Scheffler and Kerr, 1975], body length increased steadily during the first year. The mean 30-day value for this parameter was significantly greater in males than in females (P < 0.005). As noted in a previous section of this chapter, linear measurements as well as weight in *M. arctoides* increase rapidly during the first year of life, more slowly until 2.5 years of age, then increase again during the pubertal period. As reflected in Figure 20 showing CRL changes through these periods, this adolescent growth spurt was not very marked with regard to body dimensions [Faucheux et al, 1978].

Hamada [1982] has recently carried out a longitudinal somatometrical study on growth patterns in newborn Japanese monkeys (*Macaca fuscata fuscata*). The traits he measured, indicated by number, and their average values up to 12 months of age for the trunk, extremities, head and body weight are shown in Table 11a and b. Plots of increments (size at the 12th month/size at birth against percent of adult sizes) are shown in Figure 21. As shown in this figure, relating to Table 11a and b, the characters for the trunk have small birth sizes (relative to the adult) and large increments. However, tail length shows the opposite tendency.

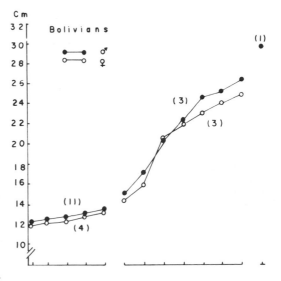

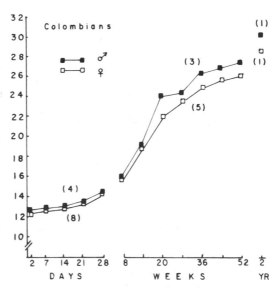

Fig. 17. Crown-rump length of squirrel monkeys from day 2 through 2 years of age. Number of subjects in group in parentheses. [From Kaack et al, 1979, with permission.]

Sitting height, anterior trunk length, biiliac breadth, chest girth, and bimammarial breadth have very small birth sizes and very large increments.

In the proboscis monkey (*Nasalis larvatus*) the chest circumference (at the level of the insertion

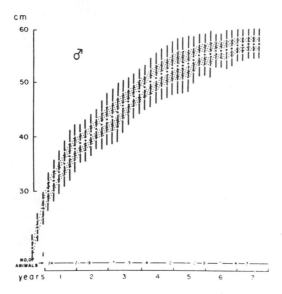

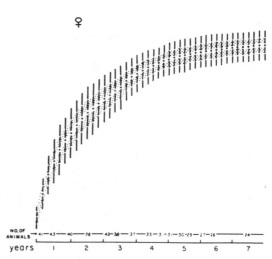

Fig. 18. Crown-rump length of male macaques in relation to chronological age. Means, with one and two standard deviations. [From van Wagenen and Catchpole, 1956, with permission.]

Fig. 19. Crown-rump length of female macaques in relation to chronological age. Means, with one and two standard deviations. [From van Wagenen and Catchpole, 1956, with permission.]

of the fourth pair of ribs) in percentage of trunk height (from suprasternal notch to upper end of pubic symphysis) decreases with growth, but increases again in males during adult life [Schultz, 1942]. The average percentage value decreased from 146.9 in the fetus to 110.4 in juveniles and 108.0 in adult females but increased again to 125.0 in adult males. The percentage value of shoulder breadth/trunk height decreased from 46.4 in fetuses to about 33 in juveniles and adult females but increased again to 38.0 in adult males. The percentage value of hip breadth to trunk height decreased to about 33 in juveniles and adult females but increased again to 36.8 in adult males [Schultz, 1942].

The percentage value of the transverse diameter of the chest to the sagittal diameter increases slightly with growth, but remains in its average below 100, in contrast to all higher primates in which it rises to far above 100 during postnatal period.

In baboons (presumably *Papio anubis* and *P. cynocephalus*) the striking weight differences between the sexes, which were illustrated in the previous section on body weight, are reflected to a great extent in the curves for linear body dimensions. As in the weight measurements, the curves

for male and female subjects are nearly identical until late in the third year when the values for males begins to exceed those for females. Figure 22 [Snow, 1967] illustrates the rate at which other body parts attain maturity in males. Trunk height is seen to be about 30% of the adult value at birth and increases to about 55% at the end of the first year. During the second year, the trunk gains only another 5%, then reaches nearly 90% by the end of the fourth year. The facial portion of the skull exhibits a more or less linear progression from birth to 4 years of age. Snow [1967] notes that the facial length at birth is only about 25% of the adult value, but the cranial portion, as indicated by head length, is about 65% of its adult size. At the age of 4 years the brain case has attained 95% of its adult size in contrast to the facial portion, which is at about 70%.

In chimpanzees (*Pan troglodytes*), the average trunk height curve is reported to have a high growth rate initially [Gavan, 1953, Fig. 5]. During the first year, the average male chimpanzee in increases 62% and the female 67.1% over their average birth measurement. Thereafter, the yearly percentage increase gradually declines and reaches a plateau at 12 years. At birth the chimpanzee trunk height is only 67% of human trunk height,

TABLE 10. Growth in Body Length

		Age (days)											
	Birth	15	30	45	60	90	120	150	180	210	240	300	360
Body length (cm) (n = 8)	30.5 ± 1.2	32.3 ± 1.3	34.1 ± 1.1	35.8 ± 1.2	37.5 ± 1.1	40.1 ± 1.2	42.8 ± 1.1	45.4 ± 1.2	46.9 ± 1.3	48.7 ± 1.3	50.2 ± 1.4	52.8 ± 1.6	55.8 ± 1.5
Rate of growth[a] (mm/m/30 days)	—	120.2 ± 44.0	109.4 ± 21.8	100.8 ± 36.5	95.3 ± 20.6	65.1 ± 13.4	68.4 ± 13.4	64.1 ± 13.2	30.1 ± 10.5	36.8 ± 4.0	31.9 ± 10.8	31.5 ± 14.0	25.3 ± 11.2

All values expressed as mean ± 1 SD.

[a]The rate of growth was calculated separately for each animal; figures represent the mean value ± 1 SD for all animals.
From Kerr et al [1969b], with permission.

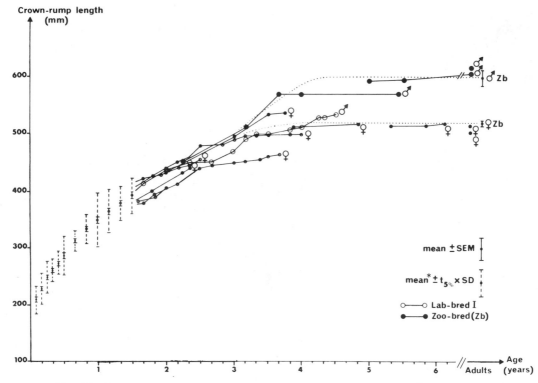

Fig. 20. Crown-rump length changes in zoo-bred and lab-bred group I. *Zoo-bred and lab-bred I males and females pooled together. [From Faucheux et al, 1978, with permission.]

but by 2 years of age male and female chimpanzees have about the same trunk height, and this is essentially the same as the human trunk height at that age in both sexes. At this time the male chimpanzee has increased his birth length 87.3% and the female 94%. In human subjects at the same age, boys have increased only 28.5% and girls 27.7%.

According to Gavan [1953], the chimpanzee continues the rapid growth, and from age 2 to 12 years the male is longer than boys of the same age. During the same period, the female chimpanzee is longer than the male and is longer than girls until at least 13 years of age. The size superiority of chimpanzees is due to the fact that male chimpanzees reach their final size at 12 years of age, whereas boys reach final size at 18 years or later. In female chimpanzees the growth period is about 60% of the human growth period. Another reason for the size superiority in chimpanzee in these periods is that the absolute growth in trunk height

in chimpanzees is greater in human subjects for a given period of time.

From these observations, Gavan [1953] points out that there are at least two variables in these growth curves—the size reached at adulthood, and the length of time required to reach that size. To determine what other differences there might be between the curves, Gavan [1953] in his Figure 6 constructed another set of curves in which the percent of adult trunk height was plotted against percent of the total growth period. The differences between chimpanzees and human subjects are now very small and show that most of the differences were due to the variables, final size and duration of growth time.

Gavan [1953] points out some additional differences, however, in that the human prenatal curves show a larger increase than in the chimpanzees. At birth (4% of the total growth period) the trunk height in the human child is about 44% of final trunk

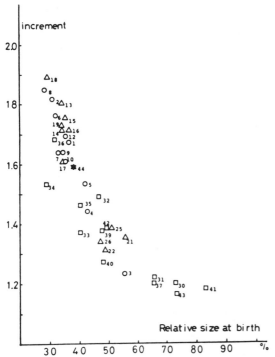

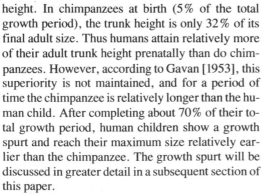

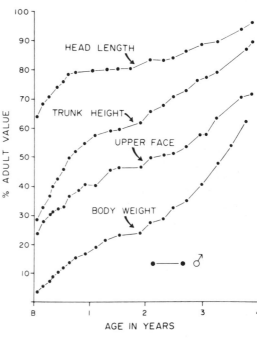

Fig. 21. Plots of increments (size at the 12th month/ size at birth) against the percent of adult sizes. Traits except body weight (No. *44) are classified into three-trunk parts (○), extremity parts (△), and head area (□). Numbers added to the signs are tabulated in Table 11a. [From Hamada, 1982, with permission.]

Fig. 22. Growth in male body weight, trunk height, upper facial height, and head length plotted as percentage of adult values. [From Snow, 1967, with permission.]

height. In chimpanzees at birth (5% of the total growth period), the trunk height is only 32% of its final adult size. Thus humans attain relatively more of their adult trunk height prenatally than do chimpanzees. However, according to Gavan [1953], this superiority is not maintained, and for a period of time the chimpanzee is relatively longer than the human child. After completing about 70% of their total growth period, human children show a growth spurt and reach their maximum size relatively earlier than the chimpanzee. The growth spurt will be discussed in greater detail in a subsequent section of this paper.

Another difference between human subjects and chimpanzees pointed out by Gavan [1953] is that in the chimpanzee curve for trunk height the male is always relatively larger than the female but the female child is usually relatively larger than the boy. Two exceptions are said to occur, at 14% and 80% of the total growth period.

In a male gorilla born at the zoo in Frankfurt, Germany, measurements of head-to-rump length, chest, abdomen, and limb dimensions were made on an approximately bimonthly schedule for a period of 6 months after birth. These measurements are shown in Table 12 [Kirchshofer, 1967] (date of measurement in left column).

Comparative data on proportional body growth in howler monkeys (*A. caraya*), rhesus monkey (*M. mulatta*), chimpanzee, and man [Malinow et al, 1966] suggest that proportional growth in howler monkeys (*A. caraya*) is greater than in the rhesus monkey (*M. mulatta*) but less than in the chimpanzee and man. Since there was no way to establish the actual chronological age of the animals used in that particular study, correlations with age were not possible.

Shea [1981] has recently conducted a series of analyses of data from wild-shot *Pan troglodytes* and *Gorilla* and from data published by Coolidge

TABLE 11a. Traits Used and Their Averages (for the three males) at the End of Each Trimonthly Period

Characters of measurement	Average values				
	0 mo	3 mo	6 mo	9 mo	12 mo
1. Sitting height (23)	202.3 mm	261.8 mm	281.8 mm	317.0 mm	345.8 mm
2. Anterior trunk length (27a)	117.4	152.4	172.4	195.0	220.3
3. Tail length (28(5))	52.8	50.0	59.5	72.0	65.2
4. Sternum length (5*)	51.0	57.7	66.0	75.0	78.5
5. Biacromial breadth (35)	56.8	72.6	74.8	92.0	91.6
6. Biiliac breadth (40)	35.1	45.3	52.7	58.0	62.3
7. Bitrochanteric breadth (42)	46.8	60.0	65.0	74.0	78.5
8. Bimammarial breadth (38)	18.5	26.0	30.3	35.0	37.5
9. Chest breadth (36)	39.6	51.9	59.4	69.0	66.3
10. Chest depth (37)	42.3	53.8	61.0	73.0	71.0
11. Circumference of neck (63)	108.3	110.5	148.3	125.0	136.0
12. Mesosternal chest girth (61)	151.7	190.2	229.4	251.0	272.5
13. Upper arm length (47)	56.6	70.2	81.0	85.0	99.3
14. Forearm length (48)	57.3	74.4	83.9	96.0	101.5
15. Thigh length (55(1))	60.4	78.2	88.6	107.0	112.2
16. Leg length (56a)	59.2	79.3	87.0	98.0	108.5
17. Max circumf of R upper arm (65)	57.5	81.5	86.0	106.0	98.0
18. Max circumf of R thigh (68)	71.8	103.0	115.3	134.0	143.5
19. Max circumf of R leg (69)	60.0	81.5	86.3	97.0	108.0
20. Min circumf of R leg (70)	49.0	61.5	61.3	72.0	73.0
21. Hand length (49)	56.2	63.4	69.4	73.0	77.7
22. Hand breadth (52)	20.4	22.5	24.4	25.0	27.2
23. 1st digit length (51a)	11.6	15.3	15.3	16.0	17.0
24. 3rd digit length (51)	28.0	34.3	34.5	35.0	36.5
25. Foot length (58)	78.0	91.7	98.0	107.0	111.7
26. Foot breadth (23*)	19.6	21.6	24.1	26.0	26.7
27. 1st toe length	15.4	19.3	18.5	20.0	23.8
28. 3rd toe length	29.4	35.3	35.8	38.0	40.0
29. Max circumf of head (45)	200.2	224.8	230.8	242.0	255.6
30. Head length (1)	66.7	74.6	78.3	81.0	79.7
31. Head breadth (3)	52.9	58.7	62.0	63.0	64.7
32. Bizygomatic breadth (6)	43.0	50.3	57.3	58.0	64.5
33. Bigonial breadth (8)	23.2	23.8	27.8	28.0	32.7
34. Upper facial height (20)	17.2	21.3	22.8	26.0	27.5
35. Facial height (18)	29.4	36.0	39.8	42.0	46.0
36. Nasal height (21)	14.6	19.5	21.5	26.0	27.0
37. Extracanthic diameter (10)	31.6	32.5	35.8	35.0	36.7
38. Intercanthic diameter (9)	8.6	9.3	8.8	9.0	8.7
39. Nasal breadth (13)	9.4	12.0	11.8	15.0	12.7
40. Total head height (16)	53.0	59.0	67.7	76.0	78.3
41. Head height (15)	33.2	34.8	40.0	40.0	40.0
42. Ear height (31)	30.2	35.8	37.5	40.0	38.7
43. Ear breadth (32)	22.6	25.5	27.5	27.0	27.7
44. Body weight (71)	558.3 gm	1,058.0 gm	1,530.0 gm	2,200.0 gm	2,426.7 gm

Numbers in parentheses are those from Martin and Saller [1957]; numbers with asterisks from Iwamoto [1971].
From Hamada [1982], with permission.

TABLE 11b. Traits Used and Their Averages (for the four females) at the End of Each Trimonthly Period

Characters of measurement	Average values				
	0 mo	3 mo	6 mo	9 mo	12 mo
1.	199.0 mm	233.5 mm	259.7 mm	304.5 mm	327.8 mm
2.	144.8	140.8	156.3	188.0	201.2
3.	53.0	48.3	50.7	63.0	64.8
4.	51.0	55.8	62.7	65.0	69.0
5.	51.9	62.2	63.3	77.5	83.8
6.	34.4	44.1	49.3	58.0	60.6
7.	44.0	53.8	57.7	63.0	70.0
8.	20.0	24.5	28.3	35.0	33.5
9	38.3	53.6	60.7	67.5	61.0
10.	42.0	56.4	61.3	71.0	67.2
11.	115.8	133.0	128.7	127.0	130.0
12.	156.7	196.8	213.7	251.5	254.0
13.	55.1	66.0	71.3	84.0	91.8
14.	56.7	70.6	74.7	83.0	94.8
15.	61.0	73.4	80.3	92.0	102.2
16.	59.7	71.4	77.3	86.5	96.4
17.	60.8	72.5	81.7	90.0	93.0
18.	72.5	93.0	109.0	125.0	129.0
19.	56.8	71.0	82.3	88.0	95.5
20.	45.0	52.5	54.0	60.0	59.5
21.	54.4	61.2	63.0	70.8	72.8
22.	19.5	22.0	22.7	24.8	25.2
23.	11.3	13.3	13.3	14.0	16.2
24.	27.3	30.3	29.7	31.0	34.4
25.	75.8	85.2	86.7	101.5	102.0
26.	19.1	21.0	22.0	24.0	25.4
27.	15.0	17.5	16.0	14.0	20.8
28.	28.5	31.5	31.3	33.0	35.6
29.	203.4	222.6	226.7	242.0	245.2
30.	68.3	76.1	78.3	81.8	82.4
31.	51.3	56.9	58.3	62.0	62.6
32.	43.0	49.3	56.3	58.0	63.4
33.	22.5	26.0	29.0	27.0	30.0
34.	17.0	18.8	22.3	25.0	25.0
35.	30.8	35.0	39.7	44.0	42.4
36.	15.0	18.5	20.0	22.0	23.4
37.	30.3	32.5	34.3	35.0	37.2
38.	8.3	8.3	8.3	7.0	8.4
39.	8.0	10.5	10.3	12.0	11.2
40.	55.2	59.5	70.3	69.5	72.0
41.	37.5	38.0	39.7	44.0	43.2
42.	28.3	33.0	33.7	32.0	36.4
43.	21.8	23.5	24.7	22.0	26.2
44.	536.7 gm	935.6 gm	1,210.0 gm	1,860.0 gm	2,006.0 gm

From Hamada [1982], with permission.

TABLE 12. Measurements in cm of the Young Gorilla Born at Frankfurt Zoo on June 22, 1965

	A	B	C	D	E	F	G	H	I	J	K	L	M
6/29/65	30.5	29.0	27.7	14.0	7.5	8.5	9.0	13.0	12.5	8.7	9.5	9.5	33.2
7/13/65	31.0	33.5	34.0	16.0	7.9	8.5	10.0	13.0	13.5	9.0	9.7	9.6	34.0
7/27/65	35.0	34.5	36.5	18.0	8.0	8.6	10.5	13.5	14.0	10.5	10.0	10.2	36.0
8/10/65	35.5	36.0	38.2	18.0	8.5	9.6	11.0	14.0	14.0	11.5	10.2	11.0	37.0
8/24/65	36.4	39.0	41.0	18.0	9.3	10.0	12.0	16.2	18.0	12.0	11.0	11.2	37.0
9/7/65	39.0	39.5	42.0	19.0	9.5	10.0	12.5	17.5	18.0	12.5	12.0	11.5	41.0
9/28/65	44.0	40.0	42.0	20.0	10.0	12.0	13.0	18.0	18.0	13.0	13.0	12.0	41.0
10/20/65	44.0	42.0	45.5	20.0	10.5	12.5	13.5	20.5	20.0	13.8	13.5	12.5	45.0
11/2/65	44.0	47.0	47.0	22.0	10.5	13.0	14.0	21.0	20.0	14.0	14.0	14.5	45.0
11/16/65	44.0	47.0	47.0	24.0	10.5	13.0	15.0	21.5	21.0	15.0	15.0	14.5	47.0
12/16/65	49.0	48.0	47.0	25.0	11.2	13.2	16.0	24.0	22.0	15.5	15.5	14.5	50.0
1/18/66	49.0	51.0	49.5	29.0	11.5	14.5	16.5	25.0	23.0	16.5	16.5	15.0	51.0
2/24/66	54.0	51.0	57.0	—	12.0	15.0	20.0	—	24.0	16.0	16.0	15.8	54.0

Key: A) chest size under the armpits; B) chest size below the ribs; C) circumference of the abdomen; D) arm length; E) hand length; F) circumference of the wrist; G) circumference of the upper arm; H) leg length; I) circumference of the thigh; J) circumference of the shank; K) circumference of the ankle joint; L) foot length; M) head-to-rump length.
From Kirchshofer et al [1967], with permission.

[1933], Rode [1941], Gavan [1953], Coolidge and Shea [1982], Biegert and Maurer [1972], and the Yerkes Primate Facility. Shea [1981] reported that at age 4 in *Pan troglodytes*, females are larger than males in all measures except head-to-fork length and basic cranial length. Since this is not true at age 3 or 5, he suggests that a growth spurt occurs in females at age 4. He notes further that such a pattern is also seen in gorillas, but it is at age 3 that females are usually larger than males. By age 4 in the gorilla, males have surpassed the females in size. Shea [1981] cites this as support for the claim that gorillas have a somewhat more accelerated developmental pattern than chimpanzees [Groves, 1970a]. Data on length of appendages reported by Shea [1981] will be described below.

Length of Appendages

Upper extremity. Hamada's [1982] studies of Japanese monkeys (*Macaca fuscata*) over a 1-year period found hand measurements to be rather large at birth and to show relatively small increments with age, although hand length increased proportionately more with age than hand breadth. Arm length and circumference, on the other hand, were relatively small at birth but showed rapid growth during the first year. Hamada's [1982] measurements show a strong inverse relation between percentage of adult size at birth and rate of growth during the first year. Viewed in this manner, head

measurements show the largest relative sizes at birth and slowest growth over the first year; next comes tail length, then hand and foot measurements. Arm and leg length and circumferences show small relative birth size but rapid growth in the first year, a pattern that is also characteristic of most trunk measures. Although male and female measurements did not differ greatly at birth, both hand and arm measurements for males increased more rapidly than in females over the first year.

Fleagle and Samonds [1975] described the physical growth of the white-fronted capuchin (*Cebus albifrons*) during the first year of life. The patterns of differential growth in the capuchin were similar to those of rhesus in that proportional growth of hand length exceeded hand breadth, and arm length (length of the radius) exceeded both hand measures over the first year. As in man and other higher primates [Tanner, 1964], the growth curve for the capuchin monkey shows a peak velocity at birth or soon thereafter and decreasing velocity during the first year, and thus far there is no evidence of a growth spurt during this period. Males are consistently larger in most measurements at all ages. However, this difference is significant only for hip breadth, hand length, and foot length as measured from x-ray plates.

Fleagle and Samonds [1975] note further that if size at 1 year is treated as an end point, and individual measurements are analyzed in terms of how they reached that size, several general patterns be-

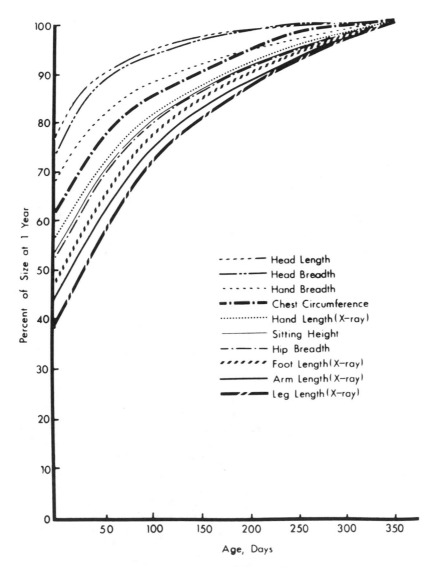

Fig. 23. Size of different body measurements relative to size at 1 year in *Cebus* monkeys (*Cebus albifrons*). [From Fleagle and Samonds, 1975, with permission.]

come evident as shown in Figure 23. A definite cranial-to-caudal maturity gradient for attainment of size is observed. For example, head measurements are closer to size at 1 year, from birth onward, than are measurements of any other part of the body. Similarly it will be observed that chest circumference is ahead of hip breadth, and arm length is ahead of leg length. Also at birth the hands and feet are closer to size at 1 year that are the long bones of the same limbs. The head measurements

actually complete over 90% of the first year's growth during the first 180 days. On the other hand, the decline in velocity occurs earliest in the more advanced head measurement and latest in limb measurements.

Comparing upper and lower extremities overall in baboons, there was no significant difference in rate between the thigh and upper arm or between the foot and hand in either sex. In both sexes the forearm grows faster than the leg. Snow [1967]

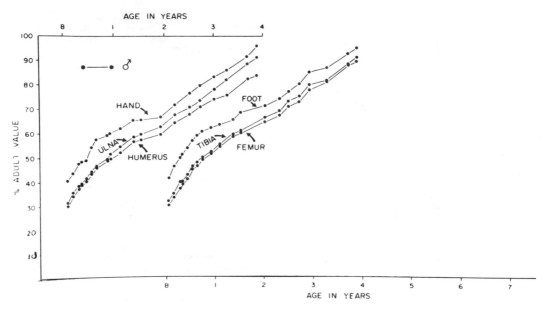

Fig. 24. Growth of limb segments of males plotted as percentages of adult value. Consistent distal-proximal maturity gradients occur in both arm and leg. [From Snow, 1967, with permission.]

plotted the growth of limb segments in male laboratory-born baboons as a percentage of adult value (Fig. 24). As noted by Snow [1967], this method of plotting allows a more direct comparison of the actual patterns of growth of segments with widely disparate initial or final size. As an example of terms of absolute growth, he notes that the humeral segment and hand are both about 6.0 cm in length at birth. However, by the end of the fourth year, the upper arm is about 5.0 cm longer than the hand. The percentage curves of these two segments, however, show them to be approximately parallel. At birth the upper arm is only 30% of the adult length, whereas the hand is about 40%. At 4 years of age the humerus has reached only about 80% of its adult length, whereas the hand has reached about 95%.

The hand, forearm, and arm in chimpanzees all grow at an initially high rate which gradually diminishes until growth ceases at about 11 years [Gavan, 1953]. From birth to nearly 2 years the sexes are of about equal size for hand, forearm, and upper-arm length. From 2 to 10 years the female is larger. When growth is completed, however, the male is larger. This indicates that the male increments are smaller but that they continue for a longer period of time. In the upper arm, however, even at 12 years, the male is still smaller than the female. Gavan [1953] illustrates these relationships in his Figure 10.

For total arm length, the sex ratio (100 × female/male) at 28 cm trunk height is 98.2% in chimpanzees. In both sexes the total arm length increases a little less than two units for every unit increase in trunk height. Total arm length increases faster than trunk height, but the comparative rate remains constant throughout the growth period.

From Gavan's [1953] figures for chimpanzees and man, it is again clear that greater proportional postnatal growth occurs for the upper arm and forearm than for hand length. Growth of hand length in terms of forearm length showed no significant sex difference in rate, but females were larger than males.

Lower extremity. The pattern of postnatal growth of the foot and the leg is closely parallel to that of the hand and arm in the Japanese monkey [Hamada, 1982]. Again the basic finding is that at birth the foot is about 50% of adult size and grows relatively slowly through the first year, whereas the leg at birth is about 35% of adult length, but grows rapidly during the first year of life.

Growth patterns of the lower extremity are also similar to those of the upper extremity in capuchins [Fleagle and Samonds, 1975], baboons [Snow, 1967], and chimpanzees [Gavan, 1953]. In chimpanzees lower-extremity length (average thigh length plus average knee height) as indicated in a regression analysis [Gavan, 1953] increases more rapidly in males than in females. Similar determinations for the average forearm (ulna) length showed that males increased faster than females.

There were no sex differences in either rate or size for growth of leg in terms of thigh length or for foot length in terms of leg length. Similarly, there were no differences in increase of total arm length in terms of total leg length for either rate or size.

Shea [1981] notes that in cross-sectional comparisons of log arm length versus log leg length in apes, the slope of the regression becomes significantly higher with increasing age. The most marked difference reported by Shea [1981] is the succesive upward transposition of each scatter, going from *Pan paniscus* (bonobo), to the common chimpanzee, to the gorilla. Thus at a given leg length, *Pan paniscus* has the shortest arms and *Gorilla* the longest. *Pan troglodytes* is intermediate. Conversely at a given arm length, the gorilla has the shortest legs and *Pan paniscus* has the longest, with *Pan troglodytes* in an intermediate position. A positive correlation of intermembral index and species size was also observed by Shea [1981].

Shea [1981] reported further that late in ontogeny the limbs slow somewhat in their growth relative to overall trunk length (head-to-fork length). This is noted to be especially marked in the gorillas, where the ratio of limbs (or limb segments) to head-to-fork length is lower in adult males than adult females. Detailed graphic illustrations of these growth phenomena are given in Shea's [1981] paper.

Head and Face

In Bolivian squirrel monkeys [Kaack et al, 1979], no differences in head circumference between sexes were observed until postnatal day 14. After that the values tended to diverge, with the males increasing more rapidly than the females through the first year (Fig. 25). In the Colombian squirrel monkeys the values for head circumference were

also greater in males than in females at all ages studied up to 2 years. The ear-to-ear measurement did not differ between the two subspecies, nor was the forehead-to-occipital measurement very different at birth. The dimensions of the heads of the infants in the two subspecies became equal at about 3 weeks of age.

In the Japanese macaque (*M. fuscata*) intercanthic breadth does not show any growth during the first year of life in either sex [Hamada, 1982]. Data on head circumference were not available for adults. Head length, head breadth, head height, extracanthic breadth, and ear breadth have larger birth sizes than the nine other head and facial characteristics studied. For these five measures, head height has the largest birth size. Head breadth and extracanthic breadth have the smallest. Increments of these five characters are smaller than the remaining nine. Certain face and head characters, including bizygomatic breadth, bigonial breadth, upper facial height, facial height, nasal height, nasal breadth, total head height, and ear height had lower birth sizes but varied considerably in growth rates.

In regard to growth rates, nasal height has the largest value. Bizygomatic breadth, upper facial height, and facial height showed the next-largest growth. Total head height has the smallest value. Bigonial breadth, ear height, and nasal breadth have the next-smallest values.

Head circumference in *M. arctoides* increased steadily in the first postnatal year, and increased 27.2% in that period of time. The corresponding figure for rhesus monkeys was 24.5% [Scheffler and Kerr, 1975]. The mean 30-day value for this parameter was significantly greater in males than in females (P < 0.001) in *M. arctoides*. Faucheux et al [1978], however, reported that there were no significant differences between male and female *M. arctoides* in regard to head and body proportions up to the age of 2 years in zoo-bred and normal lab-bred animals.

Growth of the head and face in the chimpanzee is represented by four measures—head length, head breadth, upper face height, and biorbital breadth. In all four measures initial growth was very rapid. During the first year, the average monthly increase in head length, upper face height, and biorbital breadth was from 3.0% to 3.5% and head breadth had an average monthly increase of about 2.1% [Gavan, 1953]. At 3 months, head breadth had

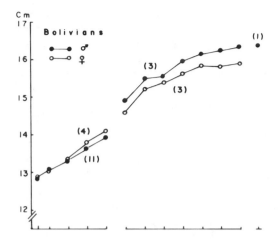

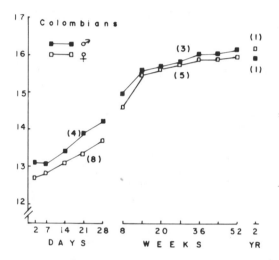

Fig. 25. Head circumference of squirrel monkeys from day 2 through 2 years of age. Number of subjects in group in parentheses. [From Kaack et al, 1979, with permission.]

attained relatively more of its final size than had head length.

In facial dimensions, biorbital breadth in chimpanzees is relatively closer to its adult size at 3 months of age than is upper-face height, but both facial dimensions are less advanced than either head diameter. This initially rapid head and face growth quickly decelerate but continue to grow slowly until age 12 years. All four measures of the chimpanzee may have reached a plateau by 12 years in that study, but the sample was too small

to be entirely certain of it. By 17 years the increase in head length in both sexes had apparently leveled off.

Adolescent Growth Spurt. One of the most characteristic features of postnatal growth in man is the increase in the rate of growth that occurs at adolescence. Brody [1945] was of the opinion that the adolescent spurt is not unique to man. He maintained that the prolongation of the total growth period, and especially the long phase of slowed juvenile growth, make the adolescent spurt obvious in man. If this is indeed the case, comparisons among nonhuman primates should reveal a regular increase in the adolescent spurt with lengthening of the growth period. The adolescent spurt in nonhuman primates would be a matter of degree rather than an all-or-nothing phenomenon.

Van Wagenen and Catchpole [1956] reported a spurt in mean growth curves for weight and crown-rump length in rhesus monkeys. The spurt in both of these dimensions was less notable in females than in males. These workers also noted that animals that matured early exhibited an earlier adolescent growth spurt. On the other hand, Gavan and Swindler [1966] calculated relative growth rates from longitudinal measurements of sitting height in rhesus monkeys and concluded that "the average rate declines from a maximum at birth in a regular sequence without showing a puberal growth spurt."

In some studies cross-sectional curves of mean animal weight gains in chimpanzees show some evidence of an adolescent acceleration in both sexes [Spence and Yerkes, 1937; Grether and Yerkes, 1940; Gavan, 1953; Smith et al, 1975]. However, the peak in females is poorly defined, and its association with the menarche is unclear. In studies by Gavan [1953], 1971] and Gavan and Swindler [1966], chimpanzee growth curves for linear dimensions did not show any evidence of an adolescent growth spurt.

In a more recent study involving serial anthropometric measurements of 16 laboratory-born rhesus monkeys (8 males, 8 females) and 12 chimpanzees (7 males, 5 females), individual longitudinal distance and velocity curves were plotted for limb dimensions of all of the animals [Watts and Gavan, 1982]. The increment curves were typically irregular, and no well-defined peak around the age of puberty was evident in most of the animals. The authors pointed out that on phylogenetic grounds, it might be expected that if the animals do exhibit an adolescent growth spurt, its magnitude would be less than in man and thus more difficult to demonstrate given irregularities in the growth curves due to measurement errors and other factors. Since it was not possible to demonstrate conclusively the presence or absence of an adolescent spurt by means of simple analysis, the authors utilized more sophisticated methods involving curve fitting by means of equations.

In an earlier investigation, Gavan [1971] tested the fit of several different equations to individual longitudinal growth data from the same chimpanzees used later in the studies of Watts and Gavan [1982]. The criterion of goodness of fit was percentage variance independent of the model. Although several equations showed very close fit to the data, the one that gave best fit for linear measurement of extremity was an exponential regression $Y = A + BR^x$. The parameter A represents the asymptote and can be used to estimate adult size. B is the overall amount of postnatal growth, and R represents the decrease in rate of growth from one age to the next. The variables, age and size, are represented by X and Y. This model depicts growth as a process that is gradually and constantly decelerating as size increases. Its use, therefore, assumes that an adolescent spurt does not exist. Since this equation gave an excellent fit to the chimpanzee data, leaving average residual variances of less than 1%, Gavan [1971] concluded that it was a good model for chimpanzee growth and that this species did not possess an adolescent acceleration.

In the more recent study, Watts and Gavan [1982] tested the fit of this equation to data on growth of limbs in rhesus monkeys and assessed the patterning of the residuals in addition to their overall magnitude in both species. As shown in their Table 1, which shows the mean variance ratios, the fit of the equation to the growth data of both the rhesus monkey and chimpanzee is seen to be quite good. The percent variance independent of the equation is very small in the chimpanzee. In the rhesus monkey data, the fit is not as good as in the chimpanzee, but still rather good.

The authors note that deviations of the observed values from the predicted curve, though slight, do show a definite age pattern. The deviations are grouped into positive and negative sets above and below the predicted curve rather than in a random scatter pattern. The observed deviations indicate that the equation is consistently underestimating actual size at certain ages and overestimating it at others. Deviations are positive in infancy, become negative during childhood, change to positive again during adolescence, and become negative again toward the end of the growth period. To test the statistical significance of the pattern, each deviation was correlated with the subsequent one. If the deviations had represented measurement error, the resulting lag correlation should be zero; however, such is not the case.

The above pattern as described by Watts and Gavan [1982] is illustrated in their Figure 1 in which the growth curve based on actual values is compared to the one predicted by the equation for thigh length in a male chimpanzee. The predicted curve shows a gradual size increase at a constantly decelerating rate. The observed curve shows a leveling off during childhood and a rise around the age of puberty. These changes give the actual curves a sigmoid shape similar to that commonly seen in human curves. Examples of plots of the deviations against a straight line for all four limb segments in representative chimpanzee and rhesus monkey subjects are shown in Figures 2 through 5 of Watts and Gavan [1982]. The authors pointed out that this method of depicting the deviations reveals their age-related pattern more clearly and shows the synchrony of changes in various dimensions measured on the same animal. It was noted that in both species there is a cluster of negative signs in the neonatal period, positive deviations during infancy, and a long series of negative ones during childhood. A second list of positive deviations indicating that growth is more rapid than predicted by the equation occurs just before the termination of growth, represented by the final negative deviations.

It was further pointed out in this study that males typically reach each phase of growth at later ages than females of the same species. The age of the first sign change occurs at nearly the same age in both species, and the differences between species for this sign change are not statistically significant. The subsequent phases of growth are much more protracted in the chimpanzee. The authors note that the patterns of growth in the two species are identical, despite the differences in absolute ages at which the changes occur. The second set of positive deviations, indicating rapid growth, prob-

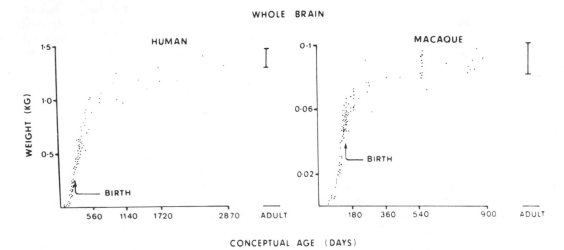

Fig. 26. Growth of the human and macaque brain with the weight scale for the macaque expanded 15-fold thus giving adult macaque and human weights a similar scale of magnitude. The age scale for the macaque was then arbitrarily expanded until a pattern approximating the human brain curve was ob-tained. The human data were derived from the work of Dobbing [1973]. The macaque data were collected by Cheek [1975] and from data provided to Dr. Cheek by Dr. Oscar Portman of the Oregon Regional Primate Research Center. [From Cheek, 1975, with permission.]

ably corresponds to the adolescent growth spurt in man, though it is much smaller in magnitude and can be discerned only when compared to the predicted curve.

In regard to the ages at the beginning of the adolescent acceleration and its peak, represented by the maximum positive deviation from the predicted curve, males are later than females in both the beginning and peak of the spurt. In chimpanzees there is a sex difference of about 2 years in the timing of adolescent growth spurt whereas in rhesus monkeys the male mean is only three-quarters of a year later than that of the females for both events.

In comparing the growth curve predicted by the equation $Y = A + BR^X$ to actual growth of the limbs in a sample of monkeys and apes, the deviations demonstrate that there are regular changes in growth rate away from the trend described by the equation. The actual curves exhibit a juvenile deceleration followed by an adolescent acceleration in growth. These features, though much less marked in the nonhuman primate, give their growth curves a shape very similar to man's and different from those of other mammals. The presence of both a juvenile growth deceleration and an adoles-cent spurt in these primates supports the idea of Brody [1945] that the two characteristics are phylogenetically related and that the long period of slowed juvenile growth between weaning and puberty brings out the adolescent spurt. Thus, the presence of an adolescent spurt in the anthropoid primates appears to be a consequence of the attenuated growth period rather than a phylogenetically novel feature in and of itself.

BRAIN GROWTH

Brain growth in all mammalian species thus far studied is characterized by a sigmoid growth pattern when brain weight is plotted against age [Laird, 1967]. The increase in total brain weight in kilograms as a function of conception age and postnatal age in days in the human and rhesus monkey is shown in Figure 26 [Cheek, 1975]. The configuration of fetal growth curves for cerebrum and cerebellum plotted individually are closely comparable to that for total brain. When brain weight is plotted on a log scale against body weight in rhesus monkey as compared to man, it is seen that the slopes of the two lines are approximately equal, thus indicating nearly proportional growth

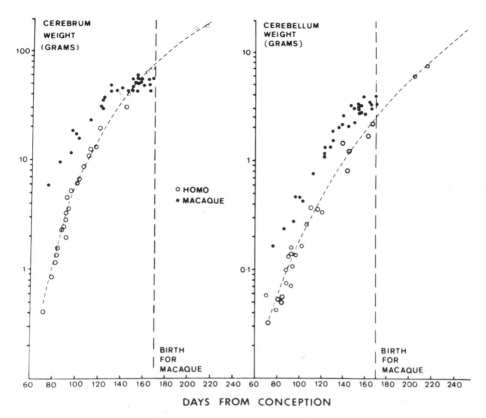

Fig. 27. A comparison of cerebral and cerebellar weights of the monkey and human during fetal life. The advanced development of the macaque brain in relation to time is evident. The macaque cerebrum weight is seen to plateau after 140 days. The human data are from the work of Howard et al as published by Cheek [1975]. [From Cheek, 1975, with permission.]

during ontogenesis, although the rhesus brain weight levels off after 140 days' gestation age. This is illustrated in Figure 27 [Cheek, 1975].

It has been shown in several species, however, that brain growth is characterized by a transient period of rapid growth which is now commonly referred to as the "brain growth spurt." As shown in Figure 28 [Dobbing and Sands, 1979], the time of the brain growth spurt in relation to the time of birth varied considerably in different species. Dobbing and Sands [1979] have pointed out certain limitations in portraying the brain growth spurt in various species in this manner. This is because different species with different life-spans and growth rates cannot be portrayed on the same time axis without making arbitrary decisions about the

choice of intervals of time described by the first-order rate curves, as well as about the manner of expressing absolute rate within those intervals. Since the increment during each arbitrarily chosen time interval has been converted to a proportion of the adult weight attained for all of the species illustrated, much of the meaning of the curves is lost since they depend greatly on the time interval chosen. Because of these problems, it is not possible to determine the relative position of each velocity peak. However, plotting the growth spurt curves in this manner does enable one to categorize a given species as a prenatal, perinatal, or postnatal brain developer from the position of its peak velocity relative to birth, and also gives a visual impression of the proportion of the brain

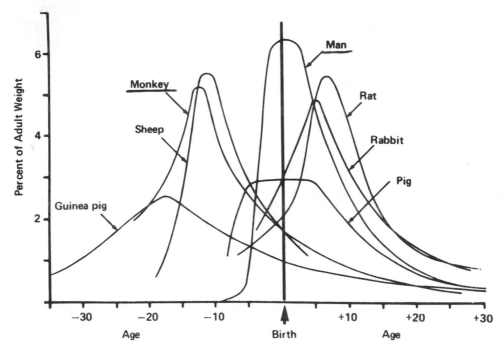

Fig. 28. The brain growth spurts of seven mammalian species expressed as first-order velocity curves of the increase in weight with age. The units of time for each species are: guinea pig (3): days; rhesus monkey (1): 4 days; sheep (9): 5 days; pig (2): weeks; man (5): months; rabbit (8): 2 days; rat (4): days. Rates are expressed as weight gain as a percentage of adult weight for each unit of time. [From Dobbing and Sands, 1979, with permission.]

growth spurt in each case that is prenatal or postnatal [Dobbing and Sands, 1979]. From this diagram, therefore, it appears that the rhesus monkey is precocial from the standpoint of brain development relative to the time of birth, whereas human subjects can be described as perinatal. Indeed the rhesus monkey brain attains about 60% of its total adult weight at birth with the cerebellum attaining over 75% of its adult weight [Cheek, 1975] whereas the human brain attains only about 30% of its adult weight at birth. The squirrel monkey brain, by comparison, attains about 55% of its adult weight at birth.

Brain Weight as a Function of Body Weight

As noted by Holt et al [1975], the curves that relate brain weight to either conception age or body weight are best expressed by convex quadratic curves, probably representing exponential or asymptotic growth patterns. These authors have further noted, citing Huxley [1932] and Needham [1931], that the conversion to a log-log basis allows a comparison of relative growth rates. In both total fetal brain and cerebrum, the value for the slope in these graphs is approximately unity. This indicates that the fetal brain is growing in constant proportion to the total body weight. Plotting data for the postnatal period on a log-log grid (brain weight vs body weight), Holt et al [1975] obtained a gradient of 0.3 which indicates that the rate of brain growth decreases to one-third of the rate in utero. They report that data for human subjects indicate a lesser gradient or rate of brain growth for less gestation, and in the postnatal period the gradient is greater than 0.3 which indicates a lesser change in growth rate. In the rhesus monkey, the brain reaches 60% of adult size before birth and is more advanced in development than is the human brain at birth.

Brain Weight as a Function of Body Length

Holt et al [1975] point out further that when fetal cerebral weight is related to body length, the points for the entire sample describe a slightly convex quadratic line. When the inspection is confined to the fetal period, it is noted that the log of cerebral weight is linearly related to body length.

Cerebellar Growth

It was reported by Holt et al [1975] that when cerebellar weight is expressed as a function of conception age, the curve approaches a sigmoid shape, because the growth of the cerebellum becomes rapid in midgestation, continues at a rapid rate through late gestation, and is about completed just before birth. These authors have pointed out that the logarithmetic transformation of the entire cycle would linearize the curve for cerebellar growth through this period. In the fetal period they observe that the log of cerebellar weight is linearly related to the conception age. Considering the growth of the cerebellum relative to total body weight, it was noted that the cerebellar relative growth rate was well in excess of that for the cerebrum or for the brain as a whole. This accelerated growth accounts for the cerebellum's achieving well in excess of 75% of its total organ size at the time of birth as compared to a brain size of 60% of its final adult weight. Postnatally, the growth rate decreases markedly.

Head circumference as well as brain weight has been used as a measure of brain growth in human subjects. In using this parameter it is assumed that it represents cranial volume which is proportional to the volume or weight of the brain it contains. Holt et al [1975] described an inverted quadratic relationship for head circumference on age from 80 days after conception to 120 days after birth.

CONCLUSIONS
Principles

Growth in body weight during the prenatal period, although approximately linear throughout much of intermediate gestation, shows a definite sigmoid shape when the extremes of gestation are considered. Growth of fetal organs tend to parallel body weight throughout gestation, with the exceptions of the lungs and thymus which show relative decreases in late gestation, and the adrenals which show relative increases.

Head circumference during prenatal growth in primates shows a negatively accelerated function of gestational age. Head volume, on the other hand, shows only a slightly decelerating function and is much more linear relative to gestational age, as is brain weight with which volume is highly correlated. Head size at birth in primates is more advanced than other morphologic measures in that head size has already reached a substantial percentage of adult size; however, head size in nonhuman primates is not as advanced at birth as that of man.

Gestation duration and adult maternal weight are clearly related, and are fairly well fit by a power function. This relationship appears to be a general principle of prenatal primate growth, and is thought to reflect differences in maternal metabolism related to size.

For a short period after birth the available data show that the newborn nursing primate infant loses weight. That weight is regained in healthy infants in 2 to 4 weeks, depending upon the species. Following this period of early postnatal weight loss, postnatal ponderal growth curves are sigmoid in all primate species.

As regards relative growth measures, there exists a cranial-to-caudal growth gradient. In terms of percent of final adult weight and growth rate during the first year, the head is more mature than the trunk, the chest is ahead of the hips, and the hands and feet are more mature than the arms and legs. During postnatal growth, most organ weights decline relative to body weight, with the exception of the spleen and testes, which increase.

Although less marked than in man, available data from rhesus monkeys and chimpanzees show signs of an adolescent growth spurt in both body weight and crown-rump length. Although it is suggested that an adolescent growth spurt is characteristic of all primate species, it is clearly variable in magnitude. Sexual dimorphism in body weight is also quite dependent upon particular species.

In several species, a perinatal period of rapid brain growth, called the brain growth spurt, has been documented. Whereas in humans maximum brain growth velocity occurs at about the time of birth, the brain growth spurt in nonhuman primates studied tends to occur prior to birth.

Trends

Reduction in Scale. Large-scale, long-term studies of growth, particularly those with large sample sizes, may be phenomena of the past. This is particularly true relative to measurements that require sacrifice of primate subjects, such as detailed studies of organ weights or brain weights. Even external measurements in more mature animals often require anesthesia, which may pose some threat to the subject. This trend toward reduction in scale of primate growth research is clearly a consequence of increased cost and decreased availability of primates as research subjects, and an increasing consciousness regarding animal welfare and species preservation.

Diversity of Species. Earlier systematic growth research concentrated mainly on the rhesus macaque, the primate model of choice for so many years. More recent studies have described growth in a much wider variety of species, usually at the unfortunate expense of smaller sample sizes and fewer parameters studied.

Self-Sustaining Colonies. With the shift in emphasis away from rhesus and larger primates toward smaller and more economic primate research models such as the squirrel monkey, a changing emphasis in primate study is clear. Such changes are brought on by lower expense, ease in raising and handling, and the viability of a self-sustaining continuous supply of colony-bred rather than wild-trapped research subjects.

Research Needs

Comprehensive and Systematic Data. It should be quite obvious from this chapter that the available data on primate growth are scattered and incomplete. There exist glaring gaps in our knowledge regarding most species other than rhesus, for which growth is reasonably well documented. Without complete comparative data on other species a comprehensive picture of growth in primates cannot emerge, nor can one clearly represent human growth within the wider context of primate growth in general. Although comprehensive data on species other than rhesus are the greatest need, any growth data on species not previously characterized are invaluable.

Newly Emerging Primate Models. The shift in research from Old World to New World primate models necessarily entails systematic data on all aspects of species such as the squirrel monkey, which has already emerged as a major competitor for rhesus as the primate research model of choice. Documentation of growth in other physically small primate species such as the marmosets, bush baby, and talapoin monkeys might set the stage for the emergence of these primates as research models if the problems of availability can be solved via self-sustaining colonies.

Problems to Be Solved

Issues of Measurements

More and more it is obvious that primates are too valuable to sacrifice in large numbers solely to study growth. On the other hand, autopsy data from animals found dead indicate that they suffered from dehydration and possible ill health prior to death. This is particularly true in trying to establish normal prenatal growth curves where in addition to the above problems, cannibalism is encountered with aborted fetuses. It is therefore essential that when primates are sacrificed for other biological or medical research thorough systematic measurements be made and filed to accumulate a data base from which growth can be later studied.

Issues of Timing

Perhaps the most difficult problem in the study of primate growth is determining age in wild-caught specimens, and in pinpointing conception in cage-reared animals. In essence, such determinations hinge on a sort of bootstrap phenomenon in that the more one knows about the growth of a given species, the more accurately ages of conception and birth can be estimated, and the better future curves characterizing growth can be derived. Clearly, true age-related data will always be superior to allometric data or relations of size or weight of one body part to another, granted that timing is reasonably accurate.

ACKNOWLEDGMENTS

The studies conducted in this laboratory on the fetal development of squirrel monkeys were supported by USPHS contract NO1 AI 82573, principal investigator, Dr. Louis Martin, and by NIH grant RR 00164.

The authors thank Dr. Susan V. Gibson and Dr. Edwin A. Watson for their participation in obtaining estimates of fetal age in squirrel monkeys.

REFERENCES

Ardito, G. Check-list of the data on the gestation length of primates. JOURNAL OF HUMAN EVOLUTION 5:213–222, 1976.

Benirshke, K.; Miller, C.J. Weights and neonatal growth of ringtailed lemurs (*Lemur catta*) and ruffed lemurs (*Lemur variegatus*). JOURNAL OF ZOO ANIMAL MEDICINE 12:107–111, 1981.

Berchelmann, M.L.; Vice, T.E.; Kalter, S.S. The hemogram of the maternally-reared neonatal and infant baboon (*Papio cynocephalus*). LABORATORY OF ANIMAL SCIENCE 21:564–571, 1971.

Berkson, G. Weight and tooth development during the first year in *Macaca irus*. LABORATORY OF ANIMAL CARE 18:352–355, 1968.

Biegert, J.; Maurer, R. Rumpfselettlänge, Allometrien und Körperproportienen bei catarrhenen Primaten. FOLIA PRIMATOLOGICA 17:142–156, 1972.

Brandes, G. Das Wachstum der Menschoffen in Vergleich zu dem das Menschen in Kurven dargestellt. DER ZOOLOGISCHE GARTEN 4:339–347, 1931.

Brody, S. BIOENERGETICS AND GROWTH. New York, Hafner, 1945.

Cheek, D.B., ed. FETAL AND POSTNATAL CELLULAR GROWTH. New York, Wiley, 1975.

Coolidge, H.J. Jr. *Pan paniscus*: Pygmy chimpanzee from south of the Congo River. AMERICAN JOURNAL OF PHYSICAL ANTHROPOLOGY (old series) 18:1–59, 1933.

Coolidge, H.J. Jr.; Shea, B.T. External body dimensions of *Pan paniscus* and *Pan troglodytes* chimpanzees. PRIMATES 23:245–251, 1982.

Cross, J.F.; Martin R.D. Calculation of gestation period and other reproductive parameters for primates. DODO, JOURNAL OF JERSEY WILDLIFE PRESERVATION TRUST 18:30–43, 1981.

Dawes, G.S.; Jacobsen, H.N.; Matt, J.D.; Shelley, H.J. Some observations of foetal and newborn rhesus monkeys. JOURNAL OF PHYSIOLOGY 152:271–298, 1960.

Dixson, A.F.; Gardner, J.S.; Bonney, R.C. Puberty in the male owl monkey (*Aotus trivirgatus griseimembra*): A study of physical and hormonal development. INTERNATIONAL JOURNAL OF PRIMATOLOGY 1:129–139, 1980.

Dobbing, J.; Sands, J. Comparative aspects of the brain growth spurt. EARLY HUMAN DEVELOPMENT 3:79–83, 1979.

Ehrlich, A. Infant development in two prosimian species: Greater galago and slow loris. DEVELOPMENTAL PSYCHOBIOLOGY 7:439–454, 1974.

Epple, G. Maintenance, breeding and development of marmoset monkeys (*Callitrichidae*) in captivity. FOLIA PRIMATOLOGICA 12:56–76, 1970.

Faucheux, B.; Bertrand, M.; Bourliere, F. Some effects of living conditions upon the pattern of growth in the stumptail macaque (*Macaca arctoides*). FOLIA PRIMATOLOGICA 30:220–236, 1978.

Fleagle, J.G.; Samonds, K.W. Physical growth of cebus monkeys (*Cebus albifrons*) during the first year of life. GROWTH 39:35–52, 1975.

Gavan, J.A. Birth order and birth weight in the chimpanzee. AMERICAN JOURNAL OF PHYSICAL ANTHROPOLOGY 10:23–30, 1952.

Gavan, J.A. Growth and development of the chimpanzee; a longitudinal and comparative study. HUMAN BIOLOGY 25:93–143, 1953.

Gavan, J.A. Longitudinal, postnatal growth in chimpanzees. Pp. 46–102 in THE CHIMPANZEE, Vol. 4. G. Bourne, ed. Basel, Karger, 1971.

Gavan, J.A.; Swindler, D.R. Growth rates and phylogeny in primates. AMERICAN JOURNAL OF PHYSICAL ANTHROPOLOGY 24:181–190, 1966.

Gijzen, A.; Tijskens, J. Growth in weight of the lowland gorilla (*Gorilla g. gorilla*) and of the mountain gorilla (*Gorilla g. beringei*). INTERNATIONAL ZOO YEARBOOK 11:183–193, 1971.

Grand, T.; Duro, E.; Montagna, W. Potto born in captivity. SCIENCE 145:663, 1964.

Grether, W.F.; Yerkes, R.M. Weight norms and relations for the chimpanzee. AMERICAN JOURNAL OF PHYSICAL ANTHROPOLOGY 28:181–197, 1940.

Gucwinska, H.; Gucwinski, A. Breeding the Zanzibar galago (*Galago senegalensis zanzibaricus*) at Wroclaw Zoo. INTERNATIONAL ZOO YEARBOOK 8:111–114, 1968.

Hamada, Y. Longitudinal somatometrical studies on the growth patterns of newborn Japanese monkeys. PRIMATES 23:542–557, 1982.

Hazama, N. Weighing wild Japanese monkeys in Arashiyama. PRIMATES 5:81–104, 1964.

Hendrickx, A.G.; Houston, M.L. Prenatal and postnatal development. Pp. 334–381 in COMPARATIVE REPRODUCTION OF NONHUMAN PRIMATES. E.S.E. Hafez, ed. Springfield, IL, Thomas, 1971.

Heuser, C.H.; Streeter, G.L. Development of the macaque embryo. CONTRIBUTIONS TO EMBRYOLOGY 29:15–55, 1941.

Holt, A.B.; Cheek, D.B.; Mellitis, E.D.; Hill, D.E. Brain size and the relation of the primate to the nonprimate. Pp. 23–44 in FETAL AND POSTNATAL CELLULAR GROWTH. D.B. Cheek, ed. New York, Wiley, 1975.

Huxley, J. PROBLEMS OF RELATIVE GROWTH. London, Methuen, 1932.

Jacobson, H.N.; Windle, W.F. Observations on mating, gestation, birth and postnatal development of *Macaca mulatta*. BIOLOGY OF THE NEONATE 2:105–120, 1960.

Kaack, B.; Walker, L.; Brizzee, K.R. The growth and development of the squirrel monkey (*Saimiri sciureus*). GROWTH 43:116–135, 1979.

Kaplan, J. Growth and behavior of surrogate-reared squirrel monkeys. DEVELOPMENTAL PSYCHOBIOLOGY 7:7–13, 1974.

Kerr, G.R.; Scheffler, G.; Waisman, H.A. Growth and development of infant *M. mulatta* fed a standardized diet. GROWTH 33:185–199, 1969b.

Kerr, G.R.; Kennan, A.L.; Waisman, H.A.; Allen,

J.R. Growth and development of the fetal rhesus monkey. I. Physical growth. GROWTH 33:201–213, 1969a.

Kerr, G.R.; Allen, J.R.; Scheffler, G.; Couture, J. Fetal and postnatal growth of rhesus monkeys (*M. mulatta*). JOURNAL OF MEDICAL PRIMATOLOGY 3:221–235, 1974.

Kihlström, J.E. Period of gestation and body weight in some placental mammals. COMPARATIVE BIOCHEMISTRY AND PHYSIOLOGY 43:673–679, 1972.

Kirchshofer, R.; Fraedrich, H.; Podolczak, D.; Podolczak, G. An account of the physical and behavioural development of the hand-reared gorilla infant *Gorilla g. gorilla* born at Frankfurt Zoo. INTERNATIONAL ZOO YEARBOOK 7:108–113, 1967.

Kirchshofer, R.; Weisse, K.; Berenz, K.; Klose, H.; Klose, I. A preliminary account of physical and behavioral development during the first 10 weeks of the hand-reared gorilla twins (*Gorilla g. gorilla*) born at Frankfurt Zoo. INTERNATIONAL ZOO YEARBOOK 8:121–128, 1968.

Kirk, J.H. Growth of maturing *Macaca mulatta*. LABORATORY ANIMAL SCIENCE 22:573–575, 1972.

Long, J.O.; Cooper, R.W. Physical growth and dental eruption in captive-bred squirrel monkeys, *Saimiri sciureus* (Letica, Colombia). Pp. 193–205 in THE SQUIRREL MONKEY. L.A. Rosenblum; R.W. Cooper, eds. New York, Academic Press, 1968.

Lorenz, R.; Heinemann, H. Contribution to the morphology and early body development of the marmoset *Callimico goeldii* (Thomas, 1904). FOLIA PRIMATOLOGICA 6:1–27, 1967.

Malinow, M.R.; Stahl, W.R.; Maruffo, C.A.; Pope, B.L.; Depaoli, R. Growth in howler monkeys. PRIMATES 7:433–447, 1966.

Manocha, S.L. Physical growth and brain development of captive-bred male and female squirrel monkeys, *Saimiri sciureus*. EXPERIENTIA 35:96–97, 1979.

McMahan, C.A.; Wigodsky, H.S.; Moore, G.T. Weight of the infant baboon (*Papio cynocephalus*) from birth to fifteen weeks. LABORATORY ANIMAL SCIENCE 26:928–931, 1976.

Napier, J.; Napier, P.H. A HANDBOOK OF LIVING PRIMATES. MORPHOLOGY, ECOLOGY AND BEHAVIOR OF NONHUMAN PRIMATES. New York, Academic Press, 1967.

Needham, J. CHEMICAL EMBRYOLOGY, Vol. 3. New York, Cambridge University Press, 1931.

Ohno, T.; Kato, Y.; Myoga, K. Growth performance and weight change of Japanese macaque under laboratory conditions. NUTRITION REPORTS INTERNATIONAL 22:935–938, 1980.

Ploog, D.; Hopf, S.; Winter, P. Ontogenese des Verhaltens von TotenkophAffen (*Saimiri sciureus*).

PSYCHOLOGISCHE FORSCHUNG 31:1–41, 1967.

Portman, A. ZOOLOGIE UND DAS NEUE BILD DES MENSCHEN. Hamburg, 1956.

Rode, R.C. Etude d'un chimpanzee pygmee adolescent (*Pan satyrus paniscus* Schwarz). MAMMALIA 5:50–68, 1941.

Rosenblum, L.A.; Smiley, J. Weight gain in bonnet and pigtail macaques. JOURNAL OF MEDICAL PRIMATOLOGY 9:247–253, 1980.

Scheffler, G.; Kerr, G.R. Growth and development of infant *M. arctoides* fed a standardized diet. JOURNAL OF MEDICAL PRIMATOLOGY 4:32–44, 1975.

Schultz, A.H. Fetal growth of man and other primates. QUARTERLY REVIEW OF BIOLOGY 1:465–521, 1926.

Schultz, A.H. Die Korperproportionen der erwachsenen catarrhinen Primaten, mit spezieller Beruchsichtigung der Menschenaffen. ANTHROPOLOGISCHER ANZEIGER 10:154–185, 1933.

Schultz, A.H. Fetal growth and development of the rhesus monkey. CONTRIBUTIONS TO EMBRYOLOGY 26:71–97, 1937.

Schultz, A.H. Growth and development of the chimpanzee. CONTRIBUTIONS TO EMBRYOLOGY 28:1–63, 1940.

Schultz, A.H. Growth and development of the orangutan. CONTRIBUTIONS TO EMBRYOLOGY 29:57–110, 1941.

Schultz, A.H. Growth and development of the proboscis monkey. BULLETIN OF THE MUSEUM OF COMPARATIVE BIOLOGY AT HARVARD UNIVERSITY 89:279–314, 1942.

Seitz, A. Notes on the body weights of newborn and young orangutans *Pongo pygmaeus*. INTERNATIONAL ZOO YEARBOOK 9:81–84, 1969.

Shea, B.T. Relative growth of the limbs and trunk in the African apes. AMERICAN JOURNAL OF PHYSICAL ANTHROPOLOGY 56:179–201, 1981.

Sigg, H.; Stolba, A.; Abegglen, J.-J.; Dasser, V. Life history of hamadryas baboons: Physical development, infant mortality, reproductive parameters and family relationships. PRIMATES 23:473–487, 1982.

Sly, D.L.; London, W.T.; Palmer, A.E.; Rice, J.M. Growth and hematologic development of the patas monkey (*Erythrocebus patas*) to one year of age. JOURNAL OF MEDICAL PRIMATOLOGY 7:156–164, 1978.

Smith, A.H.; Butler, T.M.; Pace, N. Weight growth of colony-reared chimpanzees. FOLIA PRIMATOLOGICA 24:29–59, 1975.

Snow, C.C. Some observations on the growth and development of the baboon. Pp. 187–199 in THE BABOON IN MEDICAL RESEARCH. H. Vagtborg, ed. Austin, University of Texas Press, 1967.

Spence, K.W.; Yerkes, R.M. Weight, growth and age in chimpanzee. AMERICAN JOURNAL OF PHYSICAL ANTHROPOLOGY 22:229–246, 1937.

Tanimura, T.; Tanioka, Y. Comparison of embryonic and foetal development in man and rhesus monkey. LABORATORY ANIMAL HANDBOOKS 6:205–233, 1975.

Tanner, J.M. HUMAN BIOLOGY. New York, Oxford University Press, 1964.

van Wagenen, G.; Catchpole, H.R. Physical growth of the rhesus monkey (*Macaca mulatta*). AMERICAN JOURNAL OF PHYSICAL ANTHROPOLOGY 14:245–273, 1956.

van Wagenen, G.; Catchpole, H.R.; Negri, J.; Butzko, D. Growth of the fetus and placenta of the monkey (*Macaca mulatta*). AMERICAN JOURNAL OF PHYSICAL ANTHROPOLOGY 23:23–34, 1965.

Vice, T.E.; Britton, H.A.; Ratner, I.A. Care and raising of newborn baboons. LABORATORY ANIMAL CARE 16:12–22, 1966.

Walker, L.C.; Kaack, B.; Brizzee, K.R.; Walker, M.L. Prenatal ionizing irradiation and early postnatal growth of Colombian and Bolivian squirrel monkeys (*Saimiri sciureus*). AMERICAN JOURNAL OF PRIMATOLOGY 1:379–387, 1981.

Ward, J.P.; Scott, S. Observations of two infant bush babies, *Galago senegalensis*. LABORATORY PRIMATE NEWSLETTER 9:3–6, 1970.

Watts, E.S.; Gavan, J.A. Postnatal growth of nonhuman primates: The problem of the adolescent spurt. HUMAN BIOLOGY 54:53–70, 1982.

Wilen, R.; Naftolin, F. Pubertal age, weight, and weight gain in the individual female New World monkey (*Cebus albifrons*). PRIMATES 19:769–774, 1978.

Skeletal Development

Elizabeth S. Watts

Department of Anthropology, Tulane University, New Orleans, Louisiana 70118

PRENATAL AND NEONATAL SKELETAL DEVELOPMENT
Introduction and General History

Documentation of the timing and order of prenatal skeletal ossification in primates has grown out of three primary areas of interest—the need for accurate means of assessing gestational age and progress of fetuses and neonates for biomedical research, the need to identify abnormal fetuses and high-risk infants for improved colony management, and the study of evolutionary changes that are directly related to modified ontogeny. While these research areas appear to have quite disparate goals they are interrelated in several ways. All have resulted in the accumulation of basic data on skeletal development, and phylogenetic comparisons among primate species have revealed similarities and differences in the ossification process that can aid in a more appropriate use of nonhuman primates in biomedical and other research.

Much of the early work on prenatal skeletal development of primates was carried out by a single, but indefatigable, individual, the late Adolph H. Schultz [1921, 1924, 1933, 1937, 1940, 1941, 1942, 1944]. Though his studies were based on small numbers of dead fetuses and newborns, and gestation age was not precisely known for most of them, his observations have been largely borne out by subsequent work. His pioneering work on comparative development of the primate skeleton [summarized in Schultz, 1969a, chapter 11] made two contributions of general significance. It established the existence of a phylogenetic trend for an overall delay in the *timing* of ossification within the catarrhine primates, despite the retention of largely similar *sequences* of ossification in this group. One of the best illustrations of this trend can be seen in Figure 1, showing the degree of osseous development in the upper limb of various higher primates at birth. Secondly, Schultz's work demonstrated that a number of supposed qualitative differences in the adult skeleton of primates were in fact the result of ontogenetic alterations in the ossification process. For example, in postnatal life most higher primates possess nine carpal bones in the wrist; yet man, chimpanzee, and gorilla have only eight. The possession of one less carpal bone in these three hominoids is due to early, usually prenatal, fusion of the separate os centrale with the navicular. In the other apes (orang-utans, siamangs, and gibbons) this fusion may occur late in life, and in the monkeys not at all. Thus, all the Hominoidea possess a common tendency for fusion of these two bones of the carpus, but this tendency is expressed at different ages [Schultz, 1936].

Because gestation age was not known for most of Schultz's specimens the details of his studies of ossification timing in relation to growth and other developmental indicators in various species will not be discussed here. However, one of his general findings deserves mention because of its implications for the use of osseous development as an indicator of gestational age and maturation in the late fetal and nenonatal periods. As can be seen in Figure 1, man and the apes differ from the cercopithecoid monkeys in the number of secondary centers of ossification that have appeared by the time of birth. In humans and apes the long bone diaphyses and other large skeletal elements ossify prenatally, but the radiographic appearance of the carpals, tarsals, and most epiphyses is largely confined to postnatal life. Very few of these secondary centers have appeared at birth. In contrast, in the common laboratory monkey species, the primary

Comparative Primate Biology, Volume 3: Reproduction and Development, pages 415–439
© 1986 Alan R. Liss, Inc.

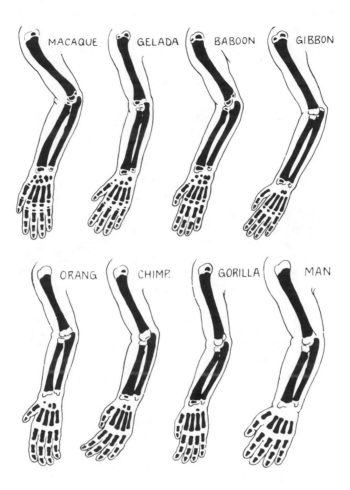

Fig. 1. Tracings of radiographs of the upper extremities in newborn catarrhine primates showing the skeletal centers ossified at birth [reprinted, with permission, from Schultz, 1969a].

centers of the skeleton ossify prenatally and the majority of the secondary centers appear before birth as well. Thus, systems for judging developmental status or age based on initial appearance of secondary centers are most useful in monkeys during the latter part of prenatal life, when most centers are appearing, but are of very limited utility for humans and apes during this period. For the latter groups they achieve maximum utility during infancy and childhood.

Data presented by Glaser [1970] and Niemitz and Sprankel [1974] on ossification at birth in a wider range of primate species, including prosimians, tarsiers, and New World monkeys, suggest that the trend noted above for an increasing delay in prenatal skeletal ossification among the catarrhine primates is limited to that group. They argue that the degree of skeletal development attained by newborn humans, New World monkeys, tarsiers,

and prosimians is very similar. It is the cercopithecoid monkeys that show notably advanced skeletal ossification at birth compared to other primate groups.

Evidence

The Genus *Macaca*. The earliest radiographic study of ossification in a sizable sample of fetuses of known conception date is that of van Wagenen and Asling [1964] on the rhesus monkey (*Macaca mulatta*). Though their investigation includes longitudinal radiographs of developing fetuses in utero their data are primarily derived from x-rays of 46 fetuses obtained by hysterotomy at roughly 20-day intervals from 50 to 177 days of gestation. They provide written descriptions, tables, and pictorial standards for ossification of the appendicular skeleton in the fetal rhesus monkey in relation to age and crown-rump length. Rough guidelines for estimating ossification progress and/or age from radiographs of fetuses in utero are also given. Their results show that ossification of the shafts of the major limb bones and girdles has already begun by 50 days and all long-bone diaphyses of the extremities show some ossification by 75 days. The secondary centers begin to appear at 90 days, the earliest being the calcaneus. By the time of parturition, at around 168 days, all but a very few secondary centers have appeared. The authors note the existence of a sex difference in the rate of prenatal osseous development, with females being advanced, but owing to the limitation of small sample size, they do not attempt to quantify this difference or adjust their standards accordingly.

Several subsequent studies provide additional normative data on ossification of laboratory-bred rhesus monkeys spanning the prenatal and neonatal periods. Wilson et al [1970] studied size, organ weights, and skeletal development in 20 rhesus monkey fetuses removed by hysterotomy at 100 days. The skeleton was stained with Alizarine Red S for visualization. The authors do not present any data on skeletal ossification but do give one figure picturing a stained and preserved fetus, sex unspecified. From this it appears that all of the long-bone shafts, the skull, and vertebrae are well ossified. The calcaneus and talus are present at this age, but none of the epiphyses can be seen. Dobbelaar and Arts [1972] present standards for estimating fetal age and parturition date based upon in utero radiographs of three fetuses taken at 4-day intervals from 70 to 168 days of gestation. Their method includes measurements of long bones, intervertebral distances, and size of the skull, as well as observation of ossification progress in several anatomical areas. In testing their method on an independent sample they found it to be most accurate between 75 and 115 days where the error of estimating parturition date was ± 5 days. Kerr and colleagues [Kerr et al, 1972; Kerr, 1975] document skeletal growth and development in a total sample of 66 fetal and infant rhesus monkeys sacrificed at 25-day age intervals during gestation and in infancy between 50 and 378 days postconception. They give standards for long-bone shaft lengths and appearance of secondary ossification centers taken from radiographs of the extremities.

Michejda and co-workers [Michejda et al, 1979; Michejda and Watson, 1979; Michejda and Bacher, 1981] have begun work on a radiographic atlas of skeletal development of the hand and wrist for the laboratory rhesus monkey. They aim to provide pictorial standards for hand/wrist ossification spanning the period from 128 days' gestational age until

complete fusion of the epiphyses at 5–6 years postnatal [Michejda, 1978]. Their prenatal data are taken from repeated radiographs of the surgically exposed hand/wrist of 20 fetuses taken at 2-week intervals. Preliminary data from the prenatal portion of this study are published in Michejda et al [1979] and Michejda and Bacher [1981]. They provide tracings representing the "most typical" radiographs of their sample at weekly intervals from 120 to 169 days of gestation along with written descriptions of secondary ossification centers at each stage. They note that the fetal rhesus monkey gains roughly one carpal center per week during the final 6 weeks of gestation. Though the existence of individual variability and sexual dimorphism in ossification timing is acknowledged, the extent of this variability is not described. Michejda and Watson [1979] report on skeletal development as an age indicator in the early postnatal period. They present x-ray standards based on longitudinal data for the period from birth to 3 months postnatal.

Prenatal and early postnatal skeletal development in the extremities of the pig-tailed macaque (*Macaca nemestrina*) has been studied extensively by Newell-Morris and colleagues [Newell-Morris and Tarrant, 1978; Newell-Morris, 1979; Newell-Morris et al, 1980]. They used more than 100 fetuses and neonates whose gestation ages were known to with ± 1 day. The fetal data were cross-sectional with observations of animals taken by cesarean section between 50 and 166 days. Most of the neonates used were followed longitudinally, some to a maximum of 356 postconception days. Ossification progress was measured by assigning each center a score of 0 when not visible, 0.5 at initial ossification (visible as a small white dot on the x-ray), and 1.0 when it was beyond this initial stage. Scores for individual centers are then summed to given a total skeletal maturity score for the hand (called NOHC, number of hand centers) and foot (NOFC). In general, timing and sequence of ossification of the extremities the pig-tailed macaque appear to be very similar to that of the rhesus though there are no studies of the latter using exactly comparable methods.

Newell-Morris and Tarrant's [1978] findings regarding the differences in ossification timing between macaques and humans extend and confirm the earlier conclusions of Schultz [1969a]. On the basis of their ossification scores the authors divide prenatal skeletal development in macaques into three main periods—a first acceleration period (roughly 50–70 days postconception) when the diaphyseal centers of the hand and foot ossify, a plateau period (70–120 days) when only two new

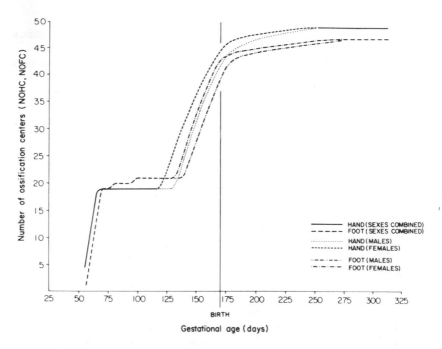

Fig. 2. Cumulative incremental curves for prenatal skeletal maturation of the hand and foot in pig-tailed macaques [reprinted, with permission, from Newell-Morris and Tarrant, 1978].

centers, the talus and calcaneus, appear, and a second acceleration period (120–275 days) when the long-bone epiphyses, carpals and remaining tarsal bones appear. Cumulative incremental curves for the skeletal maturity scores are shown in Figure 2. Comparison to a similar curve for human ossification shows that the same three phases are discernible in man, but the principal difference between humans and macaques is the shifted position of the curves with respect to the event of birth. In Figure 2 it can be seen that birth occurs in macaques towards the end of the second acceleration period, when the secondary centers are ossifying at a rapid rate. But, in man birth occurs at the end of the plateau period, at its juncture with the second acceleration period. In humans the second acceleration period begins around the time of birth and is much more protracted, occupying the first few years of postnatal life. This shift in the point at which birth occurs relative to skeletal development has produced the striking difference between man and macaque in the degree of skeletal ossification at birth that has been described by Schultz [1969a] and others. Though their gestation period is longer, humans are born with a less mature skeleton, and macaques are skeletally advanced in both absolute and relative terms. From the data available on ossification at birth in the

great apes it is apparent that they are more similar to man than to macaques in this regard [Nissen and Riesen, 1949a; Schultz, 1969a].

From the sex-specific curves depicted in Figure 2 it is evident that Newell-Morris and Tarrant [1978] found a significant sex difference in ossification progress, with females being advanced, particularly during the second acceleration period, confirming the earlier observation of Tarrant [1977] that there is significant sexual dimorphism in ossification status of newborns of this species. In a later paper Newell-Morris et al [1980] present ossification sequences in the hand and foot for the same, primarily cross-sectional, sample discussed above. They established the general order of ossification of centers in the pig-tailed macaque and compare it to sequences reported for other primates. The pig-tailed macaque shows a high degree of intraspecies variability in ossification sequence and timing. In general, however, the order of appearance of centers is similar to that of the rhesus macaque while differing from that of man in several respects. Newell-Morris et al [1979] also report the appearance of supernumerary epiphyses in their sample of fetal and infant monkeys. Extra epiphyses were found at the distal first metacarpal and metatarsal sites as an apparently normal variant in 15–20% of their animals.

Newell-Morris [1979] presents a system for determining gestational age in fetal and neonatal pigtailed macaques based on the scoring system for number of ossification centers discussed above. In the period from 130 days to birth, number of foot center (NOFC) and number of hand center (NOHC) scores are shown to be more accurate predictors of gestational age than weight, crown-rump length, or foot length, with a standard error of less than a week. Sex-specific regression equations are given for estimating gestational age from skeletal maturity scores, weight, and the two linear measurements. In applying her scoring system to abnormal fetuses Newell-Morris [1979] found ossification status to be the measure least affected by environmental stress. This finding indicates that ossification is the best criterion for estimating age, and that a discrepancy between skeletal maturity and other growth variables may serve as a sign of fetal abnormality.

Fahrenbruch et al [1979] study the effects of short gestation on birth status and subsequent development in the pig-tailed macaque. They compare size and skeletal maturity of five premature (gestation of less than 162 days) and 16 term newborns of known conception date followed from birth to 355 days postconception. Skeletal maturity scores for the hand and foot were obtained by a simple three-stage scoring method similar to that used by Newell-Morris and Tarrant [1978]. They found skeletal maturity to be more sensitive to the effects or short gestation than any of the measures of size (weight, crown-rump length, or foot length). Most of the premature infants continued to lag behind the control group in skeletal development throughout the study period. The authors conclude that skeletal immaturity is a good means of identifying premature newborns that may experience delayed maturation and other postnatal growth problems. Ossification is superior to birth weight as an index of developmental status and should be especially valuable where gestation age is unknown.

A study of fetal growth and development of the crab-eating macaque (*Macaca fascicularis*) by Mahoney [1975] includes data on ossification taken from radiographic examination of 49 in utero and 25 ex utero fetuses from dated pregnancies. Some of the fetuses in utero were examined repeatedly, and data from the two sexes were apparently combined. By 70 days the fetal skeleton is discernible in radiographs of the mother's abdomen. Age of earliest appearance of various secondary ossification centers is given for in utero and ex utero fetuses separately. Later ages of appearance are given for centers examined in utero and the author states that some of the centers were not visible in any of the in utero fetuses and that others were visible in only a small number of fetuses regardless of age. Thus, the ages of appearance based on the radiographs taken of fetuses in utero are probably less reliable as indicators of true ossification timing. Comparison of the ages of appearance for ossification centers based on fetuses radiographed ex utero show the crab-eating macaque to be broadly similar to the rhesus and pig-tailed macaques in prenatal skeletal development. Though a detailed comparison is not possible because of methodological differences in the various studies, the ages of earliest appearance of centers Mahoney [1975] gives for the crab-eating macaque are all slightly later than those reported by van Wagenen and Asling [1964] for the rhesus. Fukuda et al [1978] also studied the radiographic appearance of the skeleton in seven *Macaca fascicularis* fetuses whose gestational ages ranged from 6 to 20 weeks. Sex was not determinable in the two youngest specimens (aged 6 and 7 weeks), but the remaining five were male. All were radiographed ex utero and each age is represented by only one animal. They report bone images to be first visible in the 8-week-old fetus and the long bones to be clearly visible at 9 weeks. Length measurements (taken from x-rays) of the fetal long bones between 10 and 20 weeks are also given. Secondary ossification centers first appear in the fetus of 15 weeks, and at 20 weeks many of the long-bone epiphyses are present. The general schedule of ossification is similar to that reported for other macaque species.

A radiographic comparison of hand and foot ossification in two newborn *M. nemestrina* and three *M. fascicularis* is presented by Ardito et al [1982]. The animals used are apparently normal, term neonates obained from zoos. All died during the first week postnatal from maternal neglect or abuse. Gestation times are apparently unknown and sexes of the specimens not given, though the authors state they they were unable to discern any sexual dimorphism in skeletal development. Diagrams showing ossification in the hand/wrist and foot/ankle of the individuals are given and skeletal maturity scores assigned to each acording to the system of Newell-Morris and Tarrant [1978]. The *M. fascicularis* show higher mean scores in both extremities, but the difference between the two samples is more marked in the foot/ankle. The authors conclude that this is a significant species difference related to the greater arboreal tendencies of *M. fascicularis*; ie, advanced ossification in the foot is advantageous for arboreal grasping. Given the nature and size of the samples studied, and the wide variability in ossification status of newborn macaques due to sex, gestation time, and individual factors, such conclusions should be viewed as very tentative.

The New World Monkeys (*Ceboidea*). Very few data are available on prenatal development of New World monkeys and none are based upon animals of known gestational age. The most complete study of a callithricid is that of Phillips [1976] who investigates ossification in the fetal common marmoset (*Callithrix jacchus*). Fetuses were observed both in utero and ex utero, and 29 preserved neonates up to 50 days of postnatal age were also included. The fetuses came from 30 pregnancies but the number of specimens examined was much greater owing to the high frequency of twin and triplet pregnancies in marmosets. In addition to x-rays, alizarin preparations were used to detect the onset of ossification in the ex utero fetuses and neonates. Since fetal ages were estimated, however, the data can only provide rough guidelines for the timing of ossification in this species. Even so, they indicate some interesting contrasts with macaques that are of phylogenetic as well as practical significance. Fetal osseous development (in utero) was not visible in x-rays until more than 40 days prior to delivery. Given the usual gestation time of 150 days in this colony, the fetal skeleton does not appear until about 111 days of gestation. The earliest discernible ossification in the ex utero fetuses occurred at an estimated 95–105 days (alizarin technique) and 106–115 days (x-ray). Unless these fetal-age estimates are very much in error, the data indicate that prenatal ossification begins a good deal later in the marmoset than in the macaque where partially ossified skeletal structures are visible some 50–60 days after conception in a total gestation period of 168 days on average. Therefore, the delay is both absolute (about 50 days later from conception) and relative (a 41% lag in terms of total gestation). Phillips [1976] attributes the delay in the onset of ossification in the fetal marmoset to the fact that this species has a relatively longer embryonic period. Thus, the tempo of maturation during prenatal life may show marked differences between the New World and Old World monkeys. Such a possibility is also raised by McKim et al [1972] in their paper on prenatal growth of squirrel monkeys (*Saimiri sciureus*).

Kraus and Hampton [1969] report briefly on ossification of the foot in the fetal cotton-top tamarin (*Saguinus oedipus*). The authors give the sequence of ossification for the metatarsal and phalangeal shafts seen in eight fetuses of unknown gestational age. Alizarine preparations were used to identify ossified tissue. The results are compared to sequences reported for human fetuses. The two species appear to be very similar except for the order of ossification of the terminal phalanx of the first toe, which shows a marked difference. It is the first center to ossify in humans and the 14th in the tamarin.

Data on osseous development of the black howler monkey (*Alouatta caraya*) are given by Swindler et al [1968]. Their report is based on radiographic examination of 19 ex utero fetuses of unknown age ranging in crown-rump length from 84.0 to 170.5 mm. Skeletal development is described in relation to crown-rump length and compared to that of five known-age fetal rhesus monkeys from Schultz's [1937] study. The authors note that ossification status for a given crown-rump length is very similar in the two species, implying that the similarity in size can be used as a rough indicator of gestation age for the howler monkey fetuses. This conclusion is open to question, however, given the possibility of differential rates of prenatal growth and development between New World and Old World monkeys discussed above. It may be that the howler monkey fetuses are considerably older than those of the rhesus monkeys of similar size and ossification status.

All fetuses in the howler monkey series had ossified long-bone shafts, and some of the larger ones had a few tarsals, carpals, and epiphyseal centers present. The sequence of appearance of these secondary centers is compared to that of the rhesus monkey, chimpanzee, and man. The triquetral is the only carpal present in three of the larger howler fetuses, while the largest had this bone plus a smaller hamate. In man and chimpanzee the capitate and hamate are normally the earliest carpals to ossify, while both orders (triquetral first and capitate-hamate first) are reported for macaques [van Wagenen and Asling, 1958, 1964; Newell-Morris et al, 1980]. Obviously more research on ossification sequence variability within species is needed before definitive statements about phylogenetic differences can be made.

The Apes (*Hominoidea*). The scanty and scattered information on prenatal and neonatal ossification in apes is to be found in the works of Schultz [1933, 1940, 1941, 1944, 1969b, 1972] and in a few additional reports [Nissen and Riesen, 1949a; Hill and Spatz, 1970; Watts, 1971; Torre et al, 1978]. Sample sizes in all of these studies are small, and gestation ages are unknown for the majority of specimens. Some were undoubtedly obtained from premature births and abortions, making the data less than ideal for providing developmental norms.

Schultz's [1944] study of the gibbon included radiographic examination of nine "older" fetuses (the majority were *Hylobates lar*, though other species may have been included) and two newborn *Hylobates lar*. The primary centers for the long and irregular bones were ossified in all the fetuses examined, and the neonates possessed many of the long-bone epiphyses, two carpals, and five tarsal bones. However, Schultz's sample also included an animal several weeks old that still lacked some of the epiphyseal centers seen in the newborns. Despite this variability, however, the neonatal gibbon appears to be skeletally advanced compared to the great apes and to the three siamang (*Symphalangus syndactylus*) newborns reported by Schultz [1972]. The two female siamang neonates had two tarsals (calcaneus and talus), in the male only the calcaneus was present, and none of the three had any ossified epiphyses or carpal bones.

Ossification data on six fetal and two newborn orang-utans are reported by Schultz [1941]. All but one of the fetuses and at least one of the newborns were of the Bornean variety (*Pongo pygmaeus pygmaeus*). Crown-rump length of the fetuses ranged from 145 to 230 mm and all possessed ossified long-bone shafts. The calcaneus alone was present in the three smaller specimens, and the talus was also present in the three larger ones. One newborn female had four ossified tarsals, three carpals, and the epiphysis of the distal femur; the other, also a female, had only three tarsals and two carpal bones. The premature male Bornean orang examined by Torre et al [1978] had a postmenstrual age of 31½ weeks and a crown-rump length of 217 mm. It fits well into the larger half of Schultz's sample as regards both size and skeletal development, having well-ossified long-bone shafts plus the calcaneus and talus. A point-by-point comparison to a human fetus of 218 mm crown-rump length and estimated fetal age is described by the authors. The overall degree of ossification is similar in the two fetuses but there are some regional differences. Ossification is more advanced in the orang-utan skull and face, shoulder, and upper limb, whereas the human fetus exhibits relative advancement in the medial phalanges of the foot.

Hill and Spatz [1970] review the published information on gorilla fetal development and make comparisons to two gorilla fetuses they report for the first time. They found information on a total of 11 fetal gorillas whose sitting heights range from 71 to 240 mm. All but one are of the lowland variety (*Gorilla gorilla gorilla*). Ossification of the cranium, trunk, and limbs is discussed for the two new specimens (with sitting heights of 84 and 124 mm) as identified by x-ray and alizarin preparation. Preservation, especially of the skeleton, was poor in both fetuses, but it is apparent that all major primary centers are ossified in both, and no epiphyseal centers are present. Both apparently have some ossification of the talus and calcaneus. The authors claim to be able to identify bony deposition in six of the carpals in the larger fetus, but these were only visible in photographs of the cleared preparation.

The sample of 13 fetal chimpanzees examined by Schultz [1940] included five specimens of known gestational age, with a range of 126 to 189 days. Primary centers for all of the larger bones are well ossified in the youngest fetus and all possess the calcaneus. Of the two oldest specimens, a male of 189 days and a female of 185, the female is skeletally advanced, showing beginning ossification of the talus and hamate. In a later report based on ten neonatal chimpanzees Schultz [1969b] shows only the calcaneus and talus to be constantly present whereas the appearance of the cuboid, lateral cuneiform, hamate, capitate, and the epiphyses of the distal femur, proximal humerus, and distal radius is variable at birth.

The study of Nissen and Riesen [1949a] is the only one to report on a moderate sample of neonatal apes of known background and gestational age. These chimpanzees were colony-born, healthy animals from the Yerkes laboratories and they show considerably advanced ossification compared to the heterogeneous series of dead term fetuses and neonates examined by Schultz [1969b], a fact also noted by Schultz himself (for a comparison see Table 1). Nissen and Riesen [1949a] found substantial individual variability in skeletal development at birth, but females, as a group, are skeletally advanced over males. They explore the relationship of ossification progress to gestation time by means of rank-order correlations. From their results it is apparent that ossification shows a significant relationship to gestation time in the males of their sample ($r = +0.57$), but not in the females ($r = -0.38$). Using the same series of radiographs, Watts [1971] applied a skeletal maturity scoring system to the hand/wrist area and obtained very similar results as regards the sex difference and individual variability in these 11 newborn chimpanzees.

Though gestation age is not known for most of the fetal apes reported in the literature, it is appar-

TABLE 1. Ossification Centers Present at Birth in Apes and Humans

Genus	Author	No.	Tarsals		Carpals		Long-bone epiphyses	
			Constant	Variable	Constant	Variable	Constant	Variable
Hylobates	Schultz, 1944	2	Calcaneus Talus Cuboic Cuneiform I Cuneiform III	None	Hamate Capitate	None	Distal femur Proximal humerus Distal radius Metacarpals II–V	Distal ulna Proximal tibia
Symphalangus (*Hylobates*)	Schultz, 1972	3	Calcaneus	Talus	None	None	None	None
Pongo	Schultz, 1941	2	Calcaneus Talus Cuboid	Cuneiform III	Hamate Capitate	Navicular	None	Distal femur
Pan	Schultz, 1969	10	Calcaneus Talus	Cuboid Cuneiform III	None	Hamate Capitate	None	Distal femur Proximal humerus Distal radius
Pan	Nissen and Riesen, 1949	11	Calcaneus Talus Cuboid	Cuneiform III Cuneiform I	Hamate Capitate	None	Proximal humerus Distal femur Distal radius	Proximal tibia Proximal femur Distal tibia Distal humerus Distal fibula Distal ulna Metacarpals II–IV Proximal humerus
Homo	Hill, 1939; Francis and Werle, 1939	—	Calcaneus Talus Cuboid	Cuneiform III	None	Capitate Hamate	Distal femur Proximal tibia	Proximal humerus

ent from their size and degree of osseous development that all of them probably date from the latter half of gestation. In terms of the level of skeletal development attained, all would fall in Newell-Morris and Tarrant's [1978] plateau period where the major primary skeletal centers have already undergone ossification and the calcaneus and sometimes the talus have appeared. Some of the oldest fetal specimens and newborns have additional tarsals, carpals, and epiphyseal centers, indicating that they are beginning to enter the second acceleration period around the time of birth.

Table 1 presents a comparative summary of available data on ossification status at birth in apes and humans as reported by various authors. Given the small samples and the variability observed within species, it is not possible to demonstrate any conclusive differences in degree of ossification at birth either among the various ape genera or between apes and man. Such differences are probably quantitative rather than qualitative and will have to be demonstrated by comparing frequencies of appearance of various centers in larger samples. There is obviously some degree of overlap among all of these genera (ie, some newborn humans have as many centers present as some individual chimpanzee neonates). The demonstration of similarities and differences in sequence of appearance must likewise await work on larger samples.

Conclusions

This review makes it clear that reliable information on development of the prenatal skeleton in nonhuman primates is scanty at best. Most of the published data are for laboratory macaques, and very little is known about other species. Nevertheless, there appear to be some rather striking differences in the timing and order of prenatal ossification within the primate order. Some of them may be related to general phylogenetic trends; others probably reflect group specializations in adaptation and ecology. Obviously there is much still to be learned about prenatal skeletal development from the evolutionary point of view. However, a great deal of basic descriptive information must be gathered, and careful interspecies comparisons must be made before these evolutionary problems can be investigated further.

Skeletal ossification is an excellent means of determining level of fetal development [Hartley, 1957; Birkbeck, 1976]. The skeleton is superior to most other bodily systems for this purpose because it undergoes developmental changes that can be easily visualized and divided into stages that are relatively simple to discern and widely applicable.

As a measure of developmental status it is highly correlated with, but also somewhat independent of, fetal size and age. Therefore, it is useful in a variety of research contexts.

Much of the existing work on the prenatal skeleton has been done primarily for the purpose of establishing standards for the estimation of gestational age in fetuses of unknown conception date. For this purpose ossification is better than measures of size such as weight, crown-rump length, or foot length, because it is less variable and more highly correlated with gestation age [Newell-Morris, 1979; Fahrenbruch et al, 1979]. The data presented in Table 2 also support this finding, showing ossification status to be more highly correlated with age than is birthweight in a sample of neonatal laboratory rhesus monkeys. The data are taken from the animals described in the study of Riopelle et al [1976]. Conception date is known to within 48 hours. The radiographs and weights were taken on the day on birth. The measure of skeletal development used in these correlations was a simple count of the total number of ossification centers present in the hand. Though the correlations are not as high as those reported by Newell-Morris [1979] using a finer measure in the pig-tailed macaque, the figures are similar to hers in relative magnitude (ie, ossification shows a closer relationship to age than does weight).

There may be several reasons why ossification is a better indicator of age than are measures of size. An obvious one is that skeletal development appears to be more impervious to environmental stress [Newell-Morris, 1979]. It is also possible that ossification timing is less genetically variable than is growth in weight and length though there are no data to shed light on this possibility at present. No matter what the causes, however, the closer relationship between skeletal development and age definitely renders questionable the practice of estimating fetal age from crown-rump length and reporting ossification progress as the dependent variable, an approach sometimes used or im-

TABLE 2. Correlations of Skeletal Development and Weight With Gestation Time in Neonatal Rhesus Monkeys

	Males (n = 18)	Females (n = 16)
Ossification/gestation	0.635**	0.634*
Birthweight/gestation	0.479*	0.505*

*Significantly different from zero, $P < 0.05$.
**Significantly different from zero, $P < 0.01$.

plied in studies of human fetuses [Hill, 1939; O'Rahilly and Meyer, 1956; Garn et al, 1974].

The relationship of ossification progress to fetal age can be used either to establish time elapsed conception or to predict expected parturition date in normal pregnancies. In pathological or experimentally treated pregnancies skeletal development can also provide useful information. It can be used to estimate the age at which fetal development ceased in stillborns and abortuses [van Wagenen and Asling, 1964]. By providing a measure of developmental status that is independent of size and age it can be used to assess the effects of factors thought to retard skeletal maturation per se [Kerr et al, 1972; Riopelle et al, 1976]. And, examination of the interrelationships of fetal age, size, and osseous development can indicate cases of fetal abnormality [Newell-Morris and Tarrant, 1978; Newell-Morris, 1979].

Given that ossification of the fetal skeleton is a useful developmental indicator, what methods are best for its measurement and quantification? Beginning ossification in the fetal skeleton can be detected by means of histology, Alizarine preparation, or radiography [Meyer and O'Rahilly, 1958], and its visibility in the latter technique can be enhanced by silver nitrate impregnation [Hodges, 1953; O'Rahilly and Meyer, 1956]. Initial ossification is not identifiable as early by x-ray compared to the other techniques, but radiography is less time-consuming and does not necessarily require sacrifice of the fetus. Hence, it is more widely used. The overall utility of maturity determinations made from in utero radiographs is debatable. While this approach may be necessary if the researcher desires longitudinal data or live-born animals, there are problems with visibility of centers because of variable positioning of the fetus and other factors. For the purpose of establishing standards of osseous development, technique of repeated x-rays of surgically exposed fetuses, used by Michejda and Bacher [1981], overcomes the problem of poor visibility, but it has other drawbacks and would not be suitable for routine use. In establishing gestational or developmental age of the fetus, particularly for predicting parturition, abdominal and genital palpation of the mother were found by some workers to be as good as, or better than, radiographic examination [Mahoney, 1975; Phillips, 1976]. However, Dobbelaar and Arts [1972] obtained good results in predicting parturition from in utero radiography of rhesus monkeys using a combination of skeletal measurements and observations of ossification progress. The method was derived from a longitudinal study of three

pregnancies but showed an error of $\pm$ 5 days when tested on an independent sample of 14 pregnant females. Improved accuracy could probably be obtained by devising sex-specific prediction standards since, at least in macaques, the sexes differ in rate of prenatal osseous development [Newell-Morris and Tarrant, 1978] and in gestation time [Riopelle and Hale, 1975], males showing slower osseous development and slightly longer gestations than females.

In examining ex utero fetuses and neonates, especially living neonates, radiography is often the most practical and expedient technique. Live neonatal monkeys can be restrained and radiographed without anesthesia, but in the author's experience anesthesia is necessary for obtaining suitable x-rays of newborn apes because of their greater size and strength.

Obviously the utility of skeletal development as an age or maturational indicator is greatest at times when the fetal skeleton is most actively forming new osseous tissue. The use of simple presence or absence of centers, or counts based on radiographic appearance, is adequate during some phases of prenatal life. An example is the late fetal and neonatal period in macaques when a large number of secondary centers are appearing. (The "atlas" method described by Michejda and Bacher [1981] is probably no more useful than simple counts during this particular period since it is more difficult to apply and quantify, and its reliability and accuracy are as yet untested.) However, in every species there are periods during osseous development when few new centers are appearing (such as Newell-Morris and Tarrant's plateau period discussed above). During such phases individual morphological changes in the bones that are past the initial stage of ossification can be used as additional maturity indicators [see, for example, Birkbeck, 1976]. From the foregoing discussion it is apparent that ossification begins at different gestational ages and proceeds at different rates in various primate groups. Thus, the choice of a method of measuring ossification progress depends on the species and the time period of interest to the researcher.

POSTNATAL SKELETAL DEVELOPMENT
Introduction

Published works on postnatal osseous development in primates can, with few exceptions, be divided into two main categories: 1) studies of ossification and union of epiphyses in immature animals of unknown age. Obviously these data are not suitable for age estimation but can be used to investigate variability in the order of ossification, its phylogenetic significance, and its relationship to other developmental phenomena such as dental eruption. 2) Studies (usually radiographic) of appearance and union of epiphyses in laboratory-born animals of known age. Here the data have been used to construct a variety of systems for estimating age in wild-born animals and to provide standards for assessing maturational status in experimentally treated subjects of the same species.

Information on postnatal sequence of ossification in animals, most of unknown age, is available for tree shrews [Shigehara, 1980], tamarins [Glassman, 1983], night monkeys [Thorington and Vorek, 1976], howler monkeys [Lusted et al, 1966; Lusted and Miller, 1968], proboscis monkeys [Schultz, 1942], Japanese macaques [Hayama, 1965], baboons [Bramblett, 1969], gibbons [Schultz, 1944], orang-utans [Schultz, 1941], chimpanzees [Schultz, 1940; Kerley, 1966], and gorillas [Randall, 1943, 1944]. In addition to presenting original data on fusion of skeletal elements, several authors also give comparative reviews of the evidence for various taxonomic groups in the light of phylogenetic considerations. Todd [1930a], Washburn [1946], Curgy [1965], and Shigehara [1980] compare primates and other mammals. Schultz [1956] discusses trends within the primate order. Washburn [1943] reviews some Asian Old World monkeys, Wintheiser et al [1977] some African cercopithecids, and Tappen and Severson [1971] some New World monkeys. Adequate data on postnatal appearance of ossification centers are not available from these studies and, thus, only osseous union will be discussed here. The existing evidence suggests that there is either no relationship, or possibly a weak negative one, between the order of appearance of secondary centers and their order of fusion [Curgy, 1965]. It is, therefore, unlikely that common factors are responsible for both.

The study of the order of epiphyseal closure throughout the body is aided by using a regional approach [Washburn, 1943] since epiphyses adjacent to a given joint tend to unite around the same time even though they may belong to different bones. Thus, one can look at the order of union of regions (elbow, hip, ankle, etc) rather than of individual epiphyses, though the order of union within a region may also vary. The data available on epiphyseal union in primates are far from complete. However, it is clear even now that, though the sequence of fusion is very similar throughout the order, there is no single pattern common to all primates. The most common factor is for the epi-

physes of the elbow to unite first, a trait that is apparently universal among mammals [Shigehara, 1980]. The elbow is followed by the hip and then the ankle in all primates so far examined except the tamarins [Tappen and Severson, 1971], where the ankle is relatively advanced in *Saguinus nigricollis*. In his comparative study Shigehara [1980] shows that the hip-ankle-knee sequence in the lower extremity is common in small primitive arboreal mammals and, therefore, this pattern may be a retained ancestral feature of primates in general from which only the tamarins appear to depart. More recently, however, Glassman [1983] presents data on epiphyseal closure in the saddle-backed tamarin (*Saguinus fuscicollis*) indicating that the hip precedes the ankle, at least in the earlier stages of fusion.

The order of union of the wrist and shoulder is variable in primates although either the wrist or shoulder is always the last region to show completed union. In the orang-utan and gorilla the wrist is the last to unite whereas the shoulder is usually last in other primates with the possible exception of some of the New World monkeys [Schultz, 1956]. In macaques there is intraspecies variation in the order of fusion at these two joints. In females closure at the wrist clearly follows the shoulder whereas in males the two areas fuse at about the same time [Fukuda et al, 1978; Cheverud, 1981; Silverman et al; 1983]. This sex difference in the order of fusion is related to the fact that the usual sex difference in the ages of fusion of the wrist epiphyses (especially the distal ulna) tends to be very slight, or even reversed, in some macaque species, with males showing absolutely earlier chronological ages of fusion than females.

So far no one has been able to provide either an evolutionary or a functional hypothesis that can adequately account for the various patterns of epiphyseal union observed in primates. Washburn [1943] suggests that some of the interspecies variability may be related to differences in body proportions established late in the growth period. Shigehara [1980], following Stevenson [1924] and Simon [1978], feels that sequences of epiphyseal closure may be affected by mechanical factors related to locomotion.

Also of interest is the relationship of skeletal maturity to dental eruption and the attainment of reproductive functioning. In all primates so far studied, except humans of European origin (so-called "whites"), the permanent dentition erupts prior to the completion of epiphyseal union in the skeleton. However, Schultz [1956] demonstrates that there is a regular trend within the primate order for the delayed completion of the permanent dentition relative to epiphyseal union. In lemurs and monkeys the permanent dentition erupts relatively early, coincident with fusion in the elbow. In gibbons and orang-utans dental eruption is slightly delayed and follows union at the elbow joint. In the African apes full dental eruption is completed in the middle of the sequence of epiphyseal union. In man it is the most delayed and occurs at the very end of the sequence, coincident with, or even after, closure of the shoulder epiphysis. Sexual maturity precedes the completion of dental eruption and epiphyseal union in most primates, with the possible exception of some of the smaller New World monkeys [Shigehara, 1980; Glassman, 1983] where dental emergence is relatively advanced.

Evidence

The New World Monkeys. The only thorough study of postnatal ossification in a laboratory New World monkey is that of Thurm and colleagues [1975] of skeletal maturation in the white-fronted capuchin (*Cebus albifrons*). Developmental norms for this species were established and detailed in order to evaluate the effects of experimental nutritional deprivation on skeletal maturation [Thurm et al, 1976]. Two atlases of skeletal maturation have been constructed. One covers only the first year [Thurm et al, 1975]; the second, as yet unpublished, covers the entire maturation period (Accatino and Fleagle, unpublished). A control group of 12 animals (8 males and 4 females) provided the data for the first atlas; the second is based on a larger sample (n = 26) of animals from the same colony. These laboratory-born infants were radiographed weekly for the first 8 weeks and biweekly thereafter. The atlases provide drawings and verbal descriptions defining maturity indicators throughout the skeleton. Several developmental stages, including appearance and union, are given for most of the ossification centers. Age means and ranges at which each stage is normally reached are indicated on graphs. In the first-year atlas bone maturity scores are assigned to each stage and the scores summed for all bones to obtain a total "bone maturity score." The means for these scores are given according to age and sex. No significant sex differences were found in this sample during the first year. In addition to the original purpose of providing a basis for determining and measuring the mag-

nitude of developmental delay in experimentally treated animals, these atlases are potentially useful for estimating age in wild-born *Cebus* monkeys. Tests on animals randomly chosen from the standardizing group showed an error of less than 1½ weeks in estimating chronological age from skeletal maturity. However, larger errors should be expected in age estimates for independent groups.

Very recently Glassman [1983] has completed a cross-sectional investigation of dental eruption and epiphyseal union in saddle-backed tamarins (*Saguinus fuscicollis*) of known age. Sequence and timing of epiphyseal closure were determined by visual examination of 67 immature skeletons (26 male and 41 female) from birth to 28 months of age. Seventeen skeletons over 28 months were also examined to document union of the ischial tuberosity, iliac crest, and sphenoccipital synchondrosis. Data from animals of four subspecies (some were subspecies hybrids) and both sexes were combined. Age ranges for union of each epiphysis are given that encompass the age of the youngest animal to show beginning union and the youngest age at which all specimens exhibit complete union. The age of the youngest individual showing complete union is also given. Thus, one can establish the earliest age at which fusion begins, as well as the lower and upper limits of the range for completed fusion in this sample. Union of the long-bone epiphyses is considerably accelerated compared to the *Cebus* monkey and the macaques commencing in the tamarin distal humerus in the third postnatal month and ending with closure at the proximal humerus and distal femur at around 2 years. Regression equations are given for estimating age from skeletal and dental scores. The potential accuracy of these estimates, inferred from the standard deviations, is ± 26.5 days for dental eruption and ± 54.9 days for skeletal development, but the formulas have not been tested on an independent sample.

The Genus *Macaca*. There are some half dozen papers devoted to various aspects of postnatal skeletal development in rhesus monkeys (*Macaca mulatta*) from different colonies, but none are strictly comparable in methodology or in the ways in which the data are analyzed and presented, and, thus, their results can only be roughly compared. The earliest, and best known, of these is the study of van Wagenen and Asling [1958] on the Yale University colony. It is a mixed longitudinal study (ie, some of the subjects were x-rayed repeatedly) of a sample of 111 monkeys whose ages ranged from newborn to 10 years. The results regarding ages of appearance and union of a large number of ossification centers in the extremities are presented in sex-specific graphs, and in verbal descriptions of skeletal "maturity indicators" for each sex. The latter describe the age changes normally seen in the radiographs at 3-month intervals from birth to full skeletal maturity, which occurs at 5 years 3 months in females and 6½ years in males. Figure 3 diagrams the location of the skeletal centers investigated in this study.

This study shows females to be advanced in skeletal development from birth and to undergo epiphyseal union 6–10 months earlier than males. Individual variability in ages of appearance and fusion is acknowledged, but not quantified, by the authors. They also report that some stages of ossification and some centers are more variable than others. They conclude that, using the maturation status of a large number of centers in the appendicular skeleton, accurate judgments of chronological age and skeletal maturity can be made. Using their maturity indicators, van Wagenen and Asling [1958] report that they were able to judge the ages of rhesus monkeys from another colony to within 3 months of their true ages.

In comparing van Wagenen and Asling's [1958] study to others it must be kept in mind that the ages of appearance and union given by them are not means, or average ages. For each center they report the earliest age at which appearance (or union) occurred in their sample, and the age at which presence (or union) of a center was universal. Thus, the data given are really age ranges, representing the extremes, and are not comparable to measures of central tendency.

Gisler et al [1960] present data taken from a radiographic study of over 50 laboratory-born rhesus monkeys from the USAF Aerospace Medical Center colony. They provide bone maturation criteria and a graph for estimating age in male animals showing the state of ossification of 12 skeletal areas at quarterly intervals from 6 to 48 months. A later paper [Gisler et al, 1962] extends the aging criteria through 75 months. Included in the graphs are ages of appearance, and beginning and complete fusion of some of the epiphyses of the extremities and trunk. It is not clear how these age norms were chosen—ie, whether they represent the earliest age at which the feature was seen or the age at which

all animals possessed it. Verbal descriptions also mention the state of ossification of females, which were found to reach their maturation stages some 3–5 months ahead of males. This study includes developmental changes in some areas of the skeleton, such as the sacrum, that are not reported in van Wagenen and Asling [1958]. The stated purpose of Gisler et al [1960, 1962] is to provide a set of simplified criteria for age estimation in rhesus monkeys. But the accuracy of the system is only mentioned in the published discussion following the second [Gisler et al, 1962] paper, where it is stated to be accurate to within 3–6 months.

A longitudinal study of growth, sexual maturation, dental emergence, and skeletal development was carried out by Haigh and Scott [1965] on 13 (6 male and 7 female) captive-born rhesus monkeys in Great Britain. The age range covered is 6 months to 5½ years although all subjects were not followed to full maturity. Ossification was studied by means of radiographs of the hand/wrist. Information on ossification status by age and sex is presented in a table. All epiphyses and carpal bones had appeared by the age at which this study began (6 months). Ages of appearance of sesamoid bones and changes in shape of the articular areas of the distal radius and ulna, as well as the degree of fusion of epiphyses, are given. Another table shows the agreement among various measures of growth and development in age estimation when applied to radiographs of young animals of unknown age. Dental and skeletal development were found to be less variable with age than weight and foot length.

Watts [1975] used a bone-specific scoring system to measure skeletal maturation in the hand and wrist in rhesus monkeys from the University of Missouri colony. The study is based on serial radiographs of 43 monkeys of known age, followed from birth up to 6 years of age. As in most studies of this type, however, sample size declines with age. The skeletal maturity ratings and scores were derived from a system based on the one for measuring skeletal development in children constructed by Tanner and Whitehouse [1959] and updated by Tanner et al [1975]. Each epiphysis of the hand/wrist goes through a series of stages, and each stage is assigned a certain number of points. The points for all centers are then summed to give an overall "skeletal maturity score" for each radiograph. The means and standard deviations are given by sex and age for the sample. Females show higher mean scores than males at most ages, and the sex differ-

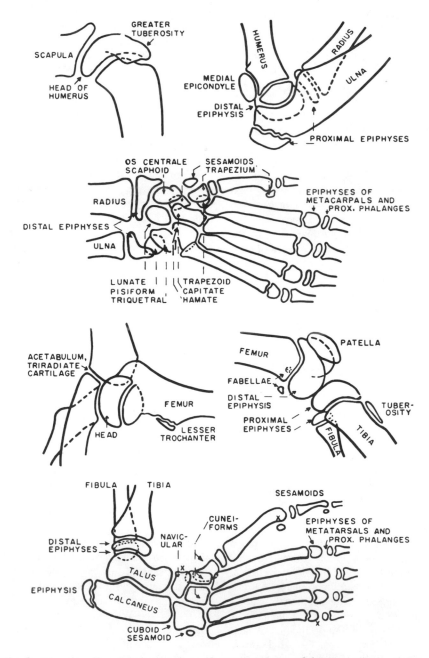

Fig. 3. Diagrams showing the locations of osseous centers of the appendicular skeleton in rhesus monkeys studied by van Wagenen and Asling [1958] (reprinted with permission).

ence is frequently significant statistically. The skeletal maturity scores have the advantage of giving a more concise measure of skeletal maturity that is more easily manipulated statistically than previously described methods. This system is not limited to appearance and union of epiphyses, but also measures intermediate stages of ossification and therefore provides a means of assessing skeletal maturation that is applicable throughout the entire period of postnatal development. It has not been tested as a method of estimating chronological age but has been used as a measure of developmental status in an experimental context [Riopelle et al, 1976].

Epiphyseal union and its relationship to age and dental eruption are reported in Cheverud's [1981] study of 299 rhesus monkey skeletons from the free-ranging colony on Cayo Santiago, Puerto Rico. The age at death, which ranges from birth to over 85 months, is known for these monkeys. The state of epiphyseal fusion was judged from the skeletal material itself rather than from radiographs. The author judged an epiphysis as fused when "it was united by bone to the diaphysis." He reports the age of union as an average age that misclassifies the fewest animals. A "misclassified" animal is one that is younger than the average age, but has the epiphysis fused, or is older than the average age with the epiphysis still unfused. The results are presented in sex-specific age tables and are compared to the ages given by van Wagenen and Asling [1959]. The two studies show a similar order but widely differing ages of fusion. The latter is not surprising since the data come from different types of colonies (free-ranging vs laboratory), used different material (skeletal vs radiographic), and had different methods of data recording and reporting. Nearly all epiphyses show later ages of fusion in the Cheverud [1981] study (see Table 3), but the cause of this apparent retardation in skeletal development is not determinable at present owing to the difficulties mentioned above.

TABLE 3. Ages in Months of Union of Long-bone Epiphyses of the Arm and Leg in Male Rhesus Monkeys

Epiphysis	Authors[a]				
	V	G	H	C	S
Humerus					
Proximal	72	72	—	77	84
Distal	24	24	—	26	—
Radius					
Proximal	48	48	—	59	61
Distal	60	63	72	77	84
Ulna					
Proximal	52	57	—	59	71
Distal	69	69	72	78	83
Femur					
Proximal	45	—	—	50	64
Distal	69	48	—	72	79
Tibia					
Proximal	69	—	—	72	80
Distal	52	—	—	62	76
Fibula					
Proximal	54	57	—	70	77
Distal	33	—	—	64	76

[a]V = van Wagenen and Asling, 1958; G = Gisler et al, 1962; H = Haigh and Scott, 1965; C = Cheverud, 1981; S = Silverman et al, 1983.

The sex difference in timing of skeletal maturation is again underscored in Cheverud's [1981] report, the average difference being on the order of 4–6 months and the greatest difference being in the ages of fusion of the epiphyses of the elbow and knee. Within-sex individual variability in age of union of epiphyses is considerable judging from the ranges reported. Multiple-regression equations are given for estimating age from epiphyseal union in animals of each sex. These equations, derived from half of the total sample and tested on the other half, can be used to estimate age to within ± 4.76 months in males and ± 5.27 months in females. In other words, age can be estimated to within about a year in unknown skeletons of rhesus monkeys between 2 and 7 years of age. Equations based on combined skeletal and dental maturation yielded slightly better results.

Most recently Silverman et al [1983] presented the results of a longitudinal radiographic study of skeletal maturation in 28 (12 female and 16 male) rhesus monkeys from the Oregon Regional Primate Research Center. The subjects were followed from 6 months to 7½ years of age, though five animals were lost from the sample during the course of the investigation. Intervals between radiographs were 25 to 200 days depending on the age of the animals. The authors give mean ages and standard deviations by sex for appearance of seven late-ossifying centers that appear radiographically after 6 months of age. The average age difference between the sexes is 139 days for appearance of these centers. As mentioned earlier, most skeletal centers have already begun to ossify in macaques by the time of birth and nearly all have appeared by 6 months after birth. Since union of epiphyses does not usually begin until after 2 years of age, these late-appearing centers are particularly useful in judging ossification status during the period between 6 months and 2 years of age. The alternative is to use a rating system, such as the one employed by Watts [1975], based upon morphological changes in the epiphyses. The rating system may have the advantage of greater sensitivity and accuracy, but its use requires some training and is time-consuming. More rapid determinations of ossification status can be made based upon simple appearance of these late-ossifying sesamoids (the patella, fabellae, and lateral tarsal sesamoid) and epiphyses (greater trochanter femur, proximal fibula, calcaneal epiphysis, and tibial tuberosity), provided they are not too variable in their timing. The data presented by Silverman et al [1983] show that some of these centers, in particular the calcaneal epiphysis, show greater variability than others and should be given less weight in estimating age or maturity status.

Also given in this paper are mean ages, standard deviations, and ranks for fusion of 14 principal epiphyses of the appendicular skeleton. Closure occurred earlier in females for 12 of these centers, the exceptions being the epiphyses of the wrist (distal radius and ulna) where fusion occurred at slightly earlier mean ages in the males. Union was complete in all epiphyses in the females at 7.18 years and in the males at 7.30 years. A series of radiographs illustrating the various stages of ossification at the shoulder, elbow, hand/wrist, hip, knee, and ankle/foot in a single female monkey are included.

Silverman et al [1983] advocate using the larger joints of the appendicular skeleton in assessments of skeletal maturity of rhesus monkeys. They cite difficulties with visibility due to positioning problems and small size as drawbacks to using the osseous centers of the hand/wrist. In the author's experience the hand/wrist is relatively easy to hold flat in the palm-down position in a fully anesthetized monkey, and a strip of Plexiglas may be placed over the fingers and held down with tape to maintain the position when necessary. Though some of the epiphyses of the digits are small, the degree of epiphyseal union can be accurately determined, with the aid of a hand lens when necessary, in all except the terminal phalanx of the thumb [Watts, 1971, 1975]. Thus it is difficult to see that Silverman et al [1983] system is "more practical" since it requires taking a larger number of x-rays. Nor can this author support their sweeping conclusion that it is "impractical to adapt human systems of skeletal assessment based on the hand and wrist to nonhuman primates."

Table 3 compares ages of fusion of some epiphyses of the appendicular skeleton in male rhesus monkeys as reported in five different studies. That there are discrepancies is not surprising given the variation in nature and size of the samples and in methodology used. Examination of these reports shows that they vary widely in what is meant by "age" and "epiphyseal fusion." With the exception of the Silverman et al [1983] figures, none of the figures given represent mean ages of fusion. Particularly noteworthy, however, is the marked contrast between the early ages given by van Wagenen and Asling [1958] and those of Cheverud [1981] and Silverman et al [1983]. The ages reported in Gisler et al [1962] are close to those of van Wagenen and Asling [1958] for most centers, but their sample size and criteria for union are not described and no further evaluation of their study is possible.

There are several possible reasons why the ages given by van Wagenen and Asling [1958] are markedly earlier than those reported in most other studies of rhesus monkeys. The first is sampling fluctuation since the sample sizes in their primarily cross-sectional study are very small for males at the later ages where union is taking place, and other studies show considerable individual variability in ages of fusion. Secondly, it could be attributed to the way in which "age of union" is defined and reported. The figures given in Table 3 represent the ages at which all animals in their sample show complete fusion of each epiphysis. These, then, represent the *latest* age at which union was attained in their study, or the upper end of the range, yet they are still a good deal earlier than the averages reported by other authors [Cheverud, 1981; Silverman et al, 1983]. Cheverud [1981] attributes the earlier ages of closure found by van Wagenen and Asling [1958] to methodological differences and suggests that their judgments of osseous union, made on the basis of radiographs, were not reliable indicators of true union. It has long been recognized that the process of epiphyseal closure appears somewhat different when viewed anatomically as opposed to radiographically [Todd, 1930b]. The major problem with the latter is that overlapping bone shadows, particularly at the larger joints, may give a false indication of union. Further difficulties may be presented by variations in positioning of the joints and in quality of the radiographs. Difficulty in determining the *onset* of fusion is mentioned by van Wagenen and Asling [1958], but they do not state that there were any problems in judging *completed* fusion. While it is possible that van Wagenen and Asling [1958] were consistently rating unfused epiphyses as fused throughout the skeleton, this seems unlikely because of the large number of epiphyses and the rather wide age discrepancies involved. Also, the radiographic study of Silverman et al [1983] shows even later ages of fusion than Cheverud's [1981]. The Silverman et al [1983] report is based on a longitudinal study, which is advantageous for judging union since epiphyses may appear to be united in a single radiograph, but observed to be unfused in subsequent x-rays of the same animal. Also, they relied on different x-ray views of the same joint to judge whether union had

taken place. However, even these methodological differences may not fully explain age differences of up to 2 years between their colony and the one studied by van Wagenen and Asling [1958].

A final possibility to account for the age differences observed between these reports is that the animals in the Yale University colony were simply very accelerated in their skeletal maturation compared to the other colonies studied. Some evidence to support this alternative can be found by comparing figures for the general growth and development of the Yale colony reported by van Wagenen and her colleagues to those given by others. For example, the average ages for the first menstrual cycle in the Yale colony, reported as 1.98 years [van Wagenen, 1952] and 1.72 years [van Wagenen, 1972], and earlier than most other published figures [see Wilen and Naftolin, 1976], and the latter is the lowest mean age yet reported for menarche in female rhesus monkeys. Also, comparisons of growth in weight between same-sex animals of the Yale colony [van Wagenen and Catchpole, 1956] and those of the USAF Aerospace Medicine colony [Kirk, 1972] show the Yale animals to be heavier at nearly all ages during the growth period. These and other comparisons with unpublished data from other colonies indicate that the Yale colony, perhaps because of superior care or genetic factors, is advanced in a number of growth and developmental indicators. It is therefore not unlikely that they show advanced skeletal maturity as well. In any case, it is not possible at present to endorse the unqualified use of the data from the Yale colony as norms for skeletal development of rhesus monkeys. Other, apparently normal, colony-dwelling rhesus monkeys show later ages of appearance and union of osseous centers and may appear to be unduly retarded when compared to the Yale standards. On the other hand, if the developmental advancement of the animals in the Yale colony is due to superior husbandry, these standards may serve as target goals, representing growth and development in an optimal environment, that keepers of other domestic rhesus colonies may wish to aim for. Also, the age differences shown in Table 3 imply that caution should be used in attempting to estimate ages of feral rhesus monkeys from epiphyseal closure in captive animals. This problem will be addressed more fully below.

A longitudinal radiographic study of skeletal development in 11 (5 male and 6 female) pig-tail macaques (*Macaca nemestrina*) is described in

Rahlman and Pace [1969]. Growth and dental eruption are also reported. The laboratory-born animals were x-rayed at intervals of 1 to 6 months starting at birth and continuing through 52 months in the males and 75 months in the females. Means, and ranges, for ages of appearance of a large number of osseous centers are reported for each sex. Also given are the *earliest* ages of epiphyseal union observed in the sample. These data are of limited value for the males since most epiphyses were still unfused at 52 months when the observations ended. While skeletal development appears to be somewhat delayed in the pig-tailed macaques of this study (see Table 4) compared to the rhesus monkeys reported by van Wagenen and Asling [1958], the small sizes of the samples and differences in the way the studies were conducted preclude any definitive conclusions on this point.

Fukuda et al [1978] studied radiographic appearance, development, and fusion of epiphyses in the six long bones of the arm and leg in 98 laboratory-bred *Macaca fascicularis* (47 males and 51 females) whose ages ranged from 6 months to 8½ years. This is a cross-sectional study and sample sizes at each age are small (the maximum number is 6). Diagrams showing ten stages in the maturation process of the long-bone epiphyses are given and graphs indicate the chronological age at which each stage is reached in both sexes. A table summarizes the sex-specific ages of epiphyseal union, but the authors do not state how they define union or how they arrived at the ages given. Females show fusion at younger ages than males for all epiphyses except the distal radius. The authors suggest that their bone maturity stages may be useful in aging wild-born animals. Some of the ages of union given in this report seem unusually late for macaques in general and for *M. fascicularis* in particular (see Tables 3, 4). For example, an age of 41 months is given for epiphyseal closure at the distal humerus and 63 months for fusion of the proximal radius in males. It is possible that these disparities are due to the cross-sectional nature and small size of the sample.

Clifton et al [1982] have developed a computerized technique for assessing skeletal age in male cynomolgus macaques (*Macaca fascicularis*) from radiographic determinations of appearance of sesmoids and union of epiphyses. The age estimates require only that the researcher score 13 ossification centers as present/absent or fused/unfused in the radiograph of an unknown animal. Apparently any degree of epiphyseal closure is scored as "fused." This information is then used in a computer program that calculates a "bone age" based on the age-specific probabilities of appearance and union. The probabilities were derived from observations of radiographic appearance and union in a standardizing sample of 59 known-age male cynomolgus macaques from five different primate laboratories. As reported in this paper the method is only useful for cynomolgus males aged 4–40 months, although it is potentially applicable to a wider range of subjects and ages. The simplicity

TABLE 4. Age Ranges (in months) for Appearance of Sesamoids and Union of Epiphyses in Male Macaques

Ossification center	M. fascicularis[a]	M. mulatta[b]	M. nemestrina[c]
Distal humerus	12–36	21–25	40–?
Proximal ulna	39–>42	34–52	>52
Radial carpal sesamoid	21–>42	25–32	42–43
1st Digital sesamoid (hand)	15–36	23–34	28–32
Proximal femur	39–>42	35–45	>52
Patella	3–12	5–6	12–15
Fabellae	18–33	12–13	45
Tibial tuberosity	15–42	26–34	>52
Lateral tarsal sesamoid	9–42	25–28	43
Calcaneus	6–36	13–14	18–28
1st Digital sesamoid (foot)	12–36	23–44	42–52
5th Digital sesamoid (foot)	18–>42	34–37	>52
2nd–4th Digital Sesamoids (foot)	15–33	34–66	46

[a]Clifton et al, 1982.
[b]van Wagenen and Asling, 1958.
[c]Rahlman and Pace, 1969.

of the scoring, good reliability, and objectivity of the system are obvious advantages. Its accuracy in estimating chronological age was tested on a subgroup of the standardizing sample with good results (an average error of 2.6 months), but it has not been tested on an independent sample. Probabilities of appearance and fusion of the 13 osseous centers used are given by age with sample sizes indicated. These data can be used to judge the ages at earliest appearance or beginning union, and those where all animals showed presence or union. Thus, rough comparisons can be made with data from other species, as seen in Table 4. Cynomolgus macaques show somewhat earlier ages of appearance and union of most centers, judging by these ranges, than do other macaque species.

The Genus *Papio*. The only data on skeletal maturation in known-age baboons (*Papio cynocephalus*) are those given by Reed [1967] apparently derived from a cross-sectional investigation of animals from the Southwest Foundation for Research and Education Colony. Sample size and sex are not specified. Radiographs were taken of the humerus, hand, and wrist, and the author presents skeletal maturity indicators in these areas, along with observations on dental calcification at 36, 46, 60, 79, and 85 months. This spans the period from beginning union of the distal humerus through complete union of the proximal humerus, which occurs by 85 months. Since the data are not presented separately by sex, and it is reasonable to assume a significant sex difference in timing of epiphyseal closure in this species, it is not possible to make meaningful detailed comparisons with other primates. However, the distal humerus is not completely united until 46 months, compared to 24–26 months in the male rhesus monkey. The age of complete closure of the proximal humeral epiphysis, one of the last to unite, is also later than the ages of union given for male rhesus monkeys. These and other rough comparisons suggest that skeletal development of the baboon is slower than that of the rhesus macaque.

The Apes (*Hominoidea*). Radiographic appearance of ossification centers in laboratory chimpanzees is reported by Nissen and Riesen [1949a]. Their 16 subjects, nine males and seven females, born and reared in the Yerkes laboratories, are known as the "Yerkes normative group" because they were kept almost exclusively for investigations of normal growth and development. This paper reports the averages and ranges for the ages of onset of ossification in some 70 skeletal centers from birth to 4 years of age. The ages of appearance were determined from serial radiographs, taken at birth and every 2 months during the first year, then every 3 months between the ages of 1 and 4 years. In addition to presenting the age norms and individual variation for beginning ossification by sex, the authors also explore the relationship of skeletal development to birth weight, gestational age, dental emergence, and postural development. On average ossification begins about 5 months earlier in females than in males. Comparisons with humans show that chimpanzees are advanced in the appearance of most skeletal centers by some 12–20 months when compared to norms for the same sex. Humans show earlier ages of ossification only for the distal epiphyses of the thumb and great toe, but tend to be relatively advanced in all of the phalangeal epiphyses.

The age norms for beginning ossification given in this study can probably be used to estimate age in feral chimpanzees and to judge the rough limits of normality in developmental timing in other laboratory chimps. However, because of the considerable individual variability seen in this sample, it would be advisable to use a large number of skeletal centers in making these kinds of judgments. The limits of variability in skeletal development in chimpanzees are probably underestimated in this study owing to the small size of the sample, the relatively uniform rearing conditions, and the high degree of genetic relatedness among the subjects. The animals were fathered by three males and there are three full siblings in the group.

Nissen and Riesen [1949b] compare skeletal development of other chimpanzees from the Yerkes colony to that of the normative group, and the results can be seen in Table 5. These animals had either been reared under different conditions or had undergone various experimental procedures. The "controls" were reared in the same manner as the normative group. With the exception of the animals that had undergone brain surgery, most of these groups tend to show slower skeletal development, as indicated by higher ages of appearance, than the normative group though the degree or retardation varies greatly as can be seen in the Z scores. The brain-operated animals had parts of their frontal association areas removed, and one of them had a portion of the parietal area removed as well. It is evident that a variety of nutritional, sensory, and hormonal deficiencies experienced by these ani-

TABLE 5. Skeletal Development of Various Groups of Yerkes Laboratory Chimpanzees Compared to the Normative Group

Group	No.	Mean gestation (days)[a]	Appearance of ossification centers		
			Compared to range[b]	Compared to mean[b]	Mean group Z score
Controls	3	232	Retarded	Retarded	+ 0.05
Mother-reared	18	223	Retarded	Retarded	+ 2.20
Home-reared	3	238	Retarded	Retarded	+ 0.09
Early deaths	7	223	Retarded	Retarded	− 0.22
Stillbirths	4	220	Retarded	Advanced	− 0.50
Castrate	1	213	Retarded	Retarded	+ 2.12
Brain operations	2	221	Advanced	Advanced	− 0.88
Light deprivation	4	217	Retarded	Retarded	+ 1.20
Restriction of tactile experience	1	212	Retarded	Retarded	+ 2.17

[a]Mean gestation of normative group is 226 days (range, 206–238).
[b]Retarded = mean % of centers above the normative range or mean exceeds that below. Advanced = mean % of centers below the normative range or mean exceeds that above.
Data from Nissen and Riesen [1949b].

mals can result in retarded ossification. However, the authors did not control for gestation time in making their comparisons. Thus, as they point out, for some of these subjects, skeletal retardation may be due to extremely short gestation, rather than to experimental or other environmental factors.

Epiphyseal union in the chimpanzee is reported in a cross-sectional study by Kerley [1966] of 30 known-age animals whose ages ranged from birth to 35 years. Fusion was studied from radiographs of the macerated skeletons, confirmed by histologic sections of the epiphyseal-metaphyseal areas. Epiphyseal closure begins in the distal humerus around 5 years of age. Because of the small numbers of animals in each age group, sex differences in ages of union are difficult to determine. Epiphyseal fusion is complete by 15 years, with the exception of one male that had an incompletely fused proximal humerus at the age of 16 years. Also reported are ages of fusion at the pubic symphysis, calcification of the costal cartilages, and changes in microstructure of the long-bone diaphyses that may be useful in age determinations for chimpanzees over 17 years.

Using a bone-specific scoring method identical to that discussed above for rhesus monkeys, Watts [1971] quantified and studied skeletal maturation in the hand/wrist of the 16 Yerkes normative chimpanzees from birth to 15 years of age. This system measures both appearance and union of epiphyses as well as morphological changes that occur be-

tween initial and completed ossification. Means and standard deviations for skeletal maturity scores by sex and age are given. The females of this sample are advanced throughout most of the growth period and reach skeletal maturity, on the average, a year earlier than males (11½ years as opposed to 12½ years).

This scoring system has not been widely applied to chimpanzees since the Yerkes normative group, for reasons stated above, is somewhat limited as a reference group. However, it has been used to measure and monitor the degree of skeletal advancement in a female chimpanzee with idiopathic precocious puberty. This laboratory-born animal developed sex skin swelling at the age of 2 months, showed elevated plasma estrogen and gonadatrophins, and her vaginal cytology was consistent with early puberty [Winterer et al, 1984]. Brief treatment with luteinizing hormone–releasing hormone (LHRH) antagonist decreased plasma gonadatrophins, estradiol, and the vaginal maturation index, but did not produce clinical reversal of the condition. Hand/wrist radiographs were taken at the ages of 16 and 32 months and rated by the modified Tanner-Whitehouse system [Watts, 1971]. Comparisons of this animal's skeletal maturity scores to those of the females in the Yerkes group show her increasingly advanced skeletal development. At 16 months her skeletal maturity score was comparable to those of Yerkes normative females whose chronological ages averaged 20.6 months (range 14–25 months), and at 32 months her score matched those of Yerkes females aged 60 months (range 51–66 months). Her first radiograph was comparable to the most advanced animal in the Yerkes group, and in the second one her chronological age was well below the range for her advanced skeletal age.

With the exception of the few cited for the chimpanzee, no other studies of skeletal development of apes of known birth date have been found. Of interest, however, is the report of Noback [1930] on radiographic appearance of skeletal centers in the hand/wrist of five infant female gorillas. All but one of these infants died from disease after having been captured in Africa and transported by ship to the United States. The fifth infant lived for some time and was examined by the author four times over a period of 20 months. Each of the dead infants was examined only once. The estimated ages of these infants, based on sitting height, weight, and dental development, are between 9 and 42 months. They fit reasonably well within the age ranges published for female chimpanzees of the Yerkes group for dental emergence [Nissen and Riesen, 1945, 1964] and ossification, but their skeletal development is somewhat delayed compared to the medians given by Nissen and Riesen [1949a]. Without further data on known-age gorillas and chimpanzees it is not possible to determine whether ossification timing actually differs between the two species or whether the apparent delay in the gorillas is due to the nature of the particular samples being compared here.

Conclusions

There is still a great deal to be learned about the development of the postnatal skeleton in primates other than man. Despite the seemingly large number of publications dealing with primate skeletal development, the amount of useful information that can be extracted from them is woefully small. There exist only a few reports on animals of known age, even fewer are based on longitudinal data, and there is no single publication that integrates skeletal development with growth and dental and sexual maturation in the same animals. With the exceptions of Todd's [1930a] data on the order of epiphyseal closure in lemurs and those of Shigehara [1980] on the common tree shrew prosimian skeletal development is virtually unknown. The apes and New World monkeys are represented by good studies of small samples of single species, but even for these the data have not been completely analyzed or published. Of the Old World monkeys only the macaques are well represented, but existing publications leave a number of questions still unanswered and sample sizes are smaller than desirable for deriving norms.

Heretofore the primary impetus for collecting and reporting information on skeletal development, especially in laboratory primates, has been the necessity of obtaining chronological age estimates for the large numbers of imported wild-born animals used in various kinds of research. With the increased domestic production and more conservative use of nonhuman primates currently seen in the United States [Wolfle, 1983] the need for age-estimating criteria can be expected to diminish. Also, though skeletal development is not one of the criteria they tested, Gavan and Hutchinson [1973] give some useful caveats concerning methods of age estimation, their derivation, testing, and general accuracy. They rightly point out that for Old World monkey species with distinct birth seasons (like the rhesus macaque) age can be estimated to within plus or minus 3 months in most cases when the year of birth can be determined. Thus, for such animals using more complicated means of age estimation is not worth the effort if they cannot be shown to have greater accuracy.

The need for normative data on osseous development in laboratory primates will still be great even should age estimation become a less pressing concern. There are still many unexplored areas of primate evolution and ontogeny for which such data are crucial. And, the continued use of nonhuman primates as experimental models in biomedical research is ensured by their close similarity to man, in skeletal development as well as in many other features. Norms are still needed for judging the degree of advancement and retardation in skeletal development caused by various experimental protocols. Likewise they are necessary for determining the efficacy of treatment for spontaneous or environmentally induced pathological conditions. Studies of humans have firmly established skeletal maturation as a useful parameter to monitor whenever there are questions about whether individuals are developing normally [for an excellent review of methodology and the utility of studying skeletal maturation see Acheson, 1966]. The use of primate skeletal development in the experimental context has not been widespread [but see, for example, Lusted et al, 1953, Kerr et al, 1973, Riopelle et al, 1976, Thurm et al, 1976].

However, it should become increasingly prevalent in the future with the development of more sophisticated research designs and more enlightened approaches to health care and maintenance of domestic colonies.

ACKNOWLEDGMENTS

I thank Dr. A.J. Riopelle for the use of the data presented in Table 2.

This research was supported in part by grant HD-07479 from the National Institute of Child Health and Human Development of the National Institutes of Health.

Gratitude is also expressed to Universe Books for permission to reprint Figure 1, and to Alan R. Liss, Inc., for the use of Figures 2 and 3.

REFERENCES

Acheson, R.M. Maturation of the skeleton. Pp. 465–502 in HUMAN DEVELOPMENT. F. Falkner, ed. Philadelphia, Saunders, 1966.

Ardito, G.; De Gennaro, T.; Pastorin, L.; Pilotti, G.; Benincasa, A.; Benso, L. Ossificazione della mano e del piede in individiu neonati del genre *Macaca (M. nemestrina-M. fascicularis)*. ARCHIVO ITALIANO DI ANATOMIA E DI EMBRIOLOGIA 88:2–28, 1982.

Birkbeck, J.A. Metrical growth and skeletal development of the human fetus. Pp. 39–68 in THE BIOLOGY OF HUMAN FETAL GROWTH. D.F. Roberts, ed. London, Taylor and Francis, 1976.

Bramblett, C.A. Non-metric age changes in the Daranjani baboon. AMERICAN JOURNAL OF PHYSICAL ANTHROPOLOGY 30:161–171, 1969.

Cheverud, J.M. Epiphyseal union and dental eruption in *Macaca mulatta*. AMERICAN JOURNAL OF PHYSICAL ANTHROPOLOGY 56:157–167, 1981.

Clifton, D.K.; Bremmer, W.J.; Steiner, R.A. An automated technique for radiographic determination of bone age. JOURNAL OF MEDICAL PRIMATOLOGY 11:147–154, 1982.

Curgy, J.-J. Apparition et soudre des points d'ossification des membres chez les mammifères. MEMOIRES DU MUSEUM NATIONALE D'HISTOIRE NATURELLE, Serie A, 33:175–307, 1965.

Dobbelaar, M.J.; Arts, T.H.M. Estimation of the fetal age in pregnant rhesus monkeys (*Macaca mulatta*) by radiography. LABORATORY ANIMALS 6:235–240, 1972.

Fahrenbruch, C.E.; Burbacher, T.M.; Sackett, G.P. Assessment of skeletal growth and maturation of premature and term *Macaca nemestrina*. Pp. 79–91 in NURSERY CARE OF NONHUMAN PRI-MATES. G.C. Ruppenthal, ed. New York, Plenum, 1979.

Francis, C.C.; Werle, P.P. The appearance of centers of ossification from birth to five years. AMERICAN JOURNAL OF PHYSICAL ANTHROPOLOGY 24:273–299, 1939.

Fukuda, S.; Cho, F.; Honjo, S. Bone growth and development of secondary ossification centers of extremities in the cynomolgus monkey (*Macaca fascicularis*). EXPERIMENTAL ANIMALS 27:387–397, 1978.

Garn, S.M.; Burdi, A.R.; Babler, W. Male advancement in prenatal hand development. AMERICAN JOURNAL OF PHYSICAL ANTHROPOLOGY 41:353–360, 1974.

Gavan, J.A.; Hutchinson, T.C. The problem of age estimation: A study using rhesus monkeys (*Macaca mulatta*). AMERICAN JOURNAL OF PHYSICAL ANTHROPOLOGY 38:69–81, 1973.

Gisler, D.B.; Wilson, S.G.; Hekhuis, G.L. Correlation of skeletal growth epiphyseal ossification with age of monkeys. ANNALS OF THE NEW YORK ACADEMY OF SCIENCES 85:800–802, 1960.

Gisler, D.B.; Wilson, S.G.; Hekhuis, G.L. Correlation of skeletal growth and epiphyseal ossification with age. II. Maturation extended through 75 months. Pp. 195–203 in PROCEEDINGS OF THE INTERNATIONAL SYMPOSIUM ON BONE MARROW THERAPY AND CHEMICAL PROTECTION IN IRRADIATED PRIMATES. Rijswijk, The Netherlands, 1962.

Glaser, D. Über die ossifikation der extremitäten bei neugebornen Primaten (*Mammalia*). ZEITSCHRIFT FÜR MORPHOLOGIE DER TIERE 79:155–163, 1970.

Glassman, D.M. Growth and development in the saddle-back tamarin: The sequence and timing of dental eruption and epiphyseal union. AMERICAN JOURNAL OF PRIMATOLOGY 5:51–59, 1983.

Haigh, M.V.; Scott, A. Some radiological and other factors for assessing age in the rhesus monkey using animals of known age. LABORATORY ANIMAL CARE 15:57–73, 1965.

Hartley, J.B. Radiological estimation of fetal maturity. BRITISH JOURNAL OF RADIOLOGY 30:561–576, 1957.

Hayama, S. Morphological studies of *Macaca fuscata*. II. The sequence of epiphyseal union by roentgenegraphic estimation. PRIMATES 6:249–269. 1965.

Hill, A.H. Fetal age assessment by centers of ossification. AMERICAN JOURNAL OF PHYSICAL ANTHROPOLOGY 24:251–272, 1939.

Hill, W.C.O.; Spatz, W.B. On two new *Gorilla* fetuses. TRANSACTIONS OF THE ROYAL SOCIETY OF EDINBURGH 68:331–359, 1970.

Hodges, P.C. Ossification in the fetal pig. ANATOMICAL RECORD 116:315–325, 1953.

Kerley, E.R. Skeletal age changes in the chimpanzee. TULANE STUDIES IN ZOOLOGY 13:71–80, 1966.

Kerr, G.R. Skeletal growth in the fetal macaque. Pp. 289–298 in FETAL AND POSTNATAL CELLULAR GROWTH. D.B. Cheek, ed. New York, Wiley, 1975.

Kerr, G.R.; Waisman, H.A.; Allen, J.A.; Wallace, J.; Scheffler, G. Malnutrition studies in *Macaca mulatta*. II. The effect on organ size and skeletal development. AMERICAN JOURNAL OF CLINICAL NUTRITION 26:620–630, 1973.

Kerr, G.R.; Wallace, J.H.; Chesney, C.F.; Waisman, H.A. Growth and development of the fetal rhesus monkey. III. Maturation and linear growth of the skull and appendicular skeleton. GROWTH 36:59–76, 1972.

Kirk, J.H. Growth of maturing *Macaca mulatta*. LABORATORY ANIMAL SCIENCE 22:573–575, 1972.

Kraus, B.S.; Hampton, J.K. Sequence of ossification of the foot in marmosets (*Saguinus oedipus*). AMERICAN JOURNAL OF PHYSICAL ANTHROPOLOGY 30:393–396, 1969.

Lusted, L.B.; Miller, R.S. Radiographic study of postnatal skeletal development. Pp. 81–89 in BIOLOGY OF THE HOWLER MONKEY. M.R. Malinow, ed. Bibliotheca Primatologica 7. Basel, Karger, 1968.

Lusted, L.B.; Miller, R.S.; Malinow, M.R. Radiographic study of the postnatal skeletal development in howler monkeys (*Alouatta caraya*). PRIMATES 7:263–270, 1966.

Lusted, L.B.; Pickering, D.E.; Fisher, D.; Smyth, F.S. Growth and metabolism in normal and thyroid-ablated infant rhesus monkeys (*Macaca mulatta*). V. Roentgenographic features of skeletal development in normal and thyroid-ablated rhesus monkeys (*Macaca mulatta*). AMERICAN JOURNAL OF DISEASES OF CHILDREN 86:426–435, 1953.

Mahoney, C.J. Practical aspects of determining early pregnancy, stage of foetal development and imminent parturition in the monkey (*Macaca fascicularis*). LABORATORY ANIMAL HANDBOOK 6:261–276, 1975.

McKim, D.; Hutchinson, T.C.; Gavan, J.A. Prenatal growth of the long bones in rhesus and squirrel monkeys (*Macaca mulatta* and *Saimiri sciureus*). AMERICAN JOURNAL OF PHYSICAL ANTHROPOLOGY 36:353–357, 1972.

Meyer, D.B.; O'Rahilly, R. Multiple techniques in the study of the onset of prenatal ossification. ANATOMICAL RECORD 132:181–193, 1958.

Michejda, M. The problem of age estimation and skeletal age. A critical review. JOURNAL OF MEDICAL PRIMATOLOGY 7:257–263, 1978.

Michejda, M.; Bacher, J. Skeletal age as a determinant of gestation in *Macaca mulatta*. JOURNAL OF MEDICAL PRIMATOLOGY 10:293–301, 1981.

Michejda, M.; Watson, W.T. Age determinants in neonatal primates: A comparison of growth factors. Pp. 61–78 in NURSERY CARE OF NONHUMAN PRIMATES. G.C. Ruppenthal, ed. New York, Plenum, 1979.

Michejda, M.; Bacher, J.; Hayes, N.; Johnson, D.; Killens, R.,; Watson, W. Estimation of gestational and skeletal age in *Macaca mulatta*. JOURNAL OF MEDICAL PRIMATOLOGY 8:143–154, 1979.

Newell-Morris, L. Age determination in macaque fetuses and neonates. Pp. 93–115 in NURSERY CARE OF NONHUMAN PRIMATES. G.C. Ruppenthal, ed. New York, Plenum, 1979.

Newell-Morris, L.; Tarrant, L.H. Ossification in the hand and foot of the macaque (*Macaca nemestrina*). I. General features. AMERICAN JOURNAL OF PHYSICAL ANTHROPOLOGY 48:441–453, 1978.

Newell-Morris, L.; Seed, J.; Tarrant, L.H.; Fahrenbruch, C. Supernumerary epiphyses in the macaque (*Macaca nemestrina*). JOURNAL OF MEDICAL PRIMATOLOGY 8:338–348, 1979.

Newell-Morris, L.; Tarrant, L.H.; Fahrenbruch, C.E.; Burbacher, T.M.; Sackett, G.P. Ossification in the hand and foot of the pigtail macaque (*Macaca nemestrina*). II. Order of appearance of centers and variability in sequence. AMERICAN JOURNAL OF PHYSICAL ANTHROPOLOGY 53:423–439, 1980.

Niemitz, C.; Sprankel, H. Early postnatal ossification in *Tarsius bancanus* Horsfield, 1821 (Mammalia, Primates) and its relation to hypothesis of nidifuguous and nidiculous animals. ZEITSCHRIFT FÜR MORPHOLOGIE DER TIERE 79:155–163, 1974.

Nissen, H.W.; Riesen, A.H. The deciduous dentition of the chimpanzee. GROWTH 9:265–274, 1945.

Nissen, H.W.; Riesen, A.H. Onset of ossification in the epiphyses and short bones of the extremities in chimpanzee. GROWTH 13:45–70, 1949a.

Nissen, H.W.; Riesen, A.H. Retardation in onset of ossification in chimpanzee related to various environmental and physiological factors. ANATOMICAL RECORD 105:665–675, 1949b.

Nissen, H.W.; Riesen, A.H. The eruption of the permanent dentition of chimpanzee. AMERICAN JOURNAL OF PHYSICAL ANTHROPOLOGY 22:285–294, 1964.

Noback, C.V. Digital epiphyses and carpal bones in the growing infant female gorilla with sitting height and estimated age. ZOOLOGICA 11:117–151, 1930.

O'Rahilly, R; Meyer, D.B. Roentgenographic investigation of the human skeleton during early fetal life. AMERICAN JOURNAL OF ROENTGENOLOGY 76:455–468, 1956.

Phillips, I.R. Skeletal development in the fetal and neonatal marmoset (*Callithrix jacchus*). LABORATORY ANIMALS 10:317–333, 1976.

Rahlman, D.F.; Pace, N. Anthropoidimetric and roentgenographic growth changes in young pig-tailed

438   Watts

monkeys (*Macaca nemestrina*). Pp. 171–180 in PROCEEDINGS OF THE SECOND INTERNATIONAL CONGRESS OF PRIMATOLOGY, Vol. 2. H.O. Hofer, ed. Basel, Karger, 1969.

Randall, F.E. The skeletal and dental development and variability of the gorilla. HUMAN BIOLOGY 15:236–254, 307–337, 1943.

Randall, F.E. The skeletal and dental development and variability of the gorilla. HUMAN BIOLOGY 16:23–76, 1944.

Reed, O.M. Cephalometric studies of the growth, development and eruption patterns of the baboon. Pp. 181–186 in THE BABOON IN MEDICAL RESEARCH, Vol. II. H. Vagtborg, ed. Austin, University of Texas Press, 1967.

Riopelle, A.R.; Hale, P.A. Nutritional and environmental factors affecting gestation length in rhesus monkeys. AMERICAN JOURNAL OF CLINICAL NUTRITION 28:1170–1176, 1975.

Riopelle, A.R.; Hale, P.A.; Watts, E.S. Protein deprivation in primates. VII. Determinants of size and skeletal maturity at birth in rhesus monkeys. HUMAN BIOLOGY 48:203–222, 1976.

Schultz, A.H. Fetuses of the Guiana howling monkey. ZOOLOGICA 3:243–262, 1921.

Schultz, A.H. Observations on colobus fetuses. BULLETIN OF THE AMERICAN MUSEUM OF NATURAL HISTORY 49:443–457, 1924.

Schultz, A.H. Chimpanzee fetuses. AMERICAN JOURNAL OF PHYSICAL ANTHROPOLOGY 18:61–79, 1933.

Schultz, A.H. Characters common to the higher primates and characters specific for man. QUARTERLY REVIEW OF BIOLOGY 11:259–283, 425–455, 1936.

Schultz, A.H. Fetal growth and development of the rhesus monkey. CARNEGIE INSTITUTE OF WASHINGTON CONTRIBUTIONS TO EMBRYOLOGY 26:73–97, 1937.

Schultz, A.H. Growth and development of the chimpanzee. CARNEGIE INSTITUTE OF WASHINGTON CONTRIBUTIONS TO EMBRYOLOGY 28:1–63, 1940.

Schultz, A.H. Growth and development of the orangutan. CARNEGIE INSTITUTE OF WASHINGTON CONTRIBUTIONS TO EMBRYOLOGY 29:57–110, 1941.

Schultz, A.H. Growth and development of the proboscis monkey. BULLETIN OF THE MUSEUM OF COMPARATIVE ZOOLOGY, HARVARD COLLEGE 89:279–314, 1942.

Schultz, A.H. Age changes and variability in gibbons: A morphological study on a population sample of a man-like ape. AMERICAN JOURNAL OF PHYSICAL ANTHROPOLOGY 2:1–129, 1944.

Schultz, A.H. Postembryonic age changes. PRIMATOLOGIA 1:887–964, 1956.

Schultz, A.H. THE LIFE OF PRIMATES, New York, Universe Books, 1969a.

Schultz, A.H. The skeleton of the chimpanzee. Pp. 50–103 in THE CHIMPANZEE, Vol. I. G.H. Bourne, ed. Basel, Karger, 1969b.

Schultz, A.H. Polydactylism in a siamang. FOLIA PRIMATOLOGICA 17:241–247, 1972.

Shigehara, N. Epiphyseal union, tooth eruption and sexual maturation in the common tree shrew, with reference to its systematic problem. PRIMATES 21:1–19, 1980.

Silverman, S.; Morgan, J.P.; Ferron, R.; McNulty, W.; Merten, D. Radiographic evaluation of appendicular skeletal maturation in the rhesus monkey. VETERINARY RADIOLOGY 24:25–34, 1983.

Simon, M.R. The effect of dynamic loading on the growth of epiphyseal cartilage in the rat. ACTA ANATOMICA 102:176–183, 1978.

Stevenson, P.H. Age order of epiphyseal union in man. AMERICAN JOURNAL OF PHYSICAL ANTHROPOLOGY 7:53–93, 1924.

Swindler, D.R.; Jenkins, T.W.; Weiss, A.W. Fetal growth and development. Pp. 28–47 in BIOLOGY OF THE HOWLER MONKEY (*ALOUATTA CARAYA*). M.R. Malinow, ed. Bibliotheca Primatologica 7. Basel, Karger, 1968.

Tanner, J.M.; Whitehouse, R.W. STANDARDS FOR SKELETAL MATURITY, PART I. Paris, International Children's Centre, 1959.

Tanner, J.M.; Whitehouse, R.H.; Marshall, W.A.; Healy, M.J.R.; Goldstein, H. ASSESSMENT OF SKELETAL MATURITY AND PREDICTION OF ADULT HEIGHT (TW2 METHOD). New York, Academic Press, 1975.

Tappen, N.C.; Severson, A. Sequence of eruption of permanent teeth and epiphyseal union in New World monkeys. FOLIA PRIMATOLOGICA 15:293–312, 1971.

Tarrant, L.H. Sex differences in skeletal maturation at birth in the pigtailed monkey. AMERICAN JOURNAL OF PHYSICAL ANTHROPOLOGY 47:163, 1977 (Abstract).

Thorington, R.W.; Vorek, R.E. Observations on the geographic variation and skeletal development of *Aotus*. LABORATORY ANIMAL SCIENCE 26:1006–1021, 1976.

Thurm, D.A.; Samonds, K.W.; Fleagle, J.G. AN ATLAS FOR THE SKELETAL MATURATION OF THE CEBUS MONKEY: THE FIRST YEAR. Boston, Department of Nutrition, Harvard School of Public Health, 1975.

Thurm, D.A.; Samonds, K.W.; Hegsted, D.M. The effects of a 20-week nutritional insult on the skeletal development of *Cebus albifrons* during the first year of life. AMERICAN JOURNAL OF CLINICAL NUTRITION 29:621–625, 1976.

Todd, T.W. Comparative youth. The physical aspect.

CHILD DEVELOPMENT 1:79–89, 1930A.

Todd, T.W. The anatomical features of epiphyseal union. CHILD DEVELOPMENT 1:79–89, 1930a.

Torre, C.; Giacobini, G.; Ardito, G. Skeletal development of an orang-utan premature newborn: A comparative study with man. JOURNAL OF HUMAN EVOLUTION 7:143–149, 1978.

van Wagenen, G. Age at menarche of the laboratory rhesus monkey. ANATOMICAL RECORD 112:436, 1952.

van Wagenen, G. Vital statistics from a breeding colony. JOURNAL OF MEDICAL PRIMATOLOGY 1:3–28, 1972.

van Wagenen, G.; Asling, C.W. Roentgenographic estimation of bone age in the rhesus monkey (*Macaca mulatta*). AMERICAN JOURNAL OF ANATOMY 103:163–165, 1958.

van Wagenen, G.; Asling C.W. Ossification in the fetal monkey (*Macaca mulatta*). AMERICAN JOURNAL OF ANATOMY 114:107–132, 1964.

van Wagenen, G.; Catchpole, H.R. Physical growth of the rhesus monkey (*Macaca mulatta*). AMERICAN JOURNAL OF PHYSICAL ANTHROPOLOGY 14:245–273, 1956.

Washburn, S.L. The sequence of epiphyseal union in Old World monkeys. AMERICAN JOURNAL OF ANATOMY 72:339–360, 1943.

Washburn, S.L. The sequence of epiphyseal union in the opossum. ANATOMICAL RECORD 94:353–363, 1946.

Watts, E.S. A comparative study of skeletal maturation in the chimpanzee and rhesus monkey and its relationship to growth and sexual maturity. Ph.D. Dissertation, University of Pennsylvania, 1971.

Watts, E.S. The assessment of skeletal development in the rhesus monkey (*Macaca mulatta*) and its relationship to growth and sexual maturity. Pp. 245–260 in THE RHESUS MONKEY, Vol. II. G.H. Bourne, ed. New York, Academic Press, 1975.

Wilen, R.; Naftolin, F. Age, weight and weight gain in the individual pubertal female rhesus monkey (*Macaca mulatta*). BIOLOGY OF REPRODUCTION 15:356–360, 1976.

Wilson, J.G.; Fradkin, R.; Hardman, A. Breeding and pregnancy in rhesus monkeys used for teratological testing. TERATOLOGY 3:59–72, 1970.

Winterer, J.; Merriam, G.R.; Gross, E.; Sly, D.L.; Faiman, C.; Loriaux, D.L.; Cutler, G.B. Jr. Idiopathic precocious puberty in the chimpanzee: A case report. JOURNAL OF MEDICAL PRIMATOLOGY 13:73–79, 1984.

Wintheiser, J.; Clauser, D.; Tappen, N. Sequence of eruption of permanent teeth and epiphyseal union in three species of African monkeys. FOLIA PRIMATOLOGICA 27:178–197, 1977.

Wolfle, T.L. Nonhuman primates in research: Trends in conservation, importation, production and use in the United States. LABORATORY ANIMALS 12:19, 21, 23–27, 1983.

Taxonomic Index

This taxonomic index is provided to assist readers in finding information on specific taxa of primates. The listings are those used in text by the authors. Inclusion of a term in this index does not imply approval of the use of that term in standard nomenclature; it simply acknowledges that there was at least one citation using that form. Consequently, it may be necessary to look under several forms to be sure all references to a species have been found. For example, the use of Leontopithecus, Leontideus, and Leontocebus for the lion tamarins is acknowledged. Wherever possible, we have cross-listed such synonyms. The listing of outdated usages is, of course, inevitable for this work, because it involves review of literature in which different nomenclature was used. In addition, traditional usage in some fields does not follow standard nomenclature protocol. As unfortunate as that may be, it is reality, and there was nothing to be gained from refusing to acknowledge such traditional uses (e.g., use of "long-tailed," "crab-eating," "cyno-molgus," "Macaca irus," etc., for Macaca fascicularis). Some of the literature is only accessible through names not technically acceptable from the standpoint of standard nomenclature; further, it is often not the technically appropriate name that is familiar to scientists working directly with the animals in laboratories or zoological parks. The inclusion of a taxonomic index seemed essential to meet the goals of **Comparative Primate Biology** *in improving interdisciplinary understanding of primates.*

J. Erwin, Series Editor

Author Index

Subject Index